Anthony

Textbook of

anatomy

and physiology

Sixth edition

Textbook of anatomy and physiology

Catherine Parker Anthony, B.A., M.S., R.N.

*Assistant Professor of Nursing, Science Department,
Frances Payne Bolton School of Nursing, Western Reserve University;
formerly Instructor of Anatomy and Physiology, Lutheran
Hospital, Cleveland, Ohio; formerly Instructor of Anatomy
and Physiology, St. Luke's Hospital, Cleveland, Ohio;
formerly Assistant Instructor of Anatomy and Physiology,
Frances Payne Bolton School of Nursing, Western Reserve University*

*With 316 illustrations, including 20 in color,
and a Trans-Vision® insert of the Human Anatomy*

Sixth edition

The C. V. Mosby Company

Saint Louis 1963

SIXTH EDITION

Copyright © 1963 by The C. V. Mosby Company

All rights reserved

Third printing

Previous editions copyrighted 1944, 1946, 1950, 1955, 1959

Printed in the United States of America

Library of Congress Catalog Card Number 63-10004

Distributed in Great Britain by Henry Kimpton, London

To my husband

T he best of the old, the best of the new." Against the background of this thought, the sixth edition of *Textbook of Anatomy and Physiology* has been prepared. In some respects, therefore, the new edition closely resembles earlier editions. For example, its primary aim remains unchanged—to present basic facts and principles of body structure and function in a way that makes the teaching of them less laborious, the learning of them less difficult, and both the teaching and learning more exhilarating and more enjoyable. And because so many of you have mentioned the helpfulness of certain features, they have been retained. Among them are such teaching-learning aids as outline surveys to introduce each chapter, outline summaries and review questions to conclude each chapter, a glossary, and many summarizing charts and tables. A new Trans-Vision® insert of the human anatomy appears in this edition.

Content of the sixth edition differs considerably from that of the fifth edition. A great deal of new material replaces old, out-of-date information. This is clearly demonstrated, for instance, in the new chapter on cells, the sections on the autonomic nervous system, the hypothalamus, and brainstem reticular formation, and the paragraphs about blood clotting, liver functions, pituitary and adrenal hormones, and kidney functions. Almost all chapters include new information about the body's responses to stress. All of them place a good deal of emphasis on the relationships between structure and function, on the formulation of principles, and on the application of facts and principles to specific situations.

Many new illustrations have been added. For example, diagrams of various homeostatic mechanisms which, it is hoped, will help students understand better their operation and significance. English terms only are used on illustrations in this edition.

Thought-provoking questions have been incorporated in the text rather frequently in the hope that they may stimulate students to read more carefully and to broaden their knowledge and to acquaint them with current physiological, clinical, and anatomical literature. Suggested Supplementary Readings for most chapters appear at the end of the book.

Appreciation keenly felt prompts the acknowledgement of indebtedness to many individuals for their suggestions, services, and intangible influences—to instructors for their thoughtful criticisms of earlier editions, to students for their enthusiasm and often their instruction, to the artist, Mrs. Mary Gund Farr, for her quick perceptions and skillful interpretations, to Mrs. Georgeanna Keefe for her fine secretarial help, to the publishers for their outstanding excellence in editing and producing the book, and, finally, to my family for making all work worthwhile.

Catherine Parker Anthony
Cleveland, Ohio

Preface to the first edition

"He teacheth ill that teacheth all." (English proverb, 1670.)

Because the course in anatomy and physiology for student nurses must cover such a large body of material in such a short time, and because this material seems difficult both for instructors to teach and for students to learn, one aim has been uppermost in the preparation of this book; namely, so to present the basic facts of body structure and function as to make the teaching of this complex subject less laborious, the learning of it less difficult, and both the teaching and learning more enjoyable.

This is primarily a teaching book, not a reference text. Since an important part of teaching skill lies in knowing what to omit, this book attempts to omit all nonessential, even though interesting, facts and to include all those facts which seem particularly pertinent for a nurse, or any beginning student of the human body, to know. The plan of teaching minimum essentials only and merely suggesting a greater wealth of material, the author believes, stimulates the student's interest and desire to discover more, and, at the same time, makes it possible for the instructor to concentrate on "driving home" the important, basic facts. Numerous devices are included which make it possible for the student to learn these basic facts more easily and quickly.

In short, the main difference between this book and other textbooks on the subject is its plan of presenting the material—a plan which minimizes the amount of time required for the instructor's preparation and which shortens and facilitates the student's learning process.

The essential features of this book are as follows:

1. Brief, topical outlines precede each chapter to help the student in following the arrangement of material and in seeing the facts in proper relationship. Paragraph headings outline the actual text so that it tallies with the topics in the outline surveys at the beginning of each chapter.

2. Only the main facts of anatomy and physiology are discussed and only the most relevant correlations with nursing and nonprofessional situations are made in the belief that too little is learned when too much is taught. Descriptions and explanations, therefore, are brief and to the point. Facts which the student should remember are emphasized, as are practical applications of those facts. Detailed facts which rightfully belong in a reference book or in a medical textbook, but which are superfluous in a text for a ninety- to one-hundred-hour course, are omitted. Consequently, the book is shorter than most texts on the subject.

3. Only those diagrams and pictures which illustrate points of particular interest or importance are included, but wherever facts are more easily understood from illustrations than from descriptions, illustrations are used. Many of the illustrations are of the simple, diagrammatic type which make such excellent teaching media.

4. The main facts, those which the student should remember, are summarized in outline form at the end of each chapter. These outlines are especially valuable for review purposes as they make it possible for the student to recognize which points are most important and to study them in a form which can be learned easily and quickly.

Also, these outline summaries constitute usable lesson plans for lecture or for discussion.

5. A complete list of review questions, some testing memory, some understanding, are included at the close of each chapter. These review questions serve several valuable purposes. They furnish a means by which the student can test herself to make sure that she has learned the facts which the text is designed to teach. They can be used as topics for classroom discussion and for oral drill.

Other features of teaching value in this book include the following:

A list of interest-arousing questions.

A vocabulary at the beginning of each chapter.

Numerous concise, simplified tables.

Study hints.

With this book go three hopes: that the nurse who studies it may gain a clear understanding of the normal body as a basis for understanding variations from the normal; that this understanding may enable her to give more intelligent care to the sick; and that the many correlations of science and nursing situations explained herein may help surround her work with an aura of interest which will make it fascinating instead of merely fatiguing!

Help and encouragement, on the part of several individuals, have made this book possible. I wish, therefore, to acknowledge my indebtedness to these friends: Miss Helen Williams, for her excellent drawings; Dr. Edmund E. Beard, for the use of his photographs of endocrine disorders; Miss Lura B. Eldredge, for her reading of parts of the manuscript and for valuable suggestions; Mr. Harry C. Biddle, for his encouragement and helpful advice; and members of my family, for their patience and faith.

Catherine Parker Anthony
Cleveland, Ohio

11

Unit four

Maintaining the metabolism of the body

Unit five

Reproduction of the human being

Unit six

Integration and control of body functions by hormones

Unit seven

Fluid, electrolyte, and acid-base balance

Study hints

If you really want to learn the subject matter in this book, do these things:

1 Start your study period with an active desire to learn the material. Approach with the attitude that what you are about to learn is both interesting and useful for you to know.

2 Have a clear idea in mind what it is you should learn from each chapter. The outline surveys at the beginning of each chapter tell you the main facts to look for and help you follow the arrangement of the material. Consult these outlines frequently while you are studying.

3 Check up on yourself to see whether or not you have learned what the material is trying to teach by answering the review questions at the end of each chapter. Testing knowledge is an important part of learning; do not neglect it.

The body as an integrated whole

Chapter 1

The body—a structural and functional unit

**The body—a unit composed of
many smaller units**
Architectural plan
Component units
Descriptive terms

**The body—one function com-
posed of many smaller func-
tions**
Survival
Homeostasis
Metabolism
Integration

Human anatomy and physiology are biological sciences; that is, they are branches of knowledge about living things. *Anatomy* is the science of the structure, and *physiology* is the science of the function of the most wondrous of all structures—the human body. Before attempting to explore details about the body, it seems feasible to examine some of its general characteristics much as it is prudent to study the map of a strange city before embarking upon an excursion through it. Two general characteristics are these.

The body is a single large structure made up of many smaller structures. It is a unit composed of smaller units.

The body performs a single large function made up of many smaller functions.

This chapter explores these two ideas briefly.

THE BODY—A UNIT COMPOSED OF MANY SMALLER UNITS

The concept of a large unit made up of lesser units is a familiar one. A city, for example, is such a unit. So, also, is a factory, or a hospital, or an automobile, or a sewing machine, or even a molecule. In each instance, the large unit is not a mere collection of the smaller units but is something more than the sum of its parts. The "something more" results from organization of the smaller units, from a relating of each one to the others in a definite way. Disorganize any large unit, break it into its separate parts, no longer arranged in a definite pattern, and you have a lesser thing than before. No longer do you have something that you recognize as one integrated whole, but, instead, several things that are clearly disintegrated, unrelated units. Consider, for example, the difference between an assembled jigsaw puzzle and its disassembled pieces. The assembled jigsaw puzzle, because of the organization or arrangement of the units that compose it, is an integrated whole. Similarly, the body, because of the organization of its component units, is an integrated whole.

17

Organization is a vital characteristic of living things. Disorganization leads to death.

Before investigating the smaller units that compose the body, we shall describe its general architectural plan.

Architectural plan of the body

The human body has a definite architectural plan, the characteristic features being a backbone, bisymmetry, and two main cavities, one on the anterior (front or ventral) surface and the other on the posterior (back or dorsal) surface. Each of these cavities, in turn, is divided into smaller cavities.

1. *ventral cavity,* separated by the diaphragm muscle into (a) a *thoracic* or chest cavity, which has pleural, pericardial, and mediastinal subdivisions, and (b) an *abdominopelvic* cavity, subdivided into an upper abdominal and a lower pelvic portion.
2. *dorsal cavity,* divided into (a) a *cranial* cavity and (b) a *spinal* cavity.

The body cavities contain the various internal organs or *viscera.* For example, in the thoracic cavity are placed the lungs, heart, trachea, esophagus, thymus gland, and certain large blood and lymphatic vessels and nerves, whereas in the abdominal cavity are located the liver, gallbladder, stomach, pancreas, intestines, spleen, kidneys, and ureters. The bladder, certain reproductive organs (uterus, uterine tubes, and ovaries in the female; prostate gland, seminal vesicles, and part of the seminal ducts in the male), and part of the large intestine (namely, the sigmoid colon and rectum) are found in the pelvic cavity.

Component units of the body

The smallest and simplest units are called cells. These are not all identical units, however, but are differentiated into four main types: epithelial, muscle, nerve, and connective. A mass of like cells with its intercellular material is called a *tissue.* Epithelial tissue, muscle tissue, nervous tissue, and connective tissue are the four primary kinds of tissues, but there are also several subtypes of each. Human cells are microscopic structures, that is, visible with a microscope but too small to be seen with the naked eye. Tissues on the other hand are macroscopic structures. Such large numbers of cells compose tissues that they need no magnification to be seen. Cells are discussed in Chapter II and tissues in Chapter III.

The next step in the integration of the member units of the body is the organization of tissues into *organs*. The stomach, for example, is an organ in which all four primary tissues are organized in a unique pattern. Muscle and connective tissue are so arranged as to form the wall of this hollow organ of specific shape. Epithelial and connective tissues are organized into a lining for the inside of the wall, and nervous tissue is distributed to both wall and lining.

Another step toward integration occurs with the organization of organs into *systems*. For example, these organs, plus several accessory ones, make up the digestive system: mouth, pharynx, esophagus, stomach, and intestines. The human body contains nine different systems of organs: skeletal, muscular, circulatory, nervous, respiratory, digestive, urinary, reproductive, and endocrine. (For names and descriptions of the organs of a system, see chapter on that system.)

In summary, the body is itself a unit but is composed of many smaller units organized into increasingly larger and more complex units. Cells are organized into tissues, tissues into organs, organs into systems, and systems into the final unit, the body.

Terms used in describing the body

Directional terms

superior toward the head end of the body; upper. Example: the hand is part of the superior extremity.

inferior away from the head; lower. Example: the foot is part of the inferior extremity.

anterior or *ventral* front. Example: the kneecap is located on the anterior side of the leg.

posterior or *dorsal* back. Example: the shoulder blades are located on the posterior side of the body.

medial or *mesial* toward the midline of the body. Example: the great toe is located at the medial side of the foot.

lateral away from the midline of the body. Example: the little toe is located at the lateral side of the foot.

proximal near or toward a point of reference, usually the trunk or the midline of the body or the beginning or source of a part. Example: the elbow is located at the proximal end of the forearm.

distal away from a point of reference, usually the trunk or midline of the body or the source of a part. Example: the hand is located at the distal end of the forearm.

Terms used in describing the planes of the body

sagittal or *longitudinal* a lengthwise plane running from front to back, dividing the body or any part of it into right and left sides (Fig. 1).

frontal or *coronal* a lengthwise plane running from side to side, dividing the body or any part of it into anterior and posterior portions (Fig. 2).

transverse or *horizontal* a crosswise plane dividing the body or any part of it into upper and lower parts (Fig. 1).

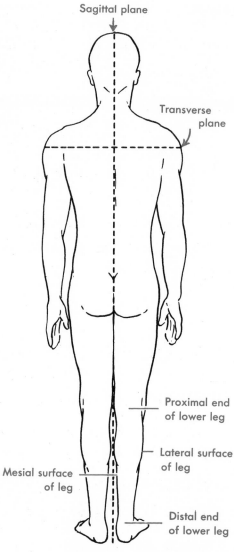

Sagittal plane

Transverse plane

Proximal end of lower leg

Lateral surface of leg

Mesial surface of leg

Distal end of lower leg

Fig. 1

Posterior view of human figure demonstrating meanings of terms used in describing the body.

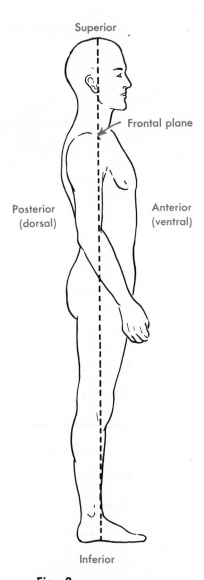

Superior

Frontal plane

Posterior (dorsal)

Anterior (ventral)

Inferior

Fig. 2

Lateral view of human figure demonstrating several terms used in describing the body.

<u>Anatomical position</u>

The term *anatomical position* refers to an erect standing position with arms at side, palms turned forward (supinated).

THE BODY—ONE FUNCTION COMPOSED OF MANY SMALLER FUNCTIONS

Survival

Survival is the one great function of the body. Numerous lesser functions—some exceedingly complex and others fairly simple—together achieve survival. Homeostasis, metabolism, and integration, for example, are some of the complex components of survival. Each of these, in turn, consists of many less complex functions. The rest of this chapter relates some general information about homeostasis, metabolism, and integration.

Homeostasis

Imagine a swimming pool with five feet of water in it and with water running into it at one end and out of it at the other but staying almost at the five-foot level all the time—perhaps rising an inch or two at times and lowering an inch or so at other times, but quickly coming back down to the five-foot level after it rises and back up to the five-foot level after it lowers. This is an illustration of a "state of dynamic equilibrium," an expression often used to describe the essential, paradoxical characteristic of homeostasis. Dynamic means moving, changing, not static. Equilibrium, on the other hand, means constancy, stability, balance. The water in the swimming pool was moving and changing; yet it stayed almost constant in amount. Its volume was stable, fluctuating only slightly above and below an equilibrium point.

Human cells require a fairly uniform or stable environment in order to maintain their life and health. Even a small shift away from the

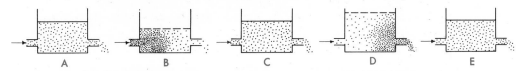

Fig. 3

A, Normal level or homeostasis; B, decreased level (compensated for by increased input and decreased output to restore normal level); C, restoration of normal level; D, increased level (compensated for by decreased input and increased output to restore normal level); E, restoration of normal level.

21

optimum state of equilibrium in the direction of either excess or deficiency interferes with the optimum functioning of the cells and indeed threatens their very survival. This requirement of steady surroundings applies to many aspects of the cellular environment—its chemical composition, its osmotic pressure, its temperature, its degree of alkalinity, etc.

Cellular environment, it must be remembered, is not synonymous with body environment. The body lives in the atmosphere surrounding it, the atmosphere of the external world. Body cells likewise live in the atmosphere surrounding them, but this is the liquid atmosphere of an internal world—specifically, the blood and interstitial fluid. Claude Bernard was one of the first to grasp and state this fundamental physiological concept that the extracellular fluid (blood and interstitial fluid) constitutes the body's internal environment and that its physical and chemical composition must be maintained relatively uniform if cells are to maintain their life and health. Later Cannon referred to the steady state of the internal environment as *homeostasis*. The term has since become a part of physiological language and is widely used today.

The principle of homeostasis is one of the most important of all physiological principles. It may be stated in this way: the body must maintain relative constancy of its chemicals and processes in order to survive. Or stated even more briefly: health and survival depend upon the body's maintaining or quickly restoring homeostasis.

All body structures play some role in maintaining the various steady states of the body. Homeostasis is virtually the job of every organ. It is, as someone has stated, the "main theme of physiology."

Metabolism

Metabolism is another part of the great work of the body, survival. In its broadest sense, metabolism means: "All the physical and chemical processes by which living organized substance is produced and maintained, and also the transformation by which energy is made available for the uses of the organism."* Hence, metabolism is a function made up of a host of other functions including the ingestion, digestion, and absorption of foods, respiration, circulation, anabolism, catabolism, secretion, excretion, and even the control of these many processes. In its narrower sense, metabolism consists of the myriad chemical reactions forever going on inside living cells. One series of

---

*From Dorland, W. A. N.: The American illustrated medical dictionary, ed. 23, Philadelphia, 1957, W. B. Saunders Co.

Body—structural
and
functional unit

22

reactions changes more complex compounds into simpler ones with the release of energy and is known as the process of *catabolism*. Another group uses energy to change simpler compounds into more complex ones and is known as the process of *anabolism*.

Catabolism supplies energy for all work done by the body, for every function it performs, whether it be movement of a finger or beating of the heart or secretion of a gland or growth of a cell or growth of the whole body or any other function whatever. Anabolism, in contrast to catabolism, uses energy instead of supplying it. Anabolism is work, in fact, one of the main kinds of physiological work, and it is done by all living cells. It is the process by which cells build their own substance (protoplasm)—by which tissues grow and repair themselves, in other words. It occurs, therefore, during reproduction of cells and of the body as a whole and during secretion by glands. In short, anabolism is the process by which cells synthesize any more complex compound from simpler compounds.

Integration

Integration means unification. The body exhibits both structural and functional integration, and both result from organization. Organization, in turn, results from control. As we have already noted, organization creates a single structure (the body) out of many structures (cells, tissues, organs, and systems). Organization also creates a single function (survival) out of many functions (digestion, respiration, circulation, movements, secretion, and all other body functions). To achieve integration of so many functions, nerve impulses and chemicals control the sequence and extent of bodily activities. Chief among control chemicals are enzymes, vitamins, and hormones.

One scientist had this to say about the importance to life of organization: ". . . we should heed the great fact of biological organization, for this, the most important characteristic of life, stands in direct opposition to the behavior of lifeless matter. The latter moves toward ever greater randomness. . . . A living organism, on the contrary, draws out from its chaotic environment particular substances and builds them into a system of ever greater and more organized complexity, thus steadily decreasing the randomness of matter. An organism is not an aggregate, but an integrate. Death releases matter from this unifying control, and the material of the body moves again toward disintegration. . . . Life *is* organization."*

---

* From Sinnott, Edmund W.: Two roads to truth, New York, 1953, The Viking Press, p. 131.

Outline summary

The body—a structural and functional unit

The body—a unit composed of many smaller units

Architectural plan

1. Backbone
2. Bilateral symmetry
3. Two main cavities
   a. ventral cavity
      1. thoracic
         a. pleural portions—contain lungs
         b. pericardial portion—contains heart
         c. mediastinal portion — area between lungs; contains trachea, esophagus, thymus gland, and certain large blood vessels, lymphatic vessels, and nerves
      2. abdominopelvic
         a. abdominal portion — contains liver, gallbladder, stomach, pancreas, intestines, spleen, kidneys and ureters
         b. pelvic portion—contains certain reproductive organs, bladder, and part of large intestine
   b. dorsal cavity
      1. cranial—contains brain, meninges, pineal and pituitary glands, and blood vessels
      2. spinal—contains spinal cord, meninges, and blood vessels

Component units of body

1. Cells—units of structure
2. Tissues—groups of like cells
3. Organs—composed of several kinds of tissues arranged in orderly manner so as to be able to carry on a special function
4. System—group of organs which work together to accomplish a complex function, such as digestion and absorption of food

Terms used in describing body

1. Directional terms
   a. superior—upper
   b. inferior—lower
   c. anterior—front
   d. posterior—back
   e. medial—toward midline
   f. lateral—away from midline
   g. proximal—toward attachment or beginning of a part
   h. distal—away from beginning of a part
2. Planes
   a. sagittal or longitudinal—lengthwise, dividing body, or any of its parts, into right and left portions
   b. frontal or coronal—lengthwise, dividing body or any of its parts into anterior and posterior portions
   c. transverse or horizontal—crosswise, dividing body or any of its parts into upper and lower sections
3. Anatomical position—erect, arms at sides, palms forward

The body—one function composed of many smaller functions

The one great function of the body—survival. Some major component functions—homeostasis, metabolism, and integration.

1. Homeostasis—a state of dynamic equilibrium; any change away from homostasis sets in operation mechanisms which tend to reverse change and restore homeostasis; principle of homeostasis one of most important physiological principles: health and survival depend upon body's maintenance of homeostasis
2. Metabolism—all chemical reactions occurring in cells
3. Catabolism—series of reactions that change more complex compounds into simpler ones with release of energy
4. Anabolism—group of reactions that use energy to build simpler compounds into more complex ones
5. Integration—control of bodily activities by nerve impulses and chemicals so that they function together to achieve survival

Review questions

The body—a structural and functional unit

1. Describe the structural organization of the body, including its general architectural plan and its component units.
2. Name the two cavities on the dorsal surface of the body. What organs do they contain?
3. Identify the divisions of the thoracic cavity and of the abdominopelvic cavity. Name the organs in each.
4. Identify four kinds of structural units of the body in order of increasing complexity.
5. State briefly the principle of homeostasis.
6. Define briefly each of the following terms:

anatomy	macroscopic
anterior	microscopic
biology	organ
cell	physiology
distal	posterior
frontal	proximal
inferior	sagittal
integration	tissue
lateral	transverse plane

Cells

Present-day knowledge about cells compared with that of ten years ago seems vast indeed. Ten years hence, in contrast, it will almost surely appear scanty and meager. For cellular research continues at a rapid pace, and every year sees the frontiers of this field pushed farther and farther out. This chapter relates a small part of the present knowledge about cells. Much of what we shall tell is old and established; some is new and tenuous. We shall start with information about an incredible substance called protoplasm.

PROTOPLASM

Protoplasm is living matter. All cells, therefore, whether plant or animal cells, are composed of protoplasm. In the words of Huxley, a nineteenth century English biologist, protoplasm is the "physical basis of life."

No unique element enters into the composition of protoplasm. Every element found in protoplasm is found also in nonliving substances.

The main elements of protoplasm are oxygen, carbon, hydrogen, and nitrogen. These and other elements* are combined to form various compounds of which water is by far the most abundant. In the water are dissolved other compounds, mainly proteins, carbohydrates, lipids (fats and fatlike compounds), and inorganic salts. But not all protoplasm has exactly the same chemical composition. For example, the protoplasm of fat cells contains a high percentage of lipids and that of muscle cells contains almost none. Red blood cell protoplasm contains the protein hemoglobin; muscle cells contain the proteins myosin and actin.

Some of the compounds dissolved in the water of protoplasm are

---

Human protoplasm (figures for elements based on analysis of entire body; for compounds, on analysis of dead mammalian striated muscle tissue; different tissues contain different kinds and proportions of elements and compounds):

Elements	%	Compounds	%
Oxygen	65	Water	75
Carbon	18	Proteins	20
Hydrogen	10	Lipids	2
Nitrogen	3	Carbohydrates	2
Calcium	2	Inorganic salts	1
Phosphorus	1		
Potassium	0.35		
Sulfur	0.25		
Chlorine	0.15		
Sodium	0.15		
Magnesium	0.05		
Iron	0.004		
Others	0.046		

The following mnemonic is an aid to remembering the elements composing the body. Each capital letter represents the chemical symbol of an element present: C. HOPKIN'S CaFe is Mighty good, a statement that should be taken with a grain of NaCl. The italicized letters symbolize carbon, hydrogen, oxygen, phosphorus, potassium, iodine, nitrogen, sulfur, calcium, iron, magnesium, sodium, and chlorine.

27

classified as *crystalloids* or *true solutes* and others as *colloids* or *colloidal solutes*.° Inorganic salts, such as sodium chloride, for example, are crystalloids, whereas proteins are colloids.

The physical state of protoplasm varies in different cells and in the same cell under different conditions; sometimes it is a sol or liquid and sometimes a gel. When protoplasm is in the sol state, its colloidal solutes are dispersed at random throughout its water, whereas in the gel state they become organized into a network that holds water bound in its spaces. Protoplasm may also be coagulated, an irreversible, fatal change in its physical state. Practical use is made of this knowledge in killing microorganisms. For example, heat and the salts of heavy metals such as bichloride of mercury and silver nitrate are thought to kill microorganisms by coagulating their protoplasm.

THE CELL

By definition a cell is the smallest unit of living matter that can maintain an independent existence and reproduce its kind. It is, as noted in Chapter I, the simplest unit in the structural organization of the body.

°The difference between crystalloids and colloids lies in the size and behavior of the dispersed particles of the solute. Five of the important characteristics which distinguish colloids from crystalloids are as follows:

1. Colloids form larger particles in solution than crystalloids. Colloid solute particles are those with diameters of about 1 up to 100 millimicrons; crystalloid solute particles are those with diameters less than about 1 millimicron. (A millimicron is one-millionth of a millimeter. Since a millimeter is one-thousandth of a meter or approximately one twenty-fifth of an inch, a millimicron is approximately one twenty-five millionth of an inch.)

2. Colloids, because they are relatively large particles, will not filter through parchment paper or through most cell membranes, whereas crystalloids will. The separation of colloids from crystalloids by passing a solution of them through a membrane which allows the crystalloids to filter through but which holds back the colloids is known as *dialysis*. Both colloids and crystalloids will pass through filter paper.

3. Colloidal solutions may exist in either a liquid state known as a *sol* or in a semisolid state called a *gel*. The blood protein, fibrinogen, a colloid in the sol state, is changed to the gel state (fibrin) during blood clotting.

4. Colloids exhibit imbibition, that is, have the power to take up large quantities of water without going into solution, much the way that a sponge takes up water. Soaking the colloid gelatin in cold water causes it to swell greatly as it takes up the water without going into solution. This property of colloids accounts for the fact that about three-fourths of the weight of the protoplasm of our tissues is water and yet they are quite firm and solid.

5. Colloidal particles bear an electrical charge; the fact that all particles of one colloid solution carry the same charge causes them to repel each other and thereby maintain their dispersion throughout the solvent.

Cells of one type differ from those of other types in shape and size as well as in chemical composition and function. Human cells vary in shape, for example, from long, slender threads to short cubes to miniature biconcave discs to highly irregular bits of protoplasm. Since all human cells probably measure less than a thousandth of an inch in diameter, they are too small to be seen with the naked eye. Yet all of them, no matter how diminutive, are tridimensional. We tend to forget this fact that cells have depth as well as breadth and length because of their flat appearance in most diagrams and microscopic sections.

Cell structure

Cells are the simplest structural units of the body, but even their complexity taxes the imagination. The electron microscope has revealed penetrating views of cell interiors, and other new techniques have disclosed additional secrets about cell structure. As a result, cells are now known to have numerous structural parts besides limiting membrane, cytoplasm, and nucleus. Cell structures we shall discuss are the following:

1. Cell membrane
2. Cytoplasmic organelles
   a. Mitochondria
   b. Ribosomes (RNA or ribonucleic acid granules)
   c. Endoplasmic reticulum
   d. Golgi apparatus
   e. Centrosome
3. Nucleus

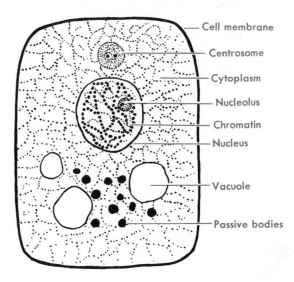

Fig. 4

Diagram of a cell based on what is seen with the light microscope. Not all of the structures shown, however, can be demonstrated in all cells.

29

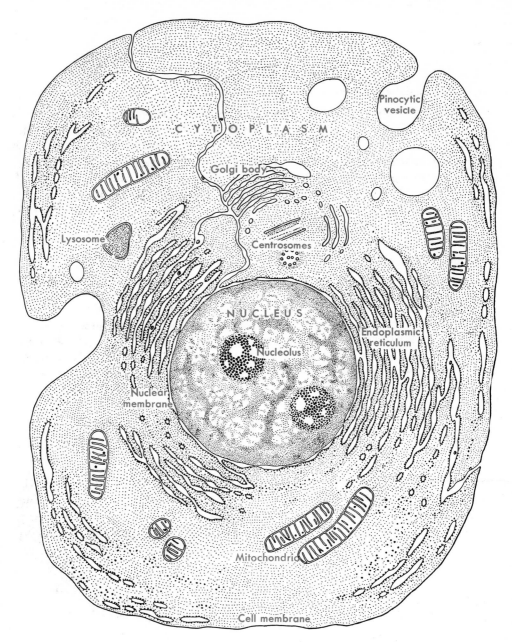

Fig. 5

Modern diagram of a typical cell. This diagram is based
on what is seen in an electron micrograph. The mitochondria
are the sites of the oxidative reactions that provide the cell
with energy. The dots that line the endoplasmic reticulum are
ribosomes, the sites of protein synthesis. In cell division
the pair of centrosomes, one shown in longitudinal section (rods)
and the other in cross section (circles), part to form poles
of spindle apparatus that separates two duplicate sets of chromosomes.
(From Brachet, J.: Scient. Am. **205**:55, 1961.)

Cell membrane

A cell membrane is an exceedingly flimsy structure only about 75 to 100 angstroms thick.* And yet this delicate structure performs life-saving functions. It acts as a barrier that protects the interior of the cell from its environment and, even more remarkable, it helps regulate the movement of water and other substances into and out of the cell. It is generally agreed that protein and lipid molecules compose the cell membrane. Presumably a single outer layer of protein molecules lies over two middle layers of lipid molecules which in turn lie over an innermost layer of protein molecules.

One more feature of cell membrane structure should be mentioned—it has holes in it, extremely tiny ones, called pores. Although no cell membrane pores have been seen, even with the powerful magnification of the electron microscope, those in red blood cells have been measured experimentally and were found to have diameters of about 7 angstroms.† Laboratory findings have suggested also that cell pores are few and far apart. In the words of one biochemist, "If one speaks of the membrane as a sieve, it is a sieve with very few holes in it."‡

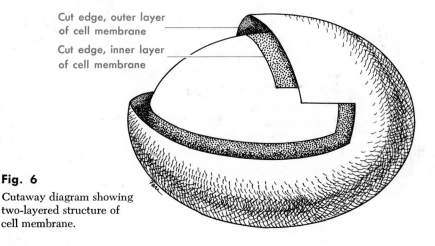

Cut edge, outer layer of cell membrane

Cut edge, inner layer of cell membrane

Fig. 6

Cutaway diagram showing two-layered structure of cell membrane.

---

*1 angstrom unit equals
   1/10th millimicron
   or
   1/10 millionth millimeter
   or a little less than
   1/250 millionth of an inch
75 angstroms, therefore, equal a little less than 3/10 millionths of an inch.
†Solomon, Arthur K.: Pores in the cell membrane, Scient. Am. **203:**146, 1960.
‡From Holter, Heinz: How things get into cells, Scient. Am. **205:**167, 1961.

Cytoplasmic organelles

Cytoplasm is cell protoplasm exclusive of the nucleus. Various laboratory techniques developed during recent years have shown that cytoplasm is not a homogeneous substance as once thought, but that its component compounds are organized into numerous small structures referred to collectively as *cytoplasmic organelles.* In electron micrographs these appear as tiny tubules, vesicles, granules, and fibrils.

Mitochondria. Mitochondria are organelles that resemble small sacs made of two delicate membranes. The inner membrane forms shelflike projections into the interior of the sac (Fig. 7). Some active cells contain two thousand or more mitochondria, whereas some less active cells may have only fifty or so. They perform a vital function. Inside them go on the series of chemical reactions that provide most of the energy for cellular work. Hence they have been described as miniature "power plants" of cells.

Ribosomes. Ribosomes (RNA granules, ergastoplasm) are the numerous granules of ribonucleic acid that stud the outer surfaces of tubules and vesicles in the cytoplasm and also lie between these structures. Their function is thought to be the important one of synthesizing cell proteins. In fact, a nickname for ribosomes is protein factories.

Endoplasmic reticulum. The endoplasmic reticulum is a complicated network of tubules and vesicles that extends in all directions throughout the cytoplasm. Some of the tubules are dotted with RNA granules, and others are smooth appearing.

Golgi apparatus. The Golgi apparatus is a cytoplasmic organelle located near the nucleus; it consists of membranous vacuoles and canals which connect, it is now generally believed, with other parts of the endoplasmic reticulum. The function of the Golgi apparatus is still not known. Recent evidence, however, suggests

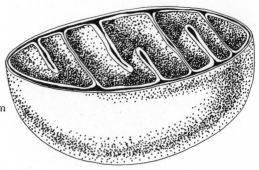

Fig. 7

Mitochondrion. Cutaway diagram showing the two-layered structure of its delicate membranous wall, similar to that of the cell membrane.

that it may segregate and condense secretions before they leave the cell.

Centrosome. The centrosome is a cytoplasmic organelle so-named because of its location near the center of the cell. Usually it lies in the same general area as the Golgi apparatus but is not part of it. Under the light microscope in a cell soon to divide, the centrosome appears as a small area of cytoplasm containing two dots, called *centrioles.* The electron microscope reveals these dots as tiny little cylinders whose walls consist of fine tubules. Two curious, astonishing observations about these structures are that one lies at right angles to the other and that a definite number of groups of tubules seems to form the walls of each centriole—nine groups with often three tubules in a group. An impressive illustration, would you not agree, of the principle that the most important characteristic of life is organization? During mitosis (cell division), the centrioles move apart and become the opposite poles of the mitotic spindle (p. 51). Presumably they play some part in organizing the fibrils of this spindle.

Nucleus

The nucleus is a spherical body located in the center of a cell. A double-layered, pore-containing membrane encloses the nucleus and separates it from the cytoplasm. In the nucleus can frequently be seen numerous deep-staining *chromatin granules.* Histologists formerly identified these as fragments of *chromosomes* (short, rodlike structures seen in the nucleus during mitosis). They believed that chromosomes broke up into chromatin granules after mitosis and that chromatin granules reassembled into chromosomes during the next cell division. More recent work has disproved this idea. It is now known that chromosomes remain intact at all times, that they do not break apart. What they do is change their shape. Their threadlike molecules coil up tightly during mitosis into short stubby rods. Then after mitosis they uncoil again except in certain segments in which the tight little coils remain. These, being denser than the thin elongated sections, absorb more stain and show up as chromatin granules.

Chromosomes are made up of *genes.* Although genes are too small to be seen even with the great magnification of an electron microscope, they have attained fame for their function as the determinants of heredity. Chromosomes consist mainly of deoxyribonucleic acid (DNA), and genes are segments of chromosomes.

Small globular bodies often seen in the nucleus are called *nucleoli.* According to some investigators, they appear to function as centers for protein and RNA synthesis.

33

Cell physiology

Each tiny cell of the body is a functional as well as a structural unit. Each cell carries on functions which characterize it as alive* and, in addition, performs some special function for the body as a whole, such as secretion by epithelial cells, contraction by muscle cells, transmission of impulses by nerve cells, etc. Each cell, in other words, fulfills its own requisites for life and, in addition, contributes to the life of the entire body. And vice versa, the body performs functions for each of its parts. It supplies them with nutrients and oxygen, and it removes their wastes, for example. In short, a relationship of mutual interdependence exists between the body as a whole and its various parts. Optimum health of the body, that is, depends upon optimum health of each of its parts, down even to the smallest cell. Conversely, optimum health of each individual part depends upon optimum health of the body as a whole. In equation form, this physiological principle of mutual interdependence might be expressed as follows:

body health ⇌ system health ⇌ organ health ⇌ tissue
health ⇌ cellular health

Some parts of the body, of course, are more important for healthy survival than others. Nerve cells that control respiration, for instance, are more important for survival than muscle cells that move the little finger.

---

*All living cells exhibit the characteristics of irritability and conductivity. Many cells also possess the property of contractility. All living cells have the ability to carry on the processes of metabolism, and most cells can reproduce themselves.

Irritability means the ability to respond to a stimulus (any change in the environment). Irritability is one of the functions of the cell membrane.

Conductivity, a property closely related to irritability, is the ability to transmit impulses from the point of stimulation to another region. Like irritability, conductivity is a function of the cell membrane. Nerve cells exhibit the highest degree of conductivity.

Contractility means literally the ability to contract or, more simply, the ability to move. It might also be described as the ability of protoplasm to change its shape. Muscle cells exhibit the highest degree of contractility.

Metabolism means essentially the release of energy and the synthesis of complex compounds. It consists of all the chemical reactions that occur inside cells and involves such functions as the movement of substances in and out of cells and growth and repair of the cell's own protoplasm.

Reproduction means the process by which a living organism produces a replica of itself. This ability varies in different cells. Blood cells, for example, do not reproduce. Some cells seem to lose the ability to reproduce with age, and the female sex cell, after union with the male sex cell, reproduces a whole new individual, not merely another cell like itself. Human cells reproduce by a mechanism known as mitosis, discussed on pp. 49 to 51.

Cell physiology deals with all kinds of cell functions, but we shall confine our discussion to the movement of substances through cell membranes, cell metabolism, and cell reproduction.

Movement of substances through cell membrane

Traffic through the cell membrane flows continuously and in both directions. Substances move through the membrane by two kinds of processes:

1. *physical processes or passive transport*—diffusion, osmosis, and filtration. In passive transport the cell does not supply the energy that drives the substance through the membrane.
2. *physiological processes*—active transport mechanisms, phagocytosis, and pincocytosis. In physiological processes cellular catabolism supplies the energy for driving the substance through the membrane.

Diffusion. Diffusion means scattering or spreading. It occurs because small particles such as molecules and ions are forever on the go. They move continuously, rapidly, and at random. Here is a convincing way to observe the results of diffusion. Place a cube of sugar on the bottom of each of two cups of water. Immediately skim off a spoonful of liquid from the top of one cup and taste it. About 10 minutes later do the same from the other cup. The second sample will taste sweet; the first will not. Sugar molecules in the second cup will have had time to move in all directions—up, out, down, in—to diffuse, that is, throughout the water. More of them, however, will have diffused up and away from the cube than down and toward it. In other words, their *net* diffusion will have been away from areas of their greater concentration toward areas of their lesser concentration. So that they eventually become evenly distributed throughout the water. Diffusion always results—if time enough elapses—in an even scattering of solute particles among solvent molecules. Water is the solvent in all body fluids.

Consider another example—two solutions, 20% and 10% sodium chloride (NaCl) separated by a membrane permeable to both NaCl and water. Sodium chloride particles and water molecules racing in all directions through the solution collide with each other and with the membrane. Some inevitably hit membrane pores from the 20% side and some from the 10% side. Just as inevitably, some bound through the pores in both directions. For a while more NaCl particles enter pores from the 20% side where they are more numerous. Net diffusion of NaCl, therefore, takes place from the more concentrated 20% side to the less concentrated 10% side. But gradually this decreases the 20% concentration and increases the 10% concentration. So that

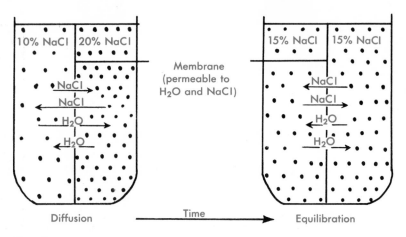

Fig. 8

Diffusion. Because the membrane separating the 10% NaCl from the 20% NaCl is permeable to both NaCl and H_2O particles, both substances diffuse through the membrane in both directions. But, as the longer arrows indicate, more NaCl particles move out of the 20% solution, where there are more of them, into the 10% solution, where there are fewer of them, than in the opposite direction. Simultaneously, more water molecules move from the 10% solution, where there are more of them, into the 20% solution, where there are fewer of them. Result: equilibration of the concentrations of the two solutions after an elapse of time. From then on equal numbers of NaCl particles diffuse in both directions, as do equal numbers of H_2O molecules.

eventually both concentrations become equal. The two solutions *equilibrate*. From that moment on, NaCl diffusion to the right through the membrane equals NaCl diffusion to the left. Similarly, water diffusion to the right equals water diffusion to the left. The two preceding illustrations point up several principles about diffusion worth remembering.

1. Diffusion is movement of solute and solvent particles in all directions through a solution or in both directions through a membrane.

2. Net diffusion of any substance occurs from the higher to the lower concentration of that substance. *Net diffusion of solute particles* takes place from a more to a less concentrated solution. But *net diffusion of water molecules* takes place from a less to a more concentrated solution, which is from the area of more water concentration to the area of less water concentration.

3. All particles not larger than the pores of a nonliving membrane diffuse through it and, given time enough, equilibrate across it. Equilibration means the same number of solute particles diffusing in both directions and the same number of water molecules diffusing in both directions. This principle does not hold true for living membranes. Sodium and potassium ions, for instance, are smaller than the pores in human cell membranes so that theoretically should diffuse through them and equilibrate as the law of diffusion dictates. But normally

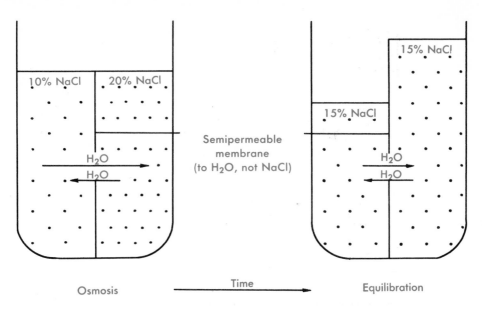

Semipermeable membrane (to H₂O, not NaCl)

Osmosis ⟶ Time ⟶ Equilibration

Fig. 9

Because the membrane separating the above solutions is semipermeable (permeable to water but not to the solute present), only water molecules move through it. As the longer arrow in the left-hand diagram indicates, more water molecules osmose from the dilute solution, where there are proportionately more of them, into the concentrated solution, where there are proportionately fewer of them, than in the opposite direction. The *net* direction of osmosis, in other words, is toward the more concentrated solution. This results in two changes—equilibration of the concentrations of the two solutions and an increase in volume of the solution which was originally more concentrated.

sodium and potassium do not equilibrate across human cell membranes. Sodium ions are more concentrated in the extracellular fluid around our cells than in the intracellular fluid within them. Potassium ions, on the other hand, are more concentrated in intracellular fluid than in extracellular fluid. Additional mechanisms other than diffusion must, therefore, operate to move sodium and potassium through cell membranes.

4. Diffusion is a passive transport mechanism because cells are passive, not active and working in this process. Cellular catabolism does not supply the energy that moves diffusing particles; the random movements of the particles themselves supply it.

Think about these diffusion principles. Make sure that you understand them, for they have many applications in physiology. Our very lives, in fact, depend upon diffusion. Evidence? Oxygen, the "breath of life," moves by diffusion from air spaces in our lungs through capillary membranes into blood and from blood through capillary membranes, interstitial fluid, and cell membranes into our cells.

Osmosis. Osmosis is the diffusion of water (or other solvent in nonliving systems) through a semipermeable membrane. A semipermeable membrane is half-permeable in the sense that it is freely permeable to water molecules but not to all solute particles present. Water diffuses rapidly through a semipermeable membrane, whereas at least one kind of solute present diffuses either not at all through it or diffuses much more slowly than does the water.

An example may reveal some clarifying principles. Assume that a semipermeable membrane separates a 10% cane sugar solution from distilled water. The membrane is impermeable to cane sugar molecules but is freely permeable to water. Or said another way, sugar is nondiffusible and water is diffusible through it. In which direction does the net movement of water occur? Into or out of the sugar solution? Why? If you are not sure, reread the diffusion principles on pp. 36 to 37. The water movement in this illustration is osmosis—a better term here than diffusion because it means specifically diffusion of water across a semipermeable membrane. Water molecules will move rapidly back and forth in both directions through the pores in the membrane. But clearly more of them enter the pores from the pure water side where no solute molecules compete for the openings. Consequently more water osmoses into the sugar solution than out of it. And as a result of this net osmosis into the sugar solution, its volume and pressure both increase. The pressure that develops in a solution due to osmosis of water into it is called *osmotic pressure*.* "The

---

*The potential osmotic pressure of a solution is directly determined by the number of solute particles it contains. The more solute particles per unit volume of solution, the greater the osmotic pressure. By experimentation it is known that 1 liter of solution that contains 1 gram molecular weight of a nonelectrolyte has a potential osmotic pressure of 17,024 mm. Hg pressure (0° C.), and that 1 liter of solution that contains 1 gram molecular weight of an electrolyte that yields 2 ions per molecule has a potential osmotic pressure of twice that amount because it contains twice as many solute particles.

The following formula for computing potential osmotic pressure derives from the preceding experimental facts.

$$\text{Potential osmotic pressure mm. Hg} = \frac{\text{Grams solute per liter}}{\text{Molecular weight solute}} \times \frac{\text{Number ions per molecule if solute electrolyte}}{} \times 17{,}024$$

Example:

What is potential osmotic pressure of 0.85% NaCl solution?
Molecular weight of NaCl = 58
NaCl forms 2 ions per molecule in solution

$$\frac{8.5}{58} \times 2 \times 17{,}024 \text{ mm. Hg} = \frac{4989.6 \text{ mm. Hg potential osmotic pressure of}}{0.85\% \text{ NaCl solution}}$$

Problem: What is potential osmotic pressure of 5% glucose? Molecular weight glucose = 180. Glucose does not ionize; it is a nonelectrolyte.

osmotic pressure is a result of the diffusion process *not a cause* of it."[*]
The footnote on the opposite page explains the method of computing
the *potential osmotic pressure* of a solution—that is, the osmotic pressure that would develop in a solution if it were separated from distilled
water by a semipermeable membrane.

Two solutions that have the same potential osmotic pressure are
said to be *isotonic* to each other. When such solutions are separated
by a semipermeable membrane, an equal amount of water osmoses
into and out of both of them. There is no net osmosis into either solution. Medical practice applies this principle by using solutions that
are isotonic to body fluids for intravenous and intramuscular injections
—isotonic NaCl solution, for example, with a concentration of about
0.9%. With such solutions, there is no net osmosis into or out of body
cells. In other words, cells neither lose or gain water; that is, they do
not become hydrated or dehydrated, changes that are injurious.

A *hypertonic* solution has a greater potential osmotic pressure than
the solution it is hypertonic to. Solution A is hypertonic to solution
B if its potential osmotic pressure is higher than that of B. Solution
B is *hypotonic* to A because its potential osmotic pressure is less than
that of A. If a semipermeable membrane separated solution A from
solution B, A would gain water and develop an actual osmotic pressure
because of net osmosis of water into it from B. We shall follow this
idea farther in the chapter on fluid and electrolyte balance. Enough
now to fix in mind the principle that net osmosis of water is *into the
hypertonic solution from the hypotonic solution* separated from it by
a semipermeable membrane. The factor that determines potential
osmotic pressure is the number of solute particles per unit volume of
solution. (See footnote, p. 38.) The more solute particles, the higher
will be the potential osmotic pressure. Therefore, of two solutions of
the same solute the more concentrated contains more solute particles
so has the higher potential osmotic pressure and is hypertonic to the
less concentrated solution. But if two solutions contain different
solutes, this may not be true. The *less* concentrated solution in such
cases may actually have more solute particles and a higher potential
osmotic pressure and may be hypertonic to the more concentrated
solution. A 2% NaCl solution, for example, is hypertonic to a 5% glucose
solution. (To prove this to yourself, read the footnote on p. 38 and
then compute the potential osmotic pressure of 2% NaCl and 5% glucose, using the formula given in the footnote.)

All body fluids contain solutes. Our cell membranes, therefore,

---

[*]From Best, Charles H., and Taylor, N. B.: The physiologic basis of medical
practice, ed. 7, Baltimore, 1961, Williams & Wilkins Co.

never separate solutions from distilled water. Yet osmosis does occur across them. They act as semipermeable membranes to several kinds of solute particles. The fluids on both sides of cell membranes contain relatively nondiffusible solutes. This is the reason that water osmoses rather than merely diffuses in and out of body cells.

Following is a summary of important principles about osmosis:

1. Osmosis is the movement of water through a semipermeable membrane. (In some nonliving systems, other solvents besides water osmose.)

2. Osmosis can occur only when at least one nondiffusible (or relatively nondiffusible) solute is present on at least one side of a membrane. If the membrane is freely permeable to all solutes and if all solutes present are freely diffusible through it, water then diffuses not osmoses across the membrane.

3. Water osmoses in both directions through a semipermeable membrane.

4. *Net* osmosis is from hypotonic into hypertonic solution.

5. Net osmosis tends to increase the volume and pressure of the originally hypertonic solution.

Suggestion: Reread and compare each of the principles just stated with corresponding diffusion principles on pp. 36 and 37.

Filtration. Filtration is the physical process by which water and dissolved substances pass through a membrane when the hydrostatic pressure on one side of the membrane is higher than on the other. Hydrostatic pressure is pressure due to the weight of a liquid. Thus, the greater the volume of water pressing on each unit of the surface area of a membrane, the greater is the hydrostatic pressure exerted against it. Hydrostatic pressure constitutes a pushing force that pushes both water and solutes through a membrane permeable to them. If a membrane separates solutions of different hydrostatic pressures, water and solutes filter through the membrane from the solution of higher hydrostatic pressure into the one of lower hydrostatic pressure for the obvious reason that the higher hydrostatic pressure pushes with more force than the lower hydrostatic pressure. Blood in the capillaries, for instance, exerts more hydrostatic pressure than does interstitial fluid on the other side of the capillary membrane. Water and true solutes, therefore, filter from blood into interstitial fluid (Fig. 10). Blood in the capillaries of the kidneys exerts a higher hydrostatic pressure than does the fluid in the microscopic funnellike structures (Bowman's capsules) encapsulating them. Water and crystalloids, therefore, filter out of the blood into the Bowman's capsules (Fig. 11). Normally, substances do not cross cell membranes by filtration but may under some abnormal conditions—in marked edema, for example.

Filtration

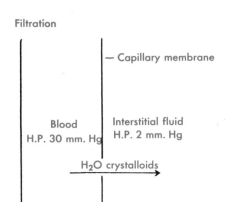

— Capillary membrane

Blood
H.P. 30 mm. Hg

Interstitial fluid
H.P. 2 mm. Hg

H_2O crystalloids

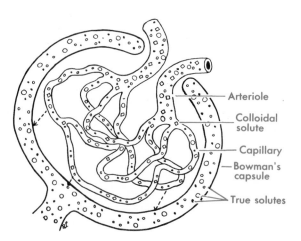

— Arteriole

— Colloidal solute

— Capillary

— Bowman's capsule

— True solutes

Fig. 10

Diagram illustrating filtration through the capillary membrane. The latter is permeable to water and crystalloids. Because blood hydrostatic pressure is greater than that of interstitial fluid, it "pushes" water and crystalloids through the capillary membrane into the interstitial fluid.

Fig. 11

Diagram to demonstrate filtration. In the kidneys, water (black dots) and true solutes (circles) filter through the walls of the glomeruli (capillaries) into the Bowman's capsules, but colloidal solutes (squares) remain in the blood because the capillary-capsule membrane is not permeable to them.

Active transport mechanisms. Although the nature of active transport mechanisms is only postulated, convincing evidence supports the concept that they exist. Most impressive, perhaps, is the fact that some substances (potassium, for example) are much more concentrated inside the cell than in the interstitial fluid around the cell, whereas others (notably, sodium) are much more concentrated outside the cell than inside it. If physical processes alone moved materials through cell membranes, such differences in concentrations could not prevail. According to the laws of diffusion and osmosis, equilibration would occur. Instead, concentration gradients (differences) of many substances prevail across cell membranes. Active transport mechanisms, therefore, are assumed to move these substances uphill with regard to their concentrations—an impossible feat for passive mechanisms. (Net diffusion, you will recall, moves a substance from the area where it is more concentrated downhill to the area where it is less concentrated and results finally in equilibration or equal movement in both directions.) Moving a substance through a membrane against its concentration gradient is work—cellular work of such importance that cells soon die if their active transportation systems fail. Such mechanisms probably handle much of the traffic through cell membranes. Energy for this vital work, as previously noted, comes from the cell's own catabolism.

41

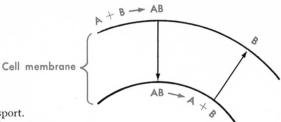

Fig. 12

Scheme to illustrate
the principle of active transport.
A, Substance transported; **B,** carrier
compound which unites with **A** at outer surface of cell membrane,
diffuses through membrane to its inner surface and there dissociates from **A.**
A moves into cytoplasm of cells; **B** moves back to outer surface of membrane
ready to transport another molecule of **A.**

Several theories about active transport mechanisms have been proposed. Most of them assume the existence of carrier compounds although none as yet has been identified. In simplest form, the theories suggest the following steps as the essential parts of an active transport mechanism:

1. On one surface of a cell membrane, a molecule of the substance to be transported (A) combines with a molecule of carrier compound (B) to form a new compound (AB).

   A + B —————————→ AB

2. Molecule AB passes through the cell membrane into or out of the cell.

3. At the other surface of the cell membrane, AB dissociates, releasing the transported substance.

   AB —————————→ A + B

4. Carrier compound molecule B moves back to the surface from which it came ready to shuttle another molecule of A through the membrane.

What substances do cells actively transport through their membranes? Some very essential ones. Some of the main ones are foods (glucose and amino acids), ions (sodium, potassium, and many or perhaps all other ions), and special substances (for example, glandular secretions). The fact that these substances are actively transported does not necessarily mean that none of them can cross cell membranes by any other methods. Glucose, sodium, and potassium, for example, probably also diffuse through them to some extent.

Phagocytosis and pinocytosis

Phagocytosis and pinocytosis are also mechanisms for moving substances through cell membranes but only in one direction—inward. More than sixty years ago Elie Metchnikoff of the Pasteur Institute saw white blood cells engulf bacteria. It reminded him of eating; therefore, from the Greek words for eating, cell, and action, he coined the word phagocytosis. Some thirty years later, in 1931, W. H. Lewis of Johns Hopkins University saw something similar in time-lapse photographs of some tissue culture cells. These cells, however, were engulfing tiny droplets of fluid instead of solid particles. They seemed to be drinking rather than eating so he named the process pinocytosis (from the Greek word for drinking). Both phagocytosis and pinocytosis consist of the same essential steps. A segment of cell membrane forms a small pocket around a bit of solid or liquid material outside the cell, pinches off from the rest of the membrane, and migrates inward as a closed vacuole or vesicle.

Cellular metabolism

Cellular metabolism is a life-maintaining function performed by every cell. It consists of two series of chemical reactions. One series, catabolism, disassembles larger molecules into smaller ones while releasing energy. The other series of reactions, anabolism, assembles smaller molecules into larger ones and in so doing uses energy. Catabolism furnishes energy for all cellular work, whereas anabolism uses some of this energy to synthesize the cell's most important products—notably enzymes and the cell's protoplasm. Thus anabolism occurs in cell growth, repair, and reproduction. Both catabolism and anabolism are as intricate as they are vital.

Catabolism. Catabolism, one of the two processes of metabolism, itself consists of two processes, glycolysis and the citric acid cycle (also called tricarboxylic acid cycle, Kreb's cycle, and cell respiration). Since the detailed study of these complex mechanisms belongs to the science of biochemistry, we shall discuss each of them only briefly.

Glycolysis. Glycolysis accomplishes two things: it partially dismembers the glucose molecule and partially releases its stored energy. More specifically, as a result of glycolysis, one glucose molecule becomes two pyruvic acid molecules (or two lactic acid molecules if oxygen is

Fig. 13

Glycolysis. Glucose, a molecule containing 6 carbon atoms is split by a series of chemical reactions into 2 molecules of pyruvic acid, each of which contain only 3 carbon atoms. Fig. 14 shows the series of intermediate reactions in brief form.

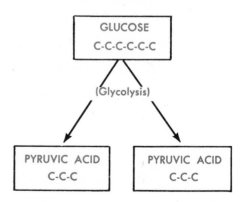

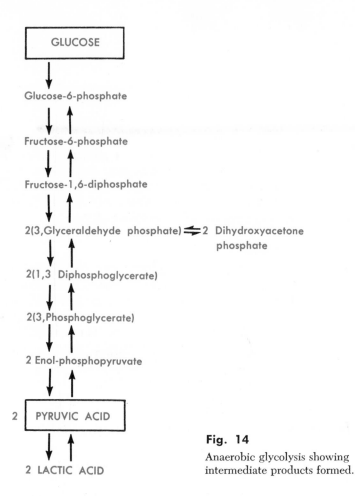

GLUCOSE

Glucose-6-phosphate

Fructose-6-phosphate

Fructose-1,6-diphosphate

2(3,Glyceraldehyde phosphate) ⇌ 2 Dihydroxyacetone phosphate

2(1,3 Diphosphoglycerate)

2(3,Phosphoglycerate)

2 Enol-phosphopyruvate

2 | PYRUVIC ACID

2 LACTIC ACID

Fig. 14

Anaerobic glycolysis showing intermediate products formed.

not plentiful in the cell). And concurrently a small part of the energy in a glucose molecule is transferred to two molecules of another compound, adenosine triphosphate (ATP), and some is transformed into heat energy. To achieve these chemical and energy changes, at least ten or eleven reactions occur in rapid-fire succession, with each one catalyzed by a specific enzyme. By the end of glycolysis the relatively large glucose molecule that contains 6 carbon atoms has been replaced by two smaller pyruvic acid molecules each of which contains only 3 carbon atoms.

Citric acid cycle. When adequate amounts of oxygen are present, pyruvic acid immediately diffuses into the mitochondria of the cell. Here, other enzymes cause it to combine with a substance called coenzyme A. This reaction splits the 3-carbon pyruvic acid molecule into a 2-carbon and a 1-carbon molecule (acetyl-coA and carbon dioxide, respectively). Acetyl-coA then combines with oxaloacetic acid to form citric acid (tricarboxylic acid). Next, citric acid undergoes a cyclical series of changes which both regenerates oxaloacetic acid and

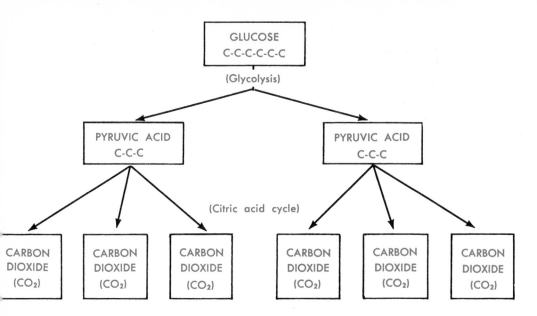

Fig. 15

Citric acid cycle splits 2 molecules of pyruvic acid (3 carbon atoms each)
formed by process of glycolysis, into 6 molecules of carbon dioxide
(1 carbon atom each) and 6 molecules of water. See Fig. 16 for intermediate
products formed during the citric acid cycle and Fig. 17 for energy changes.

forms two molecules of carbon dioxide from the acetyl-coA originally
fed into the cycle. With this, the breakdown of the glucose molecule
is completed. In summary, catabolism produces the following major
chemical changes:

1 molecule glucose

(glycolysis)

2 molecules pyruvic acid

(citric acid cycle)

6 molecules carbon dioxide + 6 molecules water

Food substances other than glucose are, of course, also catabolized
by cells, but these will be discussed in Chapter 11.

Energy changes accompany the chemical changes of both glycolysis
and the citric acid cycle. Most of the energy, however, is known to
be released during the citric acid cycle by oxidation reactions. In
barest outline, the oxidation mechanism presumably operates in this
way. Hydrogen atoms are passed along a chain of "respiratory enzymes"
to oxygen, with which they react to form water—the other end
product of catabolism besides carbon dioxide. As the hydrogen atoms
move down the respiratory enzyme chain to oxygen, small bursts of
energy are emitted and are used to drive a phosphorylation reaction
which forms ATP. In other words, part of the energy emitted during
the oxidation reactions is transferred to molecules of ATP, there to be

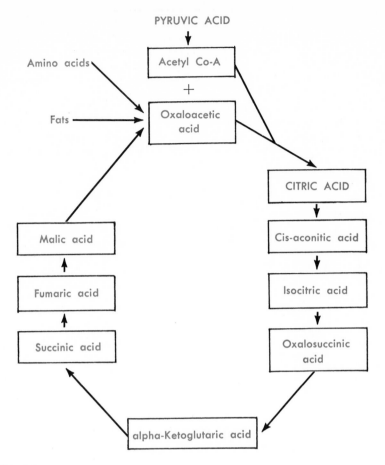

Fig. 16

Citric acid cycle showing intermediate products formed (see text).

stored until needed for cellular work, and the rest is transformed to heat (Fig. 17).

$$ADP \; + \; PO_4 \; + \; \underset{\substack{\text{(released in} \\ \text{glycolysis} \\ \text{and citric acid} \\ \text{cycle})}}{\text{ENERGY}} \longrightarrow \underset{\substack{\text{(stored} \\ \text{energy)}}}{\text{ATP}}$$

Some of the respiratory chain enzymes so far identified are DPN (diphosphopyridine nucleotide), flavoprotein, and several cytochromes. Incidentally, DPN and flavoprotein contain vitamins (niacin and riboflavin, respectively) and cytochromes contain iron. Hence, to ensure normal cellular oxidation, vitamin and mineral-containing foods must be included in the daily diet.

ATP is now recognized as the universal intracellular energy-carrier. Energy stored in ATP has an advantage over that in glucose in that it can be released more quickly. As its name suggests, ATP con-

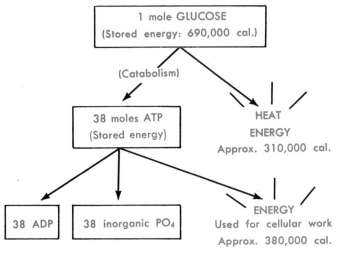

Fig. 17

Catabolism energy changes. Of 38 moles of ATP formed during
catabolism, 2 are formed during glycolysis and 36 during Krebs' citric
acid cycle. Efficiency of this energy supply mechanism is about 55%.
(Reasoning: Of the approximate total 690,000 calories stored in 1 mole of
glucose, about 380,000 are eventually made available for cellular work
by the breakdown of the 38 moles of ATP formed during catabolism
of 1 mole of glucose.)

tains three phosphate groups. The last two bonds connecting these
groups are high-energy bonds that can be broken instantaneously to
release energy the moment the cell needs it to do any of its work.

$$\text{ATP} \longrightarrow \text{ADP} + \text{PO}_4 + \text{Energy}$$

(stored   (used for cellular
energy)   work)

In contrast to this explosive release of energy from ATP by only
one reaction, the release of energy from glucose by a long series of
reactions is sluggish indeed. According to most authorities, a total
of 38 moles of ATP are formed during the catabolism of one mole of
glucose—2 during glycolysis and 36 during the citric acid cycle. These
38 ATP moles store more than half of the energy originally stored in
one mole of glucose.* The rest is transformed into heat energy, a form
of energy cells cannot use for work.

Since the citric acid cycle releases most of the energy from food

---

*One mole of glucose stores about 690,000 calories (or 690 large Calories)
of chemical energy. When 1 mole of ADP combines with phosphate to form
1 mole of ATP, there is an energy transfer of about 10,000 calories from glucose to ATP. (Some authorities say as little as 7000 and others as much as 12,000
calories.) During catabolism, therefore, a total of perhaps 380,000 calories or
about 55% of the 690,000 calories originally in 1 mole of glucose are transferred
to 38 moles of ATP. Later as needed, these 38 moles of ATP break down,
releasing approximately 380,000 calories of energy which the cell uses to do its
different kinds of work (Fig. 17).

molecules, and since this cycle of chemical reactions takes place inside mitochondria, these tiny structures are aptly described as the power plants of cells. Recent research has indicated the location of participating enzymes—citric acid cycle enzymes in the interior of mitochondria and respiratory chain enzymes in the delicate membranes that form the walls of the mitochondria. Even more amazing it is now postulated that all these enzyme molecules are placed in the mitochondria in an exact sequence, that of the chemical reactions in which they participate! Albert Lehninger, the biochemist who discovered that citric acid cycle and respiratory enzymes are located in mitochondria, writes: "If the classical engineering science of energy transformation is humbled by what is now known about the power plants of the cell, so are the newer and more glamorous branches of engineering. The technology of electronics has achieved amazing success in packaging and miniaturizing the components of a computer. But these advances still fall far short of accomplishing the unbelievable miniaturization of complex energy-transducing components that has been perfected by organic evolution in each living cell."[*]

Cell reproduction

If the title Most Important of All Compounds in the Body were to be bestowed, it might well go to deoxyribonucleic acid (DNA), the main constituent of chromosomes. For this is the substance that directs the making of each new generation of human cells. Packaged within DNA molecules are complete instructions for producing new cells like the old. We shall, therefore, relate some facts and theories about DNA before describing the mechanism of cell reproduction.

DNA is a giant molecule and is uniquely shaped, like a microscopic ladder twisted into a spiral thousands of turns long. Sugar and phosphate molecules, alternating one after the other, make up the sides of the long ladder. Deoxyribose is the name of the sugar. It is a sugar that is not sweet, and its molecules contain only 5-carbon atoms instead of 6, as do glucose molecules (deoxyribose, therefore, is classified as a pentose and glucose as a hexose).

Each rung of the DNA ladder consists of a pair of nitrogenous bases attached at the sides to sugar molecules and in the middle to each other by hydrogen. Only four kinds of nitrogenous bases occur in DNA —adenine, thymine, cytosine, and guanine. Moreover, the same two bases always pair off with each other. Adenine always pairs with thymine; cytosine always pairs with guanine. The sequence of base pairs, however, varies. Different kinds of DNA occur in different kinds of

---

[*]From Lehninger, A.: How cells transform energy, Scient. Am. **205:**62, 1961.

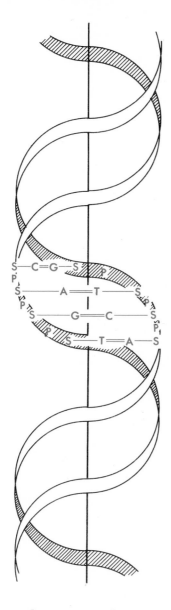

Watson-Crick structure of DNA molecule

A = adenine ⎫
C = cytosine ⎬ Classified as
G = guanine ⎭ nitrogenous bases
T = thymine
P = phosphate
S = sugar (deoxyribose)

Fig. 18

Note that each side of the DNA molecule
consists of alternating sugar and phosphate
groups, presumably thousands of them.
Each sugar group is united to the sugar
group opposite it by a pair of nitrogenous
bases, adenine-thymine or thymine-adenine
and cytosine-guanine or guanine-cytosine.
Differences in the sequences of base pairs
establishes the identity of the many
different kinds of DNA.

cells, and the difference lies in the sequence of the thousands of nitrogenous base pairs. Interestingly, a *gene* is now conceived of as a segment of a DNA molecule, with the specific sequence of adenine-
thymine and cytosine-guanine pairs determining the specific function of the gene. Each gene determines some characteristic of the
new cells formed by cell reproduction. Genes, in other words, are
heredity determinants.

Mitosis is the mechanism by which human cells reproduce. It consists of five steps or phases involving the nucleus and centrioles: interphase (or resting stage), prophase, metaphase, anaphase, and telo-

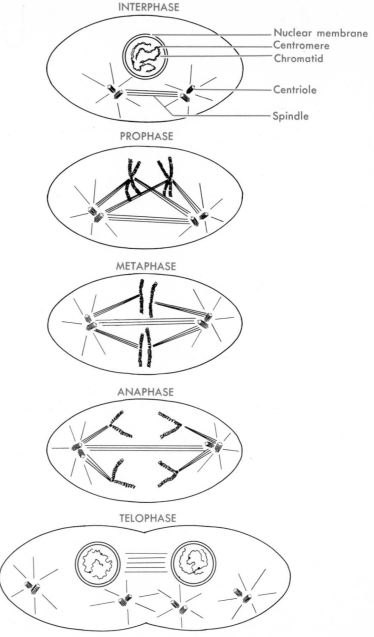

Fig. 19

Mitosis (see text for explanation).

phase. You may find it easier to follow the events of these phases if you study Fig. 19 as you read the following description.

During the *interphase* each chromosome duplicates itself and splits longitudinally into two chromatids that stay attached to each other at only one point (the centromere). The centrioles start moving away from each other, and a spindle begins to form between them. The interphase now gives way to the *prophase.* The two chromatids of each chromosome coil up tightly into short, stubby rods, the nuclear membrane disappears, the centrioles move to opposite poles of the cell, and formation of the spindle continues. The latter consists of fibers probably formed by the centrioles. Connections are established between the fibers and the chromatids.

Completion of the spindle occurs during the metaphase. Spindle fibers extend from the centrioles in all directions toward the midplane of the cell and pull attached chromatid pairs into alignment along the equator of the cell. Then in the *anaphase* the two chromatids of each pair become detached from each other and move to opposite poles. The newly separated chromatids constitute new chromosomes.

The final stage, *telophase,* now begins. A nuclear membrane forms around each set of chromosomes, and the individual chromosomes uncoil into long threads. (A few coils remain; these show up as chromatin granules under the light microscope.) Each centriole produces a new centriole. The cell becomes constricted along its midplane and then divides in two. The miracle of reproduction has again come to pass. Two new cells have replaced one old cell. Each new cell has a full set of chromosomes and all the potentialities of the cell from which it came.

To discover how cells are organized into different kinds of tissues and what special features characterize them, read the next chapter.

Outline summary

Cells

Protoplasm

1. Definition—living matter; all cells are composed of protoplasm
2. Composition
   a. main elements—carbon, hydrogen, oxygen; and nitrogen
   b. main compounds—water, proteins, carbohydrates, lipids, and inorganic salts
3. Physical state—varies: sometimes a sol; sometimes a gel

The cell

1. Definition—the smallest unit of living matter that can maintain an independent existence and reproduce its kind

2. Structure—main parts of cell are:
   a. cell membrane
      1. about 3/10 millionths inch thick according to present estimates
      2. composed of protein and lipid molecules; presumably a double layer of lipid molecules sandwiched between an inner and an outer layer of protein molecules
      3. has tiny opening or pores; few in number; spaced far apart
   b. cytoplasmic organelles
      1. mitochondria—minute membranous sacs in cytoplasm; main power plants

of cell since citric acid cycle occurs in mitochondria

2. ribosomes (RNA granules)—numerous granules that stud outer surfaces of tubules and vesicles in cytoplasm; presumably synthesize proteins

3. endoplasmic reticulum—complicated network of tubules and vesicles in cytoplasm

4. Golgi apparatus—tubules and vesicles near nucleus; believed to connect with endoplasmic reticulum; function still unknown

5. centrosome—small area of cytoplasm containing two centrioles located in same general area as Golgi apparatus but not part of it

c. nucleus

1. spherical body in center of cell; separated from cytoplasm by double-layered, pore-containing membrane

2. chromosomes located in nucleus; genes are segments of the long DNA molecules that compose chromosomes

3. Cellular physiology

a. movement of substances through cell membrane—by physical processes (diffusion, osmosis, and filtration) and by physiological processes (active transport, phagocytosis , and pinocytosis)

1. diffusion—movement of solute and solvent particles in all directions through a solution or in both directions through a membrane

a. net diffusion of solute particles—from more to less concentrated solution

b. net diffusion of water—from less to more concentrated solution

Diffusion tends to produce equilibration of solutions on opposite sides of a membrane but many exceptions to this rule when membrane is living

2. osmosis—movement of water in both directions through a semipermeable membrane

a. net osmosis—more water moves from hypotonic to hypertonic solution, that is, from solution that contains fewer to one that contains more solute particles per unit volume; osmosis tends to produce equilibration of solutions on opposite sides of a membrane

b. osmotic pressure—the pressure that develops in a solution as the result of net osmosis into it

c. isotonic solution—one that has the same potential osmotic pressure as the solution it is isotonic to; no net osmosis between isotonic solutions

d. hypertonic solution—has greater potential osmotic pressure than solution it is hypertonic to; net osmosis into hypertonic solution from hypotonic solution

e. hypotonic solution—has lower potential osmotic pressure than solution it is hypotonic to; net osmosis out of hypotonic solution into hypertonic solution

3. filtration—movement of water and solutes through a membrane from higher hydrostatic pressure area to a lower pressure area

4. active transport—movement of substance through living cell membrane

a. Direction of active transport—uphill against the concentration gradient of the substance transported, that is, from solution in which substance is less concentrated to that in which it is more concentrated. Note that this is the opposite from the direction of net diffusion of a substance; net diffusion of any substance is always from the area where it is more concentrated to that where it is less concentrated *(eating)*

5. phagocytosis—movement of solid particles into cell; segment of cell membrane forms pocket around particle outside the cell, then pinches off from rest of membrane, and migrates inward *(drinking)*

6. pinocytosis—movement of fluid into cell by process comparable to phagocytosis

b. cellular metabolism—consists of two processes, catabolism and anabolism

1. catabolism—makes energy available for

all cellular work; consists of two processes, glycolysis and citric acid cycle
a. glycolysis—a series of chemical reactions that convert one glucose molecule to two pyruvic acid molecules
and yield a small amount of high-
energy ATP and of heat
b. citric acid cycle—a series of chemical reactions that convert 2 pyruvic
acid molecules to 6 carbon dioxide
molecules and yield considerably
more heat and ATP than glycolysis
does
2. anabolism—synthesis of various compounds from simpler compounds; an
important kind of cellular work that
uses some of energy made available
by catabolism
c. cell reproduction—by mitosis, a complicated mechanism involving mainly nucleus and centrosome

Review questions

Cells

1. What are the four main elements in protoplasm?
2. What is the most abundant compound in
protoplasm?
3. What four kinds of compounds constitute
the chief solutes of protoplasm?
4. Differentiate between a crystalloid and a
colloid.
5. Name some important crystalloid compounds.
6. Name some important colloid compounds.
7. Define the terms micron and millimicron.
About how many millimicrons equals 1
inch?
8. Define the word cell.
9. Describe the structure and function of
mitochondria.
10. What are ribosomes and what is their presumed function?
11. What is the endoplasmic reticulum?
12. What is the Golgi apparatus?

13. What is the centrosome?
14. Describe the current concept of cell membrane structure.
15. Define the term angstrom. About how
many angstroms thick is a cell membrane
thought to be? How thick would this be in
terms of inches?
16. What is the current concept of chromosome and gene structure?
17. Explain the terms DNA and RNA.
18. What is meant by the expression "the
physiological principle of mutual interdependence"?
19. Distinguish between a physical and a
physiological process.
20. Write a paragraph comparing diffusion,
osmosis, and filtration. Give a specific
example of each.
21. What do the terms net diffusion and net
osmosis mean?
22. Explain the terms osmotic pressure and
potential osmotic pressure.
23. What factor directly determines the potential osmotic pressure of a solution?
24. Explain the terms isotonic, hypotonic, and
hypertonic.
25. You have three solutions: 0.9% sodium
chloride, 0.9% glucose, and 9% glucose.
Which label—isotonic, hypertonic, hypotonic—would you apply to each. Use the
formula in the footnote p. 38 before answering.
26. How does an active transport mechanism
differ from physical processes for moving
substances across cell membranes?
27. What are some of the substances believed
to be actively transported through membranes?
28. Explain the terms phagocytosis and pinocytosis.
29. Define briefly the following terms:

anabolism	citric acid cycle
ATP	glycolysis
catabolism	metabolism

30. You have often heard that you should include vitamins and minerals in your daily
diet. What scientific reason underlies this
advice?

Tissues

Tissues are organizations of cells. Nonliving intercellular substances fill in any spaces between cells. Using appearance and functions as criteria for classification, there are four basic types of tissues—epithelial, muscle, connective, and nerve—and many subtypes. Tissues differ in structure, and because structure determines function, they also differ in function. Not only do cell size, shape, and arrangement vary in different kinds of tissues, but so too does the amount and kind of intercellular substance present. Some tissues contain almost no intercellular material; others consist predominantly of it. Some intercellular substance has the form of fibers, some is unformed jelly, and some is fluid, the interstitial fluid, that bathes most living human cells.

EPITHELIAL TISSUE

Epithelial tissue performs the function of protection, secretion, and absorption and serves as a filtration and diffusion membrane. Only a fairly sturdy tissue can offer protection so that where this function is needed, epithelial tissue consists of several layers of cells. In contrast, where substances need to move through a tissue, where they need to be absorbed, to filter, or to diffuse, here epithelial tissue consists of a single layer of cells. All types of epithelial tissue are composed largely or entirely of cells. In other words, they contain little or no intercellular substance. They also contain no blood vessels. These are located in the connective tissue which epithelial tissue always overlies and adheres to firmly. Another common characteristic of all types of epithelial cells is that they undergo mitosis—a fact of practical importance since it means that old or destroyed epithelial cells can be replaced by new ones. Figs. 20 to 22 show the several varieties of epithelial tissue described in the following paragraphs.

Simple squamous epithelial tissue

Simple squamous epithelial tissue consists of only one layer of flat cells. Consequently substances can readily diffuse or filter through

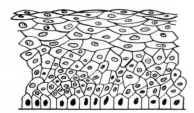

Fig. 20

Stratified squamous
epithelial tissue.

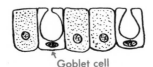

Goblet cell

Fig. 21

Columnar epithelial tissue.

Fig. 22

Ciliated epithelial tissue.

(From Francis and Farrell: Integrated anatomy and physiology, St. Louis, The C. V. Mosby Co.)

this type of tissue. The microscopic air sacs of the lungs, for example, are composed of this kind of tissue, as are the linings of blood and lymphatic vessels and the surfaces of the pleura, pericardium, and peritoneum. (Blood and lymphatic vessel linings are called *endothelium*, and the surfaces of the pleura, pericardium, and peritoneum are called *mesothelium*. Some histologists classify these as connective tissue.)

Simple columnar epithelium

Simple columnar epithelium lines the stomach and intestines and parts of the respiratory tract. A single layer of cells composes this tissue, but the cells vary in type. Goblet cells are specialized for secreting mucus. The secreting cells of glands constitute *glandular epithelial tissue*. Ciliated cells are specialized for moving mucus—upward and outward, for instance, in the respiratory tract. Still other cells are specialized for absorption through simple columnar epithelium.

Stratified squamous epithelium

Stratified squamous epithelium lines the mouth and esophagus. Its several layers of cells serve a protective function. The surface of the skin is composed of a special kind of stratified squamous epithelium (p. 71).

MUSCLE TISSUE

The specialties of muscle tissues are contraction and conduction, and its big contribution to survival is movement. Because not all muscle tissue is alike—in location, in microscopic appearance, and in nervous control—these criteria are used to classify its types. Thus, using location as the criterion, there are three kinds of muscle tissue:
1. *skeletal muscle*—attached to bones

2. *visceral muscle*—in the walls of hollow internal structures such as blood vessels, intestines, uterus, and many others.
3. *cardiac muscle*—composes the wall of the heart

With microscopic appearance as the basis of classification, there are only two types of muscle tissue: striated (named for cross striations seen in these cells) and nonstriated or smooth (no cross striations in cells).

On the basis of nervous control, there are also two kinds of muscle tissue: voluntary and involuntary.

Voluntary muscle receives nerve fibers from the cerebrospinal nervous system; therefore, its contraction can be voluntarily controlled. Involuntary muscle, on the other hand, receives nerve fibers from the autonomic nervous system so that its contraction cannot be voluntarily controlled (except in a few rare individuals). Skeletal muscle is voluntary muscle; visceral and cardiac muscle are involuntary. Visceral and cardiac muscle are also automatic,* meaning that even without nervous stimulation they continue to contract. Skeletal muscle, in contrast, cannot contract automatically. Anything that cuts off its nerve impulses paralyzes it, that is puts it immediately out of working order. This is the way poliomyelitis works, for example. It damages nerve cells that conduct impulses to skeletal muscles so that they no longer conduct, and deprived of stimulation, the muscles are paralyzed.

Finally, combining these classifications, we have the following:
1. *skeletal* or striated voluntary muscle
2. *cardiac* or striated involuntary muscle
3. *visceral* or nonstriated involuntary muscle

Because of their elongated narrow shape, muscle cells are often referred to as muscle fibers. Muscle cell cytoplasm is called sarcoplasm, and the cell membrane has the special name sarcolemma. Embedded in the sarcoplasm are many myofibrils and mitochondria. Each myofibril consists of many myofilaments, and each myofilament consists of protein molecules. According to Ham,† actin and probably tropomyosin are the proteins composing the finest myofilaments, and myosin is the protein composing the coarser ones. A single striated muscle fiber has many nuclei. It also has many cross striations.

Smooth muscle cells are also long narrow fibers but not nearly so

---

*For an account of an interesting experiment that demonstrates cardiac muscle automaticity, see Harary, I.: Heart cells in vitro, Scient. Am. **206**:141, 1962.

†The fine structure of myofilaments are discussed in Ham, Arthur W., and Leeson, Thomas S.: Histology, ed. 4, Philadelphia, 1961, J. B. Lippincott Co., pp. 426-429.

57

Fig. 23

Smooth muscle tissue. Note the tapering spindle shape of the cells
and absence of cross striations. (From Addison: Piersol's
normal histology, Philadelphia, J. B. Lippincott Co.)

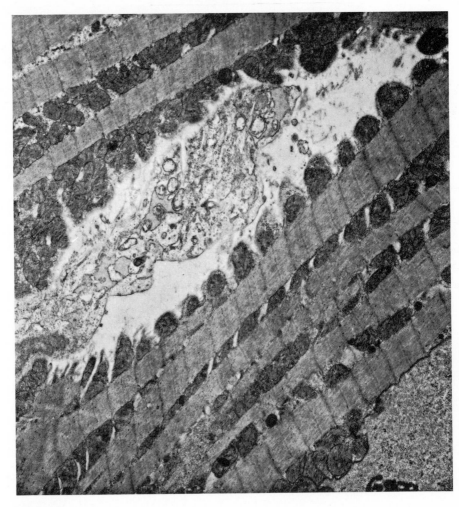

Fig. 24

Electron microphotograph of rabbit heart muscle. (x12,500.) (Courtesy
Western Reserve University Department of Pathology.)

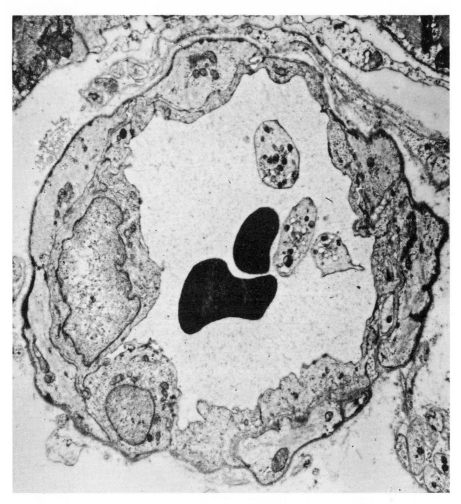

Fig. 25

Electron microphotograph of arteriole in rat heart.
(x12,500.) Note the irregularly shaped endothelial
cells lining the arteriole and the two black appearing
red blood cells inside the vessel. (Courtesy Western
Reserve University Department of Pathology.)

long as striated fibers. For example, one can see the full length
of a smooth muscle fiber in a microscopic field but only part of a
striated fiber. (According to one estimate, the longest smooth muscle
fibers measure about 500 microns and the longest striated fibers about
40,000 microns. Can you translate these measurements into millimeters and inches? If not, and if you are curious, see footnote p. 28).
Smooth muscle fibers have only one nucleus per fiber and are nonstriated or smooth in appearance.

Under the light microscope cardiac muscle fibers have cross striations and unique dark bands (intercalated disks). They also seem

to be incomplete cells that branch into each other to form a big continuous mass of protoplasm known as a syncytium. The electron microscope, however, has revealed that the intercalated disks are actually places where two cell membranes abut at the ends of adjacent cardiac fibers. Cardiac fibers do branch and anastomose, but contrary to previous belief, they do not form a syncytium. A complete cell membrane encloses each cardiac fiber—around its ends (at intercalated disks) as well as its sides.

CONNECTIVE TISSUE

Connective tissue is the most widespread and abundant tissue in the body. It connects and supports—connects tissues to each other, for example, and muscles to bones and bones to other bones. It forms a supporting framework for the body as a whole and for its organs individually. Connective tissue exists in more varied forms than the other three basic tissues. Delicate tissue paper webs, strong, tough cords, rigid bones—all are made of connective tissue. One scheme of classification lists the following types of connective tissue*:

1. Loose, ordinary, including areolar
2. Adipose
3. Dense fibrous
4. Cartilage
5. Bone
6. Hemopoietic (BLOOD)
7. Dentin

Intercellular material predominates in most connective tissues. Its qualities, therefore, determine the qualities of the different kinds of conective tissues. Some are soft, others are firm or hard, some are tough, others delicate, some are rigid, others elastic—and in each case it is their intercellular substance that makes them so.

Intercellular substance may consist, as we have already mentioned, of either fibers or shapeless jellies or more commonly of both. There are three kinds of fibers—collagenic, reticular, and elastic. They differ considerably in their properties. Collagenic fibers are tough and strong, reticular fibers are delicate, and elastic fibers are extendable and elastic. Collagenic fibers often occur in bundles—an arrangement that provides great tensile strength. Reticular fibers, in contrast, occur in networks and, although delicate, support small structures such as capillaries and nerve fibers. The protein collagen composes

---

*Blood is sometimes included as a type of connective tissue, but we shall classify it as a body fluid.

collagenic fibers. You know the hydrated form of this compound as gelatin. Collagenic fibers are also called white fibers because of their white appearance in fresh specimens.

Like intercellular fibers, intercellular jellies also vary in properties. The ground substance in loose, ordinary connective tissue, for example, is a soft, viscous jelly, whereas the matrix of bone is a very hard substance—as "hard as bone," in fact. A compound called hyaluronic acid gives the viscous quality to intercellular jellies, but it can be converted to a watery consistency by the enzyme hyaluronidase. Physicians have made use of this latter fact for some time now. They frequently give a commercial preparation of hyaluronidase intramuscularly or subcutaneously with drugs or fluids. By decreasing the viscosity of intercellular material, the enzyme hastens diffusion and absorption and thereby lessens tissue tension and pain.

Loose, ordinary connective tissue, including areolar

First, a few words of explanation about the names of this kind of tissue. It is called loose because it is stretchable and ordinary because it is one of the most widely distributed of all tissues; it is

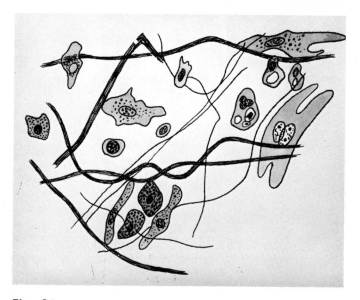

Fig. 26

Areolar connective tissue; the bundles of fibers are collagenous or white fibers; the single fibers are elastic fibers. Several kinds of connective tissue cells are shown between the fibers.

common and ordinary, not special like some kinds of connective tissue (bone and cartilage, for example) that help form comparatively few structures. Areolar was the early name for the loose, ordinary connective tissue that connects many adjacent structures of the body. It acts like a glue spread between them but an elastic glue that permits movement. The word areolar means "like a small space" and refers to the bubbles that appear as areolar tissue is pulled apart during dissection.

Although intercellular substance is prominent in loose, ordinary connective tissue, cells also are numerous and varied. Collagenic and elastic fibers are interwoven loosely and embedded in a soft viscous ground substance. Of the half dozen or so kinds of cells present, *fibroblasts* are the most common and *macrophages* are second. Fibroblasts synthesize intercellular substances of both types, that is, both fibers and jellies. Macrophages carry on phagocytosis. *Plasma cells, fat cells, mast cells,* and some *white blood cells* (leukocytes) are also found in loose ordinary connective tissue but in smaller numbers than fibroblasts and macrophages. In recent years plasma cells have come into the spotlight as antibody producers.

Adipose tissue

Adipose tissue differs from loose, ordinary connective tissue mainly in that it contains predominantly fat cells and many less fibroblasts, macrophages and mast cells. Adipose tissue occurs mainly in certain areas of the body known as fat depots.

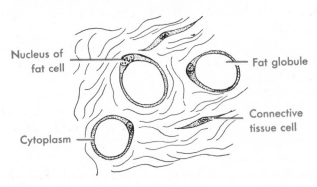

Fig. 27

Adipose tissue. Note the thin peripheral layer of cytoplasm in the adipose cells due to the fat droplet within each cell.
(From Francis and Farrell: Integrated anatomy and physiology, St. Louis, The C. V. Mosby Co.)

Dense fibrous tissue

Dense fibrous tissue consists mainly of fibrous intercellular substance with relatively few fibroblast cells. It composes structures that need great tensile strength, such as tendons and ligaments, and various other structures, including the deeper layer of the skin.

Bone and cartilage

Bone and cartilage are discussed in Chapter V.

Hemopoietic tissue

Hemopoietic tissue is discussed in Chapter IX.

Reticuloendothelial cells

Various types of connective tissue cells that carry on phagocytosis, although widely scattered throughout the body, are sometimes spoken of as the *reticuloendothelial system.* They constitute an important part of the body's defense mechanism. Opinions differ somewhat as to which cells belong in the category of reticuloendothelial cells. There does seem to be agreement, however, that the following three types of phagocytic cells belong in this classification:

1. *reticuloendothelial cells* located in the lining of blood sinusoids* in the liver, spleen, and bone marrow and in the lining of lymph channels in lymph nodes. Another name for the reticuloendothelial cells of liver sinusoids is stellate cells of von Kuppfer—stellate because of their starlike shape and von Kuppfer for the man who first described them.
2. *macrophages*—one of the commonest type cells in connective tissues; also called tissue histiocytes, resting wandering cells, and clasmatocytes.
3. *microglia*—located in the central nervous system.

Reticuloendothelial cells have a mark of distinction interesting to note: they may be either fixed or wandering cells. Many of them, especially macrophages, can come loose from their usual site and wander out into regions where their function of phagocytosis is needed, into inflamed or injured areas. Later, with their defense mission accomplished, they move back to their respective places and

---

*Sinusoids are tiny blood vessels. They are analogous to capillaries in that they connect the arterial side of circulation to the venous side, but differ in minor ways from capillaries.

remain fixed there until a future need arises. Apropos of this dual nature of reticuloendothelial cells, did you notice one of the names macrophages go by? "Resting wandering cells."

NERVE TISSUE

Nerve tissue is discussed in Chapter VII.

Table 1. Tissues

Tissue	Location	Function
Epithelial Simple squamous	Alveoli of lungs	Diffusion
	Lining blood and lymphatic vessels (called endothelium; classed as connective tissue by some histologists)	Diffusion; filtration
	Surface layer of pleura, pericardium, peritoneum (called mesothelium; classed as connective tissue by some histologists)	Diffusion
Simple columnar	Surface layer of lining of stomach, intestines, and part of respiratory tract	Absorption; secretion
Stratified squamous	Surface of lining of mouth and esophagus	Protection
	Surface of skin (epidermis)	Protection
Connective (Most widely distributed of all tissues)		
Adipose (fat)	Subcutaneously Padding at various points	Protection Insulation Support Reserve food
Dense fibrous	Tendons Ligaments Aponeuroses Deep fascia Dermis Scars Capsule of kidney, etc.	Furnish flexible but strong connection

HUMAN ANATOMY

THIRTEEN FULL-COLOR PLATES WITH SIX IN TRANSPARENT

"TRANS-VISION"® SHOWING STRUCTURES OF THE HUMAN TORSO

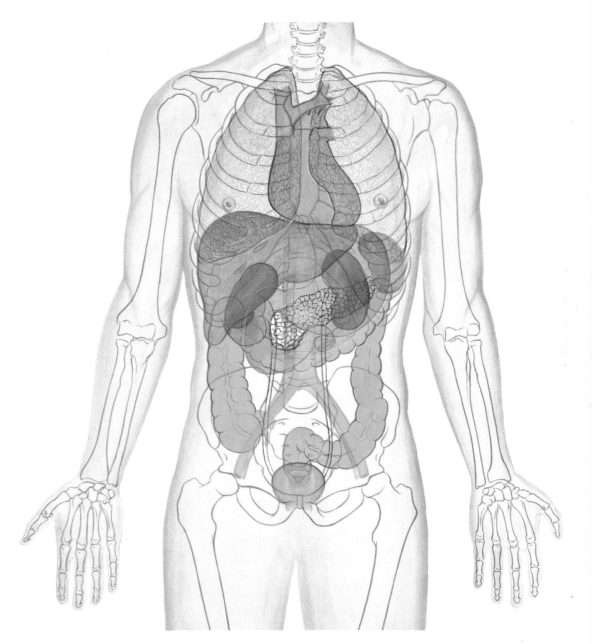

Plate I

ERNEST W. BECK, medical illustrator

in collaboration with
HARRY MONSEN , Ph.D.
Professor of Anatomy, College of Medicine, University of Illinois,

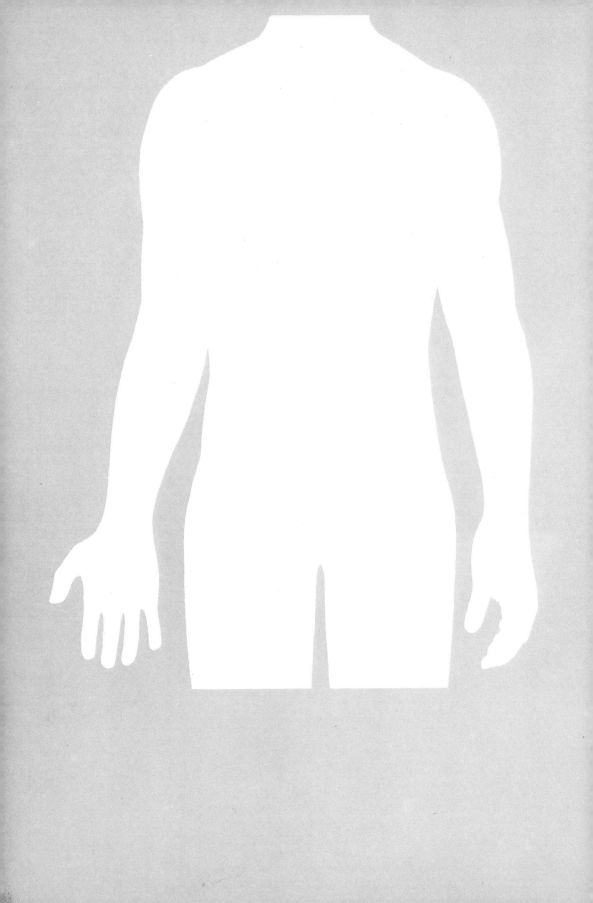

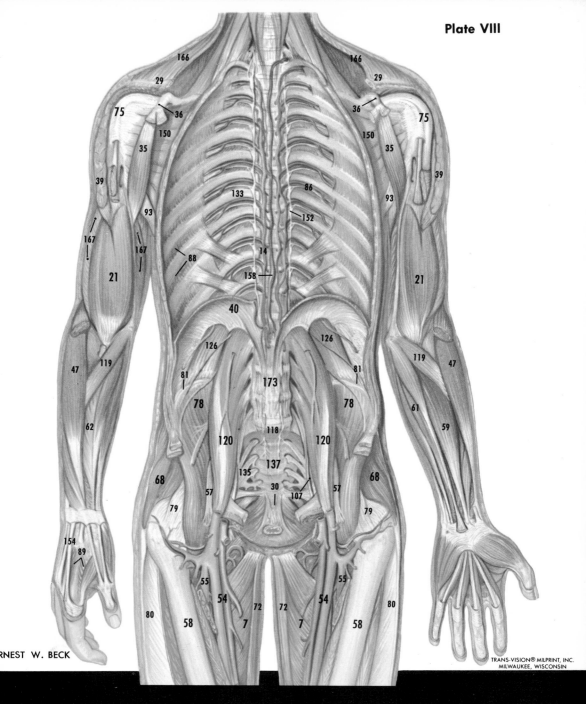

Plate VIII

ERNEST W. BECK

7. Adductor magnus muscle
14. Azygos veins
21. Brachialis muscle
29. Clavicle
30. Coccyx
35. Coracobrachialis muscle
36. Coracoid process of the scapula
39. Deltoid muscle
40. Diaphragm
47. Extensor carpi radialis longus muscle
54. Femoral artery and vein

55. Femoral artery, deep
57. Femoral nerve
58. Femur
59. Flexor carpi radialis muscle
61. Flexor digitorum profundus muscle
62. Flexor digitorum sublimus muscle
68. Gluteus medius muscle
75. Humerus
78. Iliacus muscle
79. Iliofemoral ligament
80. Iliotibial tract
81. Ilium

86. Intercostal artery, vein and nerve
88. Intercostal muscle, internal
89. Interosseous muscles, dorsal
93. Latissimus dorsi muscle
107. Obturator nerve
118. Promontory
119. Pronator teres muscle
120. Psoas muscles (major and minor)
126. Quadratus lumborum muscle

133. Rib
135. Sacral nerves
137. Sacrum
150. Subscapularis muscle
152. Sympathetic (autonomic) nerve chain
154. Tendons of extensor muscles of hand
158. Thoracic duct
166. Trapezius muscle
167. Triceps brachii muscle
173. Vertebral column

Plate IX

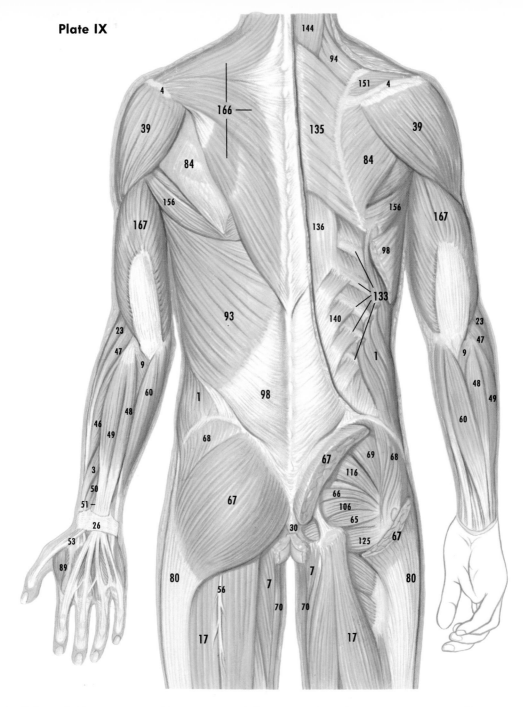

1. Abdominal oblique muscle, external
3. Abductor pollicis longus muscle
4. Acromion process of the scapula
7. Adductor magnus muscle
9. Anconeus muscle
17. Biceps femoris muscle
23. Brachioradialis muscle
26. Carpal ligament, dorsal
30. Coccyx
39. Deltoid muscle
46. Extensor carpi radialis brevis muscle

47. Extensor carpi radialis longus muscle
48. Extensor carpi ulnaris muscle
49. Extensor digitorum communis muscle
50. Extensor pollicis brevis muscle
51. Extensor pollicis longus muscle
56. Femoral cutaneous nerve, posterior
60. Flexor carpi ulnaris muscle
65. Gemellus inferior muscle

66. Gemellus superior muscle
67. Gluteus maximus muscle
68. Gluteus medius muscle
69. Gluteus minimus muscle
70. Gracilis muscle
80. Iliotibial tract
84. Infraspinatus muscle
89. Interosseous muscle, dorsal
93. Latissimus dorsi muscle
94. Levator scapulae muscle
98. Lumbodorsal fascia

106. Obturator internus muscle
116. Piriformis muscle
125. Quadratus femoris muscle
135. Rhomboideus muscle
133. Ribs (VII-XII)
136. Sacrospinalis muscle
140. Serratus posterior inferior muscle
144. Splenius capitis muscle
151. Supraspinatus muscle
156. Teres major muscle
166. Trapezius muscle
167. Triceps brachii muscle

Plate X

BONES AND SINUSES OF THE SKULL

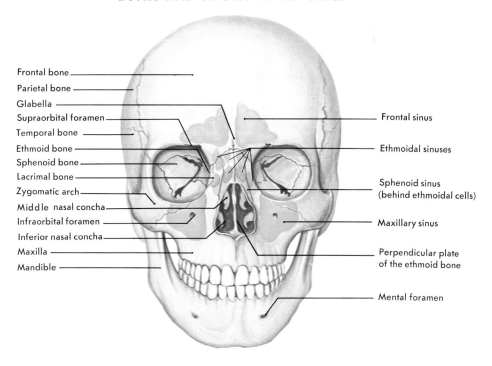

Frontal bone

Parietal bone

Glabella

Supraorbital foramen

Temporal bone

Ethmoid bone

Sphenoid bone

Lacrimal bone

Zygomatic arch

Middle nasal concha

Infraorbital foramen

Inferior nasal concha

Maxilla

Mandible

Frontal sinus

Ethmoidal sinuses

Sphenoid sinus
(behind ethmoidal cells)

Maxillary sinus

Perpendicular plate
of the ethmoid bone

Mental foramen

HEMISECTION OF THE HEAD AND NECK

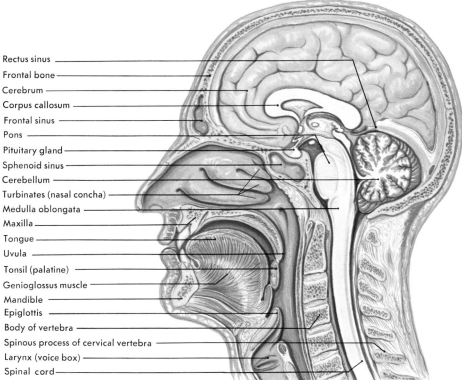

Rectus sinus

Frontal bone

Cerebrum

Corpus callosum

Frontal sinus

Pons

Pituitary gland

Sphenoid sinus

Cerebellum

Turbinates (nasal concha)

Medulla oblongata

Maxilla

Tongue

Uvula

Tonsil (palatine)

Genioglossus muscle

Mandible

Epiglottis

Body of vertebra

Spinous process of cervical vertebra

Larynx (voice box)

Spinal cord

Plate XI

ANATOMY OF THE EAR

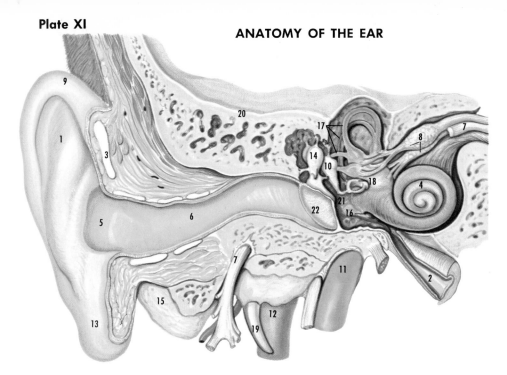

1. Antihelix	7. Facial nerve	12. Internal jugular vein	18. Stapes (stirrup)
2. Auditory tube	8. Ganglia of the vestibular	13. Lobe	19. Styloid process
3. Cartilage	nerve	14. Malleus (hammer)	20. Temporal bone
4. Cochlea	9. Helix	15. Mastoid process	21. Tympanic cavity
5. Concha (bowl)	10. Incus (anvil)	16. Round window	22. Tympanic membrane
6. External acoustic meatus	11. Internal carotid artery	17. Semicircular canals	(eardrum)

ANATOMY OF THE EYE

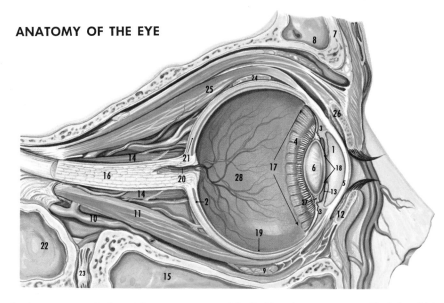

1. Aqueous chamber	8. Frontal sinus	15. Maxillary sinus	22. Sphenoid sinus
2. Choroid	9. Inferior oblique muscle	16. Optic nerve	23. Sphenopalatine ganglion
3. Ciliary muscle	10. Inferior ophthalmic vein	17. Ora serrata	24. Superior oblique muscle
4. Ciliary processes	11. Inferior rectus muscle	18. Pupil of the iris	25. Superior rectus muscle
5. Cornea	12. Inferior tarsus	19. Retina	26. Superior tarsus muscle
6. Crystalline lens	13. Iris	20. Retinal artery and vein	27. Suspensory ligament
7. Frontal bone	14. Lateral rectus muscle	21. Sclera	28. Vitreous chamber

Plate XII

SCHEMATIC BODY CELL

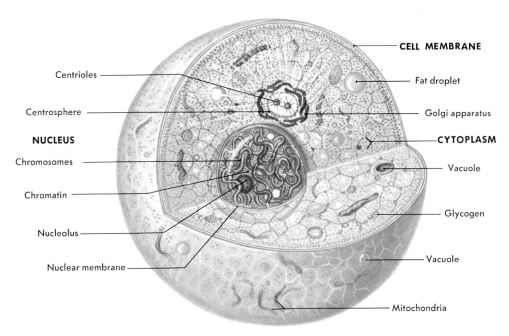

CELL MEMBRANE

Centrioles

Centrosphere

Fat droplet

Golgi apparatus

NUCLEUS

CYTOPLASM

Chromosomes

Chromatin

Vacuole

Nucleolus

Glycogen

Nuclear membrane

Vacuole

Mitochondria

Every living cell, regardless of its shape or size, has three main parts: the cell membrane, cytoplasm, and nucleus. Together they constitute protoplasm. Billions of such cells as shown above make up the tissues of our bodies.

TYPES OF CELLS

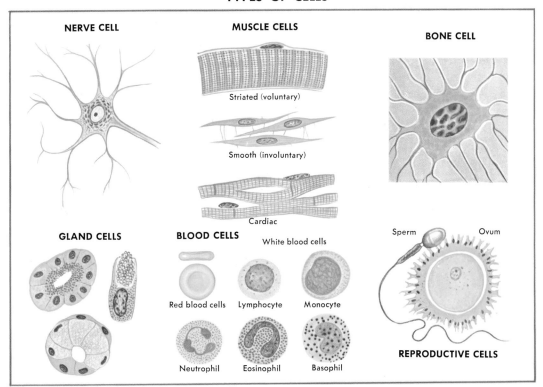

NERVE CELL

MUSCLE CELLS

BONE CELL

Striated (voluntary)

Smooth (involuntary)

Cardiac

GLAND CELLS

BLOOD CELLS

White blood cells

Sperm   Ovum

Red blood cells   Lymphocyte   Monocyte

Neutrophil   Eosinophil   Basophil

REPRODUCTIVE CELLS

Plate XIII

SKELETON

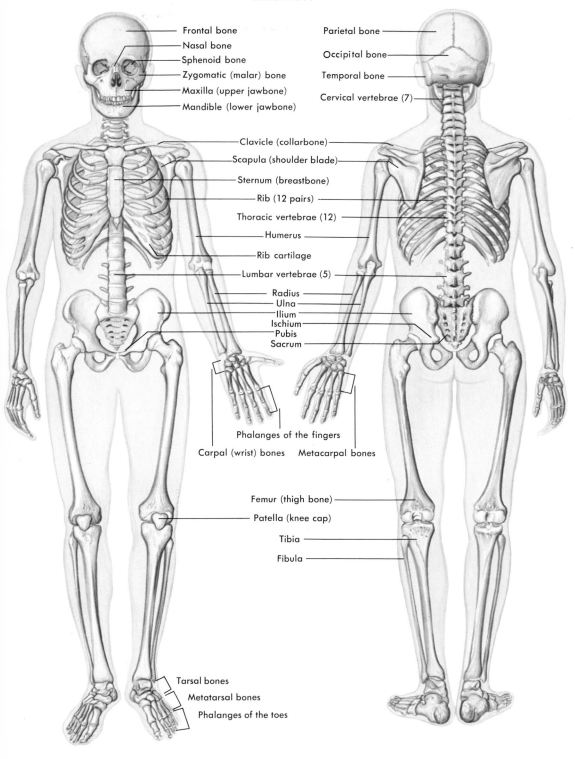

Frontal bone
Nasal bone
Sphenoid bone
Zygomatic (malar) bone
Maxilla (upper jawbone)
Mandible (lower jawbone)

Parietal bone
Occipital bone
Temporal bone
Cervical vertebrae (7)

Clavicle (collarbone)
Scapula (shoulder blade)
Sternum (breastbone)
Rib (12 pairs)
Thoracic vertebrae (12)
Humerus
Rib cartilage
Lumbar vertebrae (5)
Radius
Ulna
Ilium
Ischium
Pubis
Sacrum

Phalanges of the fingers
Carpal (wrist) bones   Metacarpal bones

Femur (thigh bone)
Patella (knee cap)
Tibia
Fibula

Tarsal bones
Metatarsal bones
Phalanges of the toes

Table 1. Tissues—cont'd

Tissue	Location	Function
Connective—cont'd		
Hemopoietic Myeloid (bone marrow)	Marrow spaces of bones	Formation of red blood cells, granular leukocytes, platelets; also reticuloendothelial cells and some other connective cells
Lymphatic	Lymph nodes Spleen Tonsils and adenoids Thymus gland	Formation of lymphocytes and monocytes; also plasma cells and some other connective tissue cells
Loose, ordinary, including areolar	Between other tissues and organs Superficial fascia	Connection
Bone	Skeleton	Support Protection
Cartilage Hyaline	Part of nasal septum Covering articular surfaces of bones Larynx Rings in trachea and bronchi	Furnish firm but flexible support
Fibrous	Discs between vertebrae Symphysis pubis	
Elastic	External ear Eustachian tube	
Muscle Skeletal (striated voluntary)	Muscles which attach to bones Extrinsic eyeball muscles Upper one third of esophagus	Movement of bones Eye movements First part of swallowing
Visceral (nonstriated involuntary or smooth)	In walls of tubular viscera of digestive, respiratory, and genitourinary tracts In walls of blood vessels and large lymphatics In ducts of glands Intrinsic eye muscles (iris and ciliary body) Arrector muscles of hairs	Movement of substances along respective tracts Control of size of blood vessels, thereby aiding in regulation of blood pressure Movement of substances along ducts Regulation of size of pupils and shape of lens Erection of hairs (gooseflesh)
Cardiac (striated involuntary)	Wall of heart	Contraction of heart
Nervous	Brain Spinal cord Nerves	Irritability and conduction

Outline summary

Tissues

1. Definition—organizations of cells with non-living intercellular substances
2. Basic types
   a. epithelial
   b. connective
   c. muscle
   d. nerve

Epithelial tissues

1. General functions—protection, secretion, diffusion, filtration, and absorption
2. Main types
   a. simple squamous—single layers of flat cells; functions—diffusion, filtration
   b. simple columnar—single layer of columnar and goblet-shaped cells and in some places, ciliated cells; functions—absorption, secretion, and moving mucus
   c. stratified squamous—several layers of cells; function—protection
   d. glandular—secreting units of all glands

Muscle tissue

1. General functions—contraction, conduction, and movement
2. Types
   a. skeletal; also called voluntary
   b. visceral; also called nonstriated or smooth involuntary
   c. cardiac; also called striated involuntary

Connective tissues

1. General functions—connections and support.
2. Main types
   a. loose, ordinary connective, including areolar

   b. adipose
   c. dense fibrous
   d. cartilage
   e. bone
   f. hemopoietic
3. General characteristics—intercellular material predominates in most connective tissues and determines their physical characteristics; consists of either fibers (collagenic, reticular, and elastic) or jellies or both

Loose, ordinary connective tissue, including areolar

One of the most widely distributed of all tissues; intercellular substance is prominent and consists of collagenic and elastic fibers loosely interwoven and embedded in soft viscous ground substance; several kinds of cells present, notably fibroblasts and macrophages, also mast cells, plasma cells, fat cells, and some white blood cells

Adipose tissue

Similar to loose, ordinary connective tissue but contains mainly fat cells

Dense fibrous tissue

Fibrous intercellular substance. (collagenic fibers) predominate; few fibroblast cells

Reticuloendothelial cells

Phagocytic cells that line small channels in lymph nodes and sinusoids in liver, spleen and marrow; macrophages and microglia also classed as reticuloendothelial cells by some authors

Review questions

Tissues

1. Name the four basic types of tissue.
2. What are the main functions of each basic type of tissue?
3. What are the names of the subtypes of connective tissue?
4. Describe intercellular substance.
5. What is the scientific basis for giving hyaluronidase with fluids or certain drugs that are injected?
6. Name several kinds of connective tissue cells.
7. What kind of cells produce intercellular substances?
8. Name three subtypes of muscle tissue; give more than one name for each.
9. What special function do reticuloendothelial cells perform?
10. What are the main locations of reticuloendothelial cells?
11. Make a list of terms you have met for the first time in this chapter; define each in your own words.

Membranes and glands

MEMBRANES

Membranes constitute a special class of organs in that they are merely thin sheets of tissues which cover or line various parts of the body. Of the numerous membranes in the body, four kinds are particularly important: mucous, serous, synovial, and cutaneous (skin). Other miscellaneous membranes (periosteum, fascia, dura mater, sclera, etc.) will be described from time to time.

Mucous membrane

Mucous membrane lines cavities or passageways of the body which open to the exterior, such as the lining of the mouth and entire digestive tract, the respiratory passages, and the genitourinary tract. It consists of a surface layer of epithelial tissue over a deeper layer of connective tissue. Its functions are protection, secretion, and absorption—protection, for example, against bacterial invasion, secretion of mucus, and absorption of water, salts, and other solutes.

Serous and synovial membranes

Serous and synovial membranes line cavities of the body which do not open to the exterior, otherwise known as closed cavities. Serous membrane that lines the thoracic cavity is called *pleura;* that which lines the abdominal cavity is called *peritoneum;* and that which lines the sac in which the heart lies is called *pericardium.*

Not only does serous membrane line the thoracic and abdominal cavities and the pericardial sac, but it also covers the organs lying in these spaces. The term *visceral layer* is applied to the part of the membrane which covers the organs, while that which lines the cavity is called the *parietal layer.* Between the two layers there is a potential space kept moist by a small amount of serous fluid. Think of the thoracic and abdominal cavities as rooms in a house. The wallpaper then becomes comparable to the parietal layer of the serous membranes. Imagine the rooms filled with furniture, each piece wrapped tightly in muslin for protection. The muslin wrappings compare with

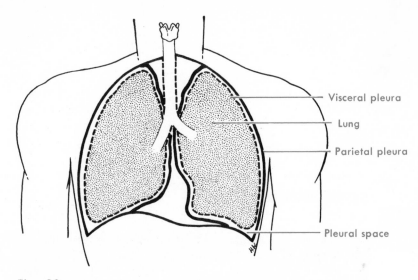

Visceral pleura

Lung

Parietal pleura

Pleural space

Fig. 28

Diagram showing the relative positions of the visceral and
parietal layers of serous membrane as found in the pleura.

the visceral serous membrane which covers each organ in the thoracic
and abdominal cavities. Even though the articles of furniture in the
rooms be stacked closely against each other and against the walls,
still there is air between the pieces and between the pieces and the
walls. This air might be likened to the small amount of lubricating
serous fluid in the potential space between the visceral and parietal
layers of serous membrane. When an organ moves against the body
wall, as the lungs do in respiration, or when the heart beats in its
serous sac, friction between the moving parts is prevented by the
presence of the very smooth moist serous sheets lining the wall surface
of the cavity and covering the organ surfaces. The mechanical principle that moving parts must have lubricated surfaces is thereby carried
out in the body.

Synovial membrane lines joint cavities, tendon sheaths, and bursae.
Its smooth moist surfaces protect against friction.

Cutaneous membrane

Vital, diverse, complex, extensive—these adjectives describe in part
the body's largest and one of its most important organs—the skin. In
terms of surface area, the skin is as large as the body itself—probably
2500 to 3000 square inches in most adults. Skin functions are crucial
to survival. They are also diverse, including such different functions
as protection, excretion, sensation, and playing a part in maintaining
fluid and electrolyte balance and normal body temperature. The skin
protects us against entry of unconquerable hordes of microorganisms
and minimizes mechanical injury of underlying structures. It bars entry

of excess sunlight and of most chemicals. Even water does not penetrate it under most circumstances. The skin protects against too much and too little heat loss. For example, if body temperature increases above certain limits, skin vessels dilate, more blood flows to the surface, and more heat is lost by radiation. And at the same time sweat glands secrete more sweat, and more heat may be lost by evaporation.

Millions of microscopic nerve endings are distributed throughout the skin. These serve as antennae or receivers for the body, keeping it informed of changes in its environment—information vital at times to survival.

Epidermis and dermis

Two main layers compose the skin: an outer and thinner layer, the *epidermis,* and an inner, thicker layer, the *dermis.* Epidermis consists of stratified squamous epithelial tissue and dermis of fibrous connective tissue. Underlying the dermis is subcutaneous tissue or superficial fascia made of areolar and in many areas adipose tissue, too. Epidermis, in all parts of the body except the palms of the hands and soles of the feet, has four layers. In the skin of the palms and soles there are five layers of epidermis. From the outside in, they are the following:

1. *stratum corneum (horny layer)*—dead cells converted to a water-repellant protein called keratin that continually flakes off (desquamates).
2. *stratum lucidum*—so named because of the presence of a translucent compound (eleidin) from which keratin forms. This layer is present only in thick skin of palms and soles.
3. *stratum granulosum*—so named because of granules visible in cytoplasm of cells; cells die in this layer.
4. *stratum spinosum (prickle cell layer)*—several layers of irregularly shaped cells.
5. *stratum germinativum (or basal layer)*—columnar shaped cells, the only cells in the epidermis that undergo mitosis. New cells are produced in this deepest stratum at the rate old keratinized cells are lost from the stratum corneum. New cells continually push surfaceward from the stratum germinativum into each successive layer, only to die, become keratinized, and eventually flake off as did their predecessors. Incidentally, this fact illustrates nicely the physiological principle that while life continues the body's work is never done. Even at rest it is producing new cells to replace millions of old ones.

An interesting characteristic of the dermis or deep layer of the skin

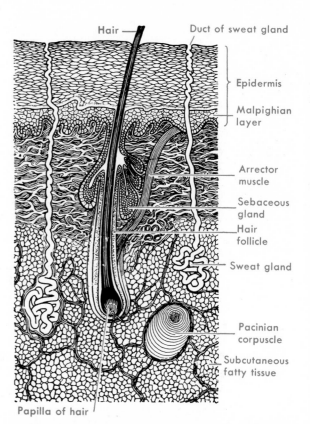

Hair — Duct of sweat gland

Epidermis

Malpighian layer

Arrector muscle

Sebaceous gland

Hair follicle

Sweat gland

Pacinian corpuscle

Subcutaneous fatty tissue

Papilla of hair

Fig. 29

Highly schematized diagram to show the microscopic structure of the skin in longitudinal section. The wavy lines in the lower part of the figure represent elastic fibers in the derma. (Modified from Cunningham; from Zoethout and Tuttle: Textbook of physiology, St. Louis, The C. V. Mosby Co.)

is its parallel ridges, suggestive on a miniature scale of the ridges of a contour plowed field. Epidermal ridges, the ones made famous by the art of fingerprinting, exist because the epidermis conforms to the underlying dermal ridges. Have you ever wondered about the array of different skin colors? Two factors are mainly responsible—pigment and blood. Black or brown compounds called melanins are the chief pigments. Special cells (melanoblasts), located mainly in the deepest layer of the epidermis, produce them as inclusions in their cytoplasm. Many factors influence the amount of skin melanins. Prolonged exposure to sunlight comes first to mind, but radiation therapy, adrenal cortex hormone deficiency, and some types of vitamin B deficiency may also cause skin darkening. The pinkish cast characteristic of skin comes from blood in the minute vessels of the dermis. But if blood contains an excess of reduced hemoglobin, then instead of the normal pinkness, the abnormal blueness of cyanosis develops. According to Lundsgaard, cyanosis appears when 100 milliliters of blood contains about 5 grams of reduced hemoglobin.*

---

*Best, Charles H., and Taylor, M. B.: The physiological basis of medical practice, ed. 7, Baltimore, 1961, Williams & Wilkins Co., p. 524.

Accessory organs of the skin

The accessory organs of the skin consist of hair, nails, and microscopic glands.

Hair. Hair is distributed over the entire body except the palms and soles. The structure of a hair has several points of similarity to that of the epidermis. Just as the epidermis is formed by the cells of its deepest layer, reproducing and forcing the daughter cells, which become horny in character, upward, so a hair is formed by a group of cells at its base multiplying and pushing upward and in so doing becoming keratinized. The part of the hair that is visible is the *shaft*, while that which is embedded in the dermis is the *root*. The root, together with its coverings (an outer connective tissue sheath and an inner epithelial coating which is a continuation of the stratum germinativum), forms the hair *follicle*. At the bottom of the follicle is a loop of capillaries enclosed in a connective tissue covering called the hair *papilla*. The cluster of epithelial cells lying over the papilla are the ones that reproduce and eventually form the hair shaft. As long as these cells remain alive, hair will regenerate even though it be cut or plucked or otherwise removed.

Each hair is kept soft and pliable by two or more *sebaceous glands* which secrete varying amounts of oily *sebum* into the follicle near the surface of the skin. Attached to the follicle, too, are small bundles of involuntary muscle known as the *arrector pili muscles.* These muscles are of interest because when they contract, the hair "stands on end," as it does in extreme fright or cold, for example. This mechanism is responsible also for gooseflesh since, as the hair is pulled into an upright position, it raises the skin around it into the familiar little goose pimples.

Hair color is due to different amounts of melanin pigments in the outer layer (cortex) of the hair. White hair contains little or no melanin.

Some hair, notably that around the eyes and in the nose and ears, performs a protective function in that it keeps out some dust and insects. For the hair on the bulk of the skin, however, no function seems apparent.

Nails. The nails are epidermal cells that have been converted to keratin. They grow from epithelial cells lying under the white crescent (lunula) at the proximal end of each nail.

Skin glands. The skin glands include three kinds of microscopic structures: sebaceous, sweat, and ceruminous glands. *Sebaceous glands* secrete oil for the hair. Wherever hairs grow from the skin there are sebaceous glands, at least two for each hair. The oil, or *sebum,* secreted by these tiny glands has value not only because it keeps the hair supple but also because it keeps the skin itself soft and pliant. Moreover, it prevents the skin from evaporating and absorbing too much water and from losing too much heat since fat is a poor heat conductor. *Sweat glands*, though very small structures, are very important and very numerous—especially on the palms, soles, forehead, and axillae (armpits). Histologists estimate, for example, that a single square inch of skin on the palms of the hands contains about three thousand sweat glands. As previously noted, sweat secretion helps maintain homeostasis of fluid and electrolytes and of body temperature. For example, if too much heat is being produced, as in strenuous exercise, or if the environmental temperature is high, these glands secrete more sweat which, in evaporating, cools the body surface. Inasmuch as sweat contains some nitrogenous wastes, the sweat glands also function as excretory organs. *Ceruminous glands* are thought to be modified sweat glands; they are located in the external ear canal. Instead of watery sweat, they secrete a waxy, pigmented substance, the *cerumen*.

Terms used in connection with the skin

The following terms are used in connection with the skin:

hypodermic beneath or under the skin.
subcutaneous same as hypodermic.
intracutaneous within the layers of the skin.
diaphoresis profuse perspiration.
pores minute openings of the sweat gland ducts on the surface of the skin; do not "open" or "close" since no muscle tissue enters into their formation; however, any agent which has an astringent action on the skin causes them to become smaller or "closed."
furuncle a boil, an infection of a hair follicle.

GLANDS

Glands consist of epithelial cells specialized for synthesizing compounds which they secrete either into ducts or blood. *Exocrine glands*

 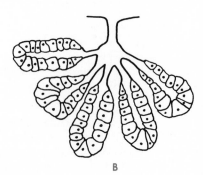

Fig. 30
A, Simple tubular gland;
B, compound tubuloalveolar gland.   A   B

secrete into ducts and *endocrine glands* into blood. Exocrine glands are further classified in several ways. Sweat glands, for example, are *simple tubular exocrine glands*. Interpreted, simple means that each gland has a single nonbranching duct, and tubular means that its secretory unit is tubular-shaped. A salivary gland, in contrast, is a *compound tubuloalveolar gland* because it has a branching duct and some tubular and some flask-shaped secretory units.

Outline summary

Membranes and glands

Membranes

1. Definition—thin sheet of tissues that either covers or lines a part of the body or divides an organ
2. Types—mucous, serous, synovial, cutaneous, and miscellaneous

Mucous membrane

1. Location—lines cavities and passages that open to exterior
2. Structure—surface layer of epithelial tissue over connective tissue
3. Functions—protection, secretion, and absorption

Serous membrane

1. Location—lines cavities that do not open to exterior
2. Functions—protection and secretion

Synovial membrane

1. Location—lines joint cavities, tendon sheaths, and bursae
2. Functions—protection and secretion

Cutaneous membrane (skin)

1. Functions
   a. protection against various factors, for example, microorganisms, sunlight, and chemicals
   b. excretion of sweat
   c. sensations
   d. fluid and electrolyte balance—skin helps maintain this by secreting varying amounts of sweat
   e. normal body temperature—skin helps

maintain this by varying amounts of blood flow through it and also by varying amounts of sweat secretion

2. Structure—two main layers—the epidermis, the outer, thinner layer of stratified squamous epithelium, and the dermis, the inner, thicker layer of connective tissue
3. Epidermis—outer layer of stratified squamous epithelial cells; surface cells dead, keratinized, and practically waterproof; only deepest layer of cells undergoes mitosis to replace surface cells that continually desquamate; melanin pigments mainly in deepest layer
4. Dermis—dense fibrous connective tissue layer underlying epidermis. Dermis of palms and soles has numerous parallel ridges
5. Subcutaneous tissue—also called superficial fascia; composed of areolar tissue or areolar and adipose tissues
6. Accessory organs
   a. hair
      1. distribution—over entire body except palms and soles
      2. shaft—visible part of hair
      3. root—part of hair embedded in dermis
      4. follicle—root with coverings
      5. papilla—loop of capillaries enclosed in connective tissue covering
      6. germinal matrix—cluster of epithelial cells lying over papilla; these cells undergo mitosis to form hair; must be intact in order for hair to regenerate
      7. sebaceous glands and arrector pili

muscles—attach to follicle; contraction of latter produces gooseflesh

8. color—due to different amounts of melanin pigments in cortex of hair

b. nails

1. are epidermal cells converted to hard keratin

2. grow from epithelial cells under the lunula ("moons")

c. skin glands

1. sebaceous—secrete oil (sebum) that keeps hair and skin soft; helps prevent excess evaporation and absorption of water and excess heat loss

2. sweat—numerous throughout skin, especially on palms, soles, forehead, and axillae; important in heat regulation

3. ceruminous—thought to be modified sweat glands; located in external ear canal; secrete ear wax or cerumen

d. terms used in connection with skin (p. 74)

Glands

Composed of epithelial cells specialized for synthesizing compounds which they secrete either into ducts or blood

1. Exocrine glands—secrete into ducts
2. Endocrine glands—secrete into blood
3. Simple glands—have nonbranching ducts
4. Tubular glands—secretory unit tubular-shaped
5. Compound glands—have branching ducts
6. Alveolar glands—flask-shaped secretory units

Review questions

Membranes and glands

1. What membranes line closed cavities? Cavities that open to the exterior?
2. What general functions do membranes serve?
3. What functions does the skin perform?
4. Describe the epidermis.
5. Describe the dermis.
6. What is keratin?
7. What is melanin and where is it found?
8. What is superficial fascia?
9. Name and describe the skin glands.
10. Define the following terms:

| alveolar gland | exocrine gland |
| endocrine gland | compound gland |

The erect
and moving
body

Chapter V

The skeletal system

Meaning

Functions
Support
Protection
Leverage; movement
Hemopoiesis
Calcium storage

Microscopic structure of bone

Microscopic structure of cartilage

Gross structure of bones
Types of bones
Structure of long bones
Structure of short bones
Structure of flat bones
Structure of irregular bones
Names and numbers of bones
Bone markings
Identification of bone markings
Differences between male and
  female skeletons
Age changes in skeleton

Joints
Classification
Movements

Bone formation and growth

Like all body structures, the skeletal and muscular systems play a part in the body's achievement of its over-all goal of survival. These two systems work together to move the body and its parts. This is a function of tremendous importance not only for the enjoyment of life but also for life itself since without movement a favorable cellular environment cannot possibly be maintained.

The body must adjust to many changes in its external environment in order to maintain homeostasis. Sometimes it adjusts the external environment; sometimes it adjusts itself. In either case movements play a part. Suppose, for instance, that environmental temperature drops below the comfort zone. The body then needs to make some kind of adjustment in order to maintain homeostasis of its internal temperature. It may change the environmental temperature back to a comfortable level (by building a fire or setting up the room thermostat, for example), or it may change itself in some way to counteract the environmental change, for instance, shivering and surface blood vessel constriction (to produce more heat and lose less, respectively).

Whichever methods the body uses, movements are necessary. Movements require the coordinated activities of nearly all of the body's systems. But, in order to gain an understanding of how movements are accomplished, we shall start by investigating the two systems whose primary business is movement: the skeletal and muscular systems.

MEANING

The term skeletal system means all the bones of the body plus the joints formed by their attachments to each other. Predominant tissues of the system are two types of connective tissue: bone and cartilage.

FUNCTIONS

The skeletal system performs five important functions:
1. *support*—bones support the body much as steel girders support our modern buildings.

2. *protection*—hard, bony "boxes" protect delicate structures enclosed by them. The skull, for example, protects the brain; the rib cage protects the lungs and heart.
3. *movement*—bones with their joints constitute levers; muscles are anchored firmly to bones; as muscles contract, force is applied to the bony levers and movement necessarily results.
4. *hemopoiesis* (blood cell formation)—The red bone marrow produces blood cells—normally, all the red cells in the adult, most types of white cells, and the platelets.
5. *calcium storage*—Bones serve as the storage depot for calcium.

MICROSCOPIC STRUCTURE OF BONE

Bone, like other tissues, consists of living cells and nonliving intercellular substance. And in bone, like other connective tissues, intercellular substance predominates over cells. But in bone the intercellular substance (matrix) is calcified. Calcium salts impregnate the cement substance of the matrix, a fact that explains the rigidity of bones and the familiar expression "as hard as bone." Embedded in the calcified matrix are collagenic fibrils. These serve to reinforce bone much as iron rods reinforce concrete. Another unique feature of bone structure is the arrangement of its intercellular substance. Concentric cylindrical layers of calcified matrix, usually less than six of them, enclose a central longitudinal canal that contains a blood vessel. Each layer of bone matrix is called a *lamella,* the central canal is an *haversian canal,* and the entire unit of canal and surrounding lamellae is an *haversian system.* According to Ham, most haversian canals contain a single large capillary, but some have a small arteriole and venule, and lymphatics have also been described in some. Bone cells *(osteocytes)* occupy minute spaces called *lacunae* between the lamellae. Microscopic canals (canaliculi), great numbers of them, radiate in all directions from the lacunae to connect them with haversian canals and provide routes for tissue fluid to reach bone cells. Each bone cell is said to lie not farther than one tenth of a millimeter from an haversian canal.

There are two types of bone based on the arrangement of lamellae—compact or dense and cancellous or spongy. In *compact bone* adjacent haversian units fit closely together with the spaces between them filled in with interstitial lamellae. In *cancellous bone,* on the other hand, there are many open spaces between thin processes of bone *(trabeculae)* which are joined together somewhat like the beams of wood in a scaffold. Arrangement of trabeculae in different ways in different bones gives structural strength along the lines of strain on individual bones.

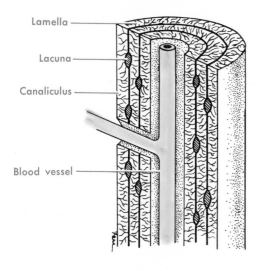

Lamella

Lacuna

Canaliculus

Blood vessel

Fig. 31

Diagram of longitudinal
section of compact bone.

Bones are not the lifeless structures they seem to be. We tend to
think of them as lifeless, perhaps because what we see when we look
at a bone is its nonliving intercellular substance. But within this hard,
lifeless material lie many living bone cells that must continually receive
food and oxygen and that must be rid of their wastes. So blood supply
to bone is important and abundant. For example, numerous blood
vessels from the periosteum (bone covering) penetrate bone by way
of *Volkmann's canals* to connect with haversian canal blood vessels.
Also, one or more arteries supply the bone marrow in the internal
medullary cavity of long bones.

MICROSCOPIC STRUCTURE OF CARTILAGE

Cartilage both resembles and differs from bone. Like bone, cartilage
consists more of intercellular substance than of cells. Abundant collagenic fibrils reinforce the matrix of both tissues. But in cartilage the
fibrils are embedded in a firm gel instead of in calcified cement substance as they are in bone. Hence cartilage has the flexibility of a firm
plastic material rather than the rigidity of bone. Another difference is
this—no canal system and no blood vessels penetrate cartilage matrix.
Cartilage is avascular and bone is abundantly vascular. Cartilage cells
like bone cells lie in lacunae. However, because no canals and blood
vessels interlace cartilage matrix, nutrients and oxygen can reach the
scattered, isolated chondrocytes (cartilage cells) only by diffusion
through the matrix gel, from capillaries in the fibrous covering of cartilage (perichondrium) or from synovial fluid in the case of articular
cartilage.

Three types of cartilage are hyaline, fibrous, and elastic. They differ
structurally mainly as to matrix fibrils. Collagenic fibrils are present
in all three types but are most numerous in fibrocartilage; hence it

81

Table 2. Bones of skeleton

Part of body	Name of bone	Number	Description
Axial skeleton (composed of 80 bones)			Bones that form upright axis of body—skull, hyoid, vertebral column, ribs, and sternum
Skull (28 bones)			
Cranium (8 bones)			Cranium forms floor for brain to rest on and helmetlike covering over it
	Frontal	1	Forehead bone; also forms most of roof of orbits (eye sockets) and anterior part of cranial floor
	Parietal	2	Prominent, bulging bones behind frontal bone; form topsides of cranial cavity
	Temporal	2	Form lower sides of cranium and part of cranial floor; contain middle and inner ear structures
	Occipital	1	Forms posterior part of cranial floor and walls
	Sphenoid	1	Keystone of cranial floor; forms its midportion; resembles bat with wings outstretched and legs extended downward posteriorly; lies behind and slightly above nose and throat; forms part of floor and side walls of orbit
	Ethmoid	1	Complicated irregular bone that helps make up anterior portion of cranial floor, medial wall of orbits, upper parts of nasal septum, and side walls and part of nasal roof; lies anterior to sphenoid, posterior to nasal bones
Face (14 bones)	Nasal	2	Small bones forming upper part of bridge of nose
	Maxillary	2	Upper jaw bones; form part of floor of orbit, anterior part of roof of mouth, and floor of nose and part of sidewalls of nose
	Zygomatic (malar)	2	Cheek bones; form part of floor and side wall of orbit
	Mandible	1	Lower jaw bone; largest, strongest bone of face
	Lacrimal	2	Thin bones about size and shape of a fingernail; posterior and lateral to nasal bones in medial wall of orbit; help form side wall of nasal cavity; often missing in dry skull
	Palatine	2	Form posterior part of hard palate, floor, and part of side walls of nasal cavity and floor of orbit
	Inferior conchae (turbinates)	2	Thin scroll of bone forming a kind of shell along inner surface of side wall of nasal cavity; lies above roof of mouth
	Vomer	1	Forms lower and posterior part of nasal septum; shaped like a ploughshare
Ear ossicles (6 bones)	Malleus (hammer)	2	Tiny bones in middle ear cavity in temporal bones; resemble, respectively, miniature hammer, anvil, and stirrups
	Incus (anvil)	2	
	Stapes (stirrups)	2	

Table 2. Bones of skeleton—cont'd

Part of body	Name of bone	Number	Description
Hyoid bone		1	U-shaped bone in neck between mandible and upper part of larynx; claims distinction as only bone in body not forming a joint with any other bone; is suspended by ligaments from styloid processes of temporal bones
Vertebral column (26 bones)			Not actually a column but a flexible segmented rod shaped like an elongated letter S; forms axis of body; head balanced above, ribs and viscera suspended in front, and lower extremities attached below; encloses spinal cord
	Cervical vertebrae	7	First or upper seven vertebrae
	Thoracic vertebrae	12	Next twelve vertebrae; twelve pairs of ribs attached to these
	Lumbar vertebrae	5	Next five vertebrae
	Sacrum	1	Five separate vertebrae until about 25 years of age; then fused to form one wedge-shaped bone
	Coccyx	1	Four or five separate vertebrae in child but fused into one in adult
Ribs and sternum (25 bones)			Ribs, sternum, and thoracic vertebrae together form bony cage known as *thorax;* ribs attach posteriorly to vertebrae, slant downward anteriorly to attach to sternum (see note after false ribs)
	True ribs	7 pairs	Upper seven pairs; fasten to sternum by costal cartilages
	False ribs	5 pairs	False ribs do not attach to sternum directly; upper three pairs of false ribs attach by means of costal cartilage of seventh ribs; last two pairs do not attach to sternum at all; therefore, are called "*floating*"
	Sternum	1	Breast bone; flat dagger-shaped bone
Appendicular skeleton (126 bones)			Bones that are appended to axial skeleton: upper and lower extremities, including shoulder and hip girdles
Upper extremities (including shoulder girdle) (64 bones)	Clavicle	2	Collar bones; shoulder girdle joined to axial skeleton by articulation of clavicles with sternum; scapula does not form joint with axial skeleton
	Scapula	2	Shoulder blades; scapulae and clavicles together comprise shoulder girdle
	Humerus	2	Long bone of upper arm
	Radius	2	Bone of thumb side of forearm
	Ulna	2	Bone of little finger side of forearm; longer than radius

Continued on next page.

Table 2. Bones of skeleton—cont'd

Part of body	Name of bone	Number	Description
Appendicular skeleton—cont'd *Upper extremities— cont'd*	Carpals (navicular, lunate, triquetrum, pisiform, greater and lesser multangular, capitate, and hamate)	16	Arranged in two rows at proximal end of hand (Fig. 55)
	Metacarpals	10	Long bones forming framework of palm of hand
	Phalanges	28	Miniature long bones of fingers, three in each finger, two in each thumb
Lower extremities (62 bones)	Ossa coxae or pelvic bones	2	The large hip bones; with sacrum and coccyx these three bones form basinlike pelvic cavity; lower extremities attached to axial skeleton by pelvic bones
	Femur	2	Thigh bone; longest, strongest bone of body
	Patella	2	Kneecap; largest sesamoid bone of body°; is embedded in tendon of quadriceps femoris muscle
	Tibia	2	Shin bone
	Fibula	2	Long, slender bone of lateral side of lower leg
	Tarsals (calcaneus, talus, navicular, first, second, and third cuneiforms, cuboid)	14	Bones that form heel and proximal or posterior half of foot (Fig. 59)
	Metatarsals	10	Long bones of feet
	Phalanges	28	Miniature long bones of toes; two in each great toe, three in other toes
Total		206°	

°An inconstant number of small, flat, round bones known as *sesamoid bones,* because of their resemblance to sesame seeds, is found in various tendons in which considerable pressure develops. Because the number of these bones varies greatly between individuals, only two of them, the patellae, have been counted among the 206 bones of the body. Generally two of them can be found in each thumb (in flexor tendon near metacarpophalangeal and interphalangeal joints) and great toe plus several others in the upper and lower extremities. *Wormian bones,* the small islets of bone frequently found in some of the cranial sutures, have not been counted in this list of 206 bones either because of their variable occurrence.

has the greatest tensile strength. Elastic cartilage matrix contains elastic fibers as well as collagenic fibers so has elasticity as well as firmness. Hyalin is the commonest type of cartilage. It resembles milk glass in appearance; in fact, its name derives from the Greek word meaning glassy. A thin layer of hyaline cartilage covers articular surfaces of bones where it helps to cushion jolts. Fibrocartilage discs between the vertebra also serve this purpose. For other locations of cartilage, see Table 1.

GROSS STRUCTURE OF BONES

Types of bones

There are four types of bones, classified according to their shapes, as follows:
1. *long bones*—femur, tibia, fibula, humerus, radius, ulna, and phalanges.
2. *short bones*—carpals and tarsals (wrist and ankle bones).
3. *flat bones*—several cranial bones, such as frontal and parietal; also ribs and scapulae.
4. *irregular bones*—vertebrae, sphenoid, ethmoid, sacrum, coccyx, and mandible.

Structure of bones

Structure of long bones

Each long bone of the body consists of the following parts (Figs. 32 and 33):
1. *diaphysis*—main shaftlike portion; several structural features accommodate it to its function of providing strong support without cumbersome weight—the thick compact bone used as construction material, for example, and the hollow cylindrical shape which offers the dual advantages of greater strength with less weight compared with a solid cylinder of the same size.
2. *epiphyses*—extremities of long bones; their somewhat bulbous shape provides generous space for muscle attachment near joints and makes for greater stability of the joint; lightness despite size is achieved by construction of porous cancellous bone with only an outer layer of dense compact bone; arrangement of the lamellae corresponding to the lines of stress gives added strength to the epiphyses; marrow fills the cancellous spaces—red marrow in the proximal epiphyses of the humerus and femur and yellow marrow in other epiphyses in the adult.
3. *articular cartilage*—thin layer of hyaline cartilage covering the

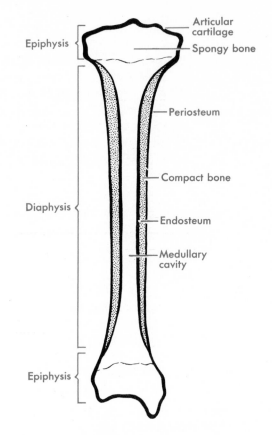

Fig. 32

Diagram to show the structure
of a long bone as seen in
longitudinal section.

articular surface of each epiphysis; resiliency of this material
cushions jars and blows.

4. *periosteum*—a dense white fibrous membrane that covers bone
except at joint surfaces, where articular cartilage forms the cover
ing; many of the periosteum's fibers penetrate the underlying
bone to weld these two structures to each other (penetrating
fibers called Sharpey's fibers); muscle tendon fibers interlace
with periosteal fibers to anchor muscles firmly to bone.

The inner layer of the periosteum of growing bones contains
osteoblasts (bone-forming cells). Because of its bone-forming
cells and blood vessels, the periosteum is necessary for bone
growth and repair and for its nutrition and, therefore, for life of
its cells. In addition it serves as the means for attaching muscle
tendons and ligaments to bone.

5. *medullary (or marrow) cavity*—a cavity running the length of the
diaphysis; contains yellow or fatty bone marrow in the adult.

6. *endosteum*—membrane that lines the medullary cavity and haversian canals; composed of cells that become active osteoblasts as
needed.

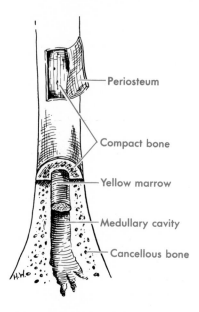

—Periosteum

—Compact bone

—Yellow marrow

—Medullary cavity

—Cancellous bone

Fig. 33

Cutaway section
of a long bone.

Structure of short bones

Short bones consist of a core of cancellous bone encased in a thin layer of compact bone.

Structure of flat bones

A layer of cancellous bone lies between two plates of compact bone; cancellous bone of the skull bones (diploe), ribs, and sternum contain red marrow.*

Structure of irregular bones

Irregular bones are similar in structure to short bones; that is, a thin layer of compact bone forms a casing over cancellous bone.

Names and numbers of bones

The human skeleton consists of two main parts: the *axial skeleton*, composed of the bones which form the upright part or axis of the body (the skull, vertebral column, ribs and sternum, and hyoid) and the *appendicular skeleton*, made up of the bones which are attached to the

---

*Note that red marrow is found in the adult in *only* a few locations: mainly in the diploe (spongy bone of the cranial bones), ribs, and sternum, in bodies of the vertebrae, and small amounts in the proximal epiphyses of the femurs and humeri and other long bones. In newborn infants and children red marrow occurs in many more bones. Because of its hemopoietic function, bone marrow is one of the most important materials of the body. Its very location, hidden within the bones, suggests its great importance. As the agent which coins millions of vital blood cells daily, it receives maximum protection from the body, the bones acting as a safe-deposit vault for it.

axial skeleton as appendages (that is, the upper and lower extremities). The names and numbers of the bones in each division of the skeleton, with an identifying remark about each, are given in Table 2. When you are trying to learn these names, locate each bone on your own body; feel its outline whenever possible. Locate each bone on a skeleton if one is available. Study Figs. 34 to 37.

Bone markings

Various points on bones are labeled according to the nature of their structure. This method of identifying definite parts of different bones proves helpful when locating other structures such as muscles, blood vessels, and nerves. Definitions of some of the common terms applied to bone markings follow.

Depressions and openings

1. *fossa*—a hollow or depression; example: mandibular fossa of temporal bone.
2. *sinus*—a cavity or spongelike space in a bone; example: the frontal sinus.
3. *foramen*—a hole; example: foramen magnum of the occipital bone.
4. *meatus*—a tube-shaped opening; example: external auditory meatus.

Projections or processes

Those projections or processes which fit into joints are as follows:
1. *condyle*—a rounded projection that enters into the formation of a joint; example: condyles of femur.
2. *head*—a rounded projection beyond a narrow necklike portion; example: head of the femur.

Those projections or processes to which muscles attach include the following:
1. *trochanter*—a very large process; greater trochanter of femur.
2. *crest*—a ridge; example: iliac crest; a less prominent ridge is called a *line*; example: ileopectineal line.
3. *spinous process or spine*—a sharp projection; example: anterior superior iliac spine.
4. *tuberosity*—a large, rounded projection; example: ischial tuberosity.
5. *tubercle*—a small, rounded projection; example: rib tubercles.

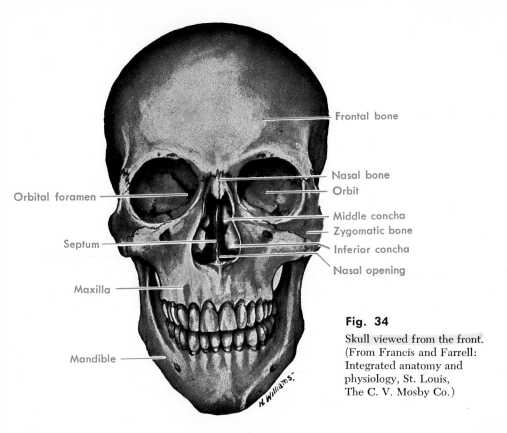

Frontal bone

Nasal bone
Orbit

Orbital foramen

Middle concha
Zygomatic bone

Septum

Inferior concha

Nasal opening

Maxilla

Fig. 34

Skull viewed from the front.
(From Francis and Farrell:
Integrated anatomy and
physiology, St. Louis,
The C. V. Mosby Co.)

Mandible

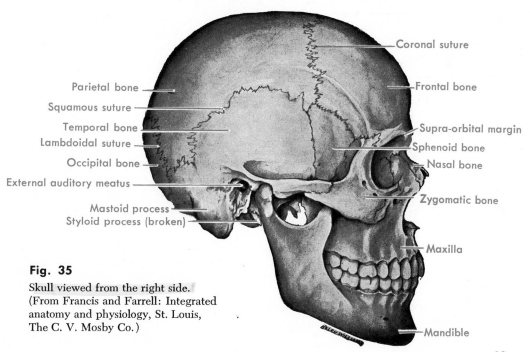

Coronal suture

Parietal bone

Frontal bone

Squamous suture

Temporal bone

Supra-orbital margin

Lambdoidal suture

Sphenoid bone

Occipital bone

Nasal bone

External auditory meatus

Mastoid process

Zygomatic bone

Styloid process (broken)

Maxilla

Fig. 35

Skull viewed from the right side.
(From Francis and Farrell: Integrated
anatomy and physiology, St. Louis,
The C. V. Mosby Co.)

Mandible

89

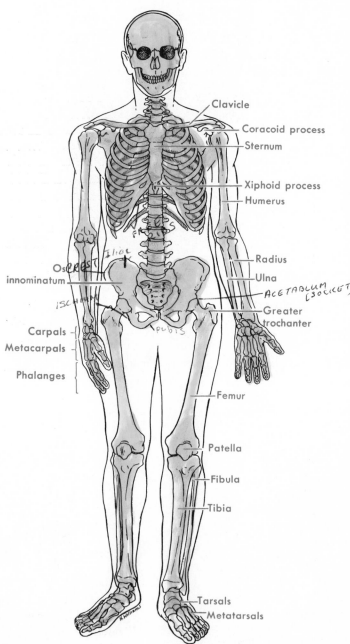

Clavicle

Coracoid process

Sternum

Xiphoid process

Humerus

Radius

Ulna

ACETABLUM (SOCKET)

Greater trochanter

Os
innominatum

IlIoc CREST

ISCHIUM

PUBIS

Carpals

Metacarpals

Phalanges

Femur

Patella

Fibula

Tibia

Tarsals

Metatarsals

H. Williams

Fig. 36
Skeleton, anterior view.

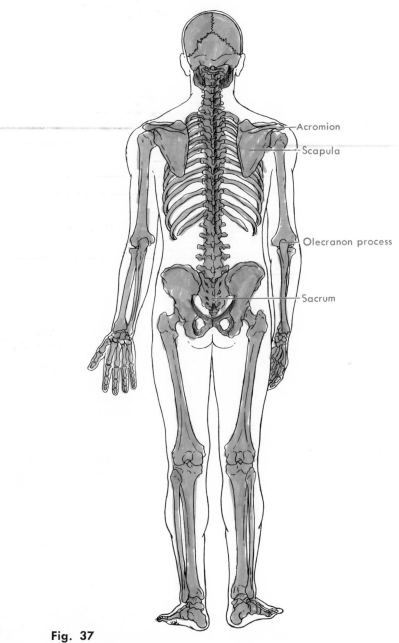

Acromion

Scapula

Olecranon process

Sacrum

Fig. 37
Skeleton, posterior view.

Identification of bone markings

Many of the markings found on bones are described in Table 3. Those which seem particularly important because they are places of muscle attachment are listed in italics in Table 3 (pp. 93 to 102).

Axial skeleton

Skull

Twenty-eight irregular-shaped bones form the skull. Eleven of these are paired bones; six are single. All but one of the skull bones are so joined to each other as to be immovable. Only the lower jawbone (mandible) is movable. The skull is composed of two anatomical entities: the cranium or brain case and the face.

Cranium. The frontal, parietal, and occipital bones form the top of the cranium, whereas the temporal bones and the great wings of the sphenoid form its sides. These same bones, plus the small cribriform plate of the ethmoid bone, make up the lower part of the cranium called the *cranial floor* or *base.* Its midportion is formed by the sphenoid bone which serves as a keystone anchoring the frontal, parietal, occipital, and ethmoid bones.

The *frontal bone* constitutes the skeletal framework for the forehead. It contains mucous-lined air-filled spaces, the *frontal sinuses,* and it forms the upper part of the orbits. It unites with the two parietal bones posteriorly, in an immovable joint, the *coronal suture.* Several of the more prominent frontal bone markings are described in Table 3.

The two *parietal bones* give shape to the bulging topsides of the cranium. They form immovable joints with several bones: the *lambdoidal suture* with the occipital bone, the *squamous suture* with the temporal bone and part of the sphenoid, and the *coronal suture,* mentioned before, with the frontal bone.

The lower sides of the cranium and part of its floor are fashioned from two *temporal bones.* They house the middle and inner ear structures and contain the *mastoid sinuses,* notable because of the occurrence of mastoiditis, an inflammation of the mucous lining of these sinus spaces. Table 3 gives a description of several other temporal bone markings.

The *occipital bone* makes the framework of the lower, posterior part of the skull. It forms immovable joints with three other cranial bones—the parietal, temporal, and sphenoid—and a movable joint with the first cervical vertebra. Consult Table 3 for a description of some of its markings.

The *sphenoid bone* resembles a bat with its wings outstretched and legs extended downward posteriorly. It constitutes the center portion of the cranial floor and forms part of the orbit floor and side walls.

Text continued on p. 103.

Table 3. Bone markings

Bone	Marking	Description
Frontal	Supra-orbital margin	Arched ridge just below eyebrows
	Frontal sinuses	Cavities inside bone just above supraorbital margin; lined with mucosa; contain air
	Frontal tuberosities	Bulge above each orbit; most prominent part of forehead
	Superciliary arches	Ridges caused by projection of frontal sinuses, eyebrows lie over these ridges
	Supraorbital notch (sometimes foramen)	Notch or foramen in the supraorbital margin slightly mesial to its midpoint; transmits supraorbital nerve and blood vessels
	Glabella	Smooth area between superciliary ridges and above nose
Temporal	Mastoid process	Protuberance just behind ear
	Mastoid sinuses	Air-filled mucosa-lined spaces within mastoid process
	External auditory meatus (or canal)	Opening into ear and tube extending into temporal bone
	Zygomatic process	Projection which articulates with malar (or zygomatic) bone
	Internal auditory meatus	Fairly large opening on posterior surface of petrous portion of bone; transmits eighth cranial nerve to inner ear and seventh cranial nerve on its way to facial structures
	Squamous portion	Thin, flaring upper part of bone
	Mastoid portion	Rough-surfaced lower part of bone posterior to external auditory meatus
	Petrous portion	Wedge-shaped process that forms part of center section of cranial floor between sphenoid and occipital bones; name derived from Greek for stone because of extreme hardness of this process; houses middle and inner ear structures
	Mandibular fossa	Oval-shaped depression anterior to external auditory meatus; forms socket for condyle of mandible
	Styloid process	Slender spike of bone extending downward and forward from under surface of bone anterior to mastoid process; often broken off in dry skull; several neck muscles and ligaments attach to styloid process
	Stylomastoid foramen	Opening between styloid and mastoid processes where facial nerve emerges from cranial cavity
	Jugular fossa	Depression on under surface of petrous portion; dilated beginning of internal jugular vein lodged here
	Jugular foramen	Opening in suture between petrous portion and occipital bone; transmits lateral sinus and ninth, tenth, and eleventh cranial nerves
	Carotid canal or foramen	Channel in petrous portion; best seen from under surface of skull; transmits internal carotid artery

Continued on next page.

Table 3. Bone markings—cont'd

Bone	Marking	Description
Occipital	*Foramen magnum*	Hole through which spinal cord enters cranial cavity
	Condyles	Convex, oval processes on either side of foramen magnum; articulate with depressions on first cervical vertebra
	External occipital protuberance	Prominent projection on posterior surface in midline short distance above foramen magnum; can be felt as definite bump
	Superior nuchal line	Curved ridge extending laterally from external occipital protuberance
	Inferior nuchal line	Less well-defined ridge paralleling superior nuchal line a short distance below it
	Internal occipital protuberance	Projection in midline on inner surface bone; groove for lateral sinuses extend laterally from this process and one for sagittal sinus upward from it
Sphenoid	*Body*	Hollow, cubelike central portion
	Great wings	Lateral projections from body; form part of outer wall of orbit
	Lesser wings	Thin, triangular projections from upper part of sphenoid body; form posterior part of roof of orbit
	Sella turcica or Turk's saddle	Saddle-shaped depression on upper surface of sphenoid body; contains pituitary gland (Fig. 38)
	Sphenoid sinuses	Irregular air-filled mucosa-lined spaces within central part of sphenoid (Fig. 42)
	Pterygoid processes	Downward projections on either side where body and greater wing unite; comparable to extended legs of bat if entire bone is likened to this animal; form part of lateral nasal wall
	Optic foramen	Opening into orbit at root of lesser wing; transmits second cranial nerve
	Superior orbital fissure	Slitlike opening into orbit; lateral to optic foramen; transmits third, fourth, and part of fifth cranial nerves
	Foramen rotundum	Opening in greater wing that transmits maxillary division of fifth cranial nerve
	Foramen ovale	Opening in great wing that transmits mandibular division of fifth cranial nerve
Ethmoid	*Horizontal (cribriform) plate*	Olfactory nerves pass through numerous holes in this plate
	Crista galli	See Figs. 42 and 44; meninges attach to this process
	Perpendicular plate	Forms upper part of nasal septum (Fig. 42)
	Ethmoidal sinuses	Honeycombed air spaces within lateral masses of bone
	Superior and middle turbinates (conchae)	Help to form lateral walls of nose (Figs. 44 and 205)
	Lateral masses	Compose sides of bone; contain many air spaces (sinuses); inner surface forms superior and middle conchae

Table 3. Bone markings—cont'd

Bone	Marking	Description
Mandible	Body	Main part of bone; forms chin
	Ramus	Process, one on either side, that projects upward from posterior part of body
	Condyle (or head)	Part of each ramus that articulates with mandibular fossa of temporal bone
	Neck	Constricted part just below condyles
	Alveolar process	Teeth set into this arch
	Mandibular foramen	Opening on inner surface of ramus; transmits nerves and vessels to lower teeth
	Mental foramen	Opening on outer surface below space between two bicuspids; transmits terminal branches of nerves and vessels which enter bone through mandibular foramen; dentists inject anesthetics through these foramina
	Coronoid process	Projection upward from anterior part of each ramus; temporal muscle inserts here
	Angle	Juncture of posterior and inferior margins of ramus
Maxilla	*Alveolar process*	Arch containing teeth
	Maxillary sinus or antrum of Highmore	Large air-filled mucosa-lined cavity within the body of each maxilla; largest of the sinuses
	Palatine process	Horizontal inward projection from alveolar process; forms anterior and larger part of hard palate
	Infraorbital foramen	Hole on external surface just below orbit; transmits vessels and nerves
	Lacrimal groove	Groove on inner surface; joined by similar groove on lacrimal bone to form canal which houses nasolacrimal duct
Palatine	Horizontal plate	Joined to palatine processes of maxillae to complete posterior part of hard palate
Special features of skull	*Sutures*	Immovable joints between skull bones
	1. *Sagittal*	1. Line of articulation between two parietal bones
	2. *Coronal*	2. Joint between parietals and frontal bone
	3. *Lambdoidal*	3. Joint between parietals and occipital bone
	Fontanels	"Soft spots" where ossification is incomplete at birth; allow some compression of skull during birth; also important in determining position of head before delivery; six such areas located at angles of parietal bones
	1. *Anterior*	1. At intersection of sagittal and coronal sutures (juncture of parietals and frontal bone); diamond shaped; largest of fontanels; usually closed by 1½ years of age
	2. *Posterior*	2. At intersection of sagittal and lambdoidal sutures (juncture of parietals and occipital bone); triangular in shape, usually closed by second month
	3. Anterolateral	3. At juncture of frontal, parietal, temporal, and sphenoid bones

Continued on next page.

Table 3. Bone markings—cont'd

Bone	Marking	Description
Special features of skull—cont'd	*Fontanels—cont'd* 4. Posterolateral	4. At juncture of parietal, occipital, and temporal bones; usually closed by second year
	Sinuses 1. *Air* (or bony)	1. Spaces or cavities within bones; those which communicate with nose called *paranasal sinuses* (frontal, sphenoidal, ethmoidal, and maxillary); mastoid cells communicate with middle ear rather than nose, therefore not included among paranasal sinuses
	2. *Blood*	2. Veins within cranial cavity (Figs. 177 and 178)
	Orbits formed by 1. Frontal 2. Ethmoid 3. Sphenoid 4. Lacrimal 5. Maxillary 6. Zygomatic 7. Palatine	1. Roof of orbit (Fig. 41) 2. Medial wall 3. Lateral wall 4. Medial wall 5. Floor 6. Lateral wall 7. Floor
	Nasal septum formed by	Partition in midline of nasal cavity; separates cavity into right and left halves
	1. Perpendicular plate of ethmoid 2. Vomer bone 3. Cartilage	1. Forms upper part of septum 2. Forms lower and posterior part 3. Forms anterior part
	Wormian bones	Small islands of bones within a suture
Vertebral column	General features	Anterior part of vertebrae (except first two cervical) consists of body; posterior part, of neural arch which, in turn, consists of two pedicles, two laminae, and seven processes projecting from laminae
	Thoracic vertebrae (Figs. 46 and 47) 1. *Body*	1. Main part; flat, round mass located anteriorly; is supporting or weight-bearing part of vertebra
	2. *Pedicles*	2. Short projections extending posteriorly from body
	3. *Laminae*	3. Posterior part of vertebra to which pedicles join and from which processes project
	4. *Neural arch*	4. Formed by pedicles and laminae; protects spinal cord posteriorly; together, neural arches form spinal cavity; congenital absence of one or more neural arches known as *spina bifida;* cord may protrude right through skin in this condition
	5. *Spinous process*	5. Sharp process projecting inferiorly from laminae in midline

Table 3. Bone markings—cont'd

Bone	Marking	Description
Vertebral column—cont'd	*Thoracic vertebrae—cont'd* 6. *Transverse processes*	6. Right and left lateral projections from laminae
	7. *Superior articulating processes*	7. Project upward from laminae
	8. *Inferior articulating processes*	8. Project downward from laminae; articulate with superior articulating processes of vertebrae below
	9. *Spinal foramen*	9. Hole in center of vertebra, formed by union of body, pedicles, and laminae; these foramina, with other vertebrae superimposed one upon other, form spinal cavity which houses spinal cord
	Cervical vertebrae 1. General features	1. Foramen in each transverse process for transmission of vertebral artery, vein, and plexus of nerves; short bifurcated spinous processes except on seventh vertebrae where it is extra long and may be felt as protrusion when head is bent forward; bodies of these vertebrae small, while spinal foramina large and triangular
	2. *Atlas*	2. First cervical vertebra; lacks body and spinous process; superior articulating processes concave ovals which act as rocker-like cradles for condyles of occipital bone; named atlas because supports head as Atlas was thought to have supported world
	3. *Axis* (*epistropheus*)	3. Second cervical vertebra; so named because atlas rotates about this bone in rotating movements of head; *dens*, or odontoid process, peglike projection upward from body of axis, forming pivot for rotation of atlas (Fig. 45)
	Lumbar vertebrae	Strong, massive; superior articulating processes directed inward instead of upward; inferior articulating processes, outward instead of downward; short, blunt spinous process
	Sacral promontory	Protuberance from anterior, upper border of sacrum into pelvis; of obstetrical importance because its size limits anteroposterior diameter of pelvic inlet
	Intervertebral foramina	Opening between vertebrae through which spinal nerves emerge (Fig. 48)
	Curves	Curves have great structural importance because increase carrying strength of vertebral column, make balance possible in upright position (if column were straight, weight of viscera would pull body forward), absorb jars from walking (straight column would transmit jars straight to head), and protect column from fracture

Continued on next page.

97

Table 3. Bone markings—cont'd

Bone	Marking	Description
Vertebral column— cont'd	*Curves—cont'd* 1. *Primary*	1. Column curves at birth from head to sacrum with convexity posteriorly; convexity persists after child stands only in *thoracic* and *sacral* regions which, therefore, are called primary curves
	2. *Secondary*	2. Concavities in *cervical* and *lumbar* regions; cervical concavity results from infant's attempts to hold head erect (3 to 4 months); lumbar concavity, from balancing efforts in learning to walk (10 to 18 months)
	3. *Abnormal*	3. *Kyphosis,* exaggerated convexity in thoracic region (hunchback); *lordosis,* exaggerated concavity in lumbar region—a very common condition; *scoliosis,* lateral curvature in any region
Sternum	*Body* *Manubrium* *Xiphoid process*	Main central part of bone Flaring, upper part Projection of cartilage at lower border of bone
Ribs	*Head*	Projection at posterior end of ribs; articulates with corresponding thoracic vertebra and one above, except last three pairs, which join corresponding vertebra only
	Neck Tubercle	Constricted portion just below head Small knob just below neck; articulates with transverse process of corresponding thoracic vertebra; missing in lowest three ribs
	Body or shaft *Costal cartilage*	Main part of rib Cartilage at sternal end of true ribs; attaches ribs (except floating ribs) to sternum
Scapula (Figs. 49 and 50)	*Borders* 1. Superior 2. Vertebral 3. Axillary *Spine*	1. Upper margin 2. Margin toward vertebral column 3. Lateral margin Sharp ridge running diagonally across posterior surface of shoulder blade
	Acromion process	Slightly flaring projection at lateral end of scapular spine; may be felt as tip of shoulder; articulates with clavicle
	Coracoid porcess	Projection on anterior surface from upper border of bone; may be felt in groove between deltoid and pectoralis major muscles, about one inch below clavicle
	Glenoid cavity	Arm socket
Humerus (Figs. 51 and 52)	*Head*	Smooth, hemispherical enlargement at proximal end of humerus
	Anatomical neck Greater tubercle	Oblique groove just below head Rounded projection lateral to head on anterior surface

Table 3. Bone markings—cont'd

Bone	Marking	Description
Humerus— cont'd	Lesser tubercle	Prominent projection on anterior surface just below anatomical neck
	Intertubercular (bicipital) groove	Deep groove between greater and lesser tubercles; long tendon of biceps muscle lodges here
	Surgical neck	Region just below tubercles; so named because of its liability to fracture
	Deltoid tuberosity	V-shaped, rough area about midway down shaft where deltoid muscle inserts.
	Radial groove	Groove running obliquely downward from deltoid tuberosity; lodges radial nerve
	Epicondyles (medial and lateral)	Rough projections at both sides of distal end
	Capitulum	Rounded knob below lateral epicondyle; articulates with radius; sometimes called radial head of humerus
	Trochlea	Projection with a deep depression through center similar to shape of a pulley; articulates with ulna
	Olecranon fossa	Depression on posterior surface just above trochlea; receives olecranon process of ulna when lower arm extends
	Coronoid fossa	Depression on anterior surface above trochlea; receives coronoid process of ulna in flexion of lower arm
Ulna (Figs. 53 and 54)	*Olecranon process*	Elbow, called funny bone because borders on humerus
	Coronoid process	Projection on anterior surface of proximal end of ulna; trochlea of humerus fits snugly between olecranon and coronoid processes
	Semilunar notch	Curved notch between olecranon and coronoid, into which trochlea fits
	Radial notch	Curved notch lateral and inferior to semilunar notch; head of radius fits into this concavity
	Head	Rounded process at distal end; does not articulate with wrist bones but with a fibrocartilaginous disc
	Styloid process	Sharp protuberance at distal end; can be seen from outside on posterior surface
Radius (Figs. 53 and 54)	*Head*	Disc-shaped process forming proximal end of radius; articulates with capitulum of humerus and with radial notch of ulna
	Radial tuberosity	Roughened projection on ulnar side, short distance below head; biceps muscle inserts here
	Styloid process	Protuberance at distal end on lateral surface (with forearm supinated as in anatomical position)
Os coxa (Fig. 56)	*Ilium*	Upper, flaring portion
	Ischium	Lower, posterior portion
	Pubic bone or pubis	Mesial, anterior section

Continued on next page.

Table 3. Bone markings—cont'd

Bone	Marking	Description
Os coxa—cont'd	Acetabulum	Hip socket; formed by union of ilium, ischium, and pubis
	Iliac crests	Upper, curving boundary of ilium
	Iliac spines	
	1. Anterior superior	1. Prominent projection at anterior end of iliac crest; can be felt externally as "point" of hip
	2. Anterior inferior	2. Less prominent projection short distance below anterior superior spine
	3. Posterior superior	3. At posterior end of iliac crest
	4. Posterior inferior	4. Just below posterior superior spine
	Greater sciatic notch	Large notch on posterior surface of ilium just below posterior inferior spine
	Gluteal lines	Three curved lines across outer surface of ilium—posterior, anterior, inferior, respectively
	Iliopectineal line	Rounded ridge extending from pubic tubercle upward and backward toward sacrum
	Iliac fossa	Large, smooth, concave inner surface of ilium above iliopectineal line
	Ischial tuberosity	Large rough, quadrilateral process forming inferior part of ischium; body rests on these tuberosities in erect sitting position
	Ischial spine	Pointed projection just above tuberosity
	Symphysis pubis	Cartilaginous, amphiarthrotic joint between pubic bones
	Superior pubic ramus	Part of pubis lying between symphysis and acetabulum; forms upper part of obturator foramen
	Inferior pubic ramus	Part extending down from symphysis; unites with ischium
	Pubic arch	Angle formed by two inferior rami
	Pubic crest	Upper margin of superior ramus
	Pubic tubercle	Rounded process at end of crest
	Obturator foramen	Large hole in anterior surface of os coxa; formed by pubis and ischium; largest foramen in body
	Pelvic brim or inlet	Boundary of aperture leading into true pelvis; formed by pubic crests, iliopectineal lines, and sacral promontory; size and shape of this inlet has great obstetrical importance since if any of it diameters are too small, infant skull cannot enter true pelvis for natural birth
	True or lesser pelvis	Space below pelvic brim; true "basin" with bone and muscle walls and muscle floor; pelvic organs located in this space
	False or greater pelvis	Broad, shallow space above pelvic brim, misnamed as is really part of abdominal cavity, but is a false "basin" in that instead of a "floor," it has only an aperture, pelvic inlet, and its bony walls, being present only at the sides and back, are less complete than those of true pelvis

Table 3. Bone markings—cont'd

Bone	Marking	Description
Os coxa— cont'd	Pelvic outlet	Irregular circumference marking lower limits of true pelvis; bounded by tip of coccyx and two ischial tuberosities
	Pelvic girdle (or bony pelvis)	Complete bony ring; composed of two hip bones (ossa coxae), sacrum, and coccyx; forms firm base by which trunk rests upon thighs and for attachment of lower extremities to axial skeleton
Femur (Fig. 57)	*Head*	Rounded, upper end of bone; fits into acetabulum
	Neck	Constricted portion just below head
	Greater trochanter	Protuberance located inferiorly and laterally to head
	Lesser trochanter	Small protuberance located inferiorly and mesially to greater trochanter
	Linea aspera	Prominent ridge extending lengthwise along concave posterior surface
	Gluteal tubercle	Rounded projection just below greater trochanter; a rudimentary third trochanter
	Supracondylar ridges	Two ridges formed by division of linea aspera at its lower end; medial supracondylar ridge extends inward to inner condyle, lateral ridge to outer condyle
	Condyles	Large, rounded bulges at distal end of femur; one on mesial and one on lateral surface
	Adductor tubercle	Small projection just above inner condyle; marks termination of medial supracondylar ridge
	Trochlea	Smooth depression between condyles on anterior surface; articulates with patella
	Intercondyloid notch	A deep depression between condyles on posterior surface; cruciate ligaments which help bind femur to tibia lodge in this notch
Tibia (Fig. 58)	*Condyles*	Bulging prominences at proximal end of tibia; upper surfaces concave for articulation with femur
	Intercondylar eminence	Upward projection on articular surface between condyles
	Crest	Sharp ridge on anterior surface
	Tibial tuberosity	Projection in midline on anterior surface
	Popliteal line	Ridge that spirals downward and inward on posterior surface of upper third of tibial shaft
	Medial malleolus	Rounded downward projection at distal end of tibia; forms prominence on inner surface of ankle
Fibula (Fig. 58)	*Lateral malleolus*	Rounded prominence at distal end of fibula; forms prominence on outer surface of ankle

Continued on next page.

Table 3. Bone markings—cont'd

Bone	Marking	Description
Tarsals (Fig. 59)	*Calcaneus*	Heel bone
	Talus	Uppermost of tarsals; articulates with tibia and fibula; boxed in by medial and lateral malleoli
	Longitudinal arches	Tarsals and metatarsals so arranged as to form arch from front to back of foot
	1. *Inner*	1. Formed by calcaneus, navicular, cuneiforms, and three medial metatarsals
	2. *Outer*	2. Formed by calcaneus, cuboid, and two lateral metatarsals
	Transverse (or *metatarsal*) *arch*	Metatarsals and distal row of tarsals (cuneiforms and cuboid) so articulated as to form arch across foot; bones kept in two arched positions by means of powerful ligaments in sole of foot and by muscles and tendons

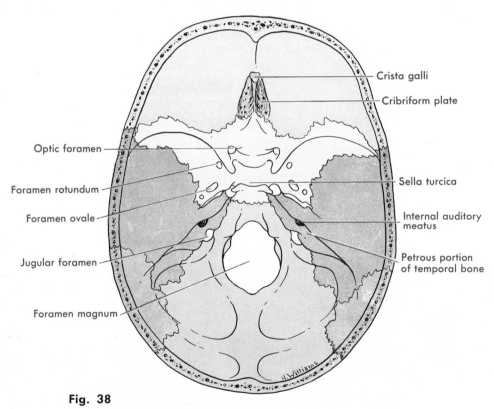

Fig. 38

Floor of the cranial cavity:
blue, frontal bone; **orange,** ethmoid and parietals; **yellow,** sphenoid;
purple, temporal; **green,** occipital.

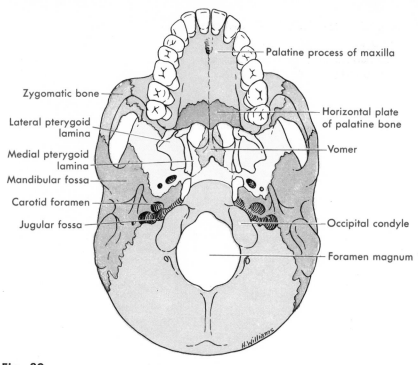

Fig. 39

Inferior surface of the skull: **green,** maxilla and occipital bones;
pink, zygomatic (malar) and vomer bones; **brown,**
palatine; **yellow,** sphenoid; **purple,** temporal.

It contains fairly large mucosa-lined air-filled spaces, the *sphenoid si-nuses.* Several prominent sphenoid markings are described in Table 3; also see Fig. 42.

The *ethmoid,* a complicated, irregular bone, lies anterior to the sphenoid but posterior to the nasal bones. It helps fashion the anterior part of the cranial floor, the medial walls of the orbits, the upper part of the nasal septum and side walls, and the part of the nasal roof perforated by small foramina through which olfactory nerve branches reach the brain. The lateral masses of the ethmoid are honeycombed with sinus spaces. More ethmoid markings are described in Table 3; also see Figs. 42 and 44.

Face bones. Fourteen bones are commonly said to form the framework of the face, but actually more are involved since some of the cranial bones, particularly the frontal and ethmoid, also help shape the face.

Just as the sphenoid acts as the keystone in the architecture of the cranium, so the *maxillae* serve in this capacity for the face. With the exception of the mandible, all the face bones articulate with the maxillae, which also articulate with each other, in the midline. The maxillae form part of the floor of the orbits, part of the roof of the mouth, and part of the floor and sidewalls of the nose. They contain the largest of

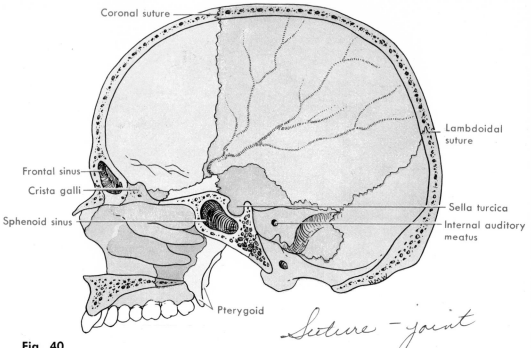

Coronal suture

Lambdoidal suture

Frontal sinus

Crista galli

Sphenoid sinus

Sella turcica

Internal auditory meatus

Pterygoid

Suture — joint

Fig. 40

Longitudinal section of the skull, nasal septum removed: **blue,** frontal bone; **pink,** nasal; **orange,** ethmoid and parietal; **purple,** inferior concha (turbinate) and temporal; **yellow,** sphenoid; **green,** maxilla and occipital; **brown,** palatine.

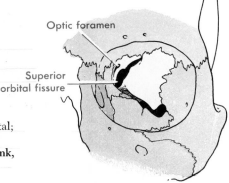

Optic foramen

Superior orbital fissure

Fig. 41

Bones that form the orbit: **blue,** frontal; **green,** maxilla; **yellow,** sphenoid; **orange,** ethmoid; **purple,** lacrimal; **pink,** malar; **fine black stripes,** palatine; **solid black,** fissures.

the paranasal sinuses, the maxillary sinuses or *antrum of Highmore.* For other markings of the maxillae, see Table 3.

Unlike the upper jaw, which is formed by a pair of bones, the lower jaw consists of a single bone, the *mandible,* due to fusion of its halves during infancy. It is the largest, strongest bone of the face. It articulates with the temporal bone in the only movable joint of the skull. Its major markings are identified in Table 3.

The cheek is shaped by the underlying *zygomatic* or malar bone. This bone also forms the outer margin of the orbit and, with the zygo-

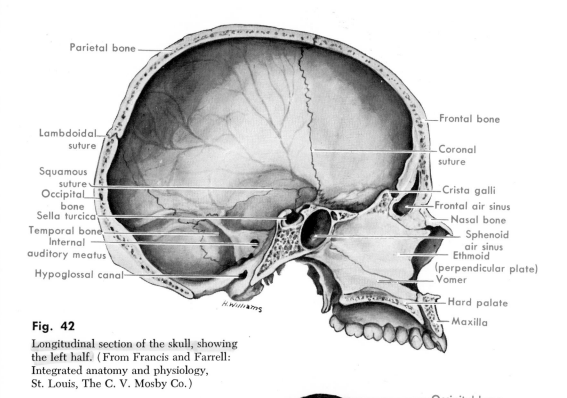

Parietal bone

Lambdoidal suture

Squamous suture

Occipital bone

Sella turcica

Temporal bone

Internal auditory meatus

Hypoglossal canal

Frontal bone

Coronal suture

Crista galli

Frontal air sinus

Nasal bone

Sphenoid air sinus

Ethmoid (perpendicular plate)

Vomer

Hard palate

Maxilla

H. Williams

Fig. 42

Longitudinal section of the skull, showing the left half. (From Francis and Farrell: Integrated anatomy and physiology, St. Louis, The C. V. Mosby Co.)

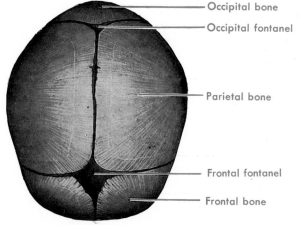

Occipital bone

Occipital fontanel

Parietal bone

Frontal fontanel

Frontal bone

Fig. 43

Skull at birth viewed from above. (From Pitzman: Fundamentals of anatomy, St. Louis, The C. V. Mosby Co.)

matic process of the temporal bone, makes the zygomatic arch. It articulates with four other face bones: the maxillae and the temporal, frontal, and sphenoid bones.

Shape is given to the nose by the two *nasal bones,* which form the upper part of the bridge of the nose, and *cartilage,* the lower part. Though small bones, the nasal bones enter into five articulations: with the perpendicular plate of the ethmoid, the cartilaginous part of the nasal septum, the frontal bone, maxillae, and with each other.

An almost paper-thin bone shaped and sized about like a fingernail

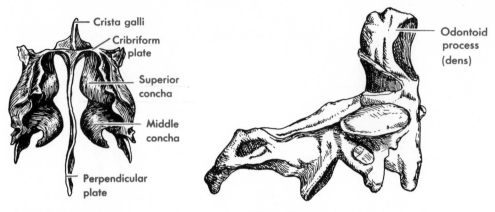

Fig. 44

Ethmoid bone viewed from behind.
(From Francis and Farrell: Integrated
anatomy and physiology, St. Louis,
The C. V. Mosby Co.)

Fig. 45

Second cervical vertebra (the axis or
epistropheus) from the side.

lies just posterior and lateral to each nasal bone. It helps form the side
wall of the nasal cavity and the medial wall of the orbit. Because it
contains a groove for the nasolacrimal duct, this bone is called the
lacrimal bone. It joins the maxilla, frontal bone, and ethmoid.

An irregular bone whose horizontal and vertical portions are joined
in such a way as to make the bone roughly **L** shaped and which forms
the framework for the inferior and lateral walls of the posterior part
of the nasal cavity is known as the *palatine bone* because it also forms
the posterior part of the hard palate. In addition, it has a small upper
projection which helps form the floor of the orbit. The two palatine
bones are united in the midline like two **L**'s facing each other. They
articulate also with the maxillae and the sphenoid.

The *inferior nasal concha* is a scroll-like bone which forms a kind of
ledge projecting into the nasal cavity from its lateral wall. In each nasal
cavity there are three of these ledges, formed respectively by the superior and middle conchae (which are projections of the ethmoid) and
the inferior concha (which is a separate bone). They are mucosa covered and divide each nasal cavity into three narrow, irregular channels, the *nasal meati*. The inferior nasal conchae form immovable joints
with the ethmoid, lacrimal, maxillary, and palatine bones.

Two structures which enter into the formation of the nasal septum
have already been mentioned, the perpendicular plate of the ethmoid
and the septal cartilage. One other structure, the *vomer bone*, completes the septum posteriorly. It is usually described as being shaped
like a ploughshare. It forms immovable joints with four bones: the
sphenoid, ethmoid, and palatine bones and the maxillae.

Ear bones. See Table 2.

Special features of the skull. Sutures, fontanels, sinuses, orbits, nasal
septum, and Wormian bones are described in Table 3.

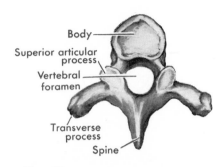

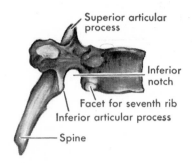

Fig. 46

Sixth thoracic vertebra viewed from
above. (From Francis and Farrell:
Integrated anatomy and physiology,
St. Louis, The C. V. Mosby Co.)

Fig. 47

Sixth thoracic vertebra viewed from the
right side. (From Francis and Farrell:
Integrated anatomy and physiology,
St. Louis, The C. V. Mosby Co.)

Hyoid bone

The hyoid bone is a single bone in the neck—a part of the axial
skeleton. Its **U** shape may be felt just above the larynx and below the
mandible where it is suspended from the styloid processes of the temporal bones. One of the pairs of extrinsic tongue muscles (hyoglossus)
originates on the hyoid bone, and certain muscles of the floor of the
mouth (mylohyoid, geniohyoid) insert on it. The hyoid claims the distinction of being the only bone in the body which does not articulate
with any other bone.

Vertebral column

The vertebral column constitutes the longitudinal axis of the skeleton. It is a flexible rather than a rigid column because it is segmented—
that is, made up of twenty-six (typical in adult) separate bones called
vertebrae, so joined to each other as to permit forward, backward, and
sideways movement of the column. The head is balanced on top of
this column, the ribs and viscera are suspended in front, the lower extremities are attached below, and the spinal cord is enclosed within.
It is, indeed, the "backbone" of the body.

The seven *cervical vertebrae* constitute the skeletal framework of the
neck; the next twelve are known as *thoracic vertebrae* because they
lie behind the thoracic cavity; the next five, which support the small
of the back, are called *lumbar vertebrae;* below the latter are the *sacrum* and *coccyx.* In the adult the sacrum is a single bone which has resulted from the fusion of five separate vertebrae, and the coccyx is a
single bone that has resulted from the fusion of four or five vertebrae.
All the vertebrae resemble each other in certain features and differ in
others. For example, all except the first cervical vertebra have a flat,
rounded mass placed anteriorly and centrally, known as the *body,* plus

107

a sharp or blunt *spinous process* projecting inferiorly in the posterior midline and two transverse processes projecting laterally. All but the sacrum and coccyx have a central opening, the *vertebral foramen*. An upward projection (the *dens*) from the body of the second cervical vertebra furnishes an axis for rotating the head. A long, blunt spinous process which can be felt at the back of the base of the neck characterizes the seventh cervical vertebra. Each thoracic vertebra has articular facets for the ribs. More detailed descriptions of separate vertebrae are given in Table 3. The vertebral column as a whole articulates with the head, ribs, and hip bones, whereas the individual vertebrae articulate with each other in joints between their bodies and articular processes. For a description of intervertebral joints, see Table 5.

In order to increase the carrying strength of the vertebral column and to make balance possible in the upright position, the vertebral column is curved. At birth there is a continuous posterior convexity from head to coccyx, but as the child learns to sit and stand, secondary posterior concavities necessary for balance develop in the cervical and lumbar regions. Not uncommonly, spinal curves deviate from the normal. For example, the lumbar curve frequently shows an exaggerated concavity *(lordosis)*, whereas any of the regions may have a lateral

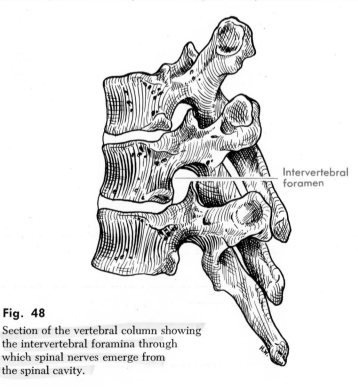

Intervertebral
foramen

Fig. 48

Section of the vertebral column showing
the intervertebral foramina through
which spinal nerves emerge from
the spinal cavity.

curvature *(scoliosis)*. The so-called hunchback is an exaggerated convexity in the thoracic region *(kyphosis)*.

Sternum

The *medial part* of the anterior chest wall is supported by the *sternum,* a somewhat dagger-shaped bone consisting of three parts: the upper handle part or *manubrium,* the middle blade part or *body,* and a blunt cartilaginous lower tip, the *xiphoid process.* The latter ossifies during adult life. The manubrium articulates with the clavicle and first rib, whereas the next nine ribs join the body of the sternum, either directly or indirectly, by means of the *costal cartilages.*

Thorax

Twelve pairs of ribs, together with the vertebral column and sternum, form the bony cage known as the *thorax.* Each rib articulates with both the body and transverse process of its corresponding thoracic vertebra. In addition, the second through the ninth ribs articulate with the body of the vertebra above. From its vertebral attachment each rib curves outward, then forward and downward, a mechanical fact important for breathing. Anteriorly each of the first seven ribs joins a costal cartilage which attaches it to the sternum. Each of the costal cartilages of the next three ribs, however, joins the cartilage of the rib above to be thus indirectly attached to the sternum. Because the two costal cartilages of the eleventh and twelfth ribs do not attach even indirectly to the sternum, they are designated floating ribs.

Appendicular skeleton
Upper extremity

The upper extremity consists of the bones of the shoulder girdle, upper arm, lower arm, wrist, and hand. Two bones, the *clavicle* and *scapula,* compose the *shoulder girdle.* Contrary to appearances, this girdle forms only one bony joint with the trunk: the sternoclavicular joint between the sternum and clavicle. At its outer end the clavicle articulates with the scapula which attaches to the ribs by muscles and tendons, not by joints. All shoulder movements, therefore, involve the sternoclavicular joint. Various markings of the scapula are described in Table 3.

The *humerus* or upper arm bone, like other long bones, consists of a shaft or diaphysis and two ends or epiphyses. The upper epiphysis bears several identifying structures: the head, anatomical neck, greater and lesser tubercles, intertubercular groove, and the surgical neck. The deltoid tuberosity and the radial groove are found on the diaphysis, and four projections, the medial and lateral epicondyles, the capitulum,

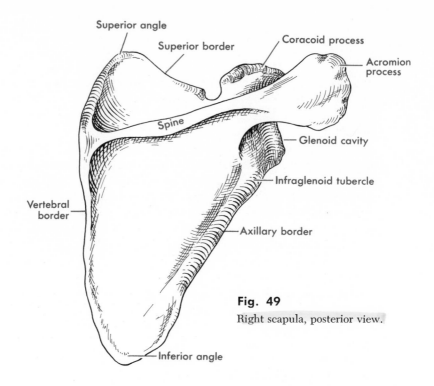

Superior angle

Superior border

Coracoid process

Acromion process

Spine

Glenoid cavity

Infraglenoid tubercle

Vertebral border

Axillary border

Fig. 49

Right scapula, posterior view.

Inferior angle

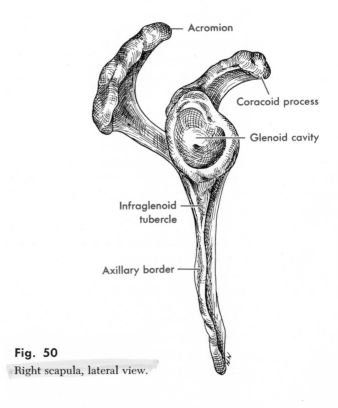

Acromion

Coracoid process

Glenoid cavity

Infraglenoid tubercle

Axillary border

Fig. 50

Right scapula, lateral view.

and the trochlea, and two depressions, the olecranon and coronoid fossae, characterize the distal epiphysis. All of these markings are described in Table 3. The humerus articulates proximally with the scapula and distally with both the radius and ulna.

Two bones form the framework for the lower arm: the *ulna* on the little finger side and the *radius* on the thumb side. At the proximal end of the ulna, the olecranon process projects posteriorly and the coronoid process anteriorly. There are also two depressions: the semilunar notch on the anterior surface and the radial notch on the lateral. The distal end has two projections: a rounded head and a sharper styloid process. For more detailed identification of these markings see Table 3. The ulna articulates proximally with the humerus and radius and distally with a fibrocartilaginous disc but not with any of the carpal bones.

The radius has three projections: two at its proximal end, the head and radial tuberosity, and one at its distal end, the styloid process (Figs. 53 and 54). There are two proximal articulations: one with the capitulum of the humerus and the other with the radial notch of the ulna. The three distal articulations are with the navicular and lunate carpal bones and with the head of the ulna.

The eight *carpal bones* (Fig. 55) form what most people think of as the upper part of their hand but what, anatomically speaking, is the wrist. Only one of these bones is evident from the outside, the *pisiform bone*, which projects anteriorly on the little finger side as a small, rounded elevation. Ligaments bind the carpals closely and firmly together in two rows of four each: proximal row (from little finger toward thumb)—pisiform, triquetrum, lunate, and navicular; distal row—hamate, capitate, and lesser and greater multangulars. The joints between the carpals and the joint between the carpals and radius permit wrist and hand movements.

Of the five *metacarpal bones* which form the framework of the hand, that of the thumb forms the most freely movable joint with the carpals, a fact of mechanical significance. Because of the wide range of movement possible between the thumb metacarpal and the greater multangular bone, particularly the ability to oppose the thumb to the fingers, the human hand has much greater dexterity than the forepaw of any animal and has enabled man to manipulate his environment effectively. The heads of the metacarpals, prominent as the proximal knuckles of the hand, articulate with the phalanges.

Lower extremity

Bones of the hip, thigh, lower leg, ankle, and foot constitute the lower extremity. Strong ligaments bind the two hip bones (*os coxae* or *os innominatum*) to the sacrum posteriorly and to each other anteriorly

111

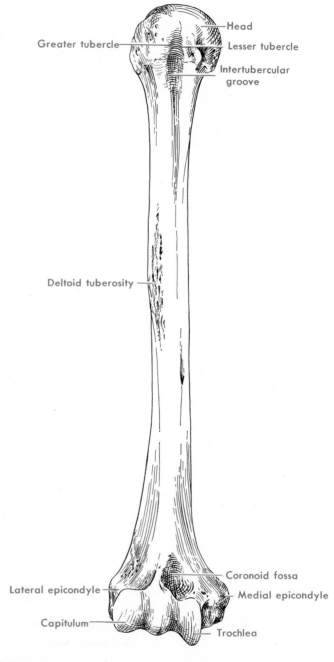

Head

Lesser tubercle

Intertubercular
groove

Greater tubercle

Deltoid tuberosity

Coronoid fossa

Lateral epicondyle

Medial epicondyle

Capitulum

Trochlea

Fig. 51

Right humerus, anterior view.

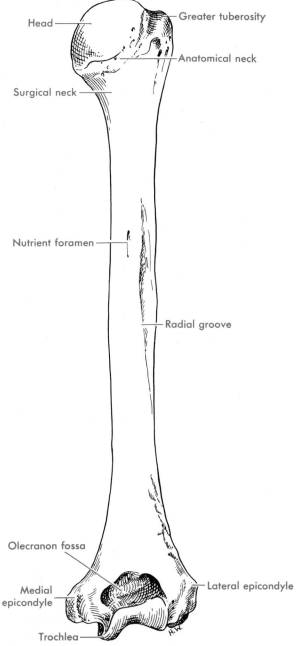

Head ———

Greater tuberosity

Anatomical neck

Surgical neck ———

Nutrient foramen ———

Radial groove

Olecranon fossa

Medial
epicondyle

Lateral epicondyle

Trochlea ———

H.W.

Fig. 52

Right humerus, posterior view.

113

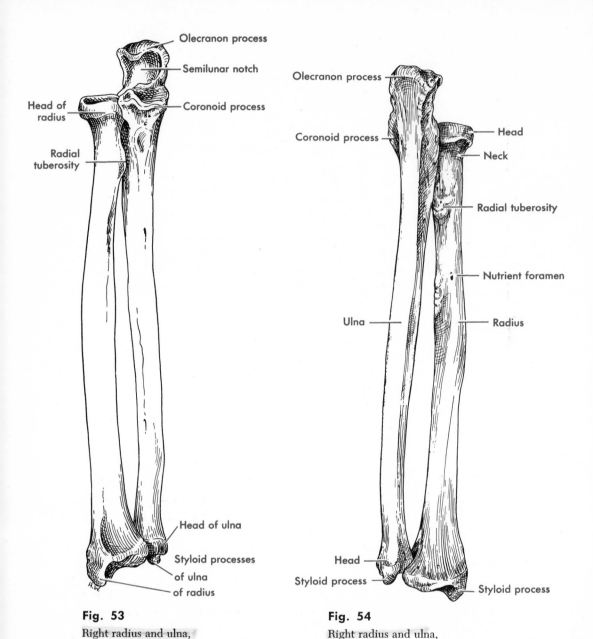

Fig. 53

Right radius and ulna,
anterior surfaces.

Fig. 54

Right radius and ulna,
posterior surfaces.

to form the *pelvic girdle*, a stable, circular base which supports the trunk and attaches the lower extremities to it. In early life each os innominatum is made up of three separate bones, but later on these fuse into a single, massive, irregular bone which is broader than any other bone in the body. The largest and uppermost of the three bones is the *ilium;* the strongest, lowermost, the *ischium;* and the anterior-most, the *pubis*. Numerous markings are present on the three bones. These are identified in Table 3; also see Fig. 56.

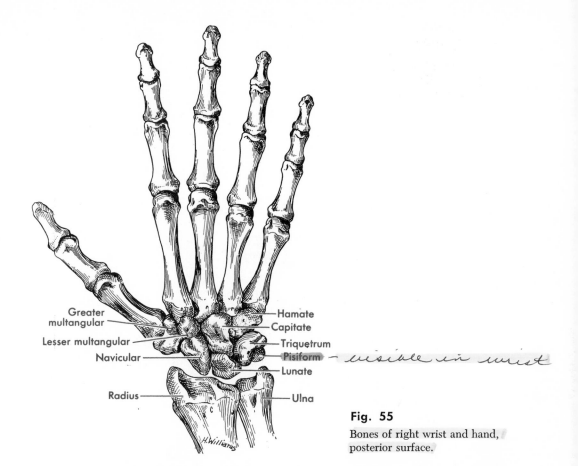

Greater multangular
Lesser multangular
Navicular
Radius

Hamate
Capitate
Triquetrum
Pisiform — *visible in wrist*
Lunate
Ulna

Fig. 55

Bones of right wrist and hand, posterior surface.

The two thigh bones or *femurs* have the distinction of being the longest and heaviest bones in the body. Several prominent markings characterize them. For example, three projections are conspicuous at each epiphysis: the head and greater and lesser trochanters proximally and the medial and lateral condyles and adductor tubercle distally (Fig. 57). Both condyles and the greater trochanter may be felt externally. For a description of the various femur markings, see Table 3.

The largest sesamoid bone in the body, and the one which is almost universally present, is the *patella* or kneecap, located in the tendon of the quadriceps femoris muscle as a protection to the underlying knee joint. When the joint is extended, the patellar outline may be distinguished through the skin, but as the knee flexes it sinks into the intercondylar notch of the femur and can no longer be delineated.

The *tibia* is the larger and stronger and the more medially and superficially located of the two lower leg bones, whereas the *fibula* is smaller and more laterally and deeply placed. The fibula articulates with the lateral condyle of the tibia, and the tibia in turn articulates with the femur in the largest and one of the most stable joints of the body. Distally the tibia articulates again with the fibula and also with the talus.

115

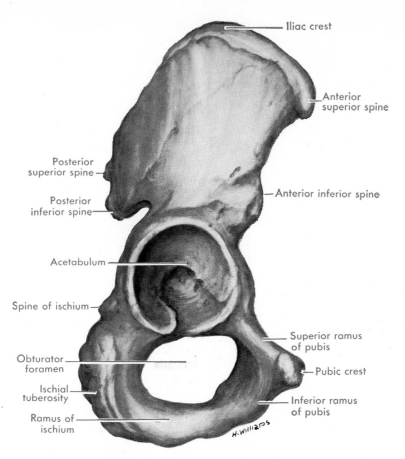

Iliac crest

Anterior superior spine

Posterior superior spine

Anterior inferior spine

Posterior inferior spine

Acetabulum

Spine of ischium

Superior ramus of pubis

Obturator foramen

Pubic crest

Ischial tuberosity

Inferior ramus of pubis

Ramus of ischium

H.Williams

Fig. 56

Right hip bone viewed from the side with the bone turned so
as to look directly into the acetabulum. (From Francis and Farrell:
Integrated anatomy and physiology, St. Louis, The C. V. Mosby Co.)

The latter fits ino a boxlike socket formed by the medial and lateral
malleoli, projections of the tibia and fibula, respectively. For other
tibial markings, see Table 3 and Fig. 58.

Structure of the *foot* is similar to that of the hand with certain differences which adapt it for supporting weight. One example of this is
the much greater solidity and the more limited mobility of the great
toes compared to the thumb. Then, too, the foot bones are held together in such a way as to form springy lengthwise and crosswise
arches. This is architecturally sound since arches are known to furnish
more supporting strength per given amount of structural material than
any other type of construction. Hence, the two-way arch construction
makes a highly stable base. The longitudinal arch has an inner or
medial portion and an outer or lateral portion, both of which are
formed by the placement of tarsals and metatarsals. Specifically some
of the tarsals (calcaneus, talus, navicular, and cuneiforms) and the
first three metatarsals form the medial longitudinal arch; the calcaneus

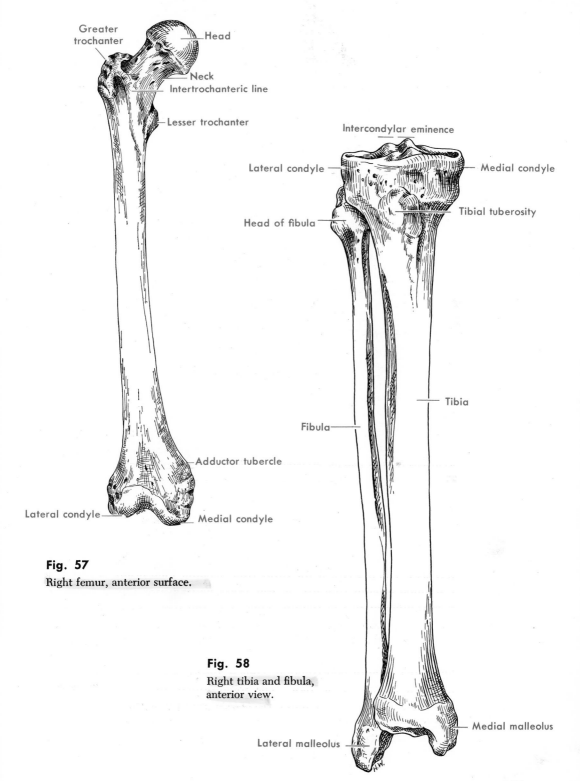

Fig. 57
Right femur, anterior surface.

Fig. 58
Right tibia and fibula,
anterior view.

117

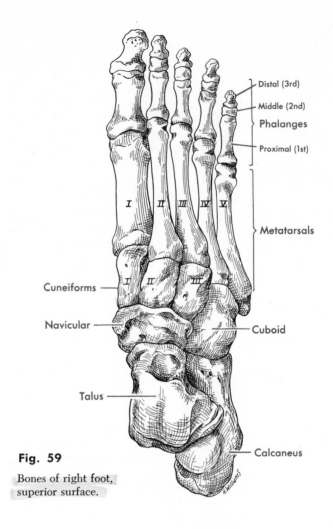

Distal (3rd)
Middle (2nd)
Phalanges
Proximal (1st)

I *II* *III* *IV* *V*

Metatarsals

Cuneiforms
I *II* *III*

Navicular

Cuboid

Talus

Calcaneus

Fig. 59

Bones of right foot,
superior surface.

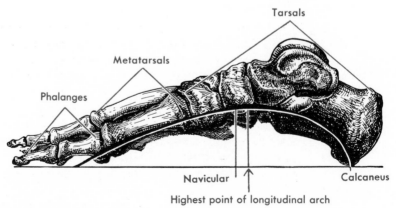

Tarsals

Metatarsals

Phalanges

Navicular

Calcaneus

Highest point of longitudinal arch

Fig. 60

Medial longitudinal arch of the foot.
(From Callander: Surgical anatomy, Philadelphia, W. B. Saunders Co.)

The skeletal
system   118

and cuboid tarsals plus the fourth and fifth metatarsals shape the lateral longitudinal arch (Figs. 59 and 60). The transverse arch results from the relative placement of the distal row of tarsals and the five metatarsals. (See Table 3 for specific bones of different arches.) Strong ligaments and leg muscle tendons normally hold the foot bones firmly in their arched positions, but not infrequently these weaken, causing the arches to flatten, a condition aptly called fallen arches or flatfeet. Note that the tarsals and metatarsals play the major role in the functioning of the foot as a supporting structure, with the phalanges relatively unimportant, whereas the reverse is true for the hand, where manipulation is the main function rather than support and where the phalanges, therefore, are all important and the carpals and metacarpals subsidiary.

Differences between male and female skeletons

Both general and specific differences exist between male and female skeletons. The general difference is one of size and weight, the male skeleton being larger and heavier; the specific differences concern the shape of the pelvic bones and cavity. Whereas in the male the pelvis is deep and funnel shaped, with a narrow pubic arch (usually less than 90 degrees), in the female the pelvis is shallow, broad, and flaring, with a wider pubic arch (usually greater than 90 degrees). The childbearing function obviously explains the necessity for these and certain other modifications of the female pelvis.

Age changes in the skeleton

Skeletal changes from infancy to adulthood are mainly changes in the size of the bones and in the proportionate sizes between different bones, whereas changes in the bones from young adulthood to old age are mainly a matter of changes in the texture and in the contour of the margins and bone markings. Some of the major modifications which occur from infancy to young adulthood are as follows:

1. The head becomes proportionately smaller. Whereas the infant head is approximately one-fourth the total height of the body, the adult head is only about one-eighth the total height.

2. The thorax changes shape, roughly speaking, from round to elliptical.

3. The pelvis becomes relatively larger and in the female relatively wider.

4. The legs become proportionately longer and the trunk proportionately shorter.

119

5. The vertebral column develops two curves not present at birth—the cervical curve when the infant starts lifting up his head (at about 3 months) and the lumbar curve when the child begins standing (toward the end of the first year); both of these curves are concave posteriorly, whereas the primary thoracic and sacral curves are convex posteriorly.

6. The cranium shows several modifications; it grows rapidly during early childhood, enlarging its capacity from approximately 350 milliliters at birth to approximately 1500 milliliters (about adult size) by 6 years of age; the fontanels close by about 1½ or 2 years of age; the sutures begin to fuse in the 20's.

7. The facial bones also show several changes between infancy and adulthood; unlike the cranial bones, their growth is slow during early childhood but rapid during the teens; whereas the infant's face compared with the entire skull bears the relationship of 1:8, the adult face bears the relationship of 1:2 to the adult skull; the sinuses are much larger in the adult—for example, at birth, only rudimentary maxillary and mastoid sinuses exist; the ethmoid and spenoid sinuses start to appear at about 6 years, the frontal at about 7; all of the bony sinuses, but especially the frontal, grow rapidly during adolescence.

8. The epiphyses of the long bones are composed of cartilage at birth but become completely ossified (except for the thin layer of articular cartilage) by adulthood; demonstration of epiphyseal cartilage by x-ray indicates that skeletal growth has not ceased.

Changes in the skeleton continue to occur from adulthood to old age. Both bone margins and projections, for example, look different in old bones than in young. Instead of clean cut, distinct margins, old bones characteristically have indistinct, shaggy appearing margins (marginal lipping and spurs)—a regrettable change because the restricted movements of old age stem partly from this piling up of bone around joint margins. Also an increase in bone along various projections develops in old age, making ridges and processes more pronounced.

Joints between bones (articulations)

Bones are joined to one another in several ingenious ways which permit of a great variety of movement. Where free movement is essential, the articulating ends of the bones are so shaped and the joint so constructed as to permit and even facilitate unhampered motion. Where only slight movement is desirable, bone shape and joint structure make only slight movement possible. Where no movement between the bones is preferable, this, too, is accomplished by bone shape and joint structure. How important normal joint structure and function are for the productiveness and enjoyment of life, probably most of us seldom consider. But disease often makes this tragically clear. Joint structure in all too many cases becomes so altered that crippling immobility results—sometimes only limitation of a single movement and sometimes almost complete immobilization. To inquire into joint structure and action is, therefore, an essential part of the study of anatomy and physiology. Basic information includes understanding the ways in which joints are classified, the ways in which they are constructed, and the kinds of movements permitted by them.

Kinds of joints

A confusing array of terms has grown up around the subject of joint classification. Different anatomists have used different criteria for identifying joint types and have muddled matters even more by using various names for the same kind of joint. One of the simpler ways of classifying joints is to divide them into two main groups based on the presence or absence of a separation (joint cavity) between the articulating bones. Using this method, there are *diarthroses* (joints with a

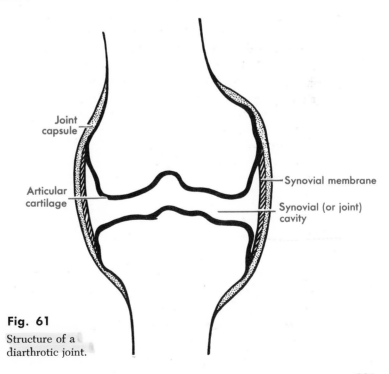

Fig. 61

Structure of a diarthrotic joint.

joint cavity) and *synarthroses* (joints without a joint cavity).* Diarthroses share several characteristics besides that of having a joint cavity. A thin layer of hyaline cartilage covers the joint surfaces of the articulating bones, a sleevelike, fibrous capsule lined with smooth, slippery synovial membrane encases the joint, and additional ligaments grow between the bones, lashing them firmly together. Crescent-shaped pieces of cartilage are found in some diarthrotic joints interposed between the articulating ends of the two bones; examples are the semilunar cartilages of the knee joint and the glenoid cartilages of the shoulder joint.

Diarthroses and synarthroses are divided into subtypes according to such characteristics as the shape of the joint surfaces of the united bones and the type connective tissue between them. See Table 4 for a summary of the main kinds of joints with examples of each.

Movements of joints

1. *flexion*—decreases the size of the angle between the anterior surfaces of articulated bones (exception, flexion of the knee and toe joints decreases the angle between the posterior surfaces of the articulated bones); flexing movements are *bending* or *folding* movements—for example, bending the head forward is flexion of the joint between the occipital bone and the atlas and bending the elbow is flexion of the elbow joint or of the lower arm. Flexing movements of the arms and legs may be thought of as "withdrawing" movements.

2. *extension*—the return from flexion; whereas bending movements are flexions, *straightening* movements are extensions; extension restores a part to its anatomic position from the flexed position. Continuation of extension beyond the anatomic position is called *hyperextension*. Examples: flexion of the head, bending it forward as in prayer, extension of the head, returning it to the upright anatomic position from the flexed position, and hyperextension of the head, stretching it backward from the upright position. Extension of the foot at the ankle joint is commonly referred to as *plantar flexion*, while flexion of the ankle joint is called *dorsal flexion*.

3. *abduction*—moves the bone away from the median plane of the body. Example: moving the arms straight out to the sides.

4. *adduction*—the opposite of abduction; moves the part toward the

---

*Another method of classifying joints recognizes three types—diarthroses, synarthroses, and amphiarthroses—and describes them, respectively, as freely movable, immovable, and slightly movable.

Table 4. Joints

Diarthroses	Synarthroses
1. **Ball and socket** *Other names:* spheroidal; enarthroses *Description:* ball-shaped head fits into concave socket *Movement:* widest range of all joints; triaxial *Examples:* shoulder and hip joints 2. **Hinge** *Other name:* ginglymus *Description:* spool-shaped surface fits into a concave surface *Movement:* in one plane about a single axis; like a hinged door movement; uniaxial *Examples:* elbow, knee, ankle, and interphalangeal joints 3. **Pivot** *Other name:* trochoid *Description:* arch-shaped surface rotates about rounded or peglike pivot *Movement:* rotation; uniaxial *Examples:* between axis and atlas; between radius and ulna 4. **Condyloid** *Other names:* ellipsoidal, ovoid *Description:* oval-shaped condyle fits into elliptical cavity *Movements:* in two planes at right angles to each other; back and forth, and side to side; biaxial *Examples:* wrist joint (between radius and carpals) 5. **Saddle** *Description:* saddle-shaped bone into socket that is concave-convex in opposite direction; a modification of condyloid joint *Movement:* same kinds of movement as condyloid joint but freer; like a rider in a saddle; biaxial *Example:* thumb, between metacarpal and carpal bones 6. **Gliding** *Other name:* arthrodia *Description:* articulating surfaces; usually flat *Movement:* gliding a nonaxial movement. *Example:* between carpal bones	1. **Cartilaginous** *Other name:* synchondrosis *Description:* cartilage grows between two articulating surfaces, usually reinforced by ligaments *Movements:* bending and twisting, or slight compression *Examples:* between bodies of vertebrae-fibrocartilaginous union permits bending, twisting movements of spine; between diaphysis and epiphysis of growing bones; replaced by bone in full-grown bones 2. **Fibrous** *Description:* thin layer of fibrous tissue; continuous with periosteum; connects articulating bones *Movement:* none *Example:* sutures of skull; in older adults fibrous connection replaced by bone

123

Table 5. Description of individual joints

Name	Articulating bones	Type	Movements
Atlantoepistro-pheal	Anterior arch of atlas rotates about dens of axis (epistropheus)	Diarthrotic (pivot type)	Pivoting or partial rotation of head
Vertebral*	Between bodies of vertebrae	Synarthrotic, cartilaginous; amphiarthrotic, by other system of classifying	Slight movement between any two vertebrae but considerable motility for column as whole
	Between articular processes	Diarthrotic (gliding)	
Clavicular Sternoclavicular	Medial end of clavicle with manubrium of sternum; only joint between upper extremity and trunk	Diarthrotic (gliding)	Gliding; weak joint that may be injured comparatively easily
Acromioclavicular	Distal end of clavicle with acromion of scapula	Diarthrotic (gliding)	Gliding; elevation, depression, protraction, retraction
Thoracic	Heads of ribs with bodies of vertebrae	Diarthrotic (gliding)	Gliding
	Tubercles of ribs with transverse processes of vertebrae	Diarthrotic (gliding)	Gliding
Shoulder	Head of humerus in glenoid cavity of scapula	Diarthrotic (ball and socket type)	Flexion, extension, abduction, adduction, rotation, and circumduction of upper arm; one of most freely movable of the joints
Elbow	Trochlea of humerus with semilunar notch of ulna; and head of radius with capitulum of humerus	Diarthrotic (hinge type)	Flexion and extension
	Head of radius in radial notch of ulna	Diarthrotic (pivot type)	Supination and pronation of lower arm and hand; rotation of lower arm on upper as in using screw driver
Wrist	Navicular, lunate, and triquetral bones articulate with radius and an articular disc	Diarthrotic (condyloid)	Flexion, extension, abduction, adduction of hand

*Joints of the vertebral column are securely maintained by a series of strong ligaments which bind the vertebrae firmly to each other in such a way that they cannot easily be moved out of position (dislocated). Two long ligaments hold the bodies of the vertebrae together; one grows out of the posterior surface of the bodies (posterior common ligament), the other from the anterior surfaces (anterior common ligament). In addition, short ligaments connect the tops of each two spinous processes (supraspinous ligaments), each two laminae (subflava ligaments), and each two spinous processes (interspinous ligaments). In the cervical region the supraspinous ligaments are known as the ligamentum nuchae.

Table 5. Description of individual joints—cont'd

Name	Articulating bones	Type	Movements
Carpal	Between various carpals	Diarthrotic (gliding)	Gliding
Hand	Proximal end of first metacarpal with greater multangular	Diarthrotic (saddle)	Flexion, extension, abduction, adduction, rotation, circumduction of thumb, and opposition to fingers; motility of this joint accounts for dexterity of human hand compared with animal forepaw
	Distal end of metacarpals with proximal end of phalanges	Diarthrotic (hinge)	Flexion, extension, limited abduction, and adduction of fingers
	Between the phalanges	Diarthrotic (hinge)	Flexion, extension of finger sections
Sacroiliac	Between sacrum and two ilia	Diarthrotic; joint cavity mostly obliterated after middle life	None or slight; for example, during late months of pregnancy and during delivery; straining of ligaments (sacroiliac strain) during movement very painful
Symphysis pubis	Between two pubic bones	Synarthrotic (or amphiarthrotic), cartilaginous	Slight, particularly during pregnancy and delivery
Hip	Head of femur in acetabulum of os coxa	Diarthrotic (ball and socket)	Flexion, extension, abduction, adduction, rotation, and circumduction
Knee	Between distal end of femur and proximal end of tibia; largest joint in body	Diarthrotic (hinge type)	Flexion and extension; slight rotation of tibia
Tibiofibular	Head of fibula with lateral condyle of tibia	Diarthrotic (gliding type)	Gliding
Ankle	Distal ends of tibia and fibula with talus	Diarthrotic (hinge type)	Flexion (dorsiflexion) and extension (plantar flexion)
Foot	Between tarsals	Diarthrotic (gliding)	Gliding; inversion and eversion
	Between metatarsals and phalanges	Diarthrotic (hinge type)	Flexion, extension, slight abduction, and adduction
	Between phalanges	Diarthrotic (hinge type)	Flexion and extension

median plane of the body. Example: bringing the arms back to the sides; adduction of the fingers means moving them toward the third finger; adduction of the toes is movement toward the second toe.

5. *rotation*—pivoting or moving the bone upon its own axis somewhat as a top turns on its axis. Example: holding the head in an upright position and turning it from one side to the other.

6. *circumduction*—causes the bone to describe the surface of a cone as it moves; the distal end of the bone describes a circle; it combines flexion, abduction, extension, and adduction in succession. Examples: dropping the head to one shoulder, then to the chest, to the other shoulder, and backward; describing a circle with the arms outstretched.

7. *special movements*—*supination,* a movement of the forearm which turns the palm forward as it is in the anatomic position; *pronation,* turning the forearm so as to bring the back of the hand forward; *inversion,* a special movement of the ankle which turns the sole of the foot inward, while *eversion* turns it outward; *protraction,* moving a part forward, as in sticking out the jaw; *retraction,* a reverse of this action.

BONE FORMATION AND GROWTH

The embryo skeleton when first formed consists of "bones" which are not really bones at all but hyaline cartilage or fibrous membrane structures shaped like bones.

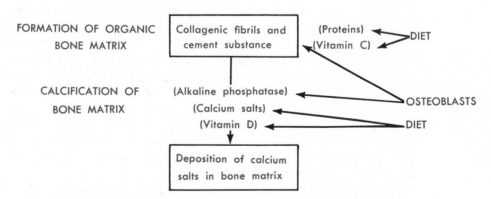

Fig. 62

Scheme to show basic steps in ossification. Osteoblasts using proteins and vitamin C supplied by diet synthesize organic bone matrix. Osteoblasts also synthesize the enzyme alkaline phosphatase. Vitamin D and alkaline phosphatase together bring about calcification of the bone matrix.

Complicated processes (the details of which belong to the study of embryology) slowly replace these structures with bone. The process called *intramembranous ossification* replaces with bone the membranous predecessors of bones and *endochondral ossification* replaces the cartilaginous forerunners. The flat skull bones, some of the face bones, and part of the clavicle are formed by intramembranous ossification. By birth most of the skeleton has been ossified but not completely so until about 25 years of age.

The mechanism of ossification is still not definitely known. Basic steps in the process, however, seem to be these: groups of *osteoblasts* (bone-forming cells) appear in the membranous or cartilaginous structures undergoing ossification and synthesize the collagenic fibrils and cement that constitute the organic substance of the new bone matrix. More or less simultaneously, Robison* suggests, they also synthesize alkaline phosphatase and release it into the matrix.

Alkaline phosphatase is an enzyme. In an alkaline medium it catalyzes the process of calcification—the deposition of complex calcium salts (presumably tricalcium phosphate, calcium carbonate and others). Vitamin D also hastens calcium salt deposition. Note that ossification, according to this concept, consists of two main processes: synthesis of the organic bone matrix by osteoblasts, followed quickly by calcification of the matrix (Fig. 62).

In long bones, endochondral ossification starts in the diaphysis and in both epiphyses and proceeds toward each other.

A layer of cartilage known as *epiphyseal cartilage* remains between the diaphyseal and epiphyseal centers of ossification. So long as bone growth continues, proliferation of epiphyseal cartilage cells brings about a thickening of the layer of cartilage from time to time. Ossification of this additional cartilage then follows; that is, osteoblasts synthesize organic bone matrix, and alkaline phosphatase facilitates calcification of the matrix, and the bone becomes longer. When epiphyseal cartilage cells stop multiplying and the cartilage has become completely ossified, bone growth has ended. This is the scientific fact that underlies the clinical practice of x-raying a child's wrist to determine whether he "will grow anymore." If the x-ray reveals a layer of epiphyseal cartilage, the answer is "yes"; if not, it is "no." He will have attained his full height.

Bones grow in diameter by the combined action of two special kinds of cells: osteoclasts and osteoblasts. The osteoclasts enlarge the diameter of the medullary cavity by eating away the bone of its walls. At

---

*Ham, Arthur W., and Leeson, Thomas S.: Histology, ed. 4, Philadelphia, 1961, J. B. Lippincott Co., p. 273.

the same time osteoblasts from the periosteum build new bone around the outside of the bone. By this dual process a bone with a larger diameter and larger medullary cavity has been produced from a smaller bone with a smaller medullary cavity.

Surprising though it seems at first thought, bones may become diseased. An example familiar to most of us is *rickets,* a condition more common to childhood than later years. Another example is *osteoporosis.* So common is this condition to old age that one authority describes it as "an almost physiological accompaniment of old age in either sex" and as "the most widespread metabolic bone disease."* The defect in this malady lies in the first step of ossification, in the synthesis of the organic bone matrix by osteoblasts. But, you may be asking, why do osteoblasts still need to synthesize bone matrix in old age? Is not ossification completed long before this in young adulthood? This seems logical, but it is not so. Bone is not formed once and for all to last a lifetime. It is not just an inert structural material. Bone is a living tissue—a fact not to be lost sight of—and as such is subject to the vicissitudes of any living tissue. It continually breaks down and is resorbed. But also it is continually being repaired and formed anew. Normally the two opposing processes balance each other. But under some circumstances they become unbalanced, and one or the other process dominates. This is exactly what happens in osteoporosis, for example. Bone formation lags behind bone breakdown. Consequently bones become thin, their density decreases, and, of course, their strength, too. With this increased fragility, fractures occur more easily. You yourself undoubtedly know some old person who has "fallen and broken his hip." But actually the sequence is often the reverse: the bone breaks first (frequently in a femur weakened by osteoporosis) and causes the fall.

Inadequate amounts of sex hormones in the blood and inadequate activity are believed to be the major factors responsible for senile osteoporosis. Estrogens (female hormones) stimulate osteoblasts to synthesize organic bone matrix.

With postmenopausal estrogen deficiency, therefore, osteoblasts lack this stimulus so fail to form matrix fast enough to keep up with the normal pace of matrix destruction. Insufficient activity operates similarly. Muscular activity puts strains on the skeleton, and these skeletal strains are natural stimulants of osteoblasts. So decreased activity means decreased osteoblasts stimulation and often the gradual development of osteoporosis.

---

*Cecil, R., and Loeb, R. F.: A textbook of medicine, ed. 10, Philadelphia, 1959, W. B. Saunders Co., p. 1389.

Suggestion: Study Fig. 62 carefully and then try to explain why a diet deficient in vitamin C or proteins might lead to osteoporosis. On the basis of the information in this diagram, do you think vitamin D deficiency might produce osteoporosis? What kind of defect in bone do you think it would produce?

Outline summary

The skeletal system

Meaning

All bones and their joints

Functions

1. Furnishes supporting framework
2. Affords protection
3. Provides levers for muscle action
4. Hemopoiesis by red bone marrow
5. Calcium storage

Microscopic structure of bone

1. Mainly calcified matrix—cement substance impregnated with calcium salts and reinforced by collagenic fibrils
2. Lamellae—concentric cylindrical layers of calcified matrix enclosing an haversian canal that contains a blood vessel
3. Haversian system—canal and surrounding lamellae
4. Lacunae—microscopic spaces containing osteocytes (bone cells); lie between lamellae
5. Canaliculi—microscopic canals radiating in all directions from lacunae, connecting them with haversian canals; routes by which tissue fluid reaches osteocytes
6. Compact bone (or solid bone)—no empty spaces; lamellae fit closely together
7. Cancellous bone (or spongy bone)—many spaces in matrix which is arranged mainly in trabeculae rather than lamellae

Microscopic structure of cartilage

1. Similar to that of bone with following exceptions:
   a. Cartilage matrix—firm gel; bone matrix—calcified cement substance
   b. Cartilage matrix no canal system, no blood vessels; bone matrix—extensive canal network

Gross structure of bones

Types of bones

1. Long (femur)
2. Short (carpals)
3. Flat (parietal)
4. Irregular (vertebrae)

Structure of bones

1. Structure of long bones—see Figs. 32 and 33.
2. Structure of short bones—thin layer of compact bone encasing a "core" of cancellous bone
3. Structure of flat bones—layer of cancellous bone between two plates of compact bone
4. Structure of irregular bones—thin layer of compact bone encasing cancellous bone

Names and numbers of bones

Total, 206 bones—Table 2, pp. 82 and 84
1. Axial skeleton (80 bones)
   a. skull (28 bones)
      1. cranium (8 bones)—frontal, parietal, temporal, occipital, sphenoid, and ethmoid
      2. face (14 bones)—nasal, maxillary, malar, mandible, lacrimal, palatine, inferior turbinates, and vomer
      3. ear ossicles (6 bones)—malleus, incus, and stapes
   b. hyoid (1 bone)
   c. spinal column (26 vertebrae)

129

d. ribs and sternum (25 bones)—7 pairs of true ribs, 5 pairs of false ribs, 2 pairs of which are floating; 1 sternum
2. Appendicular skeleton (126 bones)
   a. upper extremities (64 bones)—clavicle, scapula, humerus, ulna, radius, carpals, metacarpals, and phalanges
   b. lower extremities (62 bones)—os coxa, femur, patella, tibia, fibula, tarsal, metatarsal, and phalanges

Bone markings

1. Depressions
   a. fossa—hollow or depression
   b. sinus—cavity of spongelike air space within a bone
   c. foramen—a hole
   d. meatus—tube-shaped opening
2. Projections or processes
   a. those which fit into joints
      1. condyle—rounded projection entering into formation of a joint
      2. head—rounded projection beyond narrow neck
   b. those to which muscles attach
      1. trochanter—very large process
      2. crest—a ridge
      3. spinous process or spine—a sharp projection
      4. tuberosity—a large, rounded projection
      5. tubercle—a small, rounded projection

Identification of bone markings
See Table 3, pp. 93 to 102

Differences between male and female skeletons

1. Male skeleton larger and heavier
2. Male pelvis deep and funnel shaped with narrow pubic arch; female pelvis shallow, broad, and flaring with wider pubic arch and larger iliosacral notch

Age changes in skeletons

1. Changes in absolute and proportionate sizes of bones from infancy to adulthood
2. Changes in texture and in contour of margins and bone markings from youth to old age

Joints
1. Kinds of joints
   a. diarthroses
      1. characteristics
         a. thin layer of hyaline cartilage covers articular surfaces
         b. fibrous, synovial-lined capsule forms true joint cavity
         c. ligaments hold articulating bones firmly connected
      2. subtypes—see Table 4
   b. synarthroses
      1. characteristics
         a. no joint cavity
         b. cartilage or fibrous tissue unites articulating bones
      2. subtypes—see Table 4
2. Movements of joints
   a. flexion—angle at joint decreases
   b. extension—angle at joint increases; the return from flexion
   c. abduction—moving bone away from body's median plane
   d. adduction—moving bone back toward body's median plane
   e. rotation—pivoting a bone upon its axis
   f. circumduction—describing surface of a cone with moving part
   g. special movements
      1. supination—movement of forearm which turns palm forward
      2. pronation—movement of forearm which turns back of hand forward
      3. inversion—ankle movement turning sole of foot inward
      4. eversion—ankle movement turning sole of foot outward
      5. protraction—moving a part forward
      6. retraction—pulling part back, opposite of protraction

Bone formation and growth
Formation
1. Skeleton performed in hyaline cartilage and fibrous membranes; most of these changed into bone before birth but not complete until about twenty-five years after birth
2. Endochondral ossification—incompletely understood process which replaces hyaline cartilage "bones" with true bones; see Fig. 62 for summary of postulated basic steps of this mechanism
3. Intramembranous ossification—process

which replaces fibrous membrane "bones" with true bones

Growth

1. In length—by continual thickening of epiphyseal cartilage followed by ossification
2. In diameter—medullary cavity enlarged by osteoclasts destroying bone around it while new bone is added around circumference by osteoblasts

Correlation with bone disease; osteoporosis

Deficient synthesis of organic bone matrix by osteoblasts lacking stimulation of normal amounts of sex hormones in blood and of adequate muscular activity

Review questions

The skeletal system

1. What general functions does the skeletal system perform?
2. Describe the microscopic structure of bone and cartilage.
3. What functions does a long bone perform? Describe its structure, indicating how various structural characteristics contribute to its function.
4. Describe the general plan of the skeleton.
5. Name the bones of the adult skeleton.
6. Describe the structural features of diarthrotic joints that facilitate weight bearing and movement.
7. Give examples of several types of diarthrotic joints.
8. Explain the functions of the periosteum.
9. What joint(s) unites the shoulder girdle with the trunk? The pelvic girdle with the trunk?
10. Name the several kinds of movements possible at joints. Define each movement named.
11. Describe the intervertebral joints.
12. Name the primary curves of the spine; the secondary curves. Describe each.
13. Name the five pairs of bony sinuses in the skull.
14. Name the bones which fuse to form the coccyx.
15. What is the true pelvis? The false pelvis? Name the boundary line between the true and false pelves.
16. Through what opening does the spinal cord enter the cranial cavity?
17. Explain the basic steps in the process of ossification according to the concept described in the text.
18. Define or make an identifying statement about each of the following terms:

condyle	medullary cavity
crest	osteoblast
diaphysis	osteoclast
diarthroses	periosteum
endosteum	rotation
epiphysis	scoliosis
foramen	sinus
fossa	spinous process
haversian system	synarthroses
kyphosis	trochanter
lordosis	trabeculae

The muscular system

Man's survival depends in large part upon his ability to adjust to the changing conditions of his environment. Movements constitute the major part of this adjustment. Whereas most of the systems of the body play some role in accomplishing movement, it is the skeletal and muscular systems acting together which actually produce movements. We have investigated the architectural plan of the skeleton and have seen how its joint structures and firm supports make movement possible. But bones and joints cannot move themselves; they must be moved by something. Muscle tissue, because of its contractility, extensibility, and elasticity, is admirably suited to this function. In this chapter we shall try to discover how muscles move bones and to do this we shall try to answer many other questions—how the structure of muscles adapts them to their function, how energy is made available for their work, how muscle activity contributes to the health and survival of the whole body—to mention only a few.

MEANING OF THE MUSCULAR SYSTEM

Properly speaking, the term muscular system means all the muscles of the body—those attached to the bones, those helping to make up the walls of numerous internal structures, and the muscle which composes the wall of the heart. More commonly, however, the term refers to skeletal muscles only—those muscle masses which attach to bones and move them about, the masses of "red meat" of the body.

GENERAL FUNCTIONS

If you have any doubts about the importance of muscle function to normal life, you have only to observe a person with extensive paralysis—a victim of severe poliomyelitis, for example. Any of us possessed of normal powers of movement can little imagine life with this matchless power lost. But cardinal as it is, movement is not the only contribution muscles make to healthy survival. They also perform two other essential functions: they maintain posture and produce a large portion of body heat.

133

Movement. Movement consists sometimes of locomotion, sometimes of movements of parts of the body, sometimes of changes in the size of openings, and sometimes of propulsion of substances through tubes, for example. Propulsion of blood through arteries by heart movements is one example of the latter. Passage of food through the digestive tract by contractions of the stomach and intestines is another. By means of locomotion, adjustments are made to the external environment. Desirable objects are approached, and undesirable or dangerous ones are repelled. By means of internal movements vital adjustments and processes are accomplished. Consider the following for example: contraction and relaxation of the iris muscles which allow just the right amount of light to enter the eyes, contractions of the digestive tract muscles which promote digestion and elimination, and contractions of the heart which keep the blood circulating.

Posture. The continued partial contraction of many skeletal muscles makes possible standing, sitting, and other maintained positions of the body.

Heat production. Chemical changes that occur in muscle cells to make mechanical energy available for movement also release heat energy. In fact, they produce such a major share of total body heat that they constitute one of the most important parts of the mechanism for maintaining homeostasis of temperaure. Do you recall the term that means the series of chemical changes referred to here? If not see p. 43.

MUSCLE TISSUE—FUNCTIONAL CHARACTERISTICS

As noted in Chapter III, there are three types of muscle tissue, and they differ as to microscopic structure, nervous control, and location.

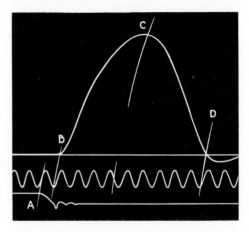

Fig. 63

The form curve of a muscle twitch; stimulus applied at **A**; beginning of contraction at **B**; relaxation, **C** to **D.** Each wave of line below form curve represents 1/100 second of time. (From Zoethout and Tuttle: Textbook of physiology, St. Louis, The C. V. Mosby Co.)

They are similar, however, as to certain functional characteristics. All three types possess a high degree of irritability, conductivity, extensibility, elasticity, and contractility.

Irritability or the ability to respond to a stimulus and *conductivity* or the ability to transmit impulses are discussed at some length in the chapter on the nervous system (pp. 192 to 194). Physiotherapists make practical use of the fact that muscle tissue is itself irritable,* independently of the nerve tissue supplying it. They cause paralyzed muscles to contract by stimulating them directly with an electrical current—a treatment aimed at preventing muscle withering from disuse.

Extensibility means the ability to be stretched; *elasticity* means the ability to resume an original length after a stretching force is removed.

Contractility is the ability to contract, to shorten, and to thicken—a property more highly developed in muscle than in any other tissue. Contractility is the functional specialty of muscle tissue—its big contribution.

TYPES OF MUSCLE CONTRACTION

Much of our information about muscle contraction has come from studies made on muscle-nerve preparations, usually the gastrocnemius muscle of a frog with its motor nerve. Electrical or sometimes other kinds of stimuli are applied to cause contraction and a graphic record is made. A common method of doing this is to attach the muscle to one end of a lever and place the wrighting point end of the lever against a smoked drum (kymograph). From such studies and others several kinds of muscle contraction have been described. Some of them are as follows.

1. *Twitch contraction*—a quick, jerky contraction in response to a single stimulus. Fig. 63 shows a kymograph record of such a contraction. It reveals that the muscle does not shorten at the instant of stimulation, but a fraction of a second later, and that it reaches a peak of shortening and then gradually resumes its former length. These three phases of contraction are spoken of, respectively, as the *latent period,*

---

*The independent excitability of muscle was first demonstrated in 1850 by the classic curare experiment of Claude Bernard. (Curare is a drug long used by the South American Indians as an arrow poison. It is known to block the passage of impulses from nerve to muscle by paralyzing the myoneural junctions.) Electrical stimulation of the motor nerve to the leg after injection of curare into the dorsal lymph sac of a frog brings about no contraction of the leg muscle, but direct stimulation of the muscle itself does evoke its contraction. Thus the muscle cells themselves are shown to be irritable, that is, able to respond to stimulation independently of their nerve supply.

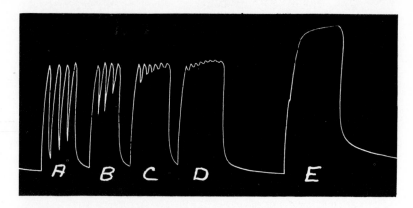

Fig. 64

Curves **A, B, C,** and **D** are of incomplete tetanus; **E,** complete
tetanus. Faradic shocks of same intensity throughout.
(From Zoethout and Tuttle: Textbook of physiology,
St. Louis, The C. V. Mosby Co.)

the *contraction phase,* and the *relaxation* phase. The entire twitch
usually lasts less than a tenth of a second. Twitch contractions do not
produce our normal movements (with the exception of the involuntary
winking movement).

2. *Tetanus* (tetanic contraction)—a more sustained contraction than
a twitch. It is produced by a series of stimuli bombarding the muscle
in rapid succession. About 30 stimuli per second, for example, evoke
a tetanic contraction by a frog gastrocnemius muscle, but the rate
varies for different muscles and different conditions. In Fig. 64 are
shown kymograph records of incomplete and complete tetanus. Our
normal smooth movements are produced by complete tetanic contractions, whereas the coarse, fine tremors that sometimes occur result
from incomplete tetanic contractions. The disease tetanus or lockjaw
produces complete tetanus of the jaw muscles, making it impossible for
the patient to terminate the contraction at will; in other words, the
jaws are "locked."

3. *Tone* (tonus; tonic contraction)—continual, partial contraction.
At any one moment a small number of the total fibers in a muscle
contract, producing a tautness of the muscle rather than a recognizable contraction and movement. Different groups of fibers scattered
throughout the muscle contract in relays. Tone is particularly important for maintaining posture. A striking illustration of this fact is the
following: when a person loses consciousness, his muscles lose their
tone, and he collapses in a heap, unable to maintain a sitting or standing posture. Muscles with less tone than normal are described as
flaccid muscles and those with more than normal tone as spastic. Impulses over stretch reflex arcs (p. 246) function in tone maintenance.

4. *Treppe* (staircase phenomenon)—increasingly stronger twitch
contractions that occur in response to constant strength stimuli re-

peated at the rate of about once or twice a second. In other words, a muscle contracts more forcefully after it has contracted a few times than when it first contracts—a principle made practical use of by athletes when they warm up but one not yet satisfactorily explained. Presumably it relates partly to the rise in temperature of active muscles and partly to their accumulation of metabolic products. After the first few stimuli, muscle responds to a considerable number of successive stimuli with maximal contractions and after these it responds with less and less strong contractions. The relaxation phase becomes shorter and finally disappears entirely (Fig. 65). In other words, the muscle stays partially contracted—an abnormal state of prolonged contraction called *contracture*.

Repeated stimulation of a muscle eventually lessens its irritability and contractility and may result in *muscle fatigue*, a condition in which the muscle does not respond to the strongest stimuli. Complete muscle fatigue, however, very seldom occurs in the body although it can be readily induced in an excised muscle.

5. *Isotonic contraction*—iso means same and tonic means pressure or tension. Therefore an isotonic contraction is one in which the pressure or tension within a muscle remains the same but its length changes; it shortens, producing movement.

6. *Isometric contraction*—a contraction in which muscle length remains the same whereas muscle tension increases. You can observe

Fig. 65

Diagram showing changes in character of contraction when muscle is stimulated repeatedly by constant strength stimuli. Curve A, Treppe or staircase phenomenon—each of first several contractions is stronger than the preceding one. Curve B, Contracture—incomplete relaxation phase in each of next series of contractions, producing a prolonged contraction. Curve C, Fatigue—no contraction in response to stimulation after a great many repetitions of the stimulus. (From Francis and Knowlton: Textbook of anatomy and physiology, St. Louis, The C. V. Mosby Co.)

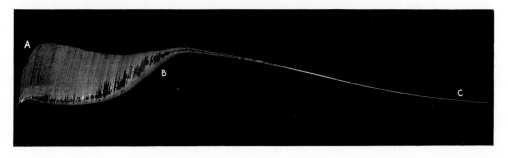

isometric contraction by pushing against a wall and feeling the tension increase in your arm muscles. Isometric contractions do not produce movements or do work; isotonic contractions both produce movement and do work.

7. *Fibrillation*—an abnormal type of contraction in which individual fibers contract asynchronously, producing a flutter of the muscle but no effective movement. Fibrillation of the heart, for example, occurs fairly often.

8. *Convulsions*—abnormal uncoordinated tetanic contractions of varying groups of muscles.

MECHANISM OF MUSCLE CONTRACTION

Nerve impulses arriving at muscle cells are believed to trigger the breakdown of adenosine triphosphate (ATP), releasing energy from these high-energy molecules. It is this energy that is utilized to do the work of contraction. Myosin, one of the proteins in muscle cells,

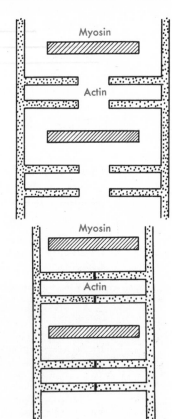

Fig. 66

Scheme to show arrangement of actin and myosin molecules in a myofibril. Upper diagram, Muscle relaxed; lower diagram, muscle contracted by actin filaments moving together. (Modified from Huxley.)

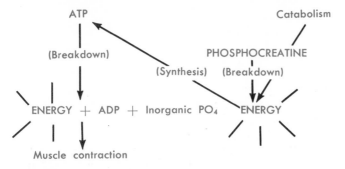

Fig. 67

Chemical changes during muscle contraction. ATP breakdown releases
energy utilized for contraction. Phosphocreatine breakdown releases energy
for more rapid replacement of ATP than occurs by catabolism. In strenuous
activity, ATP and phosphocreatin breakdown exceed their synthesis so that
net effect is a decrease of cells' stock of these high-energy compounds.

is thought to act as an enzyme, catalyzing ATP breakdown. The investigations of Huxley and Hanson a few years ago revealed amazing
detail about the fine structure of muscle cells. A single muscle cell
or fiber, they have shown, consists of many smaller fibrils embedded in
its cytoplasm (called sacroplasm in a muscle cell). Each fibril in turn
is a bundle of many smaller filaments. Some of these, composed of
molecules of the protein myosin, are coarser than others that are made
up of molecules of another protein, actin, and perhaps also tropomyosin. According to Huxley's sliding-filament hypothesis of contraction,
energy from ATP breakdown is used to slide the fine actin filaments
along the coarse myosin filaments, and this action shortens or contracts
the muscle cell.*

ATP stored in muscles comes from several sources, primarily, as we
have seen, from catabolism (re-examine p. 45 and Fig. 68). When
muscle cells are not contracting, more ATP synthesis than breakdown
goes on, and the resulting excess is stored in them for their future
energy needs. But when muscle cells become extremely active, as in
strenuous exercise, for example, ATP breakdown exceeds synthesis,
and the amount of stored ATP decreases, eventually to zero. Some
other consequences also follow. Very soon after strenuous exertion
begins, pyruvic acid starts to accumulate in muscle cells and is reduced
to lactic acid. The reason is this: respiration and circulation cannot accelerate enough to supply the cells with as much oxygen as they need
to oxidize the pyruvic acid via the citric acid cycle as rapidly as it
forms by glycolysis. Most of the lactic acid (about four fifths according to some investigators) diffuses out of the cells and is carried by the
blood to the liver there to be gradually resynthesized to glycogen or
glucose. A smaller amount remains behind in the muscle cells. Here,

*For a more complete discussion of this hypothesis see Ham, Arthur W., and
Leeson, Thomas S.: Histology, ed. 4, Philadelphia, 1961, J. B. Lippincott Co.

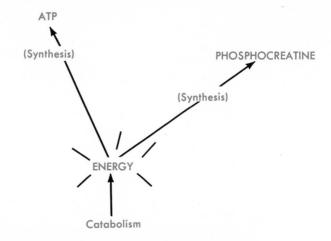

Fig. 68

Predominant chemical changes in resting muscle. ATP and phosphocreatine synthesis exceeds their breakdown. Net effect, therefore, is accumulation of reserve supply of these high-energy compounds. However, even in a resting cell some breakdown of ATP and phosphocreatine (Fig. 67) goes on to supply energy for work that cell must do to stay alive.

Fig. 69

Creation of oxygen debt during strenuous exertion.

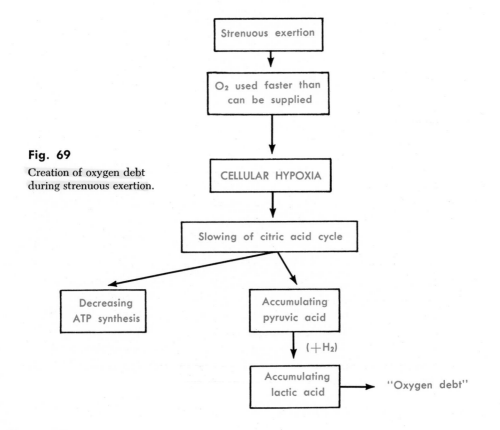

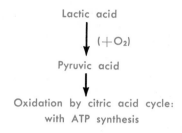

Lactic acid

$(+O_2)$

Pyruvic acid

Oxidation by citric acid cycle:
with ATP synthesis

Fig. 70

Repayment of oxygen debt after strenuous exertion.

after the strenuous bout of exercise ends, it is oxidized back to pyruvic acid and on through the citric acid cycle to carbon dioxide and water.

The amount of oxygen required for oxidation of the lactic acid accumulated during strenuous exercise is referred to as the *oxygen debt*. It is a debt that has to be repaid before exercise can continue— a fact all of us have observed when we have stopped to catch our breath during some strenuous exertion. For example, if you were to run the 100-yard dash, according to one authority* you might need more than 6 liters of oxygen to oxidize all the pyruvic acid formed by glycolysis during that short sprint. But the maximum oxygen you could consume in that same brief time would fall far short of this— probably less than 1 liter. You would, therefore, have incurred an oxygen debt of several liters which would be repaid by your breathing rapidly and deeply for some time after your strenuous exertion.

In addition to catabolism, muscle cells are thought to have at least one faster source for securing ATP—by the breakdown of phosphocreatine, another high-energy phosphate compound stored in them. When not contracting, muscle cells, as we have seen, synthesize more ATP than they need to supply energy for their work. Some of this excess ATP breaks down to yield energy for phosphocreatine synthesis. Later, when muscle cells become active, the process reverses. Phosphocreatine breaks down, releasing energy that is utilized to rebuild ATP. This, of course, prolongs the cells' supply of ATP (Figs. 67 and 68).

Muscle cells obey the all-or-none law when they contract. This means that they either contract with all the force possible under existing conditions, or they contract not at all. A strong stimulus in other words produces no stronger contraction of a single muscle cell than a weak one, provided that conditions are the same. But if conditions at the time of stimulation change, then the force of the cell's contraction changes. If, for example, at one time a muscle fiber is receiving sufficient oxygen and at another time too little oxygen, it will contract more forcefully under the adequate oxygen condition than under the deficient oxygen condition.

---

*Best, Charles H., and Taylor, M. B.: The physiological basis of medical practice, ed. 7, Baltimore, 1961, Williams & Wilkins Co., p. 879.

SKELETAL MUSCLES—GROSS STRUCTURE
Size, shape, and fiber arrangement

Skeletal muscles are organs composed mainly of skeletal muscle tissue. They vary considerably in size, shape, and arrangement of fibers. They range from extremely tiny strands, as, for example, the stapedius muscle of the middle ear, to large masses such as the muscles of the thigh. Some skeletal muscles are broad in shape and some narrow. Some are long and tapering and some short and blunt. Some are triangular, some quadrilateral, and some irregular. Some form flat sheets and others, bulky masses. Arrangement of fibers varies in different muscles. In some muscles the fibers are parallel to the long axis of the muscle, in some they converge to a narrow attachment, and in some they are oblique and either pennate (like the feathers in an old-fashioned plume pen) or bipennate (double-feathered as in the rectus femoris). Fibers may even be curved, as in the sphincters of the face, for example. The direction of the fibers composing a muscle is significant because of its relationship to function. For instance, a muscle with the bipennate fiber arrangement can produce the strongest contraction.

Connective tissue components of skeletal muscles

A fibrous connective tissue sheath *(epimysium)* envelops each muscle and extends into it as partitions between bundles of its fibers *(perimysium)* and between individual fibers *(endomysium)*. Because all three of these structures are continuous with the fibrous structures that attach muscles to bones or other structures, muscles are most firmly harnessed to the structures they pull against during contraction. The epimysium, perimysium, and endomysium of a muscle, for example, may be continuous with fibrous tissue that extends from the muscle as a *tendon*, a strong tough cord continuous at its other end with the fibrous covering of bone (periosteum). Or the fibrous wrapping of a muscle may extend as a broad, flat sheet of connective tissue *(aponeurosis)* to attach it to adjacent structures, usually the fibrous wrappings of another muscle. So tough and strong are tendons and aponeuroses that they are not often torn, even by injuries forceful enough to break bones or tear muscles. They are, however, occasionally pulled away from bones.

You may recall that a continuous sheet of loose connective tissue known as the superficial fascia lies directly under the skin. Under this lies a layer of dense fibrous connective tissue, the *deep fascia*. Extensions of the deep fascia form the epimysium, perimysium, and endomysium of muscles, their attachments to bones and other structures, and also enclose viscera, glands, blood vessels, and nerves.

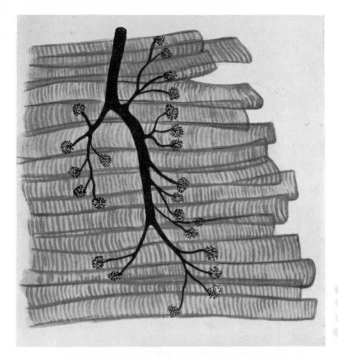

Fig. 71

A motor unit; here, a single nerve fiber branches to supply many muscle fibers. Note the motor end plates or myoneural junctions. (Modified from Bremer.)

Nerve supply of skeletal muscles

Nerve cells that transmit impulses to skeletal muscle fibers are called *somatic motor neurons.* One single motor neuron may send a single nerve fiber to a single muscle fiber or may branch to supply more than a hundred muscle fibers. It is reported, for example, that a single motor neuron supplies a single muscle fiber in one of the external eye muscles. But in the small muscles of the hand one motor neuron supplies several muscle fibers, and in large muscles such as those of the abdomen or thigh one motor neuron may send terminal branches to more than a hundred muscle fibers. A muscle's size, however, does not determine the number of its fibers innervated by a single motor neuron; the precision of the movements it performs determines this. In general, the more precise and coordinated the movements, the fewer muscle fibers are innervated by a single motor neuron, that is, the fewer the muscle fibers per motor unit. A *motor unit* is one motor neuron and the muscle fibers it supplies. At the place where a motor nerve fiber contacts a muscle fiber, the sarcoplasm of the muscle fiber projects outward like a tiny mound. This area of contact between a nerve and muscle fiber is known as the *motor end plate* or *myoneural junction*. Studies with the electron microscope have disproved the old idea that the nerve fiber penetrates the sarcolemma to terminate outside the muscle fiber. Here is a curiosity-provoking detail about the motor end plate—numerous mitochondria have been demonstrated in both the muscle and nerve fibers in this contact area. In addition to the many motor nerve endings, many sensory nerve endings are also found in skeletal muscles, but we shall save the description of these for the chapter on the nervous system.

SKELETAL MUSCLE ACTIONS

Several methods of study have been used to amass the present-day store of knowledge about muscle actions. They vary from the traditional and relatively simple procedures, such as observing and palpating muscles in action, manipulating dissected muscles to observe movements, or deducing movements from knowledge of muscle anatomy, to the newer more complicated method of electromyography (recording action potentials from contracting muscles). As a result, there is now a somewhat overwhelming amount of knowledge about muscle actions. So perhaps we will find it easier to thread our way through this maze of detail if we start with general principles and then go on to details that seem to us most useful. Here, then, are a few basic principles about skeletal muscle actions.

1. *Skeletal muscles contract only if stimulated.* They do not have the quality of automaticity inherent in cardiac and visceral muscle. Although nerve impulses are the natural stimuli for skeletal muscles, electrical and some other artificial stimuli can also activate them. A skeletal muscle deprived of nerve impulses by whatever cause is a functionless mass. One ought, therefore, to think of a skeletal muscle and its motor nerve as a physiological unit, always functioning together, either useless without the other.

2. *Skeletal muscles produce movements by pulling on bones.* Most of our muscles span at least one joint and attach to both articulating bones. When they contract, therefore, their shortening puts a pull on both bones, and this pull moves one of the bones at the joint—draws it toward the other bone, much as a pull on marionette strings moves a puppet's parts. (In case you are wondering why both bones do not move since both are pulled on by the contracting muscle, the reason is that one of them is normally stabilized by contraction of other muscles or by its own less mobile structure.)

3. *Bones serve as levers and joints serve as fulcrums of these levers.* (By definition a *lever* is any rigid bar free to turn about a fixed point called its *fulcrum.*) A contracting muscle applies a pulling force on a bone lever causing it to move about its joint fulcrum. We have already noted that a skeletal muscle and its motor nerve act as a functional unit. Now we can add bones and joints and can describe the physiological unit for movement as a neuromusculoskeletal unit. Disease of any one of these parts of the unit, as you might infer, can cause abnormal movements or complete loss of movement. Poliomyelitis, for

example, and multiple sclerosis and hemiplegia all involve the neural part of the unit. In contrast, muscular dystrophy affects the muscular part and arthritis the skeletal part.

4. *Muscles that move a part usually do not lie over that part.* In most cases the body of a muscle lies proximal to the part moved. Thus muscles that move the lower arm lie proximal to it, that is, in the upper arm. Applying the same principle, where would you expect muscles that move the hand to be located? Those that move the lower leg? The upper arm?

5. *Skeletal muscles almost always act in groups rather than singly.* In other words, most movements are produced by the coordinated action of several muscles. Some of the muscles in the group contract while others relax. To identify each muscle's special function in the group, the following classification is used:

   (a) *prime movers*—muscle or muscles whose contraction actually produces the movement.
   (b) *antagonists*—muscles which relax while the prime mover is contracting. Exception: the antagonist contracts at the same time as the prime mover when some part of the body needs to be held rigid, such as the knee joint when standing.*
   (c) *synergists*—muscles which contract at the same time as the prime mover.

Synergists may help the prime mover produce its movement, or they may stabilize a part, hold it steady, so the prime mover produces a more effective movement.

6. *Skeletal muscles contract according to the graded strength principle*—not according to the all-or-none principle, as do the individual muscle cells composing them. In other words, skeletal muscles contract with varying degrees of strength at different times—a fact of practical importance. (How else, for example, could we match the force of a movement to the demands of a task?) Several generalizations may help explain the fact of graded strength contractions. The strength of the contraction of a skeletal muscle bears a direct relationship to the initial length of its fibers, to their metabolic condition, and to the number of them contracting. If a muscle is moderately stretched at the moment when contraction begins, the force of its contraction is

---

*Antagonistic muscles have opposite actions and opposite locations; if the flexor lies anterior to the part, the extensor will be found posterior to it; for example, the pectoralis major, the flexor of the upper arm, is located on the anterior chest, while the latissimus dorsi, the extensor of the upper arm, is located on the posterior chest. The antagonist of a flexor muscle is obviously an extensor muscle; that of an abductor muscle, an adductor muscle. In Table 7 are named some frequently used antagonists.

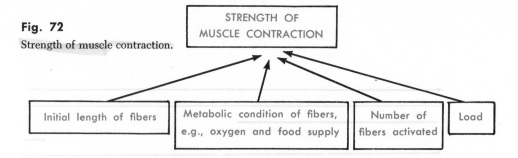

Fig. 72

Strength of muscle contraction.

increased. This principle, established years ago, applies experimentally to heart muscle (Starling's law of the heart, discussed in Chapter 9.) Outstanding among metabolic conditions that influence contraction are oxygen and food supply.

With adequate amounts of these essentials a muscle can contract with greater force than with deficient amounts. The greater the number of muscle fibers contracting simultaneously, the stronger is the contraction of a muscle. How large this number is depends upon how many motor units are activated, and this in turn depends upon the intensity and frequency of stimulation. In general, the more intense a stimulus and the more frequent, the more motor units and therefore fibers are activated and the stronger is the contraction. Contraction strength also relates to previous contraction, the warm-up principle discussed on page 137.

Another factor that influences the force of contraction is the size of the load imposed on the muscle. Within certain limits the heavier the load, the stronger is the contraction. Lift a pencil, for example, and then a heavy book and you can feel your arm muscles contract more strongly with the book.

In Fig. 72 are summarized the foregoing factors that influence muscle contraction.

Hints on how to deduce muscle actions

To understand muscle actions you need first to know certain anatomical facts such as which bones muscles attach to and which joints they pull across. Then if you relate these structural facts to functional principles—for instance, those discussed in the paragraphs just preceding—you may find your study of muscles more interesting and less difficult than you anticipate. Some specific suggestions for deducing muscle actions are as follows.

1. Start by making yourself familiar with the names, shapes, and general locations of the larger muscles. Use Table 6 (p. 149) as a guide for this.

2. Try to deduce which bones the two ends of a muscle attach to from your knowledge of the shape and general location of the muscle. For example, look carefully at the deltoid muscle as illustrated in Figs.

75 to 77. To what bones does it seem to attach? Check your deductions with Table 9 (p. 152).

3. Next, make a guess as to which bone moves when the muscle shortens. (The bone moved by a muscle's contraction is its *insertion* bone; the bone that remains relatively stationary is its *origin* bone.) In many cases you can tell by trying to move one bone and then another which one is the insertion bone. In some cases either bone may function as the insertion. Although not all muscle attachments can be deduced as readily as those of the deltoid, they can all be learned more easily by using this deduction method than by relying on rote memory alone.

4. Deduce a muscle's actions by applying the principle that its insertion moves toward its origin. Check your conclusions with the text. Here, as in steps 2 and 3 preceding, the method of deduction is intended merely as a guide and is not adequate by itself for determining muscle actions.

5. To deduce which muscle produces a given action (instead of which action a given muscle produces as in step 4), start by inferring the insertion bone (bone that moves during the action). The body and origin of the muscle will lie on one or more of the bones toward which the insertion moves—often a bone or bones proximal to the insertion bone. Couple these conclusions about origin and insertion with your knowledge of muscle names and locations to deduce the muscle that produces the action. For example, if you wish to determine the prime mover for the action of raising the upper arms straight out to the sides, you infer that the muscle inserts on the humerus since this is the bone that moves. It moves toward the shoulder, that is, the clavicle and scapula, so that probably the muscle has its origin on these bones. Because you know that the deltoid muscle fulfills these conditions, you conclude, and rightly so, that it is the muscle that raises the upper arms sidewise.

6. Do not try to learn too many details about muscle origins, insertions, and actions. Remember, it is better to start by learning a few important facts thoroughly than to half learn a mass of relatively unimportant details. Remember, too, that trying to learn too many minute facts usually results in not retaining even the main facts.

NAMES OF SKELETAL MUSCLES

Reasons for the names of muscles

Muscle names seem more logical and therefore easier to learn when one understands the reasons for the names. Each name describes one or more of the following features about the muscle.

1. *its action*—as flexor, extensor, adductor, etc.

147

2. *direction of its fibers*—as rectus or transversus.
3. *its location*—as tibialis or femoris.
4. *number of divisions composing the muscle*—as biceps, triceps, or quadriceps.
5. *its shape*—as deltoid (triangular), trapezius, or quadratus.
6. *its points of attachment*—as sternocleidomastoid.

A good way to start the study of a muscle is by trying to find out what its name means.

Muscles grouped according to location

Just as names of people are learned by associating them with their physical appearance, so the names of muscles should be learned by associating them with their appearance. As you learn each muscle name, study the illustrations to familiarize yourself with the muscle's size, shape, and general location. To help you in this task, the names of some of the major muscles are listed according to their location in Table 6.

Muscles grouped according to function

The following terms name muscles according to their main actions (Table 7, p. 150, gives examples).
1. *flexors*—decrease the angle of a joint (between the anterior surfaces of the bones except in the knee and toe joints).
2. *extensors*—return the part from flexion to normal anatomic position. Increase the angle of a joint.
3. *abductors*—move the bone away from the midline.
4. *adductors*—move the part toward the midline.
5. *rotators*—cause a part to pivot upon its axis.
6. *levators*—raise a part.
7. *depressors*—lower a part.
8. *sphincters*—reduce the size of an opening.
9. *tensors*—tense a part, that is, make it more rigid.
10. *supinators*—turn the hand palm upward.
11. *pronators*—turn the hand palm downward.

ORIGINS, INSERTIONS, FUNCTIONS, AND INNERVATIONS OF REPRESENTATIVE SKELETAL MUSCLES

In Table 6 through Table 20 is given basic information about many muscles. Each table has a description of a group of muscles that move one part of the body. Muscles that seem to the author most important for a beginning student of anatomy to learn are indicated by an asterisk and the origins and insertions so judged are printed in italics. Remember that the actions listed for each muscle are those for which it is a prime mover. Actually, a single muscle contracting alone rarely accomplishes a given action; instead, muscles act in groups as prime movers, synergists, and antagonists (p. 145) to bring about movements. As you study the muscles described in Table 6 through Table 20, try to follow the hints for studying muscle actions given on pp. 146 to 147.

Table 6. Muscles grouped according to location

Location	Muscles	Figures illustrating
Neck	Sternocleidomastoid	74
Back	Trapezius	74 through 77
	Latissimus dorsi	75
Chest	Pectoralis major	74
	Serratus anterior	74
Abdominal wall	External oblique	74, 75
Shoulder	Deltoid	74 through 77
Upper arm	Biceps brachii	76, 78
	Triceps brachii	76, 77, 79
	Brachialis	80
Forearm	Brachioradialis	76, 77
	Pronator teres	76, 78, 81
Buttocks	Gluteus maximus	75
	Gluteus medius	75
	Tensor fasciae latae	82
Thigh		
Anterior surface	Quadriceps femoris group	82
	1. Rectus femoris	82, 83
	2. Vastus lateralis	82, 84
	3. Vastus medialis	82, 85
	4. Vastus intermedius	86
Medial surface	Gracilis	82, 90
	Adductor group (longus, brevis, magnus)	82, 87, 88, 89
Posterior surface	Hamstrings	91
	1. Biceps femoris	94
	2. Semitendinosus	95
	3. Semimembranosus	96
Leg		
Anterior surface	Tibialis anterior	82
Posterior surface	Gastrocnemius	91
	Soleus	91
Pelvic floor	Levator ani	103
	Coccygeus	103

149

Table 7. Muscles grouped according to function

Part moved	Example of flexor	Example of extensor	Example of abductor	Example of adductor
Head	Sternocleidomastoid	Semispinalis capitis		
Upper arm	Pectoralis major	Trapezius Latissimus dorsi	Deltoid	Pectoralis major with latissimus dorsi
Forearm	With forearm supinated: Biceps brachii With forearm pronated: Brachialis With semisupination or semipronation: Brachioradialis	Triceps brachii		
Hand	Flexor carpi radialis and ulnaris Palmaris longus	Extensor carpi radialis, longus, and brevis Extensor carpi ulnaris	Flexor carpi radialis	Flexor carpi ulnaris
Thigh	Iliopsoas Rectus femoris (of quadriceps femoris group)	Gluteus maximus	Gluteus medius and minimus	Adductor group
Leg	Hamstrings	Quadriceps femoris group		
Foot	Tibialis anterior	Gastrocnemius Soleus	Evertors: Peroneus longus Peroneus brevis	Invertors: Tibialis anterior
Trunk	Iliopsoas Rectus abdominis	Sacrospinalis		

Table 8. Muscles that move the shoulder

Muscle	Origin	Insertion	Function	Innervation
Trapezius*	*Occipital bone* (protuberance)	*Scapula* (spine and acromion)	Raise or lower shoulders and shrug them	Spinal accessory, second, third, and fourth cervical nerves
	Vertebrae (cervical and thoracic)	*Clavicle*	Extend head when occiput acts as insertion	
Pectoralis minor*	*Ribs* (second to fifth)	*Scapula* (coracoid)	Pulls shoulder down and forward	Medial and lateral anterior thoracic nerves
Serratus anterior*	*Ribs* (upper eight or nine)	*Scapula* (anterior surface, vertebral border)	Pulls shoulder forward; abducts and rotates it upward	Long thoracic nerve

When trying to learn the origins and insertion of the muscles in this table, refer frequently to illustrations of each muscle and to the skeleton; also when possible, feel each muscle on your own body.
Italics indicate the origins and insertions to be remembered.
*Muscles that author judges are important for beginning students of anatomy to know.

Table 9. Muscles that move upper arm

Muscle	Origin	Insertion	Function	Innervation
Pectoralis major*	*Clavicle* (medial half) *Sternum* *Costal cartilages of true ribs*	*Humerus* (greater tubercle)	Flexes upper arm Adducts upper arm anteriorly; draws it across chest	Medial and lateral anterior thoracic nerves
Latissimus dorsi*	*Vertebrae* (spines of lower thoracic, lumbar and sacral) *Ilium* (crest) Lumbodorsal fascia†	*Humerus* (intertubercular groove)	Extends upper arm Adducts it posteriorly	Thoracodorsal nerve
Deltoid*	*Clavicle* *Scapula* (spine and acromion)	*Humerus* (lateral side about halfway down— deltoid tubercle)	Abducts upper arm Assists in flexion and extension of upper arm	Axillary nerve
Coracobrachialis	Scapula (coracoid process)	Humerus (middle third, medial surface)	Adduction; assists in flexion and medial rotation of arm	Musculocutaneous nerve
Supraspinatus	Scapula (supraspinous fossa)	Humerus (greater tubercle)	Assists in abducting arm	Suprascapular nerve
Teres major	Scapula (lower part, axillary border)	Humerus (upper part, anterior surface)	Assists in extension, adduction, and medial rotation of arm	Lower subscapular nerve
Teres minor	Scapula (axillary border)	Humerus (greater tubercle)	Rotates arm outward	Axillary nerve
Infraspinatus	Scapula (infraspinatus border)	Humerus (greater tubercle)	Rotates arm outward	Suprascapular nerve

When trying to learn the origins and insertion of the muscles in this table, refer frequently to illustrations of each muscle and to the skeleton; also when possible, feel each muscle on your own body.

Italics indicate the origins and insertions to be remembered.

*Muscles that author judges are important for beginning students of anatomy to know.

†Lumbodorsal fascia—extension of aponeurosis of latissimus dorsi; fills in space between last rib and iliac crest.

Table 10. Muscles that move lower arm

Muscle	Origin	Insertion	Function	Innervation
Biceps brachii*	*Scapula* (supra-glenoid tuber-osity) *Scapula* (cora-coid)	*Radius* (tubercle at proximal end)	Flexes supinated forearm Supinates forearm and hand	Musculocutaneous nerve
Brachialis*	*Humerus* (distal half, anterior surface)	*Ulna* (front of coronoid proc-ess)	Flexes pronated forearm	Musculocutaneous nerve
Brachioradialis	Humerus (above lateral epicon-dyle)	Radius (styloid process)	Flexes semipro-nated or semi-supinated fore-arm; supinates forearm and hand	Radial nerve
Triceps brachii*	*Scapula* (infra-glenoid tuber-osity) *Humerus* (poste-rior surface—lateral head above radial groove; medial head, below)	*Ulna* (olecranon process)	Extends lower arm	Radial nerve
Pronator teres	Humerus (medial epicondyle) Ulna (coronoid process)	Radius (middle third of lateral surface)	Pronates and flexes forearm	Median nerve
Pronator quad-ratus	Ulna (distal fourth, anterior surface)	Radius (distal fourth, anterior surface)	Pronates forearm	Median nerve
Supinator	Humerus (lateral epicondyle) Ulna (proximal fifth)	Radius (proximal third)	Supinates forearm	Radial nerve

When trying to learn the origins and insertion of the muscles in this table, refer frequently to illustrations of each muscle and to the skeleton; also when possible, feel each muscle on your own body.
Italics indicate the origins and insertions to be remembered.
*Muscles that author judges are important for beginning students of anatomy to know.

Table 11. Muscles that move hand

Muscle	Origin	Insertion	Function	Innervation
Flexor carpi radialis	Humerus (medial epicondyle)	Second metacarpal (base of)	Flex hand Flex forearm	Median nerve
Palmaris longus	Humerus (medial epicondyle)	Fascia of palm	Flex hand	Median nerve
Flexor carpi ulnaris	Humerus (medial epicondyle) Ulna (proximal two thirds)	Pisiform bone Third, fourth, and fifth metacarpals	Flex hand Adduct hand	Ulnar nerve
Extensor carpi radialis longus	Humerus (ridge above lateral epicondyle)	Second metacarpal (base of)	Extend hand Abduct hand (move toward thumb side when hand is supinated)	Radial nerve
Extensor carpi radialis brevis	Humerus (lateral epicondyle)	Second, third metacarpals (bases of)	Extend hand	Radial nerve
Extensor carpi ulnaris	Humerus (lateral epicondyle) Ulna (proximal three fourths)	Fifth metacarpal (base of)	Extend hand Adduct hand (move toward little finger side when hand is supinated)	Radial nerve

When trying to learn the origins and insertion of the muscles in this table, refer frequently to illustrations of each muscle and to the skeleton; also when possible, feel each muscle on your own body.

Table 12. Muscles that move thigh

Muscle	Origin	Insertion	Function	Innervation
Iliopsoas (iliacus and psoas major)*	*Ilium* (iliac fossa)	*Femur* (small trochanter)	Flex thigh	
	Vertebrae (bodies of twelfth thoracic to fifth lumbar)		Flex trunk (when femur acts as origin)	Femoral and second to fourth lumbar nerves
Rectus femoris*	*Ilium* (anterior, inferior spine)	*Tibia* (by way of patellar tendon)	Flex thigh Extend lower leg	Femoral nerve
Gluteal group 1. Maximus*	*Ilium* (crest and posterior surface) Sacrum and coccyx (posterior surface) Sacrotuberous ligament	*Femur* (gluteal tuberosity) *Iliotibial tract*†	Extend thigh—rotate outward	Inferior gluteal nerve
2. Medius*	*Ilium* (lateral surface)	*Femur* (greater trochanter)	Abduct thigh—rotate outward; stabilize pelvis on femurs	Superior gluteal nerve
3. Minimus*	*Ilium* (lateral surface)	*Femur* (greater trochanter)	Abduct thigh; stabilize pelvis on femurs Rotate thigh medially	Superior gluteal nerve
Tensor fasciae latae*	*Ilium* (anterior part of crest)	*Tibia* (by way of *iliotibial tract*)	Abduct thigh Tighten iliotibial tract†	Superior gluteal nerve
Piriformis	Vertebrae (front of sacrum)	Femur (medial aspect of greater trochanter)	Rotate thigh outward Abduct thigh Extend thigh	First or second sacral nerves
Adductor group* 1. Brevis 2. Longus 3. Magnus	*Pubic bone*	*Femur* (linea aspera)	Adduct thigh	Obturator nerve
Gracilis	Pubic bone (just below symphysis)	*Tibia* (medial surface behind sartorius)	Adduct thigh and flex and adduct leg	Obturator nerve

When trying to learn the origins and insertion of the muscles in this table, refer frequently to illustrations of each muscle and to the skeleton; also when possible, feel each muscle on your own body.
Italics indicate the origins and insertions to be remembered.
*Muscles that author judges are important for beginning students of anatomy to know.
†The iliotibial tract is part of the fascia enveloping all the thigh muscles. It consists of a wide band of white fibrous tissue attached to the iliac crest above and the lateral condyle of the tibia below. The upper part of the tract encloses the tensor fasciae latae muscle.

Table 13. Muscles that move lower leg

Muscle	Origin	Insertion	Function	Innervation
Quadriceps femoris group*				
1. Rectus femoris	Ilium (anterior, inferior spine)	Tibia (by way of patellar tendon)	Flex thigh Extend leg	Femoral nerve
2. Vastus lateralis	Femur (linea aspera)	Same	Extend leg	Femoral nerve
3. Vastus medialis	Femur	Same	Same	Femoral nerve
4. Vastus intermedius	Femur (anterior surface)	Same	Same	Femoral nerve
Sartorius*	Os innominatum (anterior, superior iliac spines)	Tibia (medial surface of upper end of shaft)	Adduct and flex leg Cross legs tailor fashion	Femoral nerve
Hamstring group*				
1. Biceps femoris	Ischium (tuberosity)	Fibula (head of)	Flex leg	Hamstring nerve (branch of sciatic nerve)
	Femur (linea aspera)	Tibia (lateral condyle)	Extend thigh	Hamstring nerve
2. Semitendinosus	Ischium (tuberosity)	Tibia (proximal end, medial surface)	Same	Hamstring nerve
3. Semimembranosus	Same	Tibia (medial condyle)	Same	Hamstring nerve

When trying to learn the origins and insertion of the muscles in this table, refer frequently to illustrations of each muscle and to the skeleton; also when possible, feel each muscle on your own body.

Italics indicate the origins and insertions to be remembered.

*Muscles that author judges are important for beginning students of anatomy to know.

Table 14. Muscles that move foot

Muscle	Origin	Insertion	Function	Innervation
Tibialis anterior*	*Tibia* (lateral condyle of upper body)	*Tarsal* (first cuneiform) Metatarsal (base of first)	Flex foot Invert foot	Common and deep peroneal nerves
Gastrocnemius*	*Femur* (condyles)	*Tarsal* (calcaneus by way of Achilles tendon)	Extend foot Flex lower leg	Tibial nerve (branch of sciatic nerve)
Soleus*	*Tibia* (underneath gastrocnemius) *Fibula*	*Same as gastrocnemius*	Extend foot (plantar flexion)	Tibial nerve
Peroneus longus	Tibia (lateral condyle) Fibula (head and shaft)	First cuneiform Base of first metatarsal	Extend foot (plantar flexion) Evert foot	Common peroneal nerve
Peroneus brevis	Fibula (lower two thirds of lateral surface of shaft)	Fifth metatarsal (tubercle, dorsal surface)	Evert foot Flex foot	Superficial peroneal nerve
Tibialis posterior	Tibia (posterior surface) Fibula (posterior surface)	Navicular bone Cuboid bone All three cuneiforms Second and fourth metatarsals	Extend foot (plantar flexion) Invert foot	Tibial nerve
Peroneus tertius	Fibula (distal third)	Fourth and fifth metatarsals (bases of)	Flex foot Evert foot	Deep peroneal nerve

When trying to learn the origins and insertion of the muscles in this table, refer frequently to illustrations of each muscle and to the skeleton; also when possible, feel each muscle on your own body.
Italics indicate the origins and insertions to be remembered.
*Muscles that author judges are important for beginning students of anatomy to know.

Table 15. Muscles that move head

Muscle	Origin	Insertion	Function	Innervation
Sternocleido-mastoid*	*Sternum* *Clavicle*	*Temporal bone* (mastoid process)	Flex head (prayer muscle) One muscle, alone, rotates head toward opposite side; spasm of this muscle alone or associated with trapezius called torticollis or wryneck	Accessory nerve
Semispinalis capitis	Vertebrae (transverse processes of upper six thoracic, articular processes of lower four cervical)	Occipital bone (between superior and inferior nuchal lines)	Extend head; bend it laterally	First five cervical nerves
Splenius capitis	Ligamentum nuchae Vertebrae (spinous processes of upper three or four)	Temporal bone (mastoid process) Occipital bone	Extend head Bend and rotate head toward same side as contracting muscle	Second, third, and fourth cervical nerves
Longissimus capitis	Vertebrae (transverse processes of upper six thoracic, articular processes of lower four cervical)	Temporal bone (mastoid process)	Extend head Bend and rotate head toward contracting side	

When trying to learn the origins and insertion of the muscles in this table, refer frequently to illustrations of each muscle and to the skeleton; also when possible, feel each muscle on your own body.
Italics indicate the origins and insertions to be remembered.
*Muscles that author judges are important for beginning students of anatomy to know.

Table 16. Muscles that move abdominal wall

Muscle	Origin	Insertion	Function	Innervation
External oblique*	*Ribs* (lower eight)	*Ossa coxae* (iliac crest and pubis by way of inguinal ligament)† *Linea alba‡ by way of an apo-neurosis§*	Compress abdo-men Important pos-tural function of all abdom-inal muscles is to pull front of pelvis upward, thereby flatten-ing lumbar curve of spine; when these muscles lose their tone, common figure faults of pro-truding abdo-men and lordo-sis develop	Lower seven inter-costal nerves and iliohypo-gastric nerves
Internal oblique*	*Ossa coxae* (iliac crest and ingui-nal ligament) *Lumbodorsal fascia*	*Ribs* (lower three) *Pubic bone Linea alba*	Same as external oblique	Last three inter-costals; iliohy-pogastric and ilioinguinal nerves
Transversalis*	*Ribs* (lower six) *Ossa coxae* (iliac crest, inguinal ligament) *Lumbodorsal fascia*	*Pubic bone Linea alba*	Same as external oblique	Last five inter-costals; iliohy-pogastric and ilioinguinal nerves

Continued on next page.

When trying to learn the origins and insertion of the muscles in this table, refer frequently to illustrations of each muscle and to the skeleton; also when possible, feel each muscle on your own body.

Italics indicate the origins and insertions to be remembered.

*Muscles that author judges are important for beginning students of anatomy to know.

†*Inguinal ligament* (or Poupart's)—lower edge of aponeurosis of external oblique muscle, extending between the anterior superior iliac spine and the spine of the pubic bone. This edge is doubled under similarly to a hem on material. The inguinal ligament forms the upper boundary of the *femoral triangle,* a large triangular area in the thigh; its other boundaries are the adductor longus muscle mesially and the sartorious laterally.

‡*Linea alba*—literally, a white line; extends from xiphoid process to symphysis pubis. Formed by fibers of aponeurosis of right abdominal muscles interlacing with fibers of aponeuroses of the left abdominal muscles; comparable to a seam up the midline of the abdominal wall, anchoring its various layers. During pregnancy the linea alba becomes pigmented and is known as the *linea niger.*

§*Aponeurosis*—sheet of white fibrous tissue which attaches one muscle to another or attaches it to bone or other movable structures; for example, the right external oblique muscle attaches to the left external oblique muscle by means of an aponeurosis.

159

Table 16. Muscles that move abdominal wall—cont'd

Muscle	Origin	Insertion	Function	Innervation
Rectus abdominis*	*Ossa coxae* (pubic bone and symphysis pubis)	*Ribs* (costal cartilage of fifth, sixth, and seventh ribs) Sternum (xiphoid process)	Same as external oblique; because abdominal muscles compress abdominal cavity, they aid in straining, defecation, forced expiration, childbirth, etc.; abdominal muscles are antagonists of diaphragm, relaxing as it contracts and vice versa Flex trunk	Last six intercostal nerves

*Muscles that author judges are important for beginning students of anatomy to know.

Table 17. Muscles that move chest wall

Muscle	Origin	Insertion	Function	Innervation
External intercostals	Rib (lower border; forward fibers)	Rib (upper border of rib below origin)	Elevate ribs	Intercostal nerves
Internal intercostals	Rib (inner surface, lower border; backward fibers)	Rib (upper border of rib below origin)	Probably depress ribs	Intercostal nerves
Diaphragm*	*Lower circumference of thorax* (of rib cage)	*Central tendon of diaphragm*	Enlarges thorax, causing inspiration	Phrenic nerves

When trying to learn the origins and insertion of the muscles in this table, refer frequently to illustrations of each muscle and to the skeleton; also when possible, feel each muscle on your own body.
Italics indicate the origins and insertions to be remembered.
*Muscles that author judges are important for beginning students of anatomy to know.

Table 18. Muscles of pelvic floor

Muscle	Origin	Insertion	Function	Innervation
Levator ani	Pubis—posterior surface Ischium (spine)	Coccyx	Together form floor of pelvic cavity; support pelvic organs; if these muscles are badly torn at childbirth, or become too relaxed, uterus or bladder may prolapse, that is, drop out	Pudendal nerve
Coccygeus (posterior continuation of levator ani)	Ischium (spine)	Coccyx Sacrum	Same as levator ani	Pudendal nerve

When trying to learn the origins and insertion of the muscles in this table, refer frequently to illustrations of each muscle and to the skeleton; also when possible, feel each muscle on your own body.

Table 19. Muscles that move the trunk

Muscle	Origin	Insertion	Function	Innervation
Sacrospinalis (erector spinae)			Extend spine; maintain erect posture of trunk Acting singly, abduct and rotate trunk	Posterior rami of first cervical to fifth lumbar spinal nerves
Lateral portion of sacrospinalis consists of 1. Iliocostalis lumborum	Iliac crest, sacrum (posterior surface), and lumbar vertebrae (spinous processes)	Ribs, lower six		
2. Iliocostalis dorsi	Ribs, lower six	Ribs, upper six		
3. Iliocostalis cervicis	Ribs, upper six	Vertebrae, fourth to sixth cervical		
Medial portion consists of 1. Longissimus dorsi	Same as iliocostalis lumborum	Vertebrae, thoracic ribs		
2. Longissimus cervicis	Vertebrae, upper six thoracic	Vertebrae, second to sixth cervical		
3. Longissimus capitis	Vertebrae, upper six thoracic and last four cervical	Temporal bone, mastoid process		
Quadratus lumborum (forms part of posterior abdominal wall)	Ilium (posterior part of crest) Vertebrae (lower three lumbar)	Ribs (twelfth) Vertebrae (transverse processes of first four lumbar)	Both muscles together extend spine One muscle alone abducts trunk toward side of contracting muscle	First three or four lumbar nerves
Iliopsoas*	See muscles that move thigh, p. 155		Flexes trunk	

When trying to learn the origins and insertion of the muscles in this table, refer frequently to illustrations of each muscle and to the skeleton; also when possible, feel each muscle on your own body.
*Muscles that author judges are important for beginning students of anatomy to know.

Table 20. Muscles of facial expression and of mastication

Muscles	Origin	Insertion	Function	Innervation
Epicranius (oc- cipitofrontalis)	Occipital bone	Tissues of eye- brows	Raises eyebrows, wrinkling fore- head, hori- zontally	Cranial nerve VII
Corrugator supercilii	Frontal bone (superciliary ridge)	Skin of eyebrow	Wrinkles fore- head vertically	Cranial nerve VII
Orbicularis oculi	Encircles eyelid		Closes eye	Cranial nerve VII
Orbicularis oris	Encircles mouth		Draws lips to- gether	Cranial nerve VII
Platysma	Fascia of upper part of deltoid and pectoralis major	Mandible—lower border Skin around cor- ners of mouth	Draws corners of mouth down— pouting	Cranial nerve VII
Buccinator	Maxillae	Skin of sides of mouth	Smiling Trumpeting	Cranial nerve VII
Muscles of mas- tication				
Masseter	Zygomatic arch	Mandible (ex- ternal surface)	Closes jaw	Cranial nerve V
Temporal	Temporal bone	Mandible	Closes jaw	Cranial nerve V
Pterygoids (in- ternal and external)	Under surface of skull	Mandible (mesial surface)	Grating teeth	Cranial nerve V

When trying to learn the origins and insertion of the muscles in this table, refer frequently to illustrations of each muscle and to the skeleton; also when possible, feel each muscle on your own body. Italics indicate the origins and insertions to be remembered.

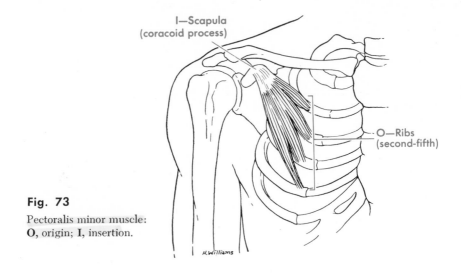

I—Scapula
(coracoid process)

O—Ribs
(second-fifth)

Fig. 73

Pectoralis minor muscle:
O, origin; **I**, insertion.

H.Williams

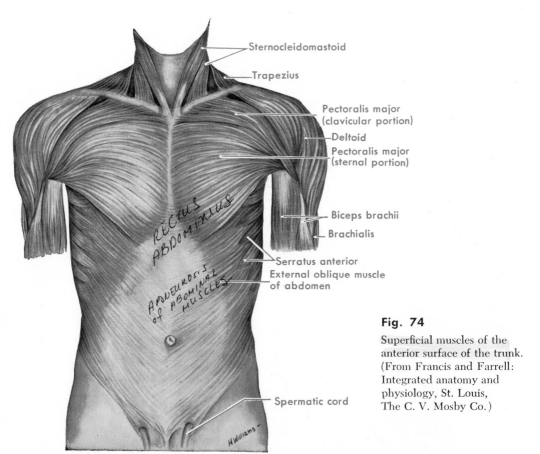

Sternocleidomastoid

Trapezius

Pectoralis major
(clavicular portion)

Deltoid

Pectoralis major
(sternal portion)

Biceps brachii

Brachialis

RECTUS ABDOMINUS

APONEUROSIS of ABDOMINAL MUSCLES

Serratus anterior

External oblique muscle
of abdomen

Fig. 74

Superficial muscles of the
anterior surface of the trunk.
(From Francis and Farrell:
Integrated anatomy and
physiology, St. Louis,
The C. V. Mosby Co.)

Spermatic cord

H.Williams

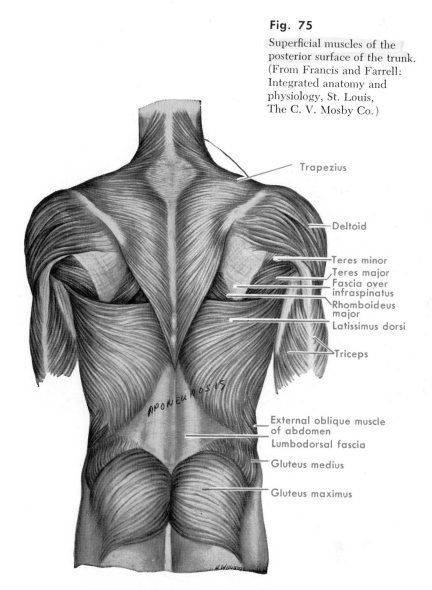

Fig. 75

Superficial muscles of the
posterior surface of the trunk.
(From Francis and Farrell:
Integrated anatomy and
physiology, St. Louis,
The C. V. Mosby Co.)

Trapezius

Deltoid

Teres minor
Teres major
Fascia over
infraspinatus
Rhomboideus
major
Latissimus dorsi

Triceps

APONEUROSIS

External oblique muscle
of abdomen
Lumbodorsal fascia

Gluteus medius

Gluteus maximus

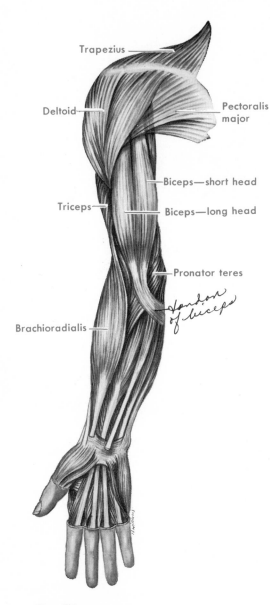

Trapezius

Deltoid

Pectoralis
major

Biceps—short head

Triceps

Biceps—long head

Pronator teres

Tendon
of biceps

Brachioradialis

Fig. 76

Muscles of the flexor surface
of the upper extremity.

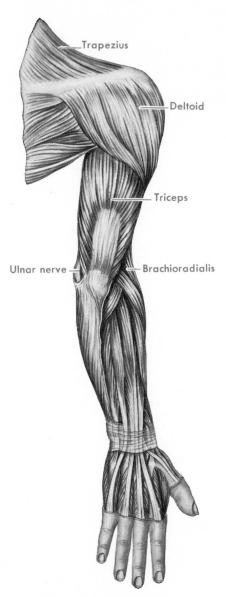

Trapezius

Deltoid

Triceps

Ulnar nerve

Brachioradialis

Fig. 77

Muscles of the extensor surface
of the upper extremity.

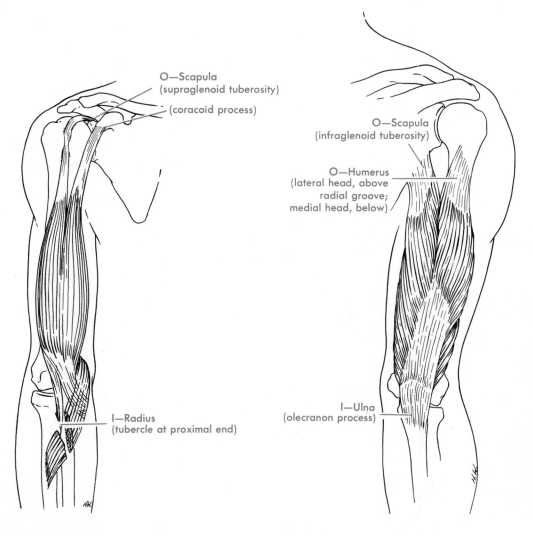

O—Scapula
(supraglenoid tuberosity)

(coracoid process)

O—Scapula
(infraglenoid tuberosity)

O—Humerus
(lateral head, above
radial groove;
medial head, below)

I—Radius
(tubercle at proximal end)

I—Ulna
(olecranon process)

Fig. 78

Biceps brachii. Pronator teres cut to
show insertion of biceps brachii:
O, origin; **I**, insertion.

Fig. 79

Triceps brachii: **O**, origin; **I**, insertion.

Fig. 80

Brachialis: **O**, origin; **I**, insertion.

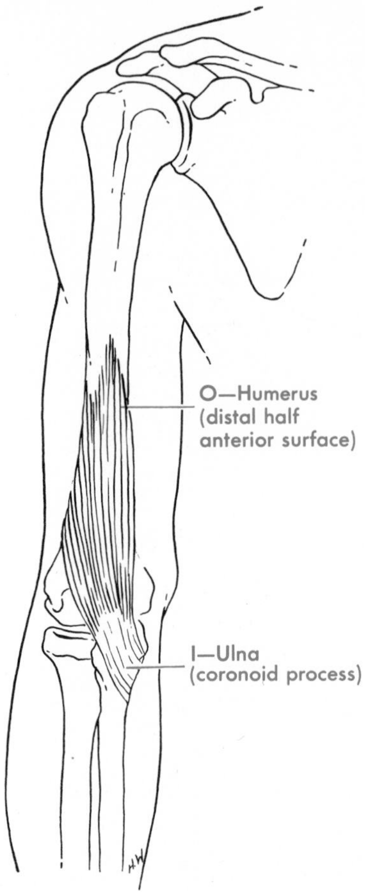

O—Humerus
(distal half
anterior surface)

I—Ulna
(coronoid process)

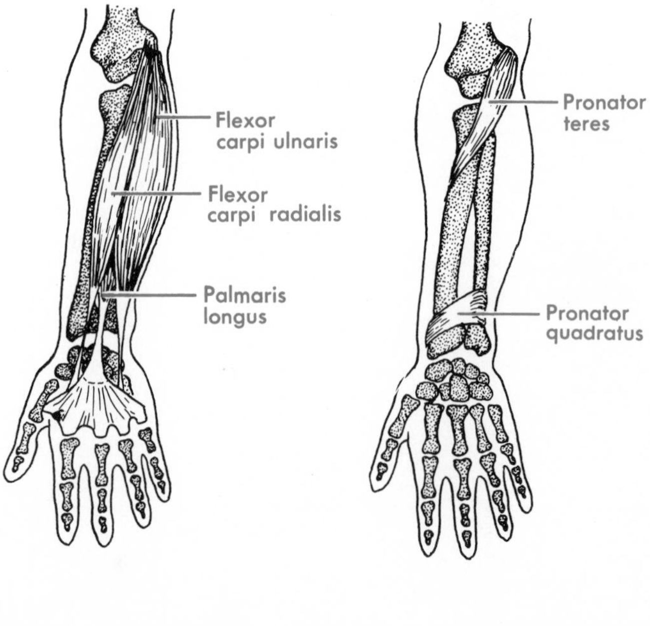

Flexor
carpi ulnaris

Flexor
carpi radialis

Palmaris
longus

Pronator
teres

Pronator
quadratus

Fig. 81

Some muscles of the
anterior aspect of the
right forearm.

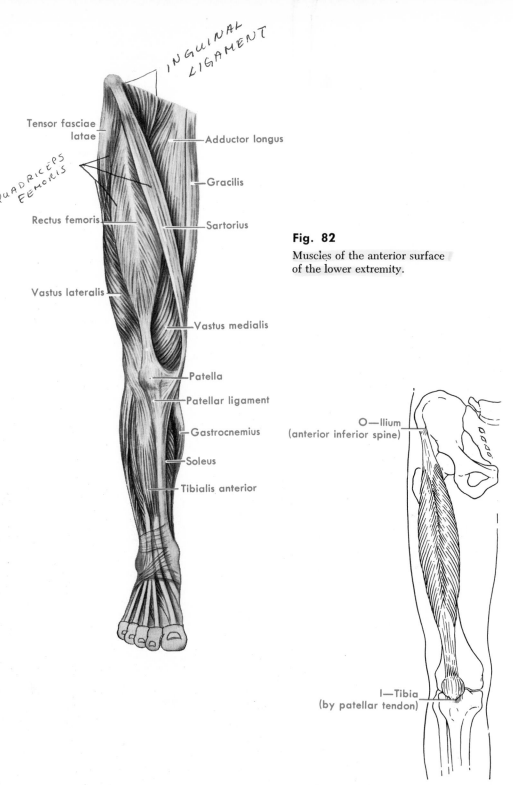

INGUINAL LIGAMENT

Tensor fasciae latae

QUADRICEPS FEMORIS

Rectus femoris

Vastus lateralis

Adductor longus

Gracilis

Sartorius

Vastus medialis

Patella

Patellar ligament

Gastrocnemius

Soleus

Tibialis anterior

Fig. 82

Muscles of the anterior surface of the lower extremity.

O—Ilium
(anterior inferior spine)

I—Tibia
(by patellar tendon)

Fig. 83

Rectus femoris: **O,** origin; **I,** insertion.

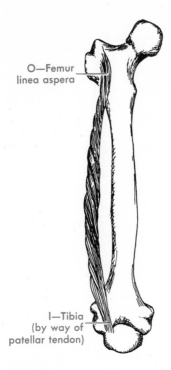

O—Femur
linea aspera

I—Tibia
(by way of
patellar tendon)

Fig. 84
Vastus lateralis muscle.

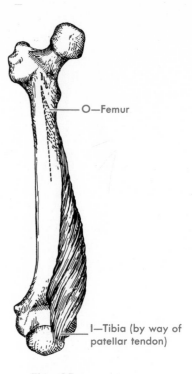

O—Femur

I—Tibia (by way of
patellar tendon)

Fig. 85
Vastus medialis muscle.

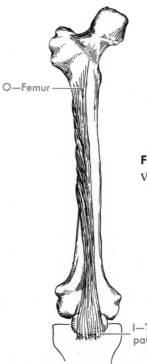

O—Femur

Fig. 86
Vastus intermedius muscle.

I—Tibia (by way of
patellar tendon)

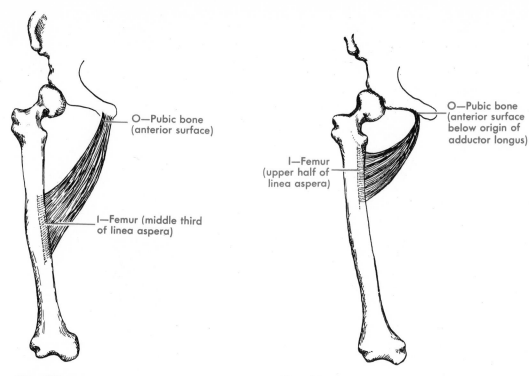

O—Pubic bone
(anterior surface)

I—Femur (middle third
of linea aspera)

O—Pubic bone
(anterior surface
below origin of
adductor longus)

I—Femur
(upper half of
linea aspera)

Fig. 87
Adductor longus muscle.

Fig. 88
Adductor brevis muscle.

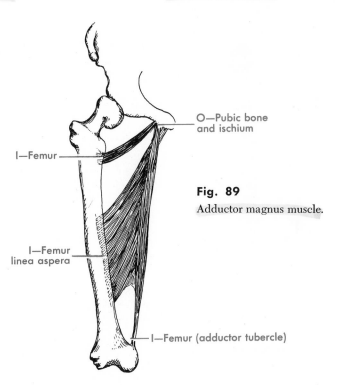

O—Pubic bone
and ischium

I—Femur

Fig. 89
Adductor magnus muscle.

I—Femur
linea aspera

I—Femur (adductor tubercle)

171

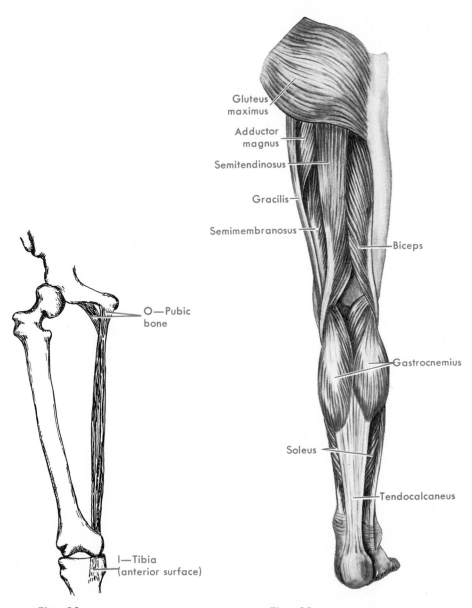

Fig. 90

Gracilis muscle.

O—Pubic bone

I—Tibia (anterior surface)

Fig. 91

Muscles of the posterior surface of the lower extremity.

Gluteus maximus

Adductor magnus

Semitendinosus

Gracilis

Semimembranosus

Biceps

Gastrocnemius

Soleus

Tendocalcaneus

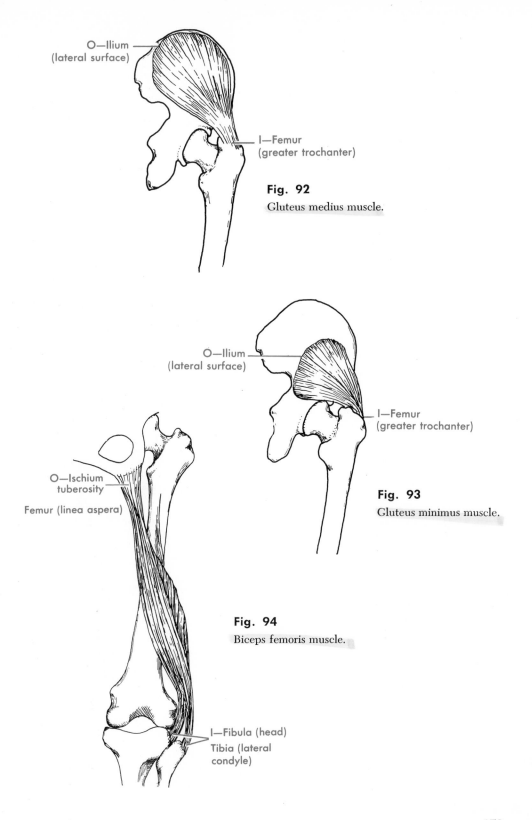

O—Ilium
(lateral surface)

I—Femur
(greater trochanter)

Fig. 92
Gluteus medius muscle.

O—Ilium
(lateral surface)

I—Femur
(greater trochanter)

O—Ischium
tuberosity

Femur (linea aspera)

Fig. 93
Gluteus minimus muscle.

Fig. 94
Biceps femoris muscle.

I—Fibula (head)
Tibia (lateral
condyle)

173

O—Ischium
tuberosity

I—Tibia

Fig. 95
Semitendinosus muscle.

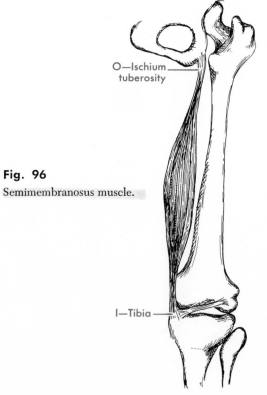

O—Ischium
tuberosity

Fig. 96
Semimembranosus muscle.

I—Tibia

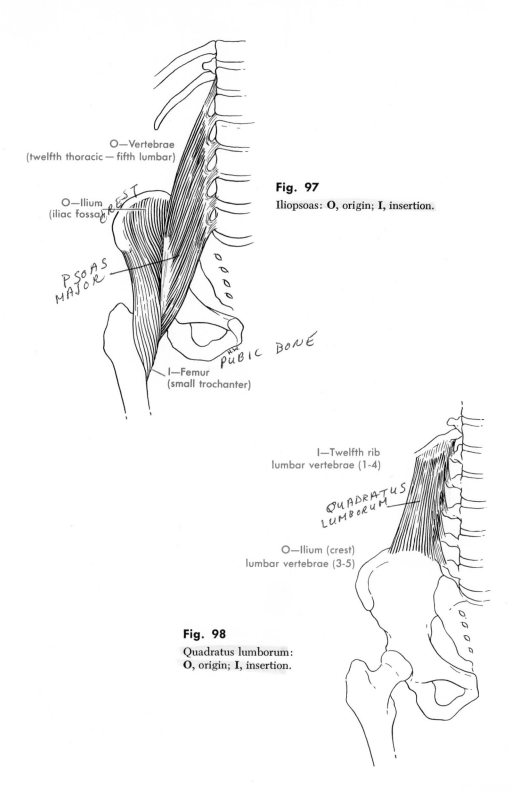

O—Vertebrae
(twelfth thoracic — fifth lumbar)

O—Ilium
(iliac fossa)

CREST

PSOAS MAJOR

PUBIC BONE

I—Femur
(small trochanter)

Fig. 97

Iliopsoas: **O**, origin; **I**, insertion.

I—Twelfth rib
lumbar vertebrae (1-4)

QUADRATUS LUMBORUM

O—Ilium (crest)
lumbar vertebrae (3-5)

Fig. 98

Quadratus lumborum:
O, origin; **I**, insertion.

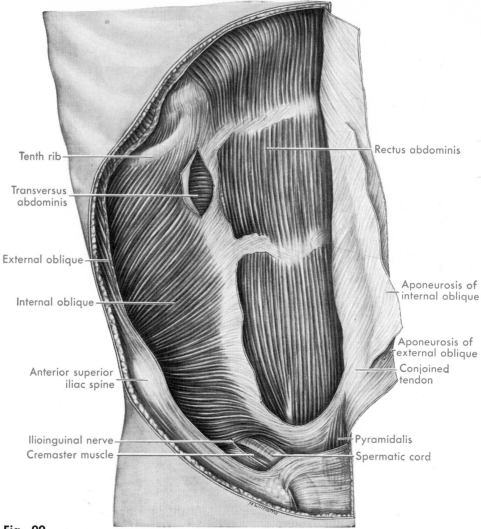

Tenth rib

Transversus abdominis

External oblique

Internal oblique

Anterior superior iliac spine

Ilioinguinal nerve
Cremaster muscle

Rectus abdominis

Aponeurosis of internal oblique

Aponeurosis of external oblique
Conjoined tendon

Pyramidalis
Spermatic cord

Fig. 99

Deep muscles of the abdominal wall. (From
Francis and Farrell: Integrated anatomy and physiology,
St. Louis, The C. V. Mosby Co.)

Rectus abdominis

Transversus
Internal oblique
External oblique

Fig. 100

Horizontal section of the anterolateral
abdominal wall. The aponeurosis
of the internal oblique muscle splits
into two sections, one lying anterior and
the other posterior to the rectus
abdominis muscle, thereby forming
an encasing sheath around this muscle.

The muscular
system   176

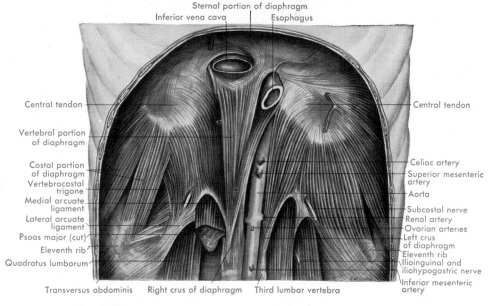

Fig. 101

Diaphragm viewed from the abdominal cavity. (From Francis and Farrell: Integrated anatomy and physiology, St. Louis, The C. V. Mosby Co.)

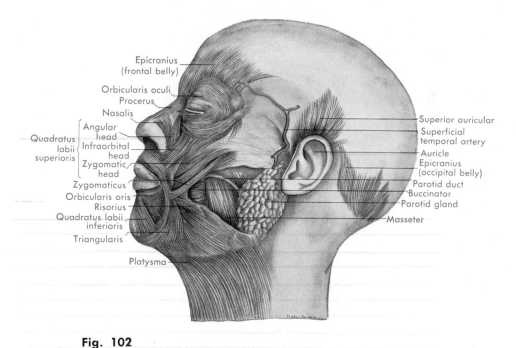

Fig. 102

Muscles of the head. These muscles make possible various facial expressions. (From Francis and Farrell: Integrated anatomy and physiology, St. Louis, The C. V. Mosby Co.)

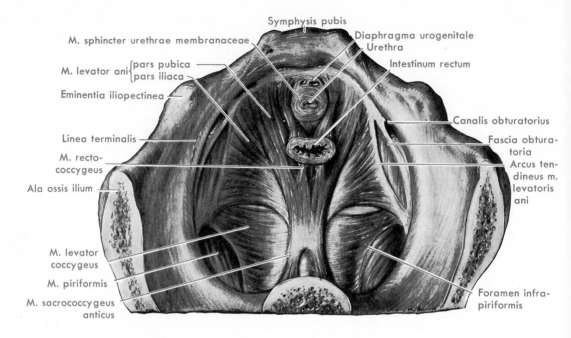

Symphysis pubis

M. sphincter urethrae membranaceae

M. levator ani { pars pubica / pars iliaca

Eminentia iliopectinea

Linea terminalis

M. recto-coccygeus

Ala ossis ilium

M. levator coccygeus

M. piriformis

M. sacrococcygeus anticus

Diaphragma urogenitale
Urethra

Intestinum rectum

Canalis obturatorius

Fascia obtura-toria

Arcus ten-dineus m. levatoris ani

Foramen infra-piriformis

Fig. 103

Pelvic floor viewed from above. (From Callander: Surgical anatomy, Philadelphia, W. B. Saunders Co.)

WEAK PLACES IN THE ABDOMINAL WALL

There are several places in the abdominal wall in which rupture (hernia) with protrusion of part of the intestine may occur. At these points the wall is weakened due to the presence of an interval or space in the abdominal aponeuroses; any undue pressure on the abdominal viscera, therefore, can force a portion of the parietal peritoneum and often a part of the intestine as well through these nonreinforced places. The weak places are (1) the *inguinal canals,* (2) the *femoral rings,* and (3) the *umbilicus.* Hernia also occurs occasionally in the diaphragm and some other areas.

Piercing the aponeuroses of the abdominal muscles are two canals, the *inguinal canals,* one on the right and the other on the left. They lie above, but parallel to, the inguinal ligaments and are about 1½ inches long. In the male the spermatic cords extend through the canals into the scrotum, whereas in the female the round ligaments of the uterus are in this location. The internal opening of each canal is a space in the aponeurosis of the transverse muscle known as the internal inguinal ring. The external openings or external inguinal rings are spaces in the aponeuroses of the external oblique muscles; they are located inferiorly and mesially to the internal rings. The fact that they are larger in the male than in the female probably explains why external inguinal hernia occurs more often in men than in women.

The *femoral rings* are openings in the groin just below the inguinal ligaments, slightly lateral to the external inguinal ring and medial to the femoral veins. They have a diameter of about ½ inch and are usually somewhat larger in females, a fact which accounts for the greater prevalence of femoral hernia in women than in men.

BURSAE

Definition

Bursae are small connective tissue sacs lined with synovial membrane and containing synovial fluid.

Locations

Bursae are located wherever pressure is exerted over moving parts, for example, between skin and bone, between tendons and bone, or between muscles, or ligaments, and bone. Some bursae which fairly frequently become inflamed (bursitis) are as follows: the subacromial bursa, between the head of the humerus and the acromion process and the deltoid muscle; the olecranon bursa, between the olecranon process and the skin; the prepatellar bursa, between the patella and the skin. Inflammation of the prepatellar bursa is known as housemaid's knee, whereas olecranon bursitis is called student's elbow.

Function

Bursae act as cushions, relieving pressure between moving parts.

TENDON SHEATHS

Definition and location

Tendon sheaths are tube-shaped structures found enclosing certain tendons, notably those of the wrist and ankle. In structure they resemble the bursae in that they are made of connective tissue lined with synovial membrane. An inner layer of synovial membrane covers the tendon surface.

Function

The moist smooth surface of the synovial membrane lining the sheath and covering the tendon facilitates the gliding movements of the tendon.

POSTURE

We have discussed two of the ways by which muscles serve the body as a whole and shall now turn our attention to a third function

179

performed by muscles. In addition to playing a major role in movement and heat production, muscles also maintain the posture of the body. Let us consider a few aspects of this important function.

Meaning

The term posture means simply position or alignment of body parts. "Good posture" means many things. It means body alignment which most favors function; it means position which requires the least muscular work to maintain, which puts the least strain on muscles, ligaments, and bones; it means keeping the body's center of gravity over its base. Good posture in the standing position, for example, means head and chest held high, chin, abdomen, and buttocks pulled in, knees bent slightly, and feet placed firmly on the ground about 6 inches apart.

How maintained

Since gravity pulls on the various parts of the body at all times, and since bones are too irregularly shaped to balance themselves upon each other, the only way the body can be held upright is for muscles to exert a continual pull on bones in the opposite direction from gravity. Gravity tends to pull the head and trunk forward and downward; muscles (head and trunk extensors) must therefore pull backward and upward on them. Gravity pulls the lower jaw downward; muscles must pull upward on it, and so on. Muscles exert this pull against gravity by virtue of their property of tonicity. Because tonicity is absent during sleep, we cannot sleep standing up.

Many structures other than muscles and bones play a part in the maintenance of posture. The nervous system is responsible for the existence of muscle tone and also regulates and coordinates the amount of pull exerted by the individual muscles. The respiratory, digestive, circulatory, excretory, and endocrine systems all contribute something toward the ability of muscle to maintain posture. This is one of many examples of the important principle that all body functions are interdependent.

Importance of posture to the body as a whole

The importance of posture can perhaps be best evaluated by considering some of the effects of poor posture. Poor posture throws more work on muscles to counteract the pull of gravity and therefore leads to fatigue more quickly than good posture. Poor posture puts more strain on ligaments. It puts abnormal strains on bones and may eventually produce deformities. It interferes with various functions such as respirations, heart action, and digestion. It probably is not going too far to say that it even detracts from one's feeling of self-confidence and joy. In support of this last claim may be cited our use of such expressions as "shoulders squared, head erect" to denote confidence and joy and "down-in-the-mouth," "long-faced," and "bowed down" to signify dejection and anxiety. The importance of posture to the body as a whole might be summed up in a single sentence: Maximal health and good posture are reciprocally related; that is, each one depends upon the other.

Outline summary

The muscular system

Meaning

All muscles of the body but especially the skeletal muscles

General functions

1. Movement—sometimes locomotion, sometimes movement within a given area
2. Maintenance of posture
3. Production of heat

Muscle tissue—functional characteristics

1. Irritability—ability to respond to a stimulus
2. Conductivity—ability to transmit impulses
3. Extensibility—ability to be stretched
4. Elasticity—ability to resume former length when stretching force is removed
5. Contractility—the ability to contract or shorten

Types of muscle contraction

1. Twitch
   a. definition—a quick, jerky contraction in response to a single stimulus
   b. form curve—reveals three successive phases in a twitch contraction: *latent period*, a fraction of a second following stimulation in which no change is apparent; *contraction period*, in which muscle fibers shorten; *relaxation period*, in which fibers return to original length
2. Tetanus
   a. definition—sustained, smooth contraction

   b. form curve—wavy line plateau for incomplete tetanus; straight line plateau for complete tetanus; normal smooth movements produced by tetanic contractions
3. Tone—continual, partial contractions; produced by activation of small groups of motor units at one time; act in relays, that is, as one group of fibers relaxes another group of motor units becomes active; characteristic of all healthy muscles
4. Treppe, contracture, and fatigue
   a. treppe—a series of increasingly stronger contractions in response to constant strength stimuli applied at rate of one or two per second; also called staircase phenomenon
   b. contracture—incomplete relaxation after repeated stimulation or certain kinds of injury
   c. fatigue—failure of muscle to contract in response to stimulation
5. Isotonic contraction—muscle shortens and performs work but tension within muscle remains unchanged
6. Isometric contraction—muscle length remains unchanged so it does no work but tension within muscle increases
7. Fibrillation—abnormal contraction in which individual fibers contract asynchronously, producing no effective movement
8. Convulsions—uncoordinated tetanic contractions of varying groups of muscles

181

Mechanism of muscle contraction

1. Stimulation of muscle triggers breakdown of ATP within muscle cells to ADP and inorganic phosphate with the release of energy
2. Energy released from ATP breakdown used to do work of muscle contraction
3. All-or-none law—applies to muscle cells but not to muscle organs; if a muscle cell contracts at all, contracts with maximal force for existing conditions
4. Sources of ATP
   a. catabolism
      1. less than 10% of ATP produced during catabolism is produced during glycolysis, the anaerobic first phase of catabolism (anerobic means chemical reactions that do not utilize oxygen); over 90% of ATP produced during the citric acid cycle, the aerobic second phase of catabolism; (aerobic means chemical reactions that do utilize oxygen); hence, without adequate oxygen supply only a small amount of ATP is produced by cell—not enough for cell to carry on its normal activities; see number 5d below
   b. phosphocreatin breakdown
      1. when phosphocreatine breaks down to creatine and inorganic phosphate, energy released and utilized for synthesizing ATP from ADP and inorganic phosphate
5. Results of strenuous muscular activity
   a. cells' rate of catabolism increased to meet increased need for ATP to supply more energy
   b. respiration and circulation unable to increase oxygen delivery to cells enough to equal their increased oxygen need (accelerated citric acid cycle uses more oxygen); in other words, oxygen supply inadequate in relation to oxygen needed
   c. citric acid cycle slows or stops
   d. ATP production decreased markedly (because of slow critic acid cycle); pyruvic acid starts accumulating and is reduced to lactic acid, thereby creating an oxygen debt; part of the lactic acid diffuses out of cells, carried to the liver,

and synthesized back to glycogen or glucose
6. Recovery after cessation of strenuous muscular activity—oxygen debt gradually repaid; lactic acid remaining in muscle cells oxidized back to pyruvic acid which is then oxidized via the citric acid cycle to carbon dioxide and water with ATP formation

Skeletal muscles—gross structure
Size, shape, and arrangement of fibers
Wide variation in different muscles

Connective tissue components

1. Epimysium—fibrous connective tissue sheath that envelops each muscle
2. Perimysium—extensions of the epimysium, partitioning each muscle into bundles of fibers
3. Endomysium—extensions of perimysium between individual muscle fibers
4. Tendon—strong, tough cord continuous at one end with fibrous wrappings (epimysium, etc.) of muscle and at other end with fibrous covering of bone (periosteum)
5. Aponeurosis—broad flat sheet of fibrous connective tissue continuous on one border with fibrous wrappings of a muscle and at other border with fibrous coverings of some adjacent structure, usually another muscle
6. Deep fascia—a layer of dense fibrous connective tissue underlying the superficial fascia under the skin; extensions of deep fascia form epimysium, etc., and also enclose viscera, glands, blood vessels, and nerves

Nerve supply of skeletal muscles
One motor neuron and the skeletal muscle fibers it supplies together constitute a *motor unit;* number of muscle fibers per motor unit varies; in general, the more precise the movements produced by a muscle, the fewer muscle fibers in each of its motor units

Skeletal muscle actions
1. Skeletal muscles contract only if stimulated
2. Skeletal muscles produce movements by pulling on insertion bones across joints

3. Bones serve as levers and joints as fulcrums of these levers
4. Muscles that move a part usually do not lie over that part but proximal to it.
5. Skeletal muscles almost always act in groups rather than singly; most movements, that is, produced by coordinated action of several muscles
6. Skeletal muscles contract according to the graded strength principle in contrast to the individual muscle cells that compose them which contract according to the all-or-none law

Hints on how to deduce muscle actions

1. Deduce bones that a muscle attaches to from illustrations of the muscle
2. Make a guess as to which bone moves (insertion)
3. Deduce movement muscle produces by applying principle that its insertion moves toward its origin

Names of skeletal muscles

1. Muscle names describe one or more of the following features about muscle
   a. its action
   b. direction of fibers
   c. its location
   d. number of divisions composing it
   e. its shape
   f. its points of attachment
2. Grouped according to location—see p. 149
3. Grouped according to function—see p. 150 muscle names which describe actions:
   a. flexors—decrease angle of joint
   b. extensors—return a part from flexion to normal anatomic position
   c. abductors—move bone away from midline of body
   d. adductors—move bone toward midline of body
   e. rotators—cause part to pivot upon its axis
   f. levators—raise a part
   g. depressors—lower a part
   h. sphincters—reduce size of an opening
   i. tensors—tense a part or make it more rigid
   j. supinators—turn hand palm upward
   k. pronators—turn hand palm downward

Origins, insertions, functions, innervations of representative skeletal muscles

See Tables 8 through 20, pp. 151 to 163.

Weak places in abdominal wall

1. Inguinal rings—right and left internal; right and left external
2. Femoral rings—right and left
3. Umbilicus

Bursae

1. Definition—small connective tissue sacs lined with synovial membrane and containing synovial fluid
2. Locations—wherever pressure is exerted over moving parts
   a. between skin and bone
   b. between tendons and bone
   c. between muscles or ligaments and bone
   d. names of bursae which frequently become inflamed (bursitis)
      1. subacromial—between deltoid muscle and head of humerus and acromion process
      2. olecranon—between olecranon process and skin; inflammation called student's elbow
      3. prepatellar—between patella and skin; inflammation called housemaid's knee
3. Function—bursae act as cushions, relieving pressure between moving parts

Tendon sheaths

1. Definition and location—tube-shaped structures which enclose certain tendons, notably those of wrist and ankle; made of connective tissue lined with synovial membrane
2. Function—facilitate gliding movements of tendon

Posture

Meaning

Position or alignment of body parts

How maintained

By continual pull of muscles on bones in opposite direction from pull of gravity; that is, posture maintained by continued partial contraction of muscles, or muscle tone; therefore, indirectly dependent on many other factors; for example, normal nervous, respiratory, and circulatory systems, health in general

Importance to body as whole

Essential for optimal functioning of most of body; for example, respiration, circulation, digestion, joint action, etc.; briefly, maximal health dependent upon good posture, good posture dependent upon health

Review questions
The muscular system

1. Differentiate between the three kinds of muscle tissue as to structure, location, and innervation.
2. Describe several physiological properties of muscle tissue.
3. What property is more highly developed in muscle than in any other tissue?
4. State a principle describing the usual relationship between a part moved and the location of muscles (insertion, body, and origin) moving the part.
5. Applying the principle stated in question 4, where would you expect muscles that move the head to be located? Name two or three muscles that fulfill these conditions.
6. Applying the principle stated in question 4, what part of the body do thigh muscles move? Name several muscles that fulfill these conditions.
7. What bone or bones serve as a lever in movements of the forearm? What structure constitutes the fulcrum for this lever?
8. Explain the meaning of the term neuro-musculoskeletal unit.

9. Name the main muscles of the back, chest, abdomen, neck, shoulder, upper arm, lower arm, thigh, buttocks, leg, and pelvic floor.
10. Name the main muscles that flex, extend, abduct, and adduct the upper arm; that raise and lower the shoulder; that flex and extend the lower arm; that flex, extend, abduct, and adduct the thigh; that flex and extend the lower leg and thigh; that flex and extend the foot; that flex, extend, abduct, and adduct the head; that move the abdominal wall; that move the chest wall.
11. Discuss the chemical reactions thought to make available energy for muscle contraction.
12. What physiological reason can you give for athletes using a warming up period before starting a game?
13. Why does an individual pant after strenuous exercise?
14. In general, where are bursae located? Give several specific locations.
15. Name several weak places in the abdominal wall where hernia may occur.
16. What and where are the inguinal canals? Of what clinical importance are they?
17. Good posture depends upon tonicity of the antigravity muscles, particularly of those which hold the head and trunk erect and the abdominal wall pulled in. Name several muscles which perform these functions.
18. Define the following terms:

aponeurosis	motor unit
bursa	origin
contraction	oxygen debt
contracture	tetanus
elasticity	tone
extensibility	treppe
fibrillation	twitch
insertion	

Integration
and control
of the body

The nervous system

If you want to understand the body, you need to remind yourself frequently of some principles stated in the first chapter of this book. Briefly, that the body is made up of millions of smaller structures that carry on a host of different activities. But—and this is the important point—together all of these diverse activities accomplish the one big, all-encompassing function of the body—survival. If you think about this for a moment, you realize that the only way many units can be made to function as a single unit (whether the units are cells, or people, or parts of a machine) is by organization, controlling their numerous activities so as to coordinate and integrate them. And this necessitates communication or in other words some means of getting information to and from the component units. The body has two ways of doing this. Nerve impulses and chemicals are its two kinds of communication devices.

The foregoing principles about a large unit composed of smaller units have many familiar applications. A hospital, to name just one example, is such a unit. Quite obviously, the activities of the hundreds of individuals who make up a modern hospital must be organized, coordinated, and integrated, and communication must take place between the individuals. Complete chaos would prevail otherwise. A disorganized hospital could not survive functionally. In no time at all it would be utterly unable to carry on its one great function of giving care to sick people.

In this chapter and the next will be discussed the nervous system, one of the body's two vital communication and integration facilities. Chapter XIV deals with chemical control devices. Facts, theories, and questions about the nervous system are as abundant and complex as they are fascinating. We shall approach this large body of material by considering cells of the nervous system first, then the coverings of the nervous system and the fluid spaces of the brain and cord, and next nervous system organs and divisions, reflexes, and the autonomic nervous system, and finally in Chapter VIII the sense organs.

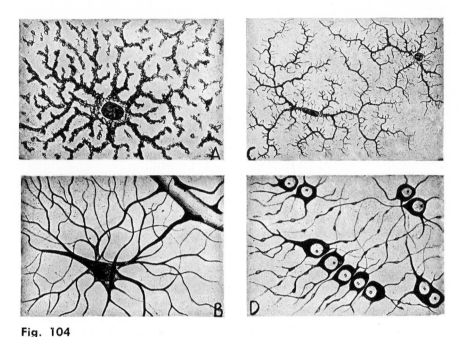

Fig. 104

Neuroglial cells of the central nervous system. **A**, Protoplasmic astrocyte; **B**, fibrous astrocyte; **C**, microglia; **D**, oligodendroglia. (After
del Río-Hortega; from Bloom and Fawcett: A textbook
of histology, Philadelphia, W. B. Saunders Co.)

CELLS OF THE NERVOUS SYSTEM

Three main kinds of cells compose nervous system structures: neurons (nerve cells), neuroglia, and microglia. We shall discuss neuroglia
and microglia first and then neurons, and in our discussion we shall
mention several subtypes of each.

Neuroglia and microglia

Neuroglia and microglia are cells intimately associated with neurons
and blood vessels in nervous tissue. (Apparently to early investigators,
these cells appeared "glued" to them since the word glia means glue.)
Neuroglia and microglia perform functions in nervous system organs
performed by connective tissue cells in other structures—support and
protection. Neurons, in contrast, specialize in the functions of irritability and conductivity. By means of little vascular feet or extensions to
blood vessels, many neuroglia form a kind of membrane between blood
vessels and neurons—said by some investigators to constitute the
blood-brain barrier which limits the exchange of certain substances
between blood and neurons. Microglia are phagocytes. As such, they

function to clear away the debris of normal cellular disintegration and become even more active in infections of the nervous system.

Neurons

Neurons—classified according to function

1. *afferent* (*sensory*)—transmit nerve impulses <u>toward</u> the central nervous system. *Conduct impulses from sense organs to spinal cord, brain, or end organs*
2. *efferent* (*motor*)—transmit nerve impulses <u>away</u> from the central nervous system; may be subdivided into motor or secretory neurons; <u>motor neurons transmit impulses to muscles</u>; <u>secretory neurons transmit impulses to glands</u>.
3. *internuncial* (*intercalated, central*)—conduct impulses from afferent to efferent neurons; lie entirely within the central nervous system.

to effector organs ← accelerator impulses that stimulate visceral or cardiac muscle

inhibitor—impulses that stop visceral or cardiac muscles

Neurons—classified according to structure

Structurally neurons fall into three classifications, unipolar, bipolar, and multipolar, depending upon the number of processes extending from the cell body.

1. *multipolar*—have several dendrites but only one axon; most brain and spinal cord neurons are multipolar.
2. *bipolar*—have only one dendrite and one axon; found in the retina and spiral ganglion of the inner ear, for example.
3. *unipolar*—true unipolar neurons have only one process, an axon, but such neurons are said to be rare except in the embryo. Pseudounipolar neurons (most sensory neurons) on the other hand are numerous. In an early stage of development they are bipolar, but later their two processes fuse for a short distance. As a result, only one process extends from the cell body, but it divides almost immediately into two branches—a <u>distal branch</u> that functions as a <u>dendrite</u> and a <u>peripheral branch</u> that functions as an <u>axon</u>.

Neurons—structure

Neuron structure, like that of other cells, illustrates the principle that structure determines function. <u>The basic function of neurons is to respond to stimuli by transmitting nerve impulses</u>. Neurons are specialists in other words in irritability and conductivity. And their unique shape is one structural feature that adapts them so well for these functions. Their cytoplasm extends out into fine processes that provide the facilities necessary for impulse conduction over distances. No other human cells are so constructed. Neuron processes or fibers, as

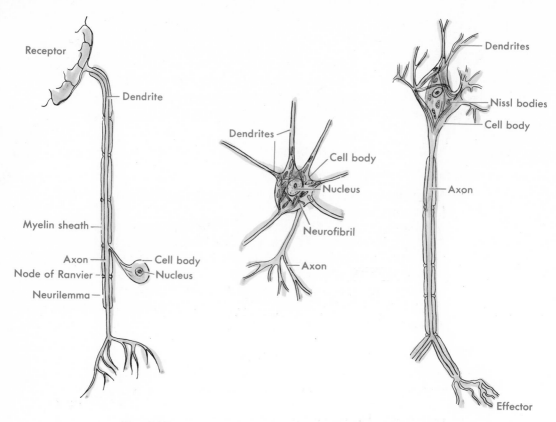

Fig. 105

Diagrammatic representation of sensory (afferent), central (internuncial),
and motor (efferent) nerve cells. Note that each type of neuron has three
parts, a cell body and two extensions, dendrite, and an axon
(see Fig. 106 for more details about axon coverings).

they are called because of their threadlike shape, vary as to length,
diameter, and number, but are of two general types—dendrites and
axons.

1. *Dendrites,* by definition, are neuron processes that respond to
stimulation by conducting impulses toward the main part of the neuron, its cell body. It is because they branch extensively like tiny
trees that they are called dendrites or dendrons (from Greek word for
tree). Most neurons have several dendrites. The distal ends of
dendrites of sensory neurons are called *receptors* because they receive
the initial stimulus (Fig. 105).

2. *Neuron cell bodies* are also sometimes called *perikaryon;* from
the Greek words, peri, meaning around, and karyon, meaning nucleus.

3. *Axons* are neuron processes that conduct impulses away from
the cell body. The word axon means axis, a term descriptive of the
long, straight shape typical of many axons. Although each neuron has
only one axon, this may have one or more side branches (*axon col-
laterals*). Moreover, axons terminate in many branched filaments.

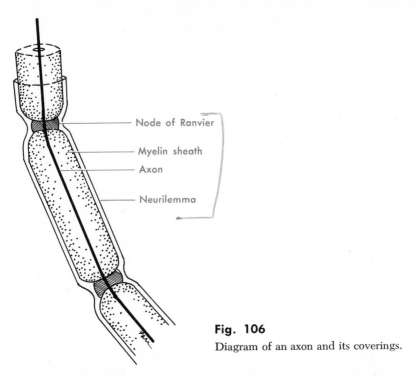

Node of Ranvier

Myelin sheath

Axon

Neurilemma

Fig. 106

Diagram of an axon and its coverings.

Axons of different neurons vary in diameter—a point of interest because it relates to velocity of impulse conduction. In general, large diameter axons conduct more rapidly than small ones. Later, we shall apply this principle to specific nerves.

4. *Neurofibrils* are fine fibrils present in dendrites, cell body, and axon. Studies made with the electron microscope (by Palay and Palade) have shown that bundles of neurofibrils interlace to form a network in neuron cytoplasm.

5. *Nissl bodies* are also called chromidial or chromaphil substance because, like the chromatin of nuclei, Nissl bodies take basic stain. The electron microscope has revealed that Nissl bodies consist of groups of flat, membranous sacs and numerous RNA granules scattered between them. In other words, they constitute the rough-surfaced vesicles of a neuron's endoplasmic reticulum (p. 32), and they occupy the minute spaces between the neurofibril bundles. Cells with numerous rough-surfaced vesicles usually specialize in protein synthesis (for example, exocrine cells of the pancreas). Reasoning from this fact, Nissl bodies would be expected to perform the same function. But why would neurons, whose specialty is conduction, also specialize in protein synthesis? No one can answer this positively as yet. But one suggestion is that it is because they must continually synthesize cytoplasm to renew the cytoplasm in their processes. And there is good reason to believe that some such vital relation exists between neuron cell body and processes. After an axon is severed, for instance, the disconnected segment soon degenerates *(axon reaction)* and Nissl substance in the cell body decreases and eventually disappears *(chromatolysis)*.

6. *Myelin sheath* is a segmented wrapping around a nerve fiber. The small gaps between segments of the myelin sheath are called *nodes of Ranviers.* Presumably myelin functions as an insulator. Also, its thickness helps determine the velocity of impulse conduction. Large diameter fast conducting fibers typically have thicker myelin than smaller slower conducting fibers.

Recent research indicates that the molecular structure of myelin and of cell membranes are essentially the same. In fact, according to present day theory, myelin consists of a double layer of the cell membrane of cells known as *Schwann cells.* These are satellite cells of nerve fibers, and a succession of them occurs along peripheral fibers. The myelin sheath is formed by one Schwann cell winding in jelly roll fashion around each segment of the fiber (each section between two successive nodes of Ranviers, that is).*

7. *Neurilemma* (also spelled neurolemma) is a continuous sheath around the segmented myelin sheath. Like the latter, the neurilemma is also thought to derive from Schwann cells. It plays an essential part in peripheral nerve fiber regeneration. But unfortunately brain and spinal cord fibers do not have a neurilemma and are not known to regenerate. This means, of course, that if disease or injury causes them to degenerate, the destruction is permanent, a fact with serious clinical implications.

In addition to the special structures just described, neurons also have many parts not unique to them. For instance, they have *mitochondria* and of course a *cell membrane.* They also have a *Golgi apparatus;* incidentally, Golgi first saw this structure in neurons.

Neuron function

The function performed by neurons is nerve impulse conduction. According to widely accepted present-day theory, a nerve impulse is a self-propagating wave of negativity that travels along the surface of the neuron membrane. Some of the major tenets of this membrane theory (first proposed in 1902 by Bernstein and modified in recent years by Hodgkin and co-workers) are the following:

1. A *potential difference* (difference in electrical charge) exists across the membrane of a nonconducting or resting neuron. It is, therefore, said to be *polarized.* More specifically, the outer surface of the membrane of a resting neuron is about 50 to 100 millivolts electropositive to its inner surface (Fig. 107). The difference in concentration of ions in the intracellular fluid of neurons and in the extra-

---

*For more details see Robertson, J. David: The membrane of the living cell, Scient. Am. **206**:65, 1962.

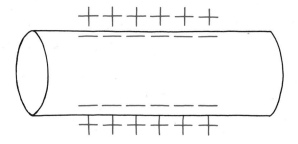

Fig. 107

Diagram to represent polarized state of membrane of nerve fiber when it is not conducting impulses.

Stimulus applied here

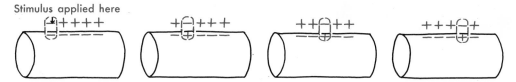

Fig. 108

Nerve impulse conduction, a self-propagating wave of depolarization along a nerve fiber membrane.

cellular fluid around them is known to produce this membrane potential difference or polarization. Details of the mechanism, however, are complex and are not yet completely worked out.

2. An adequate stimulus greatly increases the membrane's permeability to sodium ions at the point of stimulation.

3. Sodium ions rapidly diffuse through this permeable point into the nerve fiber, and potassium ions diffuse out of it.

4. Momentary *depolarization* (disappearance of the potential difference) occurs at the stimulated point but is followed immediately by the establishment of a reverse potential difference, that is, with the outer surface now perhaps 30 millivolts negative to the inner surface. In other words, at the stimulated point of the membrane an *action potential* (outer surface of membrane negative to inner) has replaced the *resting potential* (outer surface of membrane positive to inner). (Fig. 108.) Presumably inward diffusion of positive sodium ions largely accounts for development of the action potential. Because their rapid movement into the neuron leaves fewer positive charges on the outside and adds more positive charges to the inside, the outside becomes negative to the inside.

5. The stimulated point on the membrane, because it is negative, sets up a local current with the positive point adjacent to it, and the local current acts as a stimulus to this point. It therefore quickly depolarizes and becomes negative. In other words, the action potential moves to this next point on the membrane. And by repetition of the cycle, it travels the entire nerve fiber length. A wave of negativity propagates itself all along the surface of the fiber's membrane. In short, a nerve impulse is conducted.

193

6. Within thousandths of a second, the resting potential is re-established at each successive point on the membrane by reverse movement of sodium and potassium ions.

All-or-none principle. Until recently neurons have been thought to function like muscle cells on the *all-or-none principle*. Newer evidence, however, seems to indicate that only axons function on the all-or-none principle and that many dendrites and cell bodies function on the graded response principle. That is, they respond to stimuli of less than threshold strength by developing an excitatory potential and to threshold or stronger stimuli by developing an action potential and conducting an impulse. (An *excitatory potential* is merely a lowered resting potential, whereas an action potential is a reversed resting potential, see point 4 above.) Or, expressed differently, dendrites and cell bodies respond to weak stimuli, to those of less than threshold strength, by becoming "excited" or "facilitated" rather than by becoming actually stimulated to conduct. Axons, in contrast, make no response to stimuli of less than threshold strength. To stronger stimuli they respond with an action potential and impulse conduction. And the impulse travels just as fast and the action current is just as strong following stimuli of just threshold strength as following those that are stronger. In short, axons respond with maximum conduction for existing conditions or they respond not at all.

Refractory period. Neurons resemble muscle cells in that they, too, exhibit a refractory period. This means that for a brief moment, a matter of a millisecond or less, after a neuron has conducted an impulse, it is *absolutely refractory*, that is, cannot conduct again no matter how strongly stimulated. And for a slightly longer time it remains *relatively refractory* and can respond only to a stimulus of much greater than threshold strength.

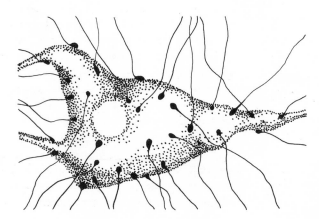

Fig. 109

End buttons on motor neuron cell body.

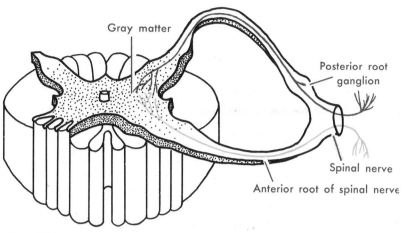

Gray matter

Posterior root ganglion

Spinal nerve

Anterior root of spinal nerve

Fig. 110

A two neuron reflex arc. **red,** Sensory neuron; **blue,** motor neuron. Nerve impulses conducted over such an arc produce the so-called stretch reflexes such as the knee jerk.

Impulse conduction at synapses and neuromuscular junction. A *synapse* is a place at which a nerve impulse is transmitted from one neuron to another. It is the contact area between the cell membrane around axon terminals of one neuron and the cell membrane of either dendrites or cell body of another neuron. The word synapse, coming as it does from the Greek verb meaning to clasp, describes the appearance of some synapses. In these, axon filaments of one neuron seem to contact dendrite filaments of another like the fingers of two clasped hands. In other synapses, one neuron's axon filaments contact another's cell body with little button-shaped endings known as *terminal buttons* (or *boutons terminaux,* or *end feet*), as shown in Fig. 109.

The widely accepted *neurohumeral theory* explains impulse transmission at synapses in this way. When an impulse reaches an axon terminal, the chemical *acetylcholine* is liberated from tiny neurovesicles in the end foot. Acetylcholine changes the permeability and therefore the potential difference of the synapsing cells' membranes and by so doing initiates impulse conduction in the next neuron. Conduction at synapses is unidirectional. It always occurs from the axon of one neuron to the dendrite or cell body of the next neuron and not in the reverse direction. Within milliseconds, an enzyme *cholinesterase* inactivates acetylcholine to stop synaptic conduction.

Neuromuscular junctions are contact places between a motor neuron's axon terminals and a muscle cell's membrane. Axons of motor neurons release acetylcholine at their junctions with skeletal muscle cells. This initiates impulse conduction along the muscle cell membrane, and contraction follows almost immediately.

195

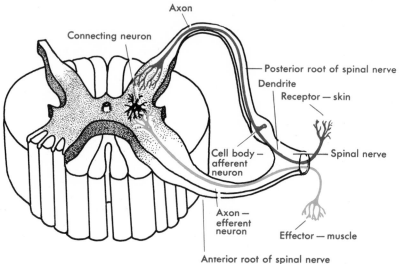

Fig. 111

Segmental ipsilateral reflex arc, consisting of an afferent, a connecting, and an efferent neuron. Nerve impulses traversing such arcs produce many spinal reflexes. Example: withdrawing the hand from a hot object.

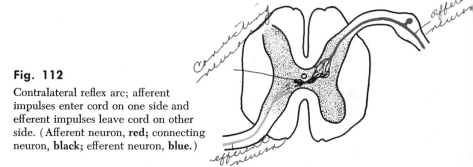

Fig. 112

Contralateral reflex arc; afferent impulses enter cord on one side and efferent impulses leave cord on other side. (Afferent neuron, **red**; connecting neuron, **black**; efferent neuron, **blue**.)

Course of impulse conduction. Impulse conduction if uninterrupted follows a set course known as a *reflex arc*. The simplest reflex arc consists of sensory neurons that synapse with motor neurons. More commonly, however, reflex arcs consist of sensory neurons that synapse with internuncial neurons that synapse with motor neurons (Figs. 110 to 113). Later on in this chapter we shall describe a few specific reflex arcs.

Rate of impulse conduction. The general principle is that the rate of impulse conduction varies directly with axon diameter—the larger the diameter, the faster the conduction. Largest diameter fibers are classed as A fibers, smallest diameter fibers as C fibers, and those of intermediate size as B fibers. Read Table 21, in which is summarized the func-

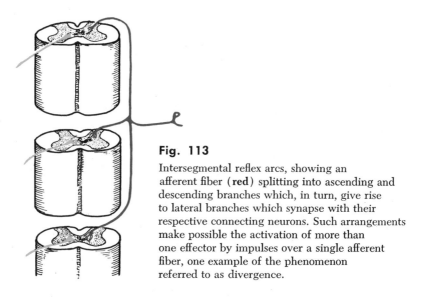

Fig. 113

Intersegmental reflex arcs, showing an afferent fiber (**red**) splitting into ascending and descending branches which, in turn, give rise to lateral branches which synapse with their respective connecting neurons. Such arrangements make possible the activation of more than one effector by impulses over a single afferent fiber, one example of the phenomenon referred to as divergence.

Table 21

	Functions of sensory fibers	Functions of motor fibers
A fibers Fastest conducting; about 100 meters per second or more than 3 miles per minute	Proprioception; touch; pressure; some heat; cold; some pain	Skeletal muscle contractions
B fibers	Some pain	Preganglionic autonomic
C fibers Slowest conducting; about ½ meter per second or 1 mile per hour	Some pain; perhaps some touch; pressure; heat; cold	Postganglionic autonomic

tions served by each class of fibers and then try to answer this question: What "survival value" do you see in the fastest conducting fibers serving the functions they do?

BRAIN AND CORD COVERINGS

Because the brain and spinal cord are both delicate and vital, nature has provided them with two protective coverings. The outer covering consists of bone: the cranial bones encase the brain and the vertebrae encase the cord. The inner covering consists of membranes, known as *meninges*, which, in turn, are composed of three distinct layers of

197

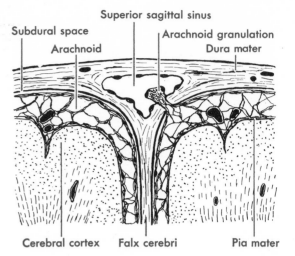

Fig. 114

Brain meninges and superior sagittal sinus in coronal section view. (After Weed; from Francis and Farrell: Integrated anatomy and physiology, St. Louis, The C. V. Mosby Co.)

tissues (Figs. 114 and 132). They are as follows: the *dura mater*, made of strong white fibrous tissue and serving both as the outer layer of the meninges and also as the inner periosteum of the cranial bones, the *arachnoid membrane*, a delicate, cobwebby layer between the dura mater and the innermost layer of the meninges, the *pia mater*, which is a transparent layer adherent to the outer surface of the brain and cord and contains blood vessels.

Three extensions of the dura mater should be mentioned: the falx cerebri, falx cerebelli, and tentorium cerebelli. The *falx cerebri* projects downward into the longitudinal fissure to form a kind of partition between the two cerebral hemispheres. The falx cerebelli separates the two cerebellar hemispheres. The *tentorium cerebelli* separates the cerebellum from the occipital lobe of the cerebrum. It takes its name from the fact that it forms a tentlike covering over the cerebellum.

Between the dura mater and the arachnoid membrane there is a small space called the *subdural space*, and between the arachnoid and the pia mater is another space, the *subarachnoid space*. Inflammation of the meninges is called *meningitis*. It most often involves the arachnoid and pia mater or the *leptomeninges*, as they are sometimes called.

BRAIN AND CORD FLUID SPACES

In addition to the bony and membranous coverings, nature has further fortified the brain and cord against injury by providing a cushion of fluid both around them and within them. The fluid is called *cerebrospinal fluid*, and the spaces containing it are (1) the subarachnoid space around the brain, (2) the subarachnoid space around the cord, (3) the ventricles and aqueduct inside the brain, and (4) the central or spinal canal inside the cord.

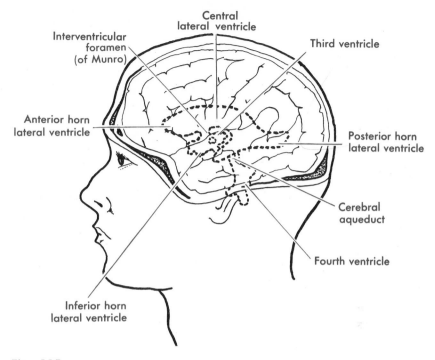

Fig. 115

The cerebral ventricles projected upon the lateral surface of the cerebrum.
(Modified from Callendar: Surgical anatomy, W. B. Saunders Co.)

The *ventricles* are cavities or spaces inside the brain. They are four in number. Two of them, the lateral (or first and second) ventricles, are located one in each cerebral hemisphere and are shaped roughly like the hemispheres themselves. The third ventricle is little more than a lengthwise slit in the cerebrum beneath the corpus callosum and longitudinal fissure at about its midpoint. The fourth ventricle is a diamond-shaped space between the cerebellum posteriorly and the medulla and pons anteriorly. Actually it is an expansion of the central canal of the cord after the cord enters the cranial cavity and becomes enlarged to form the medulla.

FORMATION AND CIRCULATION OF THE CEREBROSPINAL FLUID

Cerebrospinal fluid is a lymphlike fluid formed primarily by filtration of blood plasma from the networks of capillaries known as the choroid plexuses which are found in each of the ventricles. From each lateral ventricle the fluid seeps through an opening, the interventricular foramen (of Munro), into the third ventricle, thence through a narrow channel, the aqueduct of Sylvius (or cerebral aqueduct), into the fourth ventricle, from which it circulates into the central canal of

199

the cord. Openings in the roof of the fourth ventricle (the foramen of Magendie and foramina of Luschka) permit the flow of fluid into the subarachnoid space around the cord and thence into the subarachnoid space around the brain. From the latter space it is gradually absorbed* into the venous blood of the brain. Thus we note that the cerebrospinal fluid has made a complete circuit from its formation from the blood in the choroid plexuses, through the ventricles, central canal, and subarachnoid spaces, and back into the blood. Occasionally some condition interferes with this circuit; for example, a brain tumor may press against the cerebral aqueduct, shutting off the flow of fluid from the third to the fourth ventricle. In such an event the fluid accumulates within the lateral and third ventricles because it continues to form even though its drainage is blocked. This condition is known as *internal hydrocephalus.* If the fluid accumulates in the subarachnoid space around the brain, *external hydrocephalus* results. Subarachnoid hemorrhage, for example, may cause plugging of the arachnoid villi with clotted blood, which, in turn, causes decreased drainage of the cerebrospinal fluid from the subarachnoid space, and therefore an increased amount of it remains in the space.

Withdrawal of some of the cerebrospinal fluid from the subarachnoid space in the lumbar region of the cord is known as a *lumbar puncture.*

The amount of cerebrospinal fluid in the average man is about 135 milliliters.† Since approximately 550 milliliters† is secreted daily, the fluid must continually circulate and be reabsorbed.

ORGANS OF THE NERVOUS SYSTEM

Organs of the nervous system are few in number: the brain, spinal cord, nerves, and ganglia. (By definition, a *nerve* is "a whitish cord, made up of nerve fibers arranged in bundles, held together by a connective tissue sheath,"‡ and a *ganglion* is a cluster of neuron cell bodies.) For discussion purposes nervous system organs are classified in several ways, as follows:

1. *central nervous system* (CNS)—composed of the brain and

---

*Absorption occurs mainly through small tufts of the arachnoid which project like tiny fingers into the venous sinuses; these are called *arachnoid villi.*

†Hamilton, W. J. (editor): Textbook of human anatomy, New York, 1957, The Macmillan Co., p. 805.

‡From Stedman's medical dictionary, ed. 20, Philadelphia, 1961, Williams & Wilkins Co.

spinal cord and so named because of their central location in the body

2. *peripheral nervous system* (PNS)—composed of nerves and ganglia; so named because their locations are peripheral compared to the central locations of the brain and cord; twelve pairs of cranial nerves and many branches, thirty-one pairs of spinal nerves and many branches, and numerous autonomic nerves, and ganglia associated with all three kinds of nerves, constitute the PNS

3. *voluntary nervous system*—composed of the brain, cord, and cranial and spinal nerves (except for fibers to smooth muscle, cardiac muscle, and glands)

4. *involuntary or autonomic nervous system*—composed of ganglia and nerve fibers to smooth muscle, cardiac muscle, and glands

5. *sympathetic nervous system*—a division of the autonomic nervous system

6. *parasympathetic nervous system*—a division of the autonomic nervous system.

Brain

The brain is one of the largest of adult organs. In most adults it weighs about 3 pounds but generally is smaller in women than in men, in older persons than in younger persons, and, of course, in small persons than in large persons. It attains full size by about the eighteenth year but grows rapidly only during the first nine years or so. It consists of several parts. Those most prominent, named in the order of our discussion of them, are the cerebrum, diencephalon, midbrain, pons, medulla, and cerebellum. A more detailed classification of brain parts is the following (italicized words are ones you will probably see used most often):

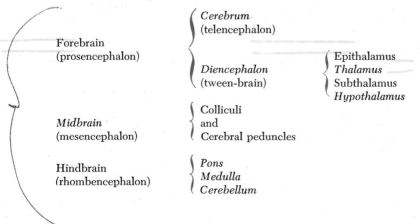

Forebrain (prosencephalon)
- *Cerebrum* (telencephalon)
- *Diencephalon* (tween-brain)
  - Epithalamus
  - *Thalamus*
  - Subthalamus
  - *Hypothalamus*

Midbrain (mesencephalon)
- Colliculi and Cerebral peduncles

Hindbrain (rhombencephalon)
- *Pons*
- *Medulla*
- *Cerebellum*

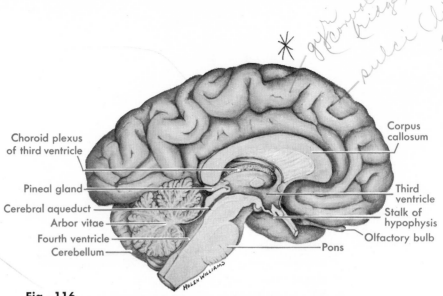

(handwritten notes in top margin: gyri convolutions (ridges), sulci (lines) groove)

Choroid plexus
of third ventricle

Corpus
callosum

Pineal gland

Cerebral aqueduct

Arbor vitae

Fourth ventricle

Cerebellum

Third
ventricle

Stalk of
hypophysis

Olfactory bulb

Pons

HELEN WILLIAMS

Fig. 116

Sagittal section through the midline of the brain showing the medial
surface of the left half of the brain (for more detailed structure,
see Fig. 117). (From Francis and Farrell: Integrated
anatomy and physiology, St. Louis, The C. V. Mosby Co.)

Cerebrum

Appearance

The cerebrum is the largest part of the human brain. A deep groove,
the *longitudinal fissure*, divides the cerebrum into two halves called
hemispheres, which are, however, not completely separated from each
other but are joined on their inferior surface by a structure composed
of white matter* and known as the *corpus callosum*. Gray matter, arranged in folds called *convolutions* or gyri, makes up the surface (*cortex*) of the cerebrum, whereas white matter composes its interior, except for a few islands of gray matter (nuclei). The entire cerebrum
has somewhat the appearance of many small sausages bound firmly
together, each convolution being comparable to a single sausage.
Between the convolutions are grooves called *sulci* when they are
shallow and *fissures* when they are deep. Prominent fissures, in addition to the longitudinal fissure already named, include the fissure of
Rolando (or central sulcus) and the fissure of Sylvius (or lateral fissure). The *fissure of Rolando* forms the boundary line between the
frontal and parietal lobes; the *fissure of Sylvius* separates the temporal
lobe below from the frontal and parietal lobes above.

Each cerebral hemisphere is subdivided into five *lobes*, each of
which, with one exception, bears the name of the bone lying over it:

*White matter is composed chiefly of myelinated nerve fibers. Gray matter, on
the other hand, consists mainly of neuron cell bodies and some nonmyelinated
fibers.

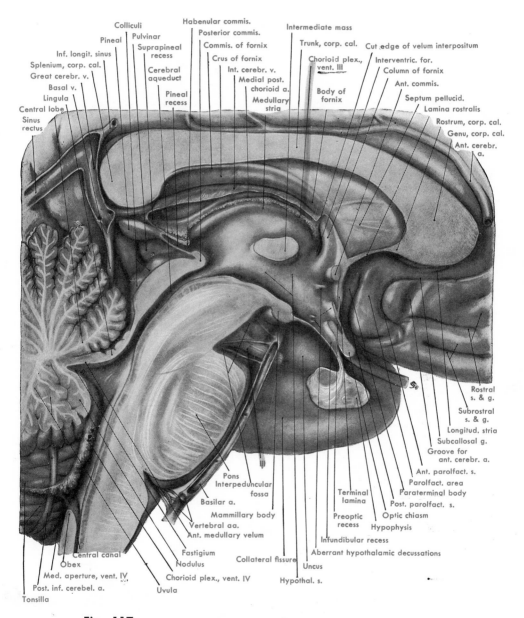

Colliculi
Pineal
Pulvinar
Suprapineal
recess
Inf. longit. sinus
Splenium, corp. cal.
Great cerebr. v.
Basal v.
Lingula
Central lobe
Sinus
rectus
Cerebral
aqueduct
Pineal
recess

Habenular commis.
Posterior commis.
Commis. of fornix
Crus of fornix
Int. cerebr. v.
Medial post.
chorioid a.
Medullary
stria

Intermediate mass
Trunk, corp. cal.
Cut edge of velum interpositum
Chorioid plex.,
vent. III
Interventric. for.
Column of fornix
Ant. commis.
Body of
fornix
Septum pellucid.
Lamina rostralis
Rostrum, corp. cal.
Genu, corp. cal.
Ant. cerebr.
a.

Rostral
s. & g.
Subrostral
s. & g.
Longitud. stria
Subcallosal g.
Groove for
ant. cerebr. a.
Ant. parolfact. s.
Parolfact. area
Paraterminal body
Post. parolfact. s.
Optic chiasm
Hypophysis

Pons
Interpeduncular
fossa
Basilar a.
Mammillary body
Vertebral aa.
Ant. medullary velum

Terminal
lamina
Preoptic
recess

Infundibular recess
Aberrant hypothalamic decussations

Central canal
Obex
Med. aperture, vent. IV
Post. inf. cerebel. a.
Tonsilla

Fastigium
Nodulus
Chorioid plex., vent. IV
Uvula

Collateral fissure
Uncus
Hypothal. s.

Fig. 117

Sagittal section of the brain to show structures around third ventricle.
(From Mettler: Neuroanatomy, St. Louis, The C. V. Mosby Co.)

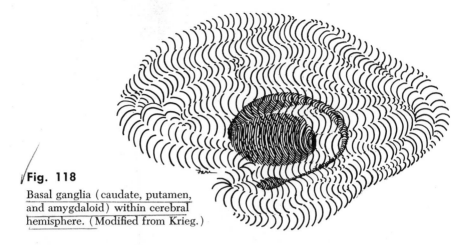

Fig. 118

Basal ganglia (caudate, putamen, and amygdaloid) within cerebral hemisphere. (Modified from Krieg.)

frontal lobe, parietal lobe, temporal lobe, occipital lobe, and island of Reil (or insula). The latter is located in the fissure of Sylvius.

Internal structure

Whereas the outer surface or cortex of the cerebrum is composed entirely of gray matter, the interior is made up of both gray and white matter. The gray matter is present in four well-defined masses embedded deep within the white matter and known collectively as the *cerebral nuclei* or *basal ganglia*. The white matter is composed of nerve fibers bound together into bundles known as *tracts*.

Cerebral nuclei. The term nucleus (when applied to the nervous system) means "a mass of gray matter, composed of nerve cells, in any part of the brain or spinal cord." *Ganglion* also means a cluster of nerve cells but usually refers to those located outside of the brain and cord. Cerebral nuclei or the *basal ganglia* constitute a large, prominent part of the interior of each cerebral hemisphere. Although all authorities do not name the same structures as parts of the basal ganglia, the following are usually included:

1. Caudate
2. Putamen
3. Globus pallidus (or, simply, the pallidum)
4. Amygdaloid
5. Claustrum

Narrow gray bands extend across the white internal capsule between the caudate and putamen. Because this gives a striped appearance to the region, it is called the *corpus striatum.* Putamen and pallidum, on the other hand, form a lens-shaped mass so that together they are known as the *lentiform nucleus.*

Knowledge of basal ganglia functions is still sketchy. It is known, for example, that they play an essential role in the production of useful voluntary movements, but just how they do this is not known. That

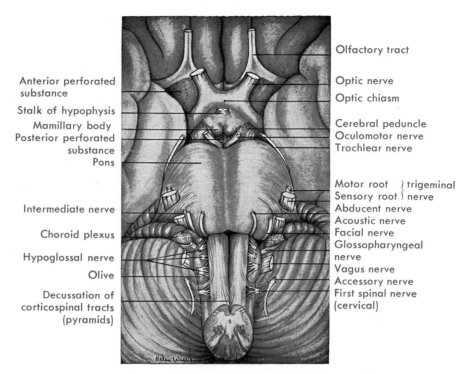

Anterior perforated substance
Stalk of hypophysis
Mamillary body
Posterior perforated substance
Pons

Intermediate nerve

Choroid plexus

Hypoglossal nerve
Olive

Decussation of corticospinal tracts (pyramids)

Olfactory tract
Optic nerve
Optic chiasm
Cerebral peduncle
Oculomotor nerve
Trochlear nerve
Motor root   } trigeminal
Sensory root } nerve
Abducent nerve
Acoustic nerve
Facial nerve
Glossopharyngeal nerve
Vagus nerve
Accessory nerve
First spinal nerve (cervical)

Fig. 119

Inferior or ventral surface of the brain stem showing attachment of the cranial nerves. (From Francis and Farrell: Integrated anatomy and physiology, St. Louis, The C. V. Mosby Co.)

disease may attack the basal ganglia is also known. Parkinsonism is one such disease—destructive lesions in the pallidum are associated with this disorder. Skeletal muscle rigidity, stiff movements, tremors, and a general poverty of movement afflict the victims of this fairly common disease. Particularly striking often is the masklike expression, resulting from loss of the movements that produce facial expression.

Tracts and nerves are comparable structures. Both consist of bundles of nerve fibers: *tracts* are bundles of axons located in the brain and cord; *nerves* are bundles of dendrites or axons or both located outside the brain and cord. In other words, tracts compose part of the central nervous system, whereas nerves and ganglia compose all of the peripheral nervous system.

Tract names indicate the location of dendrites and cell bodies of neurons whose axons compose the tract and the structure in which the axons terminate. Thus, the name corticospinal tract denotes that its fibers originate from neurons whose dendrites and cells lie in the cortex and whose axons extend through the tract to terminate in the spinal cord. In short, tract names tell us from where to where tract fibers conduct impulses.

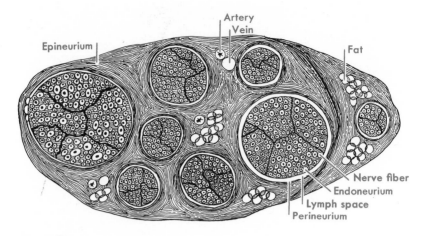

Fig. 120

Cross section of a nerve trunk. (After Harris; from Zoethout and Tuttle: Textbook of physiology, St. Louis, The C. V. Mosby Co.)

When this principle is applied, where do fibers of the spinothalamic tract begin and end? Tracts that conduct impulses upward are called sensory or *ascending projection tracts,* and those that conduct downward are referred to as motor or *descending projection tracts.* In one part of the interior of the cerebrum a group of sensory and motor projection tracts forms a large irregular mass of white matter known as the *internal capsule.* It lies between the thalamus on one side and the caudate and lentiform nuclei on the other (Figs. 118 and 135). Some tracts are short, extending from one convolution to another in the same hemisphere; these are called *association tracts.*

Functions

Knowledge of cerebral function has accumulated in various ways: by studying symptoms of patients known to have brain lesions, by studying the effects of removing or destroying various cerebral areas in animals, by studying the behavior of infants born with little or no cerebral cortex, by stimulating various cerebral areas in animals and human beings and recording objective and, in the case of human beings, subjective results, and more recently by studying brain action potentials.

Numerous microscopic studies of the cerebral cortex have revealed structural differences in different regions—for example, differences in types of neurons and arrangements of neurons into layers. Classified according to shape, there are at least three main structural types of neurons in the cortex—pyramidal, fusiform or triangular, and granule or stellate. According to Brodmann and others, these are arranged in six layers in almost all parts of the cortex, with variations in thickness

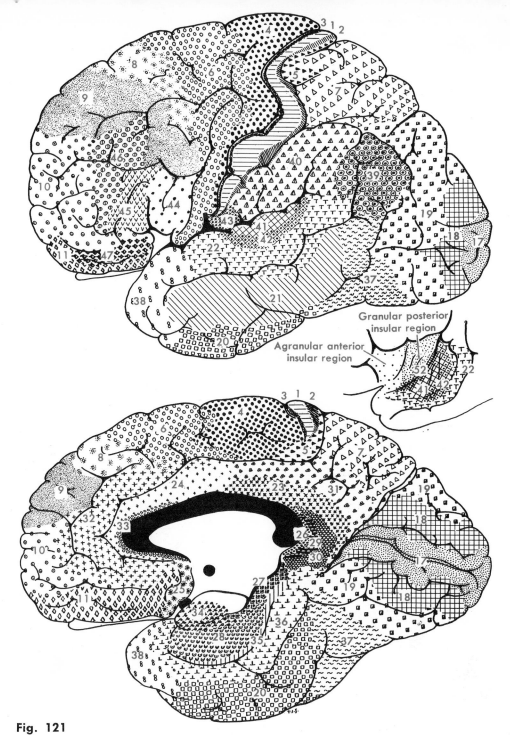

Fig. 121

Map of the human cortex according to Brodmann. Each numbered area shows different cellular structure. Some areas whose functions are best understood are these: Area 3,1,2, General somatic sensory; area 17, primary visual area; areas 18 and 19, secondary visual areas; areas 41 and 42, primary auditory areas; area 22, secondary auditory area; area 4, primary motor area; area 6, secondary motor area. (From Mettler; Neuroanatomy, St. Louis, The C. V. Mosby Co.)

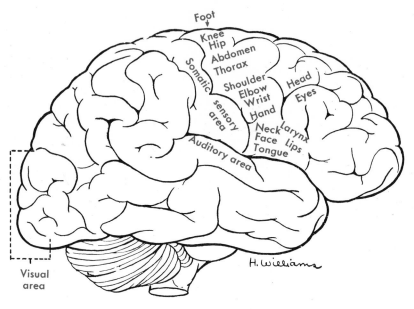

Fig. 122

Areas of cerebral localization. Neurons composing the cortex of the
cerebral convolutions marked on the diagram are known to perform definite
functions. Thus the precentral convolution controls movements of skeletal muscles,
while the postcentral convolution is responsible for general sensations such as heat,
cold, and pressure. Definite functions cannot, as yet, be assigned to the
major portion of the cerebral cortex, as suggested by the numerous unmarked
convolutions. (From Francis and Farrell: Integrated anatomy
and physiology, St. Louis, The C. V. Mosby Co.)

and cell types in different regions. On the basis of such differences,
various investigators have made cytoarchitectural maps of the cortex.
Brodmann made one in 1909 which is still widely used. His map lo-
cates 47 numbered cortical areas, each one structurally different from
the other (see Fig. 121.) Since structural differences suggest functional differences, the concept of localized cerebral functions developed. Today the concensus seems to be that definite functions can be
ascribed to comparatively few areas—control of voluntary movements
to the precentral (pre-Rolandic) area, for example—but that many
cerebral functions depend upon widespread cortical activity. And even
those areas assigned definite functions do not function independently
of other parts of the cortex.

What functions does the cerebral cortex perform? "All conscious
functions" would be the briefest and most general answer. The cortex
functions whenever we will to do anything or are conscious of anything. It is responsible for our experiencing many of the characteristics
of sensations, for our ability to produce normal voluntary movements,
and for our ability to carry on many different kinds of mental processes.

Sensations. Complex nervous mechanisms function to produce our sensations. Many structures are involved—nerves, ganglia, cord, medulla, pons, midbrain, thalamus, and cerebral cortex. Complex discriminative sensations depend upon the cerebral cortex, especially the *somesthetic area* or general sensory area (Fig. 121, areas 3, 1, and 2 in the post-central or post-Rolandic convolution). This area does more than just register separate and simple sensations. It integrates them into meaningful concepts. It makes comparisons and judgments. Suppose you were blindfolded and someone placed a cold object in your hand. Your sensations of this would be more than the simple ones of cold and touch and location. These and others would fuse so you would sense a total impression compounded of many sensations such as temperature, shape, size, weight, texture, and movement and position of body parts. You might sense, for instance, that a cold, round, fairly large, heavy, rough stone lay in your hand and that your hand and arm had moved down a bit when it was placed there, and that your muscles had tightened to hold it.

In addition to the somesthetic area, visual and auditory areas of the cerebral cortex have been identified and less definitely olfactory and gustatory (smell and taste) areas. Brodmann's area 17 in the occipital lobe constitutes the *primary visual area.* Areas 18 and 19 are secondary visual areas, sometimes called *visual psychic areas* because they are thought to interpret visual sensations.

The *primary auditory areas* lie in the temporal lobes, in the transverse convolution along each fissure of Sylvius—Brodmann's areas 41 and 42. An *auditory psychic area* in each lobe (area 22) is thought to interpret auditory sensations.

Less certainty exists about exact locations of the *olfactory and gustatory areas.* Parts of convolutions located on the ventral or undersurface of the temporal lobe are considered the primary olfactory areas by some investigators, and nearby areas in the temporal and parietal lobes and insula are suggested as primary taste areas. A small region at the lowermost part of the postcentral convolution is frequently mentioned as one taste area.

Voluntary movements. Mechanisms that control voluntary movements are extremely complex and are imperfectly understood. Many parts of the nervous system are involved, and certain areas of the cerebral cortex play an essential part in the production of normal movements. The precentral or pre-Rolandic gyrus (Brodmann's area 4) constitutes the *primary motor area.* Area 6 immediately anterior to it is a supplementary motor area and many other regions, including even the sensory somesthetic area, also contain motor neurons. A distinction is usually made between the functions of area 4 and area 6. Area 4 is said to exert control over individual muscles, especially those that produce movements of distal joints (wrist, hand, finger, ankle, foot, and toe movements). Area 6, on the other hand, controls groups of muscles simultaneously.

Mental functions. Included in this category are many diverse functions—such things as memory, foresight, emotional feelings, personality traits, speech functions, and intelligence. These and other mental and psychic functions depend more on widespread cortical activity than on localized regions. Memory, for example, once considered a function of the temporal lobes, now is viewed as a complex neural process compounded of many parts. Visual memories, stored (in some as yet unknown manner) in the occipital lobe, auditory memories in the temporal lobe, and general sensory experiences in the parietal lobe are all linked together and synthesized into complex memories by numerous association tracts between lobes. Foresight and personality traits depend largely on the prefrontal lobes. Evidence of this lies in the changes observed in patients who have undergone a prefrontal lobectomy. Most noticeable are their loss of initiative and planning ability and their lack of restraint. A housewife might, for example, become almost unable to plan a simple meal. If she were typical, she would become boastful and aggressive—personality changes indicative of a decreased ability to restrain behavior.

Speech functions consist of the use of language (speaking and writing) and the understanding of language (spoken and written). Today these faculties are believed to depend on highly integrated cortical processes, with certain areas in the frontal, parietal, and temporal lobes called speech centers serving as the focal points for integration. Lesions in different ones of these areas are associated with different types of speech defects, or *aphasias.* For example, with a lesion in *Broca's area* in the frontal lobe (Brodmann often called this area 44), the individual becomes unable to express his ideas in spoken words although he is not actually unable to speak. This condition is known as *motor aphasia.* With a lesion in the parietal lobe speech center (roughly, Brodmann's area 39) on the other hand, the individual has trouble finding the right names for things.

Diencephalon (tween-brain) — thalamus, epithalamus, subthalamus, and hypothalamus

The diencephalon is the part of the brain located between the cerebrum and the midbrain. It consists of structures around the third ventricle: the thalamus, epithalamus, subthalamus, and hypothalamus. We shall confine our discussion to the thalamus and hypothalamus.

Thalamus

Structure and location

The right thalamus is a rounded mass of gray matter about ½ inch wide and 1½ inches long, bulging into the right lateral wall of the third ventricle; the left thalamus is a similar mass in the left lateral wall. Each thalamus consists of numerous nuclei. Many of these constitute relay stations for sensory impulses on their way from the periphery to the somatic sensory area of the cerebral cortex. Others relay impulses to and from subcortical centers, notably basal ganglia in the cerebrum and dentate nuclei in the cerebellum. Still another group of thalamic nuclei relays impulses both ways between the hypothalamus and cerebral cortex.

Functions

By means of the foregoing connections, the thalamus performs the following functions:
1. It plays two parts in the mechanism responsible for sensations:
    (a) It produces conscious recognition of the cruder, less critical sensations of pain, temperature, and touch.
    (b) It relays all kinds of sensory impulses, except possibly olfactory, to the cerebrum.
2. It plays a part in the mechanism responsible for emotions by associating sensory impulses with feelings of pleasantness and unpleasantness.
3. It plays a part in the arousal or alerting mechanism.
4. It plays a part in mechanisms that produce complex reflex movements.

Hypothalamus

Structure and location

The floor and lower part of the lateral wall of the third ventricle constitute the hypothalamus. It includes an anterior portion consisting of gray matter around the optic chiasma, a medial portion consisting of the stalk of the pituitary gland and the posterior lobe of the gland, and a posterior portion consisting of the mammillary bodies and adjacent region (Fig. 117, p. 203).

Several nuclei compose the hypothalamus. Three of these of greatest functional interest are the *supraoptic nuclei* in the anterior part of the hypothalamus, above each optic tract and above and lateral to the optic chiasma, the *paraventricular nuclei*, so called because of their location close to the wall of the third ventricle in the medial part of the hypothalamus, and the *mammillary nuclei* in the mammillary bodies in the posterior part of the hypothalamus.

211

Tracts connect the hypothalamus with various parts of the central nervous system. Some are afferent, that is, conduct impulses into the hypothalamus; others are efferent, conduct impulses away from it. Some have actually been traced and therefore are known to exist; others are inferred from laboratory and clinical findings. Known afferent tracts are those that bring impulses from certain cerebral cortical regions, from the thalamus, and from the basal ganglia (pallidum and amygdaloid) to the hypothalamus. Both direct and indirect tracts connect the cortex and hypothalamus—in other words, corticohypothalamic and corticothalamohypothalamic tracts. Both are noteworthy because they provide part of the facilities by which mental processes including emotions might influence the hypothalamus.

Known efferent tracts from the hypothalamus include fibers to the thalamus, brainstem, spinal cord, and posterior pituitary gland (neurohypophysis). Fibers to the brainstem synapse with parasympathetic autonomic neurons located in nuclei of the midbrain, pons, and medulla. Those to the cord synapse with sympathetic autonomic neurons located in nuclei in the thoracic and lumbar segments of the cord. Autonomic fibers, in turn, extend out to visceral effectors (heart muscle, glands, and smooth muscle of blood vessels, digestive tract, and many other structures).

Functions

The hypothalamus is a small but functionally mighty area of the brain. It weighs little more than a quarter of an ounce yet by means of its many connections performs the following important functions.

1. The hypothalamus, via its efferent tracts to autonomic centers in brainstem and cord, integrates or coordinates autonomic functions.

2. The hypothalamus functions in the bodily expression of emotions. Because tracts connect it with both the cerebral cortex and lower autonomic centers, it is the anatomical link by which impulses from the cortex can influence internal organs such as the heart, blood vessels, and glands—the anatomical link by which emotions express themselves in changed bodily function by which the "mind influences the body" (for example, psychosomatic disease).

3. The hypothalamus helps maintain water balance by helping control both output and intake.

4. The hypothalamus helps control various reproductive functions.

5. The hypothalamus plays some part in maintaining the waking state. Presumably it functions as part of an arousal or alerting mechanism. Clinical evidence of this: somnolence characterizes some hypothalamic disorders.

6. The hypothalamus helps regulate appetite and therefore the amount of food intake. Experimental and clinical findings seem to indicate the presence of a "feeding center" in the lateral part of the hypothalamus and a "satiety center" located medially. For example, an animal with an experimental lesion in a certain area of the hypothalamus will consume tremendous amounts of food. Similarly, a human being with a tumor in the region of the hypothalamus may eat insatiably and gain an enormous amount of weight.

7. The hypothalamus helps maintain normal body temperature. Hypothalamic neurons whose fibers connect with autonomic centers for vasoconstriction and dilatation, sweating, and with somatic centers for shivering constitute heat-regulating centers. Marked elevation of body temperature frequently characterizes injuries or other abnormalities of the hypothalamus.

Cerebellum

Structure and location

The cerebellum, the second largest part of the brain, is located just below the posterior portion of the cerebrum and is partially covered by it. A transverse fissure separates the cerebellum from the cerebrum. These two parts of the brain have several characteristics in common. The exterior of the cerebellum is composed of gray matter and its interior of white matter although there is proportionately less white matter in the cerebellum, where it follows a pattern similar to the veins of a leaf, described as the *arbor vitae*. Like the cerebrum, the cerebellar surface is grooved with numerous sulci, but its convolutions are much more slender and less prominent than those of the cerebrum. The cerebellum has two large lateral masses, the cerebellar hemispheres, and a central section called the vermis because in shape it resembles a worm coiled upon itself. (For a detailed description of the several subdivisions of the cerebellum, consult a textbook on neuroanatomy.)

The internal white matter of the cerebellum is composed of some short and some long tracts. The short association tracts connect the cerebellar cortex with nuclei located in the interior of the cerebellum. The longer projection tracts connect the cerebellum with other parts of the brain and with the spinal cord. These enter or leave the cerebellum by way of its three pairs of peduncles as follows:

1. *inferior cerebellar peduncles* (or *restiform bodies*)—composed chiefly of tracts into the cerebellum from the medulla and cord; (notably, spinocerebellar, vestibulocerebellar, and reticulocerebellar tracts).

2. *middle cerebellar peduncles* (or *brachia pontis*)—composed almost entirely of tracts into the cerebellum from the pons (that is, pontocerebellar tracts).

3. *superior cerebellar peduncles* (or *brachia conjunctivum cerebelli*)—composed principally of tracts from dentate nuclei through the red nucleus of the midbrain to the thalamus.

An important pair of cerebellar nuclei are the *dentate nuclei,* one of which lies in each hemisphere. Tracts connect these nuclei with motor areas of the cerebral cortex (the dentatorubrothalamic tracts to the thalamus and thalamocortical tracts to the cortex). By means of these tracts cerebellar impulses influence the motor cortex. Impulses also travel the reverse direction. Corticopontine and pontocerebellar tracts enable the motor cortex to influence the cerebellum.

Functions

The cerebellum performs three general functions, all of which have to do with the control of skeletal muscles. It acts with the cerebral cortex to produce skilled movements by coordinating the activities of groups of muscles. It controls skeletal muscles so as to maintain equilibrium. It helps control posture. It functions below the level of consciousness to make movements smooth instead of jerky, steady instead of trembling, and efficient and coordinated instead of ineffective, awkward, and uncoordinated (asynergic).

During the years there have been many theories about cerebellar functions. One theory, based on comparative anatomy studies and substantiated by experimental methods, regards the cerebellum as three organs, each with a somewhat different function:

Synergic control of muscle action. This function, which is ascribed to the neocerebellum (superior vermis and hemispheres), is closely associated with cerebral motor activity. Normal muscle action, it is known, involves groups of muscles, the various members of which function together as a unit. In any given action, for example, the prime mover contracts, the antagonist relaxes but contracts weakly at the proper moment to act as a brake, checking the action of the prime mover, the synergists contract to assist the prime mover, and the fixation muscles of the neighboring joint contract. Through such harmonious coordinated group action normal movements are smooth, steady, and precise as to force, rate, and extent. Achievement of such movements results from cerebellar activity added to cerebral activity. Impulses from the cerebrum start the action, but those from the cerebellum synergize or coordinate the contractions and relaxations of the various muscles once they have begun. Some physiologists consider this the main, if not the sole, function of the cerebellum.

Postural reflexes. One part of the cerebellum is thought to be concerned with both exciting and inhibiting postural reflexes.

Equilibrium. Part of the cerebellum presumably discharges impulses important to the maintenance of equilibrium. Afferent impulses from the labyrinth of the ear reach the cerebellum. Here connections are made with the proper efferent fibers for contraction of the necessary muscles for equilibrium.

Cerebellar disease (abscess, hemorrhage, tumors, trauma, etc.) produces certain characteristic symptoms, among which asynergia, hypotonia, tremors, and disturbances of gait and equilibrium predominate. As examples of asynergia may be mentioned overshooting a mark or stopping before reaching it when asked to touch a given point on the body (finger-to-nose test) and drawling, scanning, or singsong speech because of asynergic action of phonation and articulation muscles. Tremors are particularly pronounced toward the end of movements and with the exertion of effort. Disturbances of gait and equilibrium vary, depending upon the muscle groups involved, but the walk is often characterized by staggering or lurching and by a clumsy manner of raising the foot too high and bringing it down with a clap. Paralysis does not result from loss of cerebellar functioning.

Medulla oblongata
Structure and location

The medulla or bulb is the part of the brain which attaches to the spinal cord; it is, in fact, an enlarged extension of the cord located just above the foramen magnum. It measures only slightly more than an inch in length and is separated from the pons above by a horizontal groove. It is composed mainly of white matter (projection tracts) and *reticular formation,* a term that means the interlacement of gray and white matter present in the cord, brainstem, and diencephalon. Nuclei in the reticular formation of the medulla include such important centers as respiratory and vasomotor centers.

On each side of the lower posterior part of the medulla are two prominent nuclei, the *nucleus gracilis* and the *nucleus cuneatus.* Here, afferent fibers from the posterior white columns (fasciculi gracilis and cuneatus) of the cord synapse with neurons whose axons extend to the thalamus and cerebellum.

The pyramids (Fig. 119) are two bulges of white matter located on the anterior surface of the medulla formed by fibers of the pyramidal projection tracts.

The olive (Fig. 119) is an oval projection appearing one on each side of the anterior surface of the medulla. It contains the *inferior*

215

olivary nucleus and two accessory olivary nuclei. Fibers from the cells of these nuclei run through the inferior cerebellar peduncles (restiform bodies) into the cerebellum. Nuclei of the ninth to twelfth cranial nerves are also located in the medulla.

Functions

Nuclei in the medulla contain a number of reflex centers, some of which are necessary to life and are, therefore, called the *vital centers.* They are the cardiac, vasomotor, and respiratory centers, and they function as parts of neural mechanisms for controlling heart action, blood vessel diameter, and respirations. Because the medulla contains these centers, it is the most vital part of the entire brain—so vital, in fact, that injury or disease of the medulla often proves fatal. Blows at the base of the skull and bulbar poliomyelitis, for example, cause death if they interrupt impulse conduction by the vital respiratory centers.

The medulla functions in mechanisms that control many nonvital reflexes. It contains centers, for example, for vomiting, coughing, sneezing, hiccoughing, and swallowing.

All projection tracts between the cord and brain necessarily pass through the medulla; hence it functions in a great many sensory and motor mechanisms. Fibers of the crossed corticospinal tracts decussate, that is, cross from one side to the other in the pyramids of the medulla—an anatomical fact that explains why one side of the brain is said to control the other side of the body.

Pons varolii

Structure and location

Just above the medulla lies the pons, composed like the medulla of white matter and a few nuclei. Fibers which run transversely across the pons and through the brachia pontis (middle cerebellar peduncles) into the cerebellum make up the external white matter of the pons and give it its bridgelike appearance. The reticular formation extends into the pons from the medulla. One important reticular nucleus in the pons is called the *pneumotaxic center;* it functions in the control of respirations. Nuclei of the fifth to eighth cranial nerves are located in the upper part of the pons.

Midbrain

The midbrain lies below the inferior surface of the cerebrum and above the pons. It consists mainly of white matter with some internal gray matter around the cerebral aqueduct, the cavity within the midbrain. The *cerebral peduncles* form the ventral part of the midbrain, and the corpora *quadrigemina* or *colliculi* form the dorsal part. The cerebral peduncles are two ropelike masses of white matter which extend divergently from the pons to the undersurface of the cerebral hemispheres (Fig. 119). In other words, the cerebral peduncles are made up of tracts which constitute the main connection between the forebrain and hindbrain. Hence the midbrain, by function as well as by location, is well named.

The *corpora quadrigemina* consist of four rounded eminences, the two superior and the two inferior colliculi (Fig. 117) which form the dorsal part of the midbrain. Certain auditory reflex centers lie in the inferior colliculi and visual centers in the superior colliculi.

An important nucleus in the midbrain reticular formation is the *red nucleus,* a large gray mass ventral to the superior colliculi. Fibers from the cerebellum and from the frontal lobe of the cerebral cortex end here, and fibers which extend into the rubrospinal tracts of the cord have their cells of origin here. Nuclei of the third and fourth cranial nerves and the anterior part of the nucleus of the fifth cranial nerve are located deep in the midbrain. Also, as mentioned in the preceding paragraph, nuclei for certain auditory and visual reflexes lie in the colliculi of the midbrain.

Functions of the pons and midbrain

The upper part of the brainstem serves as conduction pathways (projection tracts) between the cord and other parts of the brain. The pupillary center, which controls the size of the pupil, is an important center located in the midbrain.

Spinal cord
Location

The spinal cord lies within the spinal cavity, extending from the foramen magnum to the lower border of the first lumbar vertebra, a distance of 17 or 18 inches in the average body. The meninges of the cord, however, continue on down for some distance. The pia mater forms a slender filament known as the *filum terminale,* which blends with the dura mater at the level of the third segment of the sacrum, forming a fibrous cord which disappears in the periosteum of the coccyx. This extension of the meninges beyond the cord is an anatomical feature of great convenience in performing lumbar punctures. By in serting the needle between the third and fourth or fourth and fifth lumbar vertebrae into the subarachnoid space, cerebrospinal fluid can

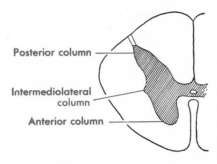

Fig. 123

Distribution of gray and white matter as seen in a cross-section view of the thoracic section of the spinal cord (diagrammatic).

Posterior column

Intermediolateral column

Anterior column

be withdrawn without danger of injuring the spinal cord which ends more than an inch above that point. The fourth lumbar vertebra is easily located because it lies on a line with the iliac crest. Placing the patient on his side and arching his back by drawing the knees and chest together separates the vertebra sufficiently to introduce the needle. The cord does not completely fill the spinal cavity which also contains the meninges, spinal fluid, a cushion of adipose tissue, and blood vessels.

Structure

The cord is an oval-shaped cylinder which tapers slightly from above downward and has two bulges, one in the cervical region and the other in the lumbar region. Gray matter, shaped roughly like a three-dimensional letter H, composes the inner core of the cord and white matter composes the outer portion. Different portions of the gray matter are identified as the anterior gray column and as the posterior and lateral gray columns or as the anterior, posterior, and lateral horns of gray matter. Six lengthwise grooves divide the white matter into long columns. The deepest of these grooves, the *anterior median fissure*, together with the somewhat shallower *posterior median sulcus*, just misses dividing the cord into separate symmetrical halves. The anterolateral sulcus and posterolateral sulcus subdivide each half of the cord into three *columns* (or funiculi): the anterior, posterior, and lateral white columns. These columns consist of large bundles of nerve fibers arranged in tracts.

Important tracts of each white column are given in Tables 22 and 23; also see Fig. 124.

Functions

Two words suggest the two big functions of the spinal cord: conduction and connection. Spinal cord tracts serve as two-way conduction paths between peripheral nerves and the brain. Spinal cord nuclei serve as connecting centers between sensory and motor neurons; in short, they serve as reflex centers.

Two-way conduction. Both ascending and descending tracts compose the white matter of the cord. Tracts, as we have already noted,

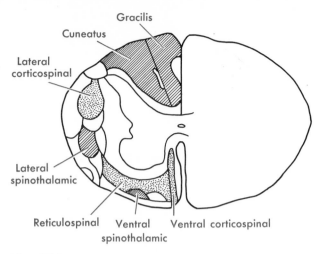

Fig. 124

Location in spinal cord of some major projection tracts. Striped areas, *sensory:* Gracilis and cuneatus (muscle sense and discriminating touch); lateral spinothalamic (pain and temperature); ventral spinothalamic (crude touch). Dotted areas, *motor:* Lateral corticospinal (voluntary movements); reticulospinal (some inhibitory and some facilitatory impulses to anterior horn neurons); ventral corticospinal (voluntary movements).

are structural organizations—that is, they are made up of groups of axons, all of which originate in the same structure and terminate in the same structure. Fibers of the spinothalamic tract, for example, all originate in the spinal cord (they are axons of neurons whose cell bodies lie in gray matter of the cord) and all terminate in the thalamus. But tracts are also functional organizations, which means that they are groups of fibers that serve one general function. For instance, fibers of the lateral spinothalamic tract serve a sensory function. Some of them transmit pain impulses (impulses initiated by stimulation of pain receptors) and some temperature impulses (impulses initiated by stimulation of temperature receptors). Because so many different tracts make up the white columns of the cord, we shall mention only a few that seem most important in man. Locate each tract in Fig. 124. Table 22 and Table 23 give more information about tracts. Four important ascending or sensory tracts and their functions, stated very briefly are as follows:

1. *lateral spinothalamic tracts*—pain and temperature.
2. *ventral spinothalamic tracts*—crude touch.
3. *fasciculi gracilis and cuneatus*—discriminating touch and conscious kinesthesia.
4. *spinocerebellar tracts*—unconscious kinesthesia.

Four important descending or motor tracts and their functions in brief are as follows:

1. *lateral corticospinal tracts*—voluntary movement; contraction of individual or small groups of muscles, particularly those moving hands, fingers, feet, and toes on opposite side of body.

219

Table 22. Major ascending tracts of spinal cord

Name	Function	Location	Origin*	Termination†
Lateral spino-thalamic	Pain, temperature opposite side	Lateral white columns	Posterior gray column opposite side	Thalamus
Ventral spino-thalamic	Crude touch	Anterior white columns	Same	Same
Fasciculus gracilis and cuneatus	Conscious kinesthesia; sensations of deep touch and pressure; two-point discrimination; vibration	Posterior white columns	Spinal ganglia same side	Medulla
Spinocerebellar	Unconscious kinesthesia	Lateral white columns	Posterior gray column	Cerebellum

*Location of cell bodies of neurons from which axons of tract arise.
†Structure in which axons of tract terminate.

Table 23. Major descending tracts of spinal cord

Name	Function	Location	Origin*	Termination†
Lateral cortico-spinal (or crossed pyramidal)	Voluntary movement; contraction of individual or small groups of muscles, particularly those moving hands, fingers, feet, and toes of opposite side	Lateral white columns	Motor areas cerebral cortex (mainly areas 4 and 6) opposite side from tract location in cord	Intermediate or anterior gray column
Ventral cortico-spinal (direct pyramidal)	Same as lateral corticospinal	Same as lateral corticospinal	Motor cortex but on same side as tract location in cord	Same as lateral corticospinal
Lateral reticulo-spinal	Mainly facilitory influence on motor neurons to skeletal muscles	Lateral white columns	Reticular formation midbrain, pons, and medulla	Intermediate or anterior gray columns
Medial reticulo-spinal	Mainly inhibitory influence on motor neurons to skeletal muscles	Anterior white columns	Reticular formation medulla mainly	Intermediate or anterior gray columns

*Location of cell bodies of neurons from which axons of tract arise.
†Structure in which axons of tract terminate.

2. *ventral corticospinal tracts*—same as preceding except mainly muscles of same side of body.

3. *lateral reticulospinal tracts*—mainly facilitory impulses to anterior horn motor neurons to skeletal muscles.

4. *medial reticulospinal tracts*—mainly inhibitory impulses to anterior horn motor neurons to skeletal muscles.

Spinal cord injuries may be extremely disabling, depending upon which tracts and centers and how many are damaged. Only a single pair of tracts, for example, may be involved, with consequent limited impairment of function, or several tracts and centers may be injured, with extensive or even fatal loss of function. The disease *tabes dorsalis* or *locomotor ataxia,* which may result from syphilis of the central nervous system, illustrates the way damage of one pair of tracts may alter function. In this disease, some of the fibers in some of the spinal nerve posterior roots and posterior columns of the cord degenerate. Those most often damaged are the fibers which transmit impulses from the lower extremities, from proprioceptors in muscles, tendons, and joints, and from certain discriminating touch receptors. As a result, the victim of this disease may lose much of his sense of position. For instance, he may not be able to tell you the exact position of his feet or toes if his eyes are closed so that he cannot look to see where they are. But, strangely enough, if you were to put a hot object on his foot, he would feel it and know where it was. Why? What tracts would still be functioning to make possible touch sensations?

Fracture dislocations of vertebrae frequently compress the spinal cord, injuring many or all of its tracts and centers, with extensive and serious functional consequences. If, for example, fracture of one or more cervical vertebrae occurs (broken neck), all cord tracts may be injured so they can no longer function. Sensory impulses (from parts of the body supplied by spinal nerves that come off the cord below the injury) can no longer reach the brain, and the patient has "no feeling" in these parts. Moreover, if all cord tracts have been damaged by the injury, motor impulses from the brain can no longer reach muscles below the injury, and the patient is paralyzed as well as without sensation in the affected parts.

Reflex center function of the spinal cord. A reflex center is the place at which incoming sensory impulses become outgoing motor impulses. Some reflex centers are merely synapses between sensory and motor neurons, whereas others are internuncial neurons interposed between sensory and motor neurons. Spinal cord gray matter contains all the reflex centers for spinal reflexes (responses produced by activation of these centers; see p. 246). This means, of course, that a spinal reflex can occur only when the cord segment that contains its reflex center is

221

functionally intact. It means also that when disease or injury or drugs or any agent makes cord reflex centers unable to function, the corresponding spinal reflexes then cannot occur. For example, with lesions of the lumbar segments of the cord the knee jerk is absent.

Cranial nerves

Twelve pairs of nerves arise from the undersurface of the brain, some from each division with the exception of the cerebellum, and pass through small foramina in the skull to their respective destinations. They are numbered in the order in which they emerge from front to back and, in addition, bear names descriptive of their distribution or of their function. Some of these nerves consist of afferent fibers only, some of efferent fibers mainly, and some of both afferent and efferent fibers, in which case they are called mixed nerves. Cell bodies of the efferent fibers lie in the various nuclei of the brainstem; cell bodies of the afferent fibers, with few exceptions, are located in ganglia (for example, the semilunar or gasserian ganglion of the fifth cranial nerve) outside the brainstem. The first, second, and eighth pairs are purely afferent.

First cranial nerve (olfactory). The olfactory nerves are composed of axons of neurons whose dendrites and cell bodies lie in the nasal mucosa, high up along the septum and superior conchae (turbinates). Axons of these neurons form about twenty small fibers which pierce each cribriform plate and terminate in the olfactory bulbs, where they synapse with olfactory neurons II whose axons comprise the olfactory tracts. Summarizing:

Olfactory neurons I

dendrites ⎫
cell body ⎬ in nasal mucosa

axons   in small fibers which extend through cribriform plate to olfactory bulb

Olfactory neurons II

dendrites ⎫
cell body ⎬ in olfactory bulb

axons   in olfactory tracts

Second cranial nerve (optic). Axons from the third and innermost layer of neurons of the retina compose the second cranial nerves. After entering the cranial cavity through the optic foramina, the two optic nerves unite to form the *optic chiasma*, in which some of the fibers of each nerve cross to the opposite side and continue in the *optic tract* of that side. Thus each optic nerve contains only fibers from the retina of the same side, whereas each optic tract has fibers in it from both retinae, a fact of importance in interpreting certain visual disorders (Fig. 148, p. 278). Most of the optic tract fibers terminate in the thalamus (in the portion known as the lateral geniculate body). From here a new relay of fibers runs to the visual area of the occipital lobe cortex. A few optic tract fibers terminate in the midbrain where they synapse with motor fibers to the external eye muscle (third, fourth, and sixth cranial nerves).

Third cranial nerve (oculomotor). Fibers of the third cranial nerve originate from cells in the oculomotor nucleus in the ventral part of the midbrain and extend to the various external eye muscles, with the exception of the superior oblique and the lateral rectus. Autonomic fibers whose cells lie in a nucleus of the midbrain (the Edinger-Westphal nucleus) are also contained in the oculomotor nerves. These fibers terminate in the ciliary ganglion where they synapse with cells whose postganglionic fibers supply the intrinsic eye muscles (ciliary and iris). Still a third group of fibers are found in the third cranial nerves, namely, sensory fibers from proprioceptors in the eye muscles.

Fourth cranial nerve (trochlear). Motor fibers of the fourth cranial nerve have their origin in cells in the midbrain, from whence they extend to the superior oblique muscles of the eye. Afferent fibers from proprioceptors in these muscles are also contained in the trochlear nerves.

Fifth cranial nerve (trifacial or trigeminal). Three sensory branches (ophthalmic, maxillary, and mandibular nerves) carry afferent impulses from the skin and mucosa of the head and teeth to cell bodies in the

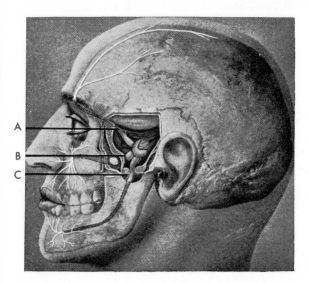

A
B
C

Fig. 125

Gasserian ganglion and the three main branches of the fifth cranial nerve. A, Deep exit of first division at sphenoidal fissure; B, deep exit of second division at foramen rotundum; C, deep exit of third division at foramen ovale. (From Campbell: A textbook of surgical anatomy, Philadelphia, W. B. Saunders Co.)

223

semilunar or gasserian ganglion (a swelling on the nerve, lodged in the petrous portion of the temporal bone) (Fig. 125). Fibers extend from the ganglion to the main sensory nucleus of the fifth cranial nerve situated in the pons. A smaller motor root of the trigeminal nerve originates in the trifacial motor nucleus located in the pons just medial to the sensory nucleus. Fibers run from the motor root to the muscles of mastication by way of the mandibular nerve.

Sixth cranial nerve (abducens). The sixth cranial nerve is a motor nerve with fibers originating from a nucleus in the pons in the floor of the fourth ventricle and extending to the lateral rectus muscles of the eyes. It contains also some afferent fibers from proprioceptors in the lateral rectus muscles.

Seventh cranial nerve (facial). The motor fibers of the seventh cranial nerve arise from a nucleus in the lower part of the pons, whence they extend by way of several branches to the superficial muscles of the face and scalp and to the submaxillary and sublingual glands. Sensory fibers from the taste buds of the anterior two thirds of the tongue run in the facial nerve to cell bodies in the geniculate ganglion, a small swelling on the facial nerve where it passes through a canal in the temporal bone. From the ganglion, fibers extend to the nucleus solitarius in the medulla.

Eighth cranial nerve (acoustic or auditory). The eighth cranial nerve has two distinct divisions, both of which are sensory. Fibers from the semicircular canals run to the vestibular ganglion (in the internal auditory meatus) where their cell bodies are located and whence fibers extend to the vestibular nuclei in the pons and medulla. Together these fibers constitute the *vestibular nerve.* Some of its fibers run to the cerebellum. The *cochlear nerve,* the other branch of the acoustic nerve, consists of fibers which start in the organ of Corti in the cochlea, have their cell bodies in the spiral ganglion in the cochlea, and terminate in the cochlear nuclei located between the medulla and pons. The vestibular nerve is sensory for balance and the cochlear nerve for hearing.

Ninth cranial nerve (glossopharyngeal). Both sensory and motor fibers compose the ninth cranial nerve, and, as the name implies, are distributed to the tongue and the pharynx. Sensory fibers, with their receptors in the pharynx and posterior third of the tongue, have their cell bodies in the jugular (superior) and petrous (inferior) ganglia, located respectively in the jugular foramen and the petrous portion of the temporal bone. From these, fibers extend to the nucleus solitarius in the medulla. The motor fibers of the ninth cranial nerve originate in cells in the nucleus ambiguus in the medulla and run to muscles of the pharynx. There are also secretory fibers in this nerve, with cells of origin in the nucleus salivatorius (at the junction of the pons and medulla). These fibers run to the otic ganglion, whence postganglionic fibers extend to the parotid gland.

Tenth cranial nerve (vagus or pneumogastric). The tenth cranial nerve is widely distributed and contains both sensory and motor fibers. Its sensory fibers supply the phaynx, larynx, trachea, heart, lungs, bronchi, esophagus, stomach, small intestine, and gallbladder. Cell bodies for these sensory dendrites lie in the jugular and nodose ganglia, located respectively in the jugular foramen and just inferior to it on the trunk of the nerve. Centrally the sensory axons terminate in the medulla (in the nucleus solitarius) and in the pons (in the nucleus of the trigeminal nerve). Motor fibers of the vagus originate in cells in the medulla (in the dorsal motor nucleus of the vagus) and extend to various autonomic ganglia in the vagal plexus, whence postganglionic fibers run to muscles of the pharynx, larynx, and thoracic and abdominal viscera.

Eleventh cranial nerve (accessory or spinal accessory). The eleventh cranial nerve is a motor nerve. Part of its fibers originates in cells in the medulla (in the dorsal motor nucleus of the vagus and in the nucleus ambiguus) and pass by way of vagal branches to thoracic and abdominal viscera. The rest of the fibers have their cells of origin in the anterior gray column of the first five or six segments of the cervical spinal cord and extend through the spinal root of the accessory nerve to the trapezius and sternocleidomastoid muscles.

Twelfth cranial nerve (hypoglossal). Motor fibers with cell bodies in the medulla (in the hypoglossal nucleus) compose the twelfth cranial nerve. They supply the muscles of the tongue. According to some anatomists, this nerve also contains sensory fibers from proprioceptors in the tongue.

Table 24 summarizes the main facts about the distribution and function of each of the cranial nerve pairs.

Neuralgia of the trifacial nerve, known as tic douloureux, is an extremely painful condition which can be relieved by removing the gasserian (or semilunar) ganglion, the large ganglion on the posterior root of the nerve (Fig. 125) containing the cell bodies of the nerve's afferent fibers. After such an operation, the patient's face, scalp, teeth, and conjunctiva on the side treated show anesthesia. Special care, such as wearing protective goggles and irrigating the eye frequently, is therefore prescribed. The patient is instructed also to visit his dentist regularly since he can no longer experience a toothache as a warning of diseased teeth.

Severe head injuries often damage one or more of the cranial nerves, producing symptoms analogous to the functions of the nerve affected.

Table 24. Cranial nerves

Nerve	Sensory fibers			Motor fibers		Functions*
	Receptors	Cell bodies	Termination	Cell bodies	Termination	
I. Olfactory†	Nasal mucosa‡	Nasal mucosa‡	Olfactory bulbs (new relay of neurons to olfactory cortex)			Sense of smell
II. Optic	Retina	Retina	Nucleus in thalamus (lateral geniculate body); some fibers terminate in superior colliculus of midbrain			Vision
III. Oculomotor	External eye muscles except superior oblique and lateral rectus	?	?	Midbrain (oculomotor nucleus and Edinger-Westphal nucleus)†	External eye muscles except superior oblique and lateral rectus; fibers from E-W nucleus terminate in ciliary ganglion and thence to ciliary and iris muscles	Eye movements; regulation of size of pupil; accommodation; proprioception (muscle sense)
IV. Trochlear	Superior oblique	?	?	Midbrain	Superior oblique muscle of eye	Eye movements; proprioception
V. Trigeminal	Skin and mucosa of head; teeth	Gasserian ganglion	Pons (sensory nucleus)	Pons (motor nucleus)	Muscles of mastication	Sensations of head and face; chewing movements; muscle sense
VI. Abducens	Lateral rectus			Pons	Lateral rectus muscle of eye	Abduction of eye; proprioception

				Pons	Superficial muscles of face and scalp	
VII. Facial	*Taste buds of anterior two-thirds of tongue*	*Geniculate ganglion*	*Medulla (nucleus solitarius)*		**Superficial muscles of face and scalp**	*Facial expressions;* **secretion of saliva;** *taste*
VIII. Acoustic 1. Vestibular branch	*Semicircular canals and vestibule*	*Vestibular ganglion*	*Pons and medulla (vestibular nuclei)*			*Balance or equilibrium sense*
2. Cochlear or auditory branch	*Organ of Corti in cochlea*	*Spiral ganglion*	*Pons and medulla (cochlear nuclei)*			*Hearing*
IX. Glossopharyngeal	*Pharynx and posterior one-third of tongue*	*Jugular and petrous ganglia*	*Medulla (nucleus solitarius)*	**Medulla (nucleus ambiguus)**	**Muscles of pharynx**	*Taste and other sensations of tongue;* **swallowing movements; aid in reflex control of blood pressure and respirations; secretion of saliva**
	Carotid sinus and carotid body	*Same*	*Medulla (respiratory and vasomotor centers)*	**Medulla at junction of pons (nucleus salivatorius)**	**Otic ganglion and thence to parotid gland**	

Continued on next page.

*An aid for remembering the general function of each cranial nerve is the following twelve-word saying: "Some Say Marry Money But My Brothers Say Bad Business Marry Money." Words beginning with S indicate sensory function of cranial nerves of the same numbers; words beginning with M indicate motor function; words beginning with B indicate both sensory and motor functions. For example, the first, second, and eighth words start with S, which indicates sensory function of cranial nerves 1, 2, and 8.

†The first letters of the words in the following sentences are the first letters of the names of the cranial nerves. Many generations of anatomy students have used it as an aid to memorizing these names. It is, "On Old Olympus Tiny Tiny Tops, A Finn and German Viewed Some Hops." (There are several slightly differing versions of this sentence.)

‡Italics indicate sensory fibers and functions; boldface type indicates motor fibers and functions.

Table 24.   Cranial nerves—cont'd

Nerve	Sensory fibers			Motor fibers		Functions[*]
	Receptors	Cell bodies	Termination	Cell bodies	Termination	
X. Vagus	Pharynx, larynx, and thoracic and abdominal viscera	Jugular and nodose ganglia	Medulla (nucleus solitarius); pons (nucleus of fifth cranial nerve)	Medulla (dorsal motor nucleus)	Ganglia of vagal plexus and thence to muscles of pharynx, larynx and thoracic and abdominal viscera	Sensations and movements of organs supplied; for example, slows heart, increases peristalsis, and contracts muscles for voice production
XI. Spinal accessory	?	?	?	Medulla (dorsal motor nucleus of vagus and nucleus ambiguus)	Muscles of thoracic and abdominal viscera and pharynx and larynx	Shoulder movements; turning movements of head; movements of viscera; voice productions; proprioception?
				Anterior gray column of first five or six cervical segments of spinal cord	Trapezius and sternocleidomastoid muscle	
XII. Hypoglossal	?	?	?	Medulla (hypoglossal nucleus)	Muscles of tongue	Tongue movements; proprioception?

[*]An aid for remembering the general function of each cranial nerve is the following twelve-word saying: "Some Say Marry Money But My Brothers Say Bad Business Marry Money." Words beginning with S indicate sensory function of cranial nerves of the same members; words beginning with M indicate motor function; words beginning with B indicate both sensory and motor functions. For example, the first, second, and eighth words start with S, which indicates sensory function of cranial nerves 1, 2, and 8.

For example, injury of the sixth cranial nerve causes the eye to turn in, due to paralysis of the abducting muscle of the eye, whereas injury of the eighth cranial nerve produces deafness. Injury to the facial nerve results in a poker-faced expression and a drooping of the corner of the mouth due to paralysis of the facial muscles.

An aneurysm of one of the middle cerebral arteries with resulting pressure on the nearby oculomotor nerve is not uncommon. In such cases the pupil on the same side remains dilated; in addition, the eye may turn outward and the lid may droop.

The second cranial nerve is particularly susceptible to atrophy, resulting in total blindness on the affected side.

Spinal nerves

Origin

Thirty-one pairs of nerves have their origin on the spinal cord. Unlike the cranial nerves, they have no special names but are merely numbered according to the level of the spinal column at which they emerge from the spinal cavity. Thus, there are eight cervical, twelve thoracic, five lumbar, and five sacral pairs and one coccygeal pair of spinal nerves. The first cervical nerve emerges in the space between the occipital bone and the first cervical vertebra, whereas the rest of the cervical and all the thoracic nerves pass out of the spinal cavity horizontally through the intervertebral foramina of their respective vertebrae. The lumbar, sacral, and coccygeal nerves, on the other hand, have to descend from their point of origin at the lower end of the cord (which terminates at the level of the first lumbar vertebra) before reaching the intervertebral foramina of their respective vertebrae, through which they then emerge. This gives the lower end of the cord, with its attached spinal nerves, the appearance of a horse's tail. In fact, it bears the name *cauda equina* (Latin equivalent for horse's tail).

Each spinal nerve, instead of attaching directly to the cord, attaches indirectly by means of two short roots, anterior and posterior. The posterior roots are readily recognized by the presence on them of a swelling, the posterior root ganglion or *spinal ganglion* (microscopically a ganglion consists chiefly of neuron cell bodies). The roots lie within the spinal cavity with the ganglia in the intervertebral foramina (Fig. 48, p. 108).

Distribution

After each spinal nerve emerges from the spinal cavity, it divides into two main branches, the anterior and posterior rami (Fig. 127). The posterior rami then subdivide into lesser nerves which extend into

Text continued on p. 234.

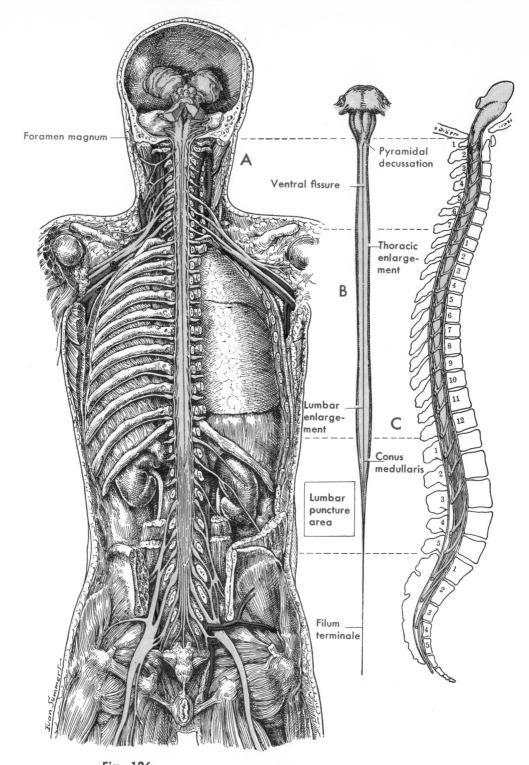

Foramen magnum

A

Ventral fissure

B

Pyramidal
decussation

Thoracic
enlarge-
ment

C

Lumbar
enlarge-
ment

Conus
medullaris

Lumbar
puncture
area

Filum
terminale

Ivan Summers

Fig. 126

Relation of spinal cord, part of brain, and some of spinal
nerves to surrounding structures. (From Mettler: Neuroanatomy,
St. Louis, The C. V. Mosby Co.)

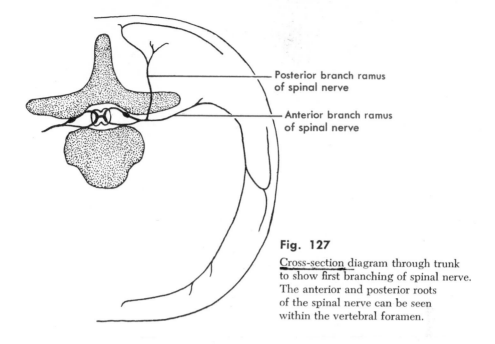

Fig. 127

Cross-section diagram through trunk
to show first branching of spinal nerve.
The anterior and posterior roots
of the spinal nerve can be seen
within the vertebral foramen.

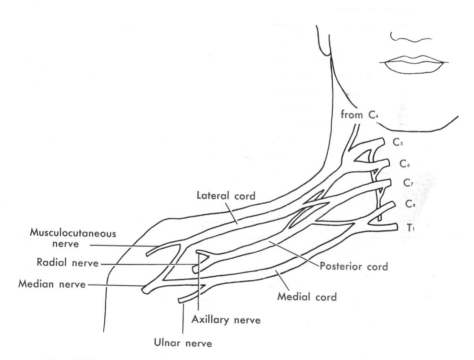

Fig. 128

Brachial plexus; intermixing of fibers from lower four cervical and first
thoracic nerves.

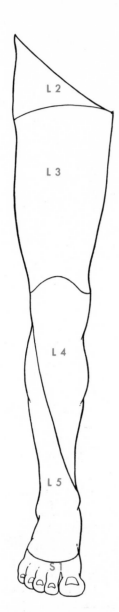

Fig. 129

Diagram to show segmental distribution of spinal nerves to the front of the lower extremity: L, lumbar segments; S, sacral segments. (After Collier and Purves-Stewart; from Francis and Farrell: Integrated anatomy and physiology, St. Louis, The C. V. Mosby Co.)

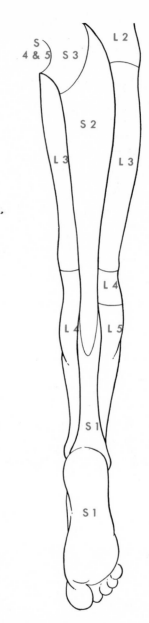

Fig. 130

Diagram to show segmental distribution of spinal nerves to the back of the lower extremity: L, lumbar segments; S, sacral segments. (After Collier and Purves-Stewart; from Francis and Farrell: Integrated anatomy and physiology, St. Louis, The C. V. Mosby Co.)

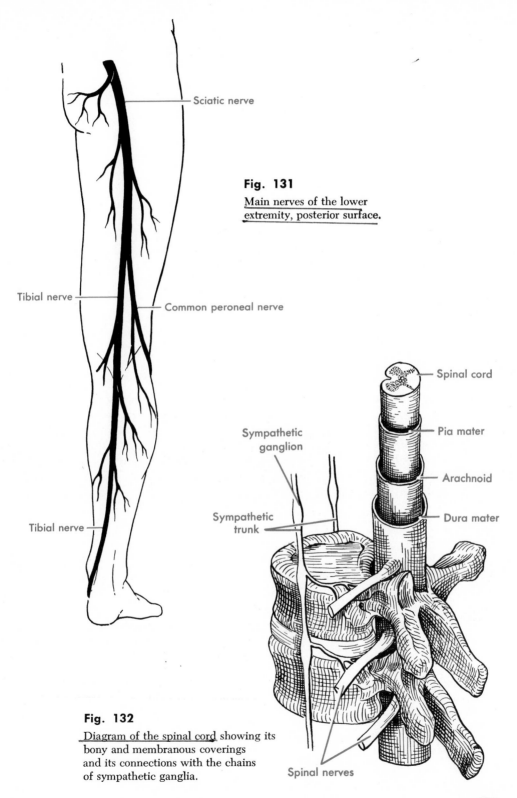

Sciatic nerve

Fig. 131

Main nerves of the lower
extremity, posterior surface.

Tibial nerve

Common peroneal nerve

Tibial nerve

Sympathetic
ganglion

Sympathetic
trunk

Spinal cord

Pia mater

Arachnoid

Dura mater

Fig. 132

Diagram of the spinal cord showing its
bony and membranous coverings
and its connections with the chains
of sympathetic ganglia.

Spinal nerves

233

the muscles and skin of the posterior surface of the head, neck, and trunk. The anterior rami (except those of the thoracic nerves) subdivide in a more complicated fashion, forming plexuses or complex networks of nerves (Table 25). For example, fibers from the lower four cervical and first thoracic nerves intermix in such a way as to form a fairly definite, although apparently hopelessly confused, pattern called the *brachial plexus* (Fig. 128). Emerging from this plexus are smaller nerves bearing names descriptive of their locations, such as the median nerve, the musculocutaneous nerve, and the ulnar nerve. These nerves (each containing fibers from more than one spinal nerve) divide further into smaller and smaller branches, resulting ultimately in the complete innervation of the hand and most of the arm. The brachial plexus is located in the shoulder region from the neck to the axilla. It is of clinical significance since it is sometimes stretched or torn at birth, causing paralysis and numbness of the baby's arm on that side. If untreated, it results in a withered arm. Branching from this plexus are several nerves to the skin and to voluntary muscles. The right and left phrenic nerves whose fibers come from the third and fourth or fourth and fifth cervical spinal nerves before formation of the plexus have considerable clinical interest since they supply the diaphragm muscle. If the neck is broken in a way that severs or crushes the cord above this level, nerve impulses from the brain can, of course, no longer reach the phrenic nerves, and therefore the diaphragm stops contracting. Unless artificial respiration of some kind is provided, the patient dies of respiratory paralysis as a result of the broken neck. Poliomyelitis which attacks the cord between the third and fifth cervical segments also paralyzes the phrenic nerve and, therefore, the diaphragm.

Another spinal nerve plexus is the *lumbar plexus*, formed by the intermingling of fibers from the first four lumbar nerves. This network of nerves is located in the lumbar region of the back in the psoas muscle. The large femoral nerve is one of several nerves emerging from the lumbar plexus. It divides into many branches which supply the thigh and leg.

Fibers from the fourth and fifth lumbar nerves and the first, second, and third sacral nerves form the *sacral plexus*, located in the pelvic cavity on the anterior surface of the piriformis muscle. Among others nerves which emerge from the sacral plexus are the tibial and common peroneal nerves which, in the thigh, form the largest nerve in the body, namely, the great sciatic nerve. It pierces the buttocks and runs down the back of the thigh; its many branches supply nearly all the skin of the leg, the posterior thigh muscles and the leg and foot muscles. Sciatica or neuralgia of the sciatic nerve is a fairly common and very painful condition.

Table 25. Spinal nerves and peripheral branches

Spinal nerves	Plexuses formed from anterior rami	Spinal nerve branches from plexuses	Parts supplied
Cervical 1 2 3 4	Cervical plexus	Lesser occipital Great auricular Cutaneous nerve of neck Anterior supraclavicular Middle supraclavicular Posterior supraclavicular Branches to numerous neck muscles	Sensory to back of head, front of neck, and upper part of shoulder; motor to numerous neck muscles
Cervical 5 6 7 8 Thoracic (or dorsal) 1	Brachial plexus	Suprascapular and dorsoscapular	Superficial muscles° of scapula
		Thoracic nerves, medial and lateral anterior	Pectoralis major and minor
		Long thoracic nerve	Serratus anterior
		Thoracodorsal	Latissimus dorsi
		Subscapular	Subscapular and teres major muscles
		Axillary (circumflex)	Deltoid and teres minor muscles and skin over deltoid
		Musculocutaneous	Muscles of front of arm (biceps brachii, coracobrachialis, and brachialis) and skin on outer side of forearm
		Ulnar	Flexor carpi ulnaris and part of flexor digitorum profundus; some of muscles of hand; sensory to medial side of hand, little finger, and medial half of fourth finger
2 3 4 5 6 7 8 9 10 11 12	No plexus formed; branches run directly to intercostal muscles and skin of thorax	Median	Rest of muscles of front of forearm and hand; sensory to skin of palmar surface of thumb, index, and middle fingers
		Radial	Triceps muscle and muscles of back of forearm; sensory to skin of back of forearm and hand
		Medial cutaneous	Sensory to inner surface of arm and forearm
		Phrenic (branches from cervical nerves before formation of plexus; most of its fibers from fourth cervical nerve)	Diaphragm

Continued on next page.

°Although nerves to muscles are considered motor, they do contain some sensory fibers which transmit proprioceptive impulses.

Table 25. Spinal nerves and peripheral branches—cont'd

Spinal nerves	Plexuses formed from anterior rami	Spinal nerve branches from plexuses	Parts supplied
		Iliohypogastric ⎱ Some- times	Sensory to anterior abdominal wall
		Ilioinguinal ⎰ fused	Sensory to anterior abdominal wall and external genitalia; motor to muscles of abdominal wall
		Genitofemoral	Sensory to skin of external genitalia and inguinal region
Lumbar 1		Lateral cutaneous of thigh	Sensory to outer side of thigh
2 3 4 5		Femoral	Motor to quadriceps, sartorius, and iliacus muscles; sensory to front of thigh and to medial side of lower leg (saphenous nerve)
Sacral 1 2	Lumbrosacral plexus	Obturator	Motor to adductor muscles of thigh
3 4 5		Tibial* (medial popliteal)	Motor to muscles of calf of leg; sensory to skin of calf of leg and sole of foot
Coccygeal 1		Common peroneal† (lateral popliteal)	Motor to evertors and dorsiflexors of foot; sensory to lateral surface of leg and dorsal surface of foot
		Nerves to hamstring muscles	Motor to muscles of back of thigh
		Gluteal nerves, superior and inferior	Motor to buttocks muscles and tensor fasciae latae
		Posterior cutaneous nerve	Sensory to skin of buttocks, posterior surface of thigh, and leg
		Pudendal nerve	Motor to perineal muscles; sensory to skin of perineum

*Sensory fibers from the tibial and peroneal nerves unite to form the *medial cutaneous* (or sural) *nerve* which supplies the calf of the leg and the lateral surface of the foot. In the thigh the tibial and common peroneal nerves are usually enclosed in a single sheath to form the *sciatic nerve*, the largest nerve in the body with its width of approximately three-quarters of an inch. About two-thirds of the way down the posterior part of the thigh it divides into its component parts. Branches of the sciatic nerve extend into the hamstring muscles.

Microscopic structure

Unlike cranial nerves, <u>all spinal nerves are *mixed nerves;*</u> that is, <u>they are composed of both sensory and motor fibers.</u> Some of the motor fibers terminate in visceral effectors (sweat glands and smooth muscle of blood vessels and hairs). These are called visceral or autonomic fibers because functionally they belong to the autonomic nervous system. Other spinal nerve motor fibers terminate in skeletal muscles and are referred to as somatic fibers. They are axons of neurons whose dendrites and cell bodies lie in the anterior gray columns of the cord. The autonomic fibers in spinal nerves are also axons, but their cell bodies are located in autonomic ganglia.

Sensory fibers in spinal nerves are dendrites. They have their origin in the millions of receptors located all over the body—in skin, mucosa, muscles, tendons, joints, viscera, etc. (everywhere except in structures supplied by cranial nerves). Grouped together in spinal nerves and their branches, sensory dendrites extend all the way from the receptors to the spinal ganglia located just outside the cord on the posterior roots of the spinal nerves. Here their cell bodies are located. Microscopically, then, posterior root ganglia consist of clusters of sensory cell bodies.

Table 26. Cranial nerves contrasted with spinal nerves

	Cranial nerves	*Spinal nerves*
Origin	Base of brain	Spinal cord
Distribution	Mainly to head and neck	Skin, skeletal muscles, joints, blood vessels, sweat glands, and mucosa except of head and neck
Structure	Some composed of sensory fibers only; some of both motor axons and sensory dendrites; some motor fibers belong to voluntary nervous system, some to autonomic	All of them composed of both sensory dendrites and motor axons; some of latter, somatic or voluntary, some autonomic
Function	Vision, hearing, olfactory sense, eye movements, etc.	Sensations, movements, and sweat secretion

Functions

Spinal nerve functions are easily deduced from the facts just presented about the kinds of fibers composing them. They serve as two-way conduction paths between the periphery nerves and spinal cord. They constitute the first part of the sensory neural mechanism; therefore sensation is partly a function of spinal nerves. They also constitute the last part of the motor neural mechanism; therefore skeletal muscle contractions and contractions of the smooth muscle of blood vessels and hairs and secretion by sweat glands are also partly functions of spinal nerves. Consequently, anything which interferes with the functioning of a spinal nerve produces both anesthesia and paralysis and

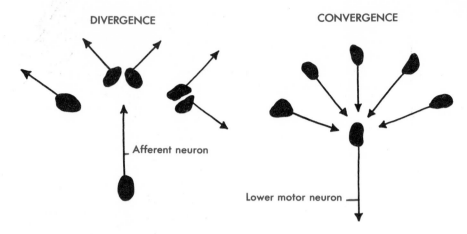

DIVERGENCE

CONVERGENCE

Afferent neuron

Lower motor neuron

Fig. 133

Scheme to show how a single afferent neuron may activate several other neurons (the anatomical basis for a single stimulus initiating multiple responses) and how many neurons activate a single lower motor neuron (the basis for multiple stimuli influencing a single response).

sometimes autonomic effects in the part innervated by that nerve. Spinal nerve *branches,* however, may be sensory, motor, or mixed (Table 25, p. 235).

Sensory neural pathways

Sensory impulses reach the cerebral cortex by way of a three-neuron relay. Sensory neuron I, of the relay conducts from the periphery to the cord or brainstem, sensory neuron II, from the cord or brainstem to the thalamus, and sensory neuron III, from the thalamus to the general sensory area in the parietal lobe of the cerebral cortex. Most axons of sensory neurons II decussate in their ascent to the thalamus. So, for the most part, one side of the brain registers sensations of the other side of the body. As a general rule, sensory fibers synapse with many internuncial neurons at different levels in the cord and brain and therefore have potential connections with numerous effectors and can function simultaneously in many reflex arcs. This principle of divergence has great protective value—somewhat as if a single line into a telephone exchange were to connect with a hospital, doctor's office, and police and fire departments all at the same time. Table 27 summarizes briefly the conduction pathways followed by several kinds of sensory impulses.

Arousal or alerting mechanism

Sensory impulses of all kinds feed into the reticular formation of the cord, brainstem, thalamus, and hypothalamus and are relayed from it

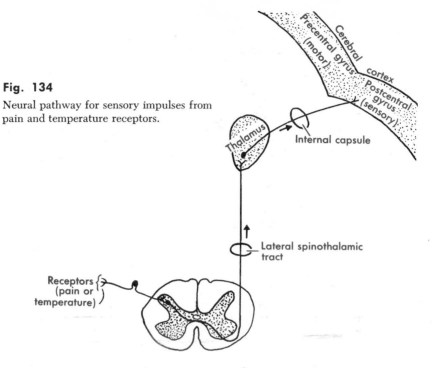

Fig. 134

Neural pathway for sensory impulses from pain and temperature receptors.

Table 27. Sensory neural pathways

Neurons	Organs in which neuron parts are located
1. Pain and temperature	
Sensory neuron I	
Receptors	In skin, mucosa, muscles, tendons, viscera
Dendrite	In spinal nerve and branches
Cell body	In spinal ganglion, on posterior root of spinal nerves
Axon	In posterior root of spinal nerve; terminates in posterior gray column of cord
Sensory neuron II	
Dendrite	Posterior gray column
Cell body	Posterior gray column
Axon	Decussates and ascends in lateral spinothalamic (Fig. 124, p. 219, and Fig. 134) tract; terminates in thalamus
Sensory neuron III	
Dendrite	Thalamus
Cell body	Thalamus
Axon	Thalamus via thalamocortical tract in internal capsule to general sensory area of cerebral cortex, that is, post-central gyrus in parietal lobe

Continued on next page.

239

Table 27. Sensory neural pathways—cont'd

Neurons	Organs in which neuron parts are located
2. Crude touch stimuli	
Sensory neuron I	Same as sensory neuron I for pain and temperature stimuli
Sensory neuron II	
Dendrite	Posterior gray column; same as sensory neuron II for pain and temperature
Cell body	
Axon	In ventral spinothalamic tract (Fig. 124) to thalamus
Sensory neuron III	Same as sensory neuron III for pain and temperature stimuli
3. Discriminating touch (two-point discrimination, vibrations) deep touch, and pressure and conscious proprioception	
Sensory neuron I	Same as sensory neuron I for pain, temperature, and crude touch stimuli, except that axon extends up cord in posterior white columns (fasciculi gracilis and cuneatus, Fig. 124) to nuclei gracilis and cuneatus in medulla, instead of terminating in posterior gray columns of cord
Sensory neuron II	
Dendrite	In nuclei gracilis and cuneatus of medulla
Cell body	
Axon	Decussates and ascends in medial lemniscus (broad band of fibers in medulla and midbrain) to terminate in thalamus
Sensory neuron III	Same as sensory neuron III for pain, temperature, and crude touch stimuli

to all parts of the cerebral cortex where they produce arousal or alerting of the individual. In fact, this reticular formation transmission is believed essential for maintenance of the waking state. Unconsciousness ensues when it is suppressed; incidentally, this is thought to be largely the action of general anesthetics. On the other hand, amphetamine and epinephrine, drugs which stimulate the reticular formation, produce wakefulness. In addition to its arousal function, the reticular formation also serves motor functions. For example, impulses from the bulboinhibitory centers in the reticular formation of the medulla tend to decrease skeletal muscle activity, and impulses from facilitatory reticular centers tend to increase it.

Motor neural pathways to skeletal muscles

Because neural pathways to skeletal muscles are extremely complex and because there are still so many unknowns about them, we shall confine our discussion to basic facts related to two major principles about these pathways. The first is the *principle of the final common path*. It might be stated this way. Motor neurons whose dendrites and cells lie in the anterior gray horn of the spinal cord constitute the final common path which all impulses to skeletal muscles must traverse because the only motor fibers terminating in skeletal muscles are axons of anterior horn neurons. Anterior horn neurons are also referred to as *lower motor neurons*.

The second major principle about motor neural pathways to skeletal muscles is the *principle of convergence*. Briefly it is that axons of a great many neurons converge upon, that is, synapse with each lower motor neuron. Hence many impulses from diverse sources continually bombard it, and together their combined or summated effect controls its functioning.

Motor pathways from the cerebral cortex down to anterior horn motor neurons are numerous and complex. Two methods are used to classify them—one based on the way their fibers enter the spinal cord

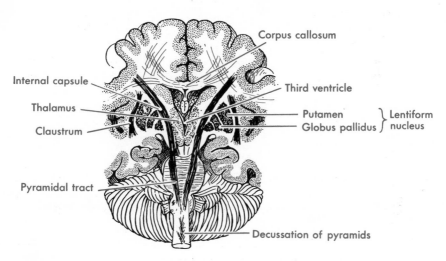

Fig. 135

Coronal section through the brain in the axis of the brain stem showing the lateral corticospinal (crossed pyramidal) tracts, the main motor tracts of the body. The paralysis accompanying apoplexy (a "stroke") is frequently the result of injury of nerve fibers in the internal capsule (part of the crossed pyramidal tract) due to hemorrhage from blood vessels in or near the internal capsule.

241

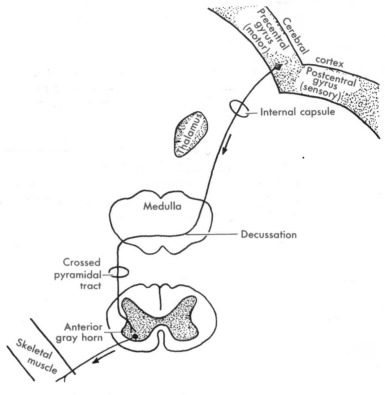

Fig. 136

Crossed pyramidal tract—the neural pathway
for impulses from giant pyramidal cells
of Betz and other cells in motor cortex.

and the other on their influence on the lower motor neurons. The first
method divides them into pyramidal and extrapyramidal tracts, and
the second classifies them as facilitatory and inhibitory tracts.

Pyramidal tract fibers come together in the medulla to form the
pyramids—hence their name. Pyramidal tracts are also called corticospinal tracts because of the uninterrupted extension of their fibers from
the cerebrum (primarily area 4, Fig. 121) to the cord. Impulses over
these tracts stimulate contractions of individual muscles to produce
voluntary small discrete movements, especially of the hands and feet.
They also help maintain muscle tone.

Extrapyramidal tracts are much more complex than pyramidal tracts.
They consist of all pathways between the motor cortex and anterior
horn cells except pyramidal tracts. Complicated incompletely worked
out relays between the cortex, basal ganglia, thalamus, and brainstem
form the upper portions of extrapyramidal tracts, and reticulospinal
tracts constitute one of the main lower portions. Extrapyramidal tracts
serve three general functions: facilitation, stimulation, and inhibition.
Impulses over some of the fibers either facilitate anterior horn neurons

or stimulate them to cause simultaneous contractions of groups of muscles to produce large coordinated movements. Impulses over others inhibit anterior horn neurons and thereby tend to decrease muscle tone.

Facilitatory tracts are so called because of their effect on lower motor neurons. They decrease the electrical charge that exists across the neuron's membrane. When they lower it to a level above the neuron's *threshold of excitation* (level at which impulse conduction starts), *facilitation* of the neuron is said to have occurred, rather than actual stimulation. Facilitatory tracts, then, are those whose impulses either

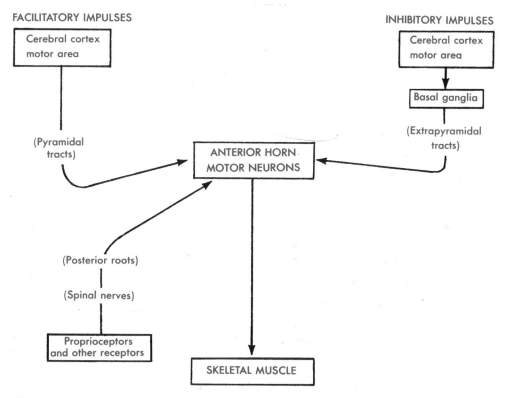

Fig. 137

Shows the main sources of impulses converging on the lower motor neuron. Impulses via the pyramidal tracts and via proprioceptive and other sensory neurons exert a stimulating or facilitatory effect on the lower motor neuron. Some impulses relayed through the basal ganglia and other extrapyramidal tracts exert an inhibitory effect on these cells. Many other impulses also impinge on the anterior horn cells but are not shown in this diagram.

Table 28. Pyramidal efferent path from cerebral cortex

Microscopic structures	Macroscopic structures in which neurons located
Upper motor neuron (Betz cell)	
Dendrite	Motor area of cerebral cortex
Cell body	Motor area of cerebral cortex
Axon	Motor area of cerebral cortex; descends in corticospinal (pyramidal) tract through cerebrum and brainstem; decussates in medulla and continues descent in lateral corticospinal (crossed pyramidal) tract in lateral white column; or may descend uncrossed in ventral, or direct, pyramidal tract in anterior white column and decussate just prior to terminating in anterior gray column (Fig. 136, p. 242)
Lower motor neuron	
Dendrite	Anterior gray column
Cell body	Anterior gray column
Axon	Anterior gray column to anterior root of spinal nerve to spinal nerve and branches
Effector	Skeletal muscle

facilitate or stimulate lower motor neurons. If sufficient facilitatory impulses reach a neuron simultaneously or in rapid enough succession, summation occurs and produces stimulation of the neuron rather than just facilitation. Inhibitory tract impulses have the opposite effect on lower motor neurons. They increase the electrical charge across their membranes and so inhibit them.

Fig. 137 shows some of the main sources of facilitatory impulses converging upon the lower motor neuron. All pyramidal tracts, some extrapyramidal tracts (for example, facilitatory reticulospinal fibers from cells in the *bulbofacilitatory centers* in the reticular formation of the midbrain, pons, and medulla), and sensory neurons all transmit facilitatory impulses to lower motor neurons either directly or indirectly via internuncial neurons. Inhibitory impulses reach lower motor neurons by way of certain extrapyramidal tracts, mainly by inhibitory reticulospinal fibers (those whose cells lie in the *bulboinhibitory center* in the reticular formation of the medulla largely, below the level of entrance of the vestibular nerve, it is thought). The cerebral cortex transmits to this center by way of certain tracts through the basal ganglia, especially through the pallidum and caudate.

Normally, the ratio of facilitatory and inhibitory impulses converging upon lower motor neurons is such as to maintain normal muscle tone. In other words, facilitatory impulses somewhat exceed inhibitory impulses. But disease sometimes alters this ratio. Parkinson's disease and "strokes," for example, may interrupt transmission by inhibitory extra-pyramidal paths through basal ganglia to bulboinhibitory centers. Facilitatory impulses then predominate, and excess muscle tone (rigidity or spasticity) develops. Injury of *upper motor neurons* (those whose dendrites and cells are located in the cerebral cortex and whose axons lie in either pyramidal or extrapyramidal tracts) produces symptoms known as the *upper motor syndrome*—loss of voluntary movement of involved muscles (due to injury of pyramidal tract upper motor neurons) and abnormal muscle tone, most often rigidity (due to injury of extrapyramidal tract inhibitory motor neurons). The *lower motor neuron syndrome*, in contrast, results from injury of anterior horn neurons and is characterized by flaccid paralysis, that is, loss of both voluntary and reflex movements of the skeletal muscles innervated by the damaged cord segments and by loss of muscle tone.

Reflexes

Definition

The action which results from a nerve impuse passing over a reflex arc is called a *reflex*. In other words, a reflex is a response to a stimulus; it may or may not be conscious. Usually the term is used to mean

Table 29. Correlation of microscopic and macroscopic structures of a segmental reflex arc*

Microscopic structures	Macroscopic structures in which neurons located
Afferent neuron	
Receptor	In skin or mucosa
Dendrite	In spinal nerve and branches
Cell body	In spinal ganglion on posterior root of spinal nerve
Axon	Posterior root of spinal nerve; terminates in posterior gray column of cord
Central neuron	
Dendrite	Posterior gray column
Cell body	Posterior gray column
Axon	Central gray matter of cord, extending into anterior gray column
Efferent neuron	
Dendrite	Anterior gray column
Cell body	Anterior gray column
Axon	Anterior gray column, extending into anterior root of spinal nerve, spinal nerve, and its branches
Effector	In skeletal muscles

*See Figs. 111 and 112.

only involuntary responses rather than those directly willed (that is, involving cerebral cortex activity).

Some reflexes of clinical importance

Clinical interest in reflexes stems from the fact that they deviate from normal in certain diseases. So the testing of reflexes is a valuable diagnostic aid. Physicians frequently test the following reflexes.

Knee jerk. The knee jerk or patellar reflex is an extension of the lower leg in response to tapping of the patellar tendon. The tap stretches both the tendon and its muscle, the quadriceps femoris, and thereby stimulates muscle spindles (receptors) in the muscle and initiates conduction over the following reflex arc:

1. *sensory fibers*—in second to fourth lumbar spinal nerves.
2. *reflex center*—in second to fourth lumbar segment of cord.
3. *motor fibers*—in second to fourth lumbar spinal nerves.

Note that this is a *two-neuron reflex arc.* It is also a *segmental arc*—impulses enter and leave the same segment of the cord—and an *ipsilateral arc* because impulses come from and go to the same side of the body (Fig. 110, p. 195).

Because of the kind of stimulation used to evoke it, the knee jerk is classified as a *stretch reflex* or *myotatic reflex* (Greek, mys, muscle + tasis, stretching). It is also classed as a *tendon reflex,* for obvious reasons, and as a *spinal cord reflex* because the reflex center of the arc mediating it lies in cord gray matter. And, finally, on the basis of the deep location of the receptor stimulated, it is classified as a *deep reflex* (in contrast to *superficial reflexes* elicited by stimulation of skin or mucosa receptors). Clinical interpretation of exaggerated or decreased or absent deep reflexes is based on the following physiological principles.

1. Impulse conduction over spinal reflex arcs is essential for producing deep reflexes.
2. Pyramidal tract impulses and some extrapyramidal impulses tend to facilitate deep reflexes. Pyramidal tract impulses are also necessary for voluntary movement.
3. Some extrapyramidal impulses tend to inhibit deep reflexes.

Applying these principles—poliomyelitis, by damaging anterior horn cells, interrupts spinal reflex arc conduction and is therefore characterized by the absence of at least some deep reflexes. Why do victims of poliomyelitis have also some paralysis or loss of voluntary movement? (See p. 241 if you are not sure.) Cerebral vascular accidents (hemorrhage, blood clots, strokes, etc.) frequently interrupt both pyramidal and extrapyramidal conduction. If deep reflexes are exaggerated, it indicates damage of inhibitory extrapyramidal upper motor neurons. Why do you think patients are so often paralyzed after strokes? Paralysis in these individuals must indicate injury of which tracts?

Ankle jerk. Ankle jerk or Achilles reflex is an extension (plantar flexion) of the foot in response to tapping of the Achilles tendon; it is a deep reflex mediated by two-neuron spinal arcs with centers in the first and second sacral segments of the cord.

Babinski reflex. The Babinski reflex is an extension of the great toe, with or without fanning of the other toes, in response to stimulation of the outer margin of the sole of the foot. Normally, except during the first few months of infancy, the response to such stimulation is plantar flexion of all five toes. Therefore a positive Babinski, except in infants under a few months old, is an abnormal reflex. It "is a sign only of interruption of corticospinal fibers which innervate the musculature of the great toe."*

Corneal reflex. The corneal reflex is winking in response to touching the cornea. It is mediated by reflex arcs with sensory fibers in the ophthalmic branch of the fifth cranial nerve, centers in the pons, and motor fibers in the seventh cranial nerve.

Pupillary light reflex. The pupillary light reflex is constriction of the pupil in response to bright light cast into the eye. It is mediated by complex arcs with sensory fibers in the second cranial nerve, motor fibers in the third cranial nerve, and centers in the midbrain.

Abdominal reflex. The abdominal reflex is drawing in of the abdominal wall in response to stroking the side of the abdomen. It is mediated by arcs with sensory and motor fibers in the ninth to twelfth thoracic spinal nerves and centers in these segments of the cord and is classified as a superficial reflex. A decrease in this reflex or its absence indicates lesions involving pyramidal tract upper motor neurons.

AUTONOMIC NERVOUS SYSTEM
Definition

By definition, the autonomic nervous system is the part of the nervous system that sends efferent fibers to visceral effectors. The term *visceral effectors* may be defined in two ways: in terms of tissues or of organs. In terms of tissues visceral effectors consist of cardiac muscle, smooth muscle, and glandular epithelium. In terms of organs visceral effectors consist of the heart, blood vessels, iris, ciliary muscle, hair muscles, various thoracic and abdominal organs, and the body's many glands. All of these structures innervated by the autonomic nervous system, you will note, are ones we think of as involuntary, that is, beyond our conscious control. They are our automatic parts. They

---

*From Best, Charles H., and Taylor, M. B.: The physiological basis of medical practice, ed. 7, Baltimore, 1961, Williams & Wilkins Co., p. 1205.

function without our willing them to and for the most part without our even being conscious of them at all.

Divisions

Two anatomically and physiologically separate divisions compose the autonomic nervous system: the sympathetic (or thoracolumbar) division and the parasympathetic (or craniosacral) division. Both divisions consist of numerous ganglia and fibers.

Sympathetic ganglia lie lateral to the anterior surface of the spinal cord. Short fibers connect them with the cord and with each other. Because of the latter fact, sympathetic ganglia* have somewhat the appearance of two chains of beads, one chain on each side of the spinal column from the level of the second cervical vertebra to the coccyx.

Parasympathetic ganglia, on the other hand, lie in or near visceral effectors. One example is the ciliary ganglion located in the posterior part of the orbit near the iris and ciliary muscle.

Autonomic neurons

As we have seen, autonomic neurons are efferent neurons.† A relay of two neurons conducts impulses from the central nervous system to visceral effectors—a fact noteworthy because it is the most fundamental structural difference between visceral effector and somatic effector in-

---

*_Sympathetic ganglia_—There are three cervical, ten or eleven thoracic, four lumbar, and four sacral ganglia in each sympathetic chain.

A few sympathetic ganglia, notably the celiac, superior, and inferior mesenteric ganglia, are located a short distance from the cord and therefore are called _collateral ganglia._

Celiac ganglia (solar plexus)—two fairly large, flat masses located on either side of celiac artery just below the diaphragm. They consist of dendrites and cell bodies of postganglionic neurons and their synapses with preganglionic axons which reach the celiac ganglia via the splanchnic and vagus nerves.

Superior mesenteric ganglion—small mass of postganglionic cells and synapses located near beginning of superior mesenteric artery.

Inferior mesenteric ganglion—small mass of postganglionic cells located close to beginning of inferior mesenteric artery.

†This does not mean that afferent neurons play no part in autonomic functioning. Quite the contrary, for like the voluntary nervous system the autonomic system functions on the reflex arc principle. But sensory neurons do not belong exclusively to one system or the other. Many of them function in both somatic and autonomic reflex arcs. For example, stimulation of skin heat receptors may initiate reflex contraction of smooth muscle in surface blood vessels (an autonomic reflex) as well as contraction of skeletal muscles (a somatic reflex). And stimulation of visceral sensory neurons (receptors located in an internal organ) may initiate a somatic reflex, as when an individual pulls his legs up in response to painful stimulation of intestinal receptors, for example, with "gas pains," as well as an autonomic reflex.

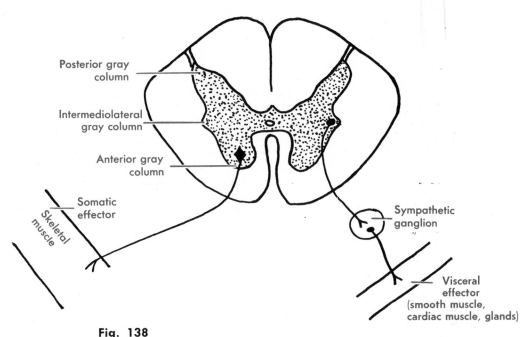

Fig. 138

Cross-section diagram of spinal cord showing location of sympathetic cells on one side of diagram and of somatic anterior cells on the other side.

nervation. Only one motor neuron, you will recall, conducts from the central nervous system to a skeletal muscle cell (Fig. 138). The first neuron in the two-neuron autonomic relay conducts from the cord or brainstem to an autonomic ganglion and is therefore referred to as a *preganglionic neuron.* The second neuron conducts from the autonomic ganglion to a visceral effector and is therefore called a *postganglionic neuron.*

Preganglionic neurons of the sympathetic system. The preganglionic neurons of the sympathetic system (Figs. 138 and 139 and Table 30) have their cell bodies in the lateral gray columns of the thoracic and first three or four lumbar segments of the cord. Axons from these cells extend through the anterior roots of the corresponding spinal nerves and through small side branches (the white rami) to the respective sympathetic ganglia. Here, some of them synapse with postganglionic neurons (each axon synapsing with several postganglionic neurons). Other preganglionic axons send branches up and down the sympathetic chain to terminate in ganglia above and below their point of origin. Still others extend through the sympathetic ganglia, out through the splanchnic nerves,* and terminate in the collateral ganglia.

---

*The three splanchnic nerves constitute the main branches from the thoracic sympathetic trunk. Since their fibers synapse in the celiac and other collateral ganglia with postganglionic neurons to abdominal structures, they form the main route for sympathetic stimulation of abdominal viscera.

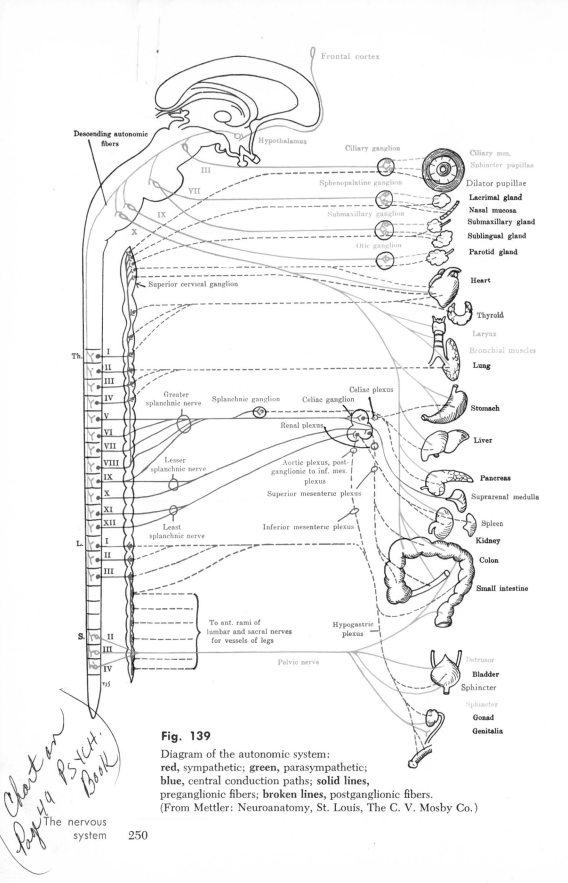

Frontal cortex

Descending autonomic fibers

Hypothalamus

III

VII

IX

X

Ciliary ganglion

Ciliary mm.
Sphincter pupillae
Dilator pupillae

Sphenopalatine ganglion

Lacrimal gland
Nasal mucosa

Submaxillary ganglion

Submaxillary gland
Sublingual gland

Otic ganglion

Parotid gland

Superior cervical ganglion

Heart

Thyroid
Larynx
Bronchial muscles
Lung

Th.

I
II
III
IV
V
VI
VII
VIII
IX
X
XI
XII

Greater
splanchnic nerve

Splanchnic ganglion

Celiac ganglion

Celiac plexus

Renal plexus

Lesser
splanchnic nerve

Aortic plexus, post-
ganglionic to inf. mes.
plexus
Superior mesenteric plexus

Stomach

Liver

Pancreas

Suprarenal medulla

Spleen

L.

I
II
III

Least
splanchnic nerve

Inferior mesenteric plexus

Kidney

Colon

Small intestine

S.

II
III
IV

To ant. rami of
lumbar and sacral nerves
for vessels of legs

Hypogastric
plexus

Pelvic nerve

Detrusor
Bladder
Sphincter

Sphincter
Gonad
Genitalia

Fig. 139

Diagram of the autonomic system:
red, sympathetic; **green**, parasympathetic;
blue, central conduction paths; **solid lines**,
preganglionic fibers; **broken lines**, postganglionic fibers.
(From Mettler: Neuroanatomy, St. Louis, The C. V. Mosby Co.)

The nervous
system   250

Table 30. Locations of autonomic neurons

Autonomic neurons (efferent)	Macroscopic structures in which located
Sympathetic division	
Preganglionic neurons	
Dendrites and cell bodies	In lateral gray columns of thoracic and first four lumbar segments of spinal cord
Axons (preganglionic fibers)	In anterior roots of spinal nerves to spinal nerves (thoracic and first four lumbar) to white rami and thence in any of three following pathways: 1. Through white rami to sympathetic ganglia where they synapse with several postganglionic neurons 2. Through white rami to and through sympathetic ganglia, thence up or down sympathetic trunk before synapsing in a sympathetic ganglion with several postganglionic neurons 3. Through white rami to and through sympathetic ganglia, to and through splanchnic nerves to collateral ganglia (celiac, superior, and inferior mesenteric ganglia), where they synapse with several postganglionic neurons
Postganglionic neurons	
Dendrites and cell bodies	In sympathetic or collateral ganglia
Axons (postganglionic fibers)	In autonomic nerves which form various plexuses before supplying thoracic and abdominal viscera and blood vessels in these body cavities, or Through gray rami to spinal nerves to cutaneous blood vessels, sweat glands, and smooth muscles of hair follicles
Parasympathetic division	
First order or preganglionic neurons	
Dendrites and cell bodies	In midbrain or medulla, (or lateral gray columns of sacral cord)
Axons (preganglionic fibers)	From midbrain to third cranial nerve to ciliary ganglion or From pons to seventh cranial nerve to sphenopalatine ganglion or submaxillary ganglion or From medulla to 1. Ninth cranial nerve to otic ganglion or 2. Tenth and eleventh cranial nerves to cardiac and celiac ganglia
Second order or postganglionic neurons	
Dendrites and cell bodies	In various ganglia (ciliary, sphenopalatine, submaxillary, otic, cardiac, and celiac) located in or near organs
Axons (postganglionic fibers)	In short nerve filaments to various viscera, glands, blood vessels, and intrinsic eye muscles

251

But no matter which course a sympathetic preganglionic axon follows, it synapses with many postganglionic neurons, and these frequently terminate in widely separated organs. This anatomical fact explains a well-known physiological principle—sympathetic responses are usually widespread, involving many organs and not just one.

Postganglionic neurons of the sympathetic system. The postganglionic neurons of the sympathetic system have their dendrites and cell bodies in the sympathetic chain ganglia or in collateral ganglia. Their axons are distributed by both spinal nerves and separate autonomic nerves. They reach the spinal nerves via small filament (gray rami) which connect the sympathetic ganglia with the spinal nerves. They then travel in the spinal nerves to blood vessels, sweat glands, and arrector hair muscles all over the body. The course of postganglionic axons through autonomic nerves is somewhat more complex. These nerves form complicated plexuses before fibers are finally distributed to their respective destinations. For example, postganglionic fibers from the celiac and superior mesenteric ganglia pass through the celiac plexus before reaching the abdominal viscera, those from the inferior mesenteric ganglion pass through the hypogastric plexus on their way to the lower abdominal and pelvic viscera, and those from the cervical ganglion pass through the cardiac nerves and the cardiac plexus at the base of the heart and are then distributed to the heart.

Preganglionic neurons of the parasympathetic system. The preganglionic neurons of the parasympathetic system have their cell bodies in nuclei in the brainstem or in the lateral gray columns of the sacral cord. Their axons are contained in certain cranial and pelvic nerves and extend a considerable distance before synapsing with postganglionic neurons. For example, axons of neurons with cell bodies in the vagus nuclei (located in the medulla) travel in the vagus nerve for a distance of a foot or more before reaching their terminal ganglia in the chest and abdomen (Fig. 139 and Table 30).

Postganglionic neurons of the parasympathetic system. The postganglionic neurons of the parasympathetic system have their dendrites and cell bodies in the outlying parasympathetic ganglia and send short axons into the nearby structures. Each parasympathetic preganglionic neuron synapses, therefore, only with postganglionic neurons to a single structure. For this reason, parasympathetic stimulation frequently involves response by only one organ as contrasted with sympathetic responses which, as noted before, usually involve numerous organs.

Functions

The autonomic system controls visceral effectors, causing them to respond in ways that tend to maintain or restore homeostasis. Regulation of homeostatic mechanisms, in other words, is the general function of the autonomic nervous system. But it does not accomplish this vital task alone. The voluntary nervous system and various chemicals (hormones and carbon dioxide, for example) assist and supplement the autonomic nervous system in the control of homeostatic mechanisms.

Here are some general principles that may help you understand and remember specific autonomic functions.

1. *Principle of dual autonomic innervation.* Most visceral effectors receive both sympathetic and parasympathetic fibers. Examples are cardiac muscle, smooth muscle of iris, ciliary body, bronchial tubes, and digestive tract, and some glands (Fig. 139).

2. *Principle of single autonomic innervation.* Some visceral effectors are believed to receive only sympathetic fibers. Examples are smooth muscle of hairs, smooth muscle of most blood vessels, sweat glands, and medulla of adrenal glands.

3. *Principle of autonomic antagonism.* Sympathetic and parasympathetic impulses tend to produce opposite effects, but according to modern theory both kinds of impulses play continually upon dually innervated visceral effectors. Hence the algebraic sum of the two opposing forces actually controls their rate of activity.

For instance, at any one moment sympathetic impulses tend to accelerate the heartbeat and parasympathetic impulses to slow it, and the algebraic sum of these two opposing forces determines the actual rate. A speeding up of the rate, therefore, might result from increased sympathetic or decreased parasympathetic impulses, or both.

4. *Principle of chemical mediation of impulses.* Chemicals mediate impulse transmission across autonomic synapses and neuromuscular and neuroglandular junctions, as they do across somatic neuromuscular junctions and presumably all synapses. Autonomic axons are classified as either cholinergic or adrenergic fibers, depending upon the chemical they release. *Cholinergic fibers** liberate acetylcholine. *Adrenergic fibers** release adrenaline (epinephrine, sympathin) or similar sub-

---

*Cholinergic fibers
1. All preganglionic axons, both sympathetic and parasympathetic
2. All or almost all parasympathetic postganglionic axons (authorities disagree about this)
3. Sympathetic postganglionic fibers to sweat glands, to blood vessels of skeletal muscles and of some skin areas and some sympathetic fibers to coronary arteries
4. Somatic motor axons

*Adrenergic fibers
1. Most sympathetic postganglionic axons

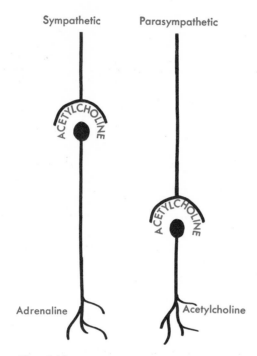

Fig. 140

Diagram to show release of chemicals at autonomic fiber terminals. Fibers
which release adrenaline are called adrenergic; those which release
acetylcholine, cholinergic. Note that only postganglionic fibers of the
sympathetic system are adrenergic (even a few of these are cholinergic,
notably those to the sweat glands, uterus, and stomach). All preganglionic
fibers and parasympathetic postganglionic fibers are cholinergic as are
also motor fibers to voluntary muscle. Acetylcholine normally is rapidly
destroyed by the enzyme cholinesterase. However, its action can be
prolonged by certain drugs, such as eserine, which inhibit the enzyme.

stances, hence their name. Some are now known to liberate noradrena-
line (norepinephrine; thought to be Cannon's sympathin E) and others
to release adrenaline (epinephrine; thought to be Cannon's sympathin
I) (Fig. 140).

   5. *Principle of nonautonomy.* The autonomic nervous system is not
autonomous. It is neither anatomically nor physiologically independent
of the rest of the nervous system. It and all parts of the nervous system
work together as a single functional unit. As evidence of the nonautonomy of the autonomic system, consider the following facts. All preganglionic neurons have their dendrites and cells located in the brain
and cord gray matter, in the "lower autonomic centers." Moreover, numerous central neurons synapse with preganglionic neurons. And therefore impulses from various higher centers impinge upon and control

Table 31. Autonomic functions

Visceral effectors	Parasympathetic effects	Sympathetic effects
Cardiac muscle	Slows heart rate	Accelerates rate
Smooth muscle		
1. Of most blood vessels	None	Adrenergic fibers; vasoconstriction
2. Of skeletal muscle blood vessels	None	Mainly cholinergic sympathetic fibers; vasodilatation
3. Of coronary arteries	Not established	Cholinergic sympathetic fibers, vasodilatation; adrenergic fibers, vasoconstriction
4. Of digestive tract	Increases peristalsis	Decreases peristalsis
5. Of urinary bladder	Stimulates	Inhibits
6. Of urinary sphincter	Inhibits	Stimulates
7. Iris and ciliary muscle	Constricts pupil; accommodation for near vision	Dilates pupil
Glands		
1. Sweat	None	Cholinergic fibers stimulate sweat glands
2. Salivary	Stimulates secretion	Confusing evidence; sympathetic fibers may supply only blood vessels of gland, causing constriction
3. Pancreas including islets	Stimulates secretion	Confusing evidence; same as for salivary glands
4. Liver	None	Stimulates glycogenolysis which tends to increase blood sugar
5. Adrenal medulla	None	Stimulates adrenalin secretion which tends to increase blood sugar, blood pressure, and heart rate and to produce many other changes

the lower autonomic centers. The hypothalamus, for example, is the most notable of the known "higher autonomic centers" (so called because they are groups of neurons whose dendrites and cells lie in the brain, that is, in higher up locations than those of the lower autonomic centers).

You may be wondering why the name autonomic system was ever chosen in the first place if the system is really not autonomous. Originally the term seemed appropriate. The autonomic system seemed to be self-regulating and independent of the rest of the nervous system. Common observations furnished abundant evidence of its independence from cerebral control, from direct control by the will, that is. But later even this was found to be not entirely true. Some rare and startling exceptions were discovered. I have seen one such exception—a man who sat in a brightly lighted amphitheater in front of a class of medical students and made his pupils change from small, constricted dots (normal response to bright light) to widely dilated circles. This same man also willed gooseflesh to appear on his arms by contracting the smooth muscles of the hairs.

Functions of the parasympathetic (craniosacral) division. A suggested principle about parasympathetic function is that it so regulates the activities of visceral effectors as to have a conserving, upbuilding effect. For example, parasympathetic impulses slow the heartbeat and stimulate peristalsis and digestive juice secretion. Table 31 lists specific parasympathetic functions.

Functions of the sympathetic (thoracolumbar) division. A suggested principle about sympathetic function is that it so regulates the activities of visceral effectors as to prepare the body for maximum energy expenditure and to enable it to defend itself against various threats to survival. Sympatheic impulses usually dominate in times of stress—whether this be threatened bodily danger, or strenuous exercise, or intense emotional experience. Study Table 31 to discover specific sympathetic functions.

Psychosomatic disorders illustrate the principle that emotions not outwardly expressed tend to be inwardly expressed—that is, emotions not expressed through somatic effectors (skeletal muscle contractions) tend to be expressed through visceral effectors, through disordered autonomic functions. Sympathetic control, as previously mentioned, usually dominates in times of stress, but curiously enough parasympathetic impulses frequently take over the control of some effectors at such times. For instance, one of the first symptoms of emotional stress may be a feeling of hunger and wanting to eat more than usual, presumably due in part at least to increased gastric motility, a parasympathetic response. Most famous of parasympathetic disorders is peptic ulcer, stemming from excess parasympathetic stimulation of hydrochloric acid glands.

Numerous drugs mimic or oppose the effects of autonomic impulses on visceral effectors. Epinephrine and ephedrine, for example, mimic sympathetic effects, and methacholine and pilocarpine mimic parasympathetic effects. Atropine and scopolamine, on the other hand, block parasympathetic effects.

Outline summary

The nervous system

Cells of the nervous system

Neuroglia and microglia

1. Neuroglia—cells that attach to neurons and adjacent blood vessels; may constitute blood-brain barrier, limiting exchange of certain substances between blood and neurons
2. Microglia—phagocytic cells found in nervous tissue

Neurons

1. Classified according to function
   a. afferent or sensory—transmit impulses toward central nervous system
   b. efferent or motor—transmit away from central nervous system
   c. internuncial (intercalated, central)— conduct from sensory to motor neurons
2. Classified according to structure
   a. Multipolar—several dendrites, one axon
   b. bipolar—one dendrite, one axon
   c. unipolar—axon only, but this type rare after birth; pseudo-unipolar neurons— originally unipolar, but two processes fuse for short distance then divide into dendrite and axon
3. Structure
   a. See Fig. 105 and text, pp. 189 to 192
4. Function
   a. conduction of nerve impulses—self-propagating waves of negativity pass along neuron membrane; see pp. 192 to 194
   b. axons function on all-or-none principle; conduct maximally for given condition or not at all
   c. dendrites and cell bodies function on graded response principle; respond to subthreshold stimuli by facilitation (decrease in electrical charge across membrane) and to threshold and greater stimuli by conduction
   d. neurons exhibit refractory period, brief moment after stimulation during which it cannot again be stimulated
   e. conduction across synapses and neuromuscular junctions; chemical acetylcholine mediates conduction at skeletal muscle junctions and presumably at all synapses
   f. course of nerve impulse—reflex arcs, most of which consist of sensory neurons synapsing with internuncial neurons synapsing with motor neurons
   g. rate of impulse conduction—see Table 21, p. 197

Brain and cord coverings

1. Bony—cranial bones around brain; vertebrae around cord
2. Membranous—called meninges and consist of three layers
   a. dura mater—white fibrous tissue outer layer
   b. arachnoid membrane—cobwebby middle layer
   c. pia mater—transparent; adherent to outer surface of brain and cord; contains blood vessels; therefore, nutritive layer

Brain and cord fluid spaces

1. Subarachnoid space around brain
2. Subarachnoid space around cord

257

3. Ventricles and cerebral aqueduct inside brain—four cavities within brain
   a. first and second lateral ventricles—large cavities, one in each cerebral hemisphere
   b. third ventricle—vertical slit in cerebrum beneath corpus callosum and longitudinal fissure
   c. fourth ventricle—diamond-shaped space between cerebellum and medulla and pons; is expansion of central canal of cord
4. Central canal inside cord

Formation and circulation of cerebrospinal fluid

1. Formed by plasma filtering from network of capillaries (choroid plexus) in each ventricle
2. Circulates from lateral ventricles to third ventricle, cerebral aqueduct, fourth ventricle, central canal of cord, subarachnoid space of cord and brain; venous sinuses

Organs of the nervous system

Classified according to location

1. Central nervous system consisting of
   a. brain
   b. spinal cord
2. Peripheral nervous system consisting of
   a. cranial nerves, twelve pairs
   b. spinal nerves, thirty-one pairs
   c. autonomic nervous system

Classified according to function

1. Cerebrospinal or voluntary system consisting of
   a. brain
   b. spinal cord
   c. cranial nerves (except for fibers to smooth muscle, cardiac muscle, and glands)
   d. spinal nerves (except for fibers to smooth muscle, cardiac muscle, and glands)
2. Autonomic or involuntary system consisting of
   a. autonomic ganglia
   b. preganglionic and postganglionic fibers

Brain

Cerebrum, diencephalon, cerebellum, medulla oblongata, pons varolii, midbrain; another classification divides brain into forebrain (prosencephalon), midbrain (mesencephalon), and hindbrain (rhombencephalon)

Cerebrum

1. General description—largest part of human brain; incompletely divided by longitudinal fissure into two hemispheres (connected by corpus callosum) each hemisphere divided by fissures into 5 lobes: frontal, parietal, temporal, occipital, and island of Reil (insula)
2. Cortex—outer layer of gray matter arranged in ridges called convolutions or gyri
3. Interior—consists of masses of gray matter called cerebral nuclei or basal ganglia embedded in white matter
   a. cerebral nuclei names—see p. 204; function: help produce normal movements
   b. white matter in cerebrum arranged in tracts (bundles of axons); ascending projection tracts transmit impulses toward or to brain; descending projections tracts transmit impulses down from brain to cord; commissural tracts transmit from one hemisphere to other; association tracts transmit from one convolution to another in same hemisphere
4. Functions—in general, all conscious functions; for example, analysis, integration, and interpretation of sensations, control of voluntary movements, use and understanding of language, and all other mental functions

Diencephalon (tween-brain)

1. Thalamus
   a. a large rounded mass of gray matter in each cerebral hemisphere, lateral to third ventricle; composed of many nuclei
   b. relays afferent impulses to cerebral cortex
   c. conscious recognition of crude sensations of pain, temperature, and touch
   d. involved in emotional component of sensations; feelings of pleasantness or unpleasantness
   e. involved in alerting or arousal mechanism
   f. involved in production of complex reflex movements

2. Hypothalamus
   a. structure and location
      1. gray matter around optic chiasma, the pituitary stalk, posterior lobe of pituitary, mammillary bodies, and adjacent regions; made up of many nuclei, notably supraoptic, paraventricular, and mammillary
      2. afferent tracts conduct impulses to hypothalamus from cerebral cortex, thalamus, and basal ganglia
      3. efferent tracts conduct from hypothalamus to autonomic centers in brainstem and cord, to thalamus, and to posterior pituitary gland
   b. functions
      1. coordinates autonomic functions
      2. makes it possible for emotions to express themselves in changed bodily functions (psychosomatic disease)
      3. helps maintain water balance
      4. helps control various reproductive functions
      5. helps maintain waking state
      6. helps regulate appetite
      7. helps maintain normal body temperature

Cerebellum
Second largest part of human brain
1. Structure and location
   a. has two hemispheres and center section, vermis
   b. surface grooved with sulci
   c. slightly raised, slender convolutions
   d. internal white matter arranged in pattern like veins of leaf
   e. three pairs of tracts in cerebellum—inferior, middle, and superior cerebellar peduncles
   f. most important cerebellar nucleus—dentate nucleus
2. Functions
   a. synergic control of muscle action
   b. postural reflexes
   c. equilibrium

Medulla oblongata
1. Structure and location
   a. part of brain formed by enlargement of cord as it enters cranial cavity
   b. mainly white matter (projection tracts); also reticular formation (interlacement of gray and white matter, containing many nuclei)
   c. various autonomic centers in reticular formation, for example, cardiac and vasomotor; also respiratory, vomiting, coughing, hiccoughing, sneezing, and swallowing centers
2. Functions
   a. helps control heartbeat, blood pressure, and respirations
   b. mediates reflexes of vomiting, coughing, hiccoughing, etc.
   c. conducts impulses between cord and brain

Pons varolii
1. Structure and location
   a. located just above medulla
   b. white matter with few nuclei
2. Functions
   a. contains projection tracts between cord and various parts of brain
   b. centers for fifth to eighth cranial nerves

Midbrain
1. Location and structure
   a. located above pons, just below cerebrum
   b. white matter with few nuclei
   c. cerebral aqueduct within midbrain
   d. cerebral peduncles are two tracts composing ventral part of midbrain and connecting pons to cerebrum
   e. corpora quadrigemina — four rounded eminences (two superior and two inferior colliculi) on dorsal surface of midbrain
   f. important nucleus—red nucleus
2. Functions
   a. projection tracts function in sensations and movements
   b. pupillary center functions in pupillary reflexes

Spinal cord
1. Location
   a. in spinal cavity, from foramen magnum to first lumbar vertebra
   b. meninges continue below that point
2. Structure
   a. core of gray matter shaped like three-dimensional letter H
   b. white matter present in columns, ante-

rior, lateral, and posterior, composed of numerous projection tracts

3. Functions
   a. sensory and motor conduction pathways between peripheral nerves and brain; names and functions of tracts see p. 220
   b. composite of reflex centers—for all segmental and intersegmental responses

Cranial nerves

Twelve pairs—see Table 24, p. 226, for distribution and function

Spinal nerves

Thirty-one pairs; originate by anterior and posterior roots from cord, emerge through intervertebral foramina; spinal ganglion on each posterior root; branches of spinal nerves distributed to skin, mucosa, skeletal muscles; branches form plexuses, such as brachial plexus, from which nerves emerge to supply various parts; microscopically spinal nerves consist of sensory dendrites and motor axons; that is, are mixed nerves; also contain autonomic postganglionic fibers; see Table 25, p. 235, for peripheral branches of spinal nerves; functions of spinal nerves summarized in Table 26, p. 237)

Sensory neural pathways (Table 27, p. 239)

1. A three-neuron relay conducts impulses from periphery to cerebral cortex:
   a. sensory neuron I conducts from periphery to cord or to brainstem
   b. sensory neuron II conducts from cord or to brainstem to thalamus
   c. sensory neuron III conducts from thalamus to general sensory area of cerebral cortex (areas 3, 1, 2)
2. Most sensory neuron II axons decussate; so one side of brain registers mainly sensations for opposite side of body
3. Principle of divergence applies to sensory impulse conduction; each sensory neuron synapses with more than one neuron; hence impulses over any sensory neuron diverge and may activate many effectors
4. Arousal or alerting mechanism—cerebral cortex stimulated by impulses from reticular formation which is stimulated by sensory impulses of all kinds reaching it

Motor neural pathways

1. Principle of the final common path—motor neurons in anterior gray horns of cord constitute final common path for impulses to skeletal muscles; are the only neurons transmitting impulses into skeletal muscles
2. Principle of convergence—axons of many neurons synapse with each anterior horn motor neuron
3. Motor pathways from cerebral cortex to anterior horn cells classified according to way fibers enter cord:
   a. pyramidal tracts (or corticospinal tracts) —dendrites and cells in cortex, axons enter cord by way of pyramids of medulla, synapse directly with anterior horn cells or indirectly via internuncial neurons
      1. functions—voluntary contractions of individual muscles to produce small discrete movements; also help maintain muscle tone
   b. extrapyramidal tracts—all pathways between motor cortex and anterior horn cells, except pyramidal tracts; upper extrapyramidal tracts relay impulses between cortex, basal ganglia, thalamus, and brainstem; reticulospinal tracts main lower extrapyramidal tracts
4. Motor pathways from cerebral cortex to anterior horn cells also classified according to influence on anterior horn cells:
   a. facilitatory tracts—have facilitating or stimulating effect on anterior horn cells; all pyramidal tracts and some extrapyramidal tracts facilitatory, notably the facilitatory reticulospinal fibers
   b. inhibitory tracts—have inhibiting effect on anterior horn cells; inhibitory reticulospinal fibers are main inhibitory tracts
5. Ratio of facilitatory and inhibitory impulses impinging on anterior horn cells controls activity; normally, slight predominance of facilitatory impulses maintains muscle tone

Reflexes

1. Definitions—action resulting from conduction over a reflex arc; a reflex is a response (either muscle contraction or glandular secretion) to a stimulus; usually term reflex used to mean only involuntary responses

2. Some reflexes of clinical importance—see pp. 246 to 247

Autonomic nervous system

Definition

Part of nervous system that sends efferent fibers to internal organs, blood vessels, glands, and ciliary muscle; in other words, innervates visceral effectors (smooth and cardiac muscle and glands)

Divisions

1. Sympathetic or thoracolumbar
2. Parasympathetic or craniosacral

Macroscopic structure

1. Sympathetic division consists of two chains of ganglia, one on either side of backbone, from which preganglionic fibers extend to cord, postganglionic fibers to smooth muscle, cardiac muscle, and glandular tissue
2. Parasympathetic division consists of ganglia located on or near viscera with preganglionic fibers between ganglia and brainstem and between ganglia and sacral region of cord, postganglionic fibers from ganglia into viscera and glands

Microscopic structure

1. Cell bodies of preganglionic neurons of sympathetic system in lateral gray columns of thoracic and lumbar segments of cord
2. Cell bodies of postganglionic neurons of sympathetic system in sympathetic chain ganglia or in collateral ganglia (celiac, superior and inferior mesenteric)
3. Cells of preganglionic neurons of parasympathetic system in various nuclei of brainstem and in gray matter of sacral segments of cord
4. Cells of postganglionic neurons of parasympathetic system in ganglia on or near organs innervated

Functions

1. General function autonomic system—controls visceral effectors so they respond in ways that tend to maintain or restore homeostasis; in other words, regulation of homeostatic mechanisms (with help of voluntary nervous system and various chemicals)
2. Parasympathetic division—controls visceral effectors so their activities have conserving, upbuilding effect; see Table 31, p. 255, for specific parasympathetic functions
3. Sympathetic division—controls visceral effectors so their activities make possible maximum energy expenditure; part of body's defense in times of stress; see Table 31, p. 255, for specific sympathetic functions

Review questions

The nervous system

1. In a word or two, what general function does the nervous system perform?
2. What other system serves the same general function?
3. Explain the following abbreviations: CNS and PNS.
4. Make an identifying statement about each of the three types of neurons.
5. What physiological properties are more highly developed in nervous tissue than in any other?
6. Describe the structural characteristics of neurons which adapt them for this functional property.
7. What microscopic structures compose gray matter? White matter?
8. What function is the myelin sheath thought to perform? The neurilemma? Which neurons lack a neurilemma?
9. Distinguish between a nerve and a tract.
10. Distinguish between a ganglion, a nucleus, and a reflex center.
11. Where is a lumbar puncture done? Why?
12. What general name is given to the membranous coverings of the brain and cord? What three layers compose this covering?
13. What are the cavities inside the brain called? How many are there? What do they contain?
14. Describe the circulation of cerebrospinal fluid.
15. What is the function of the cerebrospinal fluid?
16. What name is given to the outer portion

of the cerebrum? Describe its appearance. What structure connects its hemispheres?

17. Describe the general structure of the interior of the cerebrum.
18. Describe the general functions performed by the cerebral cortex.
19. State at least one specific function performed by each of the lobes of the cerebral cortex: frontal, parietal, temporal, and occipital.
20. Explain what projection tracts are.
21. Explain the system for naming individual tracts. Cite the names of a few specific tracts to clarify your explanation.
22. Describe the structure, location, and general functions of the thalamus, hypothalamus, and cerebellum.
23. Describe the gross structure and general functions of the spinal cord.
24. Explain briefly the general function of the autonomic nervous system; of the sympathetic system; of the parasympathetic system.
25. Sympathetic stimulation produces massive, widespread responses, whereas reactions to parasympathetic stimulation are highly localized. What anatomical difference between the two systems explains this physiological difference?
26. Injury of which cranial nerve would produce blindness? Deafness? Loss of the sense of smell? One eye to turn in?
27. Distinguish between a reflex arc, a reflex center, and a reflex.
28. Explain each of the following: lower motor neuron, upper motor neuron, and final common path.
29. Name the tracts that transmit impulses from each of the following types of receptors to the brain; state in which column of the cord each tract is located: pain and temperature receptors, crude touch receptors, proprioceptors (name two tracts for these), and discriminating touch receptors (two tracts).
30. Where are cell bodies of lower motor neurons located?
31. Explain the roles the following substances are thought to play in nervous system functioning: acetylcholine, norepinephrine, and cholinesterase.

32. Explain briefly the following principles:
    (a) All-or-none principle as applied to neurons
    (b) Principle of convergence
    (c) Principle of divergence
    (d) Principle of autonomic antagonism
33. A patient has suffered a cerebral hemorrhage into the right internal capsule. What major symptoms would you expect this to produce? Explain.
34. Digitalis, a drug said to have a stimulating effect on the vagus nerve, has been administered to a patient. What effect, if any, would you expect it to have on the patient's pulse?
35. When a physician does a neurological examination he tests various reflexes, for example, the knee jerk, ankle jerk, and abdominal reflex. Answer the following questions about each of these three reflexes:
    (a) What movement constitutes the reflex?
    (b) How is it elicited?
    (c) What nerves contain the sensory dendrites of its reflex arc?
    (d) What nerves contain the motor axons of its reflex arcs?
    (e) Which of the following words classify the reflex: bulbar or cord, contralateral or ipsilateral; deep or superficial, segmental or intersegmental, and two-neuron or three-neuron?
36. Describe the sensory neural pathway from periphery to cerebral cortex.
37. Describe briefly the relationship between the autonomic nervous system and the rest of the nervous system.
38. Compare impulse conduction by nerve fibers, across synapses, and across neuromuscular junctions.
39. Contrast these two neural paths: from the central nervous system to somatic effectors; from the central nervous system to visceral effectors.
40. Classify the following structures as somatic effectors, visceral effectors, or neither: adrenal glands, biceps femoris muscle, heart, iris, and skin.
41. Explain briefly the arousal or alerting mechanism.
42. What two general functions is the reticular formation thought to perform?

43. Distinguish between the terms action potential, excitatory potential, and resting potential.
44. Compare parasympathetic and sympathetic effects on the heart, blood vessels, digestive tract, sweat glands, and adrenal medulla.
45. Define the following terms briefly:

axon	kinesthesia
cortex	plexus
decussation	potential difference
dendrite	proprioception
depolarization	receptor

Sense organs

The body has millions of sense organs. All of its receptors, the beginnings of dendrites of all its sensory neurons, are its sense organs. They serve two vital general functions—sensations and reflexes. All sensations and all reflexes result from stimulation of receptors. In short, receptors are the structures that detect changes in our external and internal environment and that initiate the responses necessary for adjusting the body to these changes so as to maintain or restore homeostasis. One more point —a matter more of interest than importance—we have more than just the "five senses," vision, hearing, taste, smell, and touch. For example, some of our other senses are warmth, cold, pain, and proprioception.

Receptors are located all over the body, inside as well as on its surfaces. Sherrington classified receptors according to their location as exteroceptors, visceroceptors, and proprioceptors. Exteroceptors are surface receptors. They are located in the skin, mucosa, eye, and ear. Visceroceptors and proprioceptors are both located internally. Visceroceptors are found, for example, in the walls of the blood vessels, stomach, intestines, and various other organs. Proprioceptors are located in muscles, tendons, joints, and internal ear.

Structurally receptors differ considerably. Some, such as those in the eye and ear, constitute highly specialized sense organs. Others are simply naked or free nerve fibers, and still others are encapsulated nerve fibers. (Fig. 141.)

According to the principle of specificity of receptors, specific kinds of receptors mediate specific sensations because they are sensitive to specific kinds of stimuli. Although generally accepted, this principle is now questioned by some investigators who think one kind of receptor may mediate more than one kind of sensation and that one kind of sensation may be mediated by more than one kind of receptor. Table 32 and Fig. 141 present generally accepted ideas about which types of receptors mediate which sensations.

Because stimulation of pain receptors may give warning of potentially harmful environmental changes, pain receptors are also called *nociceptors* (L. *noceo*, to injure). Any type of stimulus, provided that

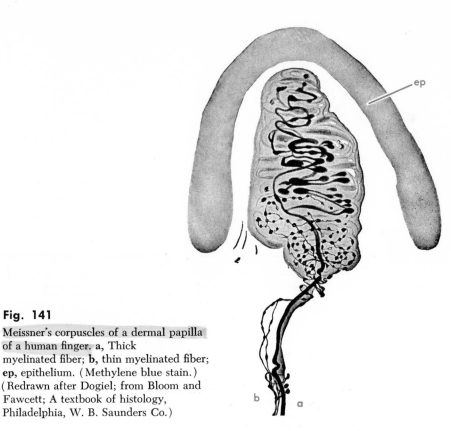

Fig. 141

Meissner's corpuscles of a dermal papilla
of a human finger. **a,** Thick
myelinated fiber; **b,** thin myelinated fiber;
ep, epithelium. (Methylene blue stain.)
(Redrawn after Dogiel; from Bloom and
Fawcett; A textbook of histology,
Philadelphia, W. B. Saunders Co.)

it be sufficiently intense, seems to be adequate for stimulating nociceptors in the skin and mucosa. In contrast, nociceptors in the viscera are stimulated only by marked changes in pressure and by certain chemicals. Cutting, crushing, or burning the intestinal wall, for example, are none of them painful procedures. But if the intestine becomes markedly distended or contracts with excessive force, severe pain results. That ischemia of the heart due to coronary occlusion causes pain is common knowledge. Presumably, the resulting cellular oxygen deficiency leads to the formation or accumulation of chemicals that stimulate nociceptors in the heart.

Two main types of pain are recognized: somatic and visceral.

Somatic pain may be *superficial,* as when it arises from stimulation of skin receptors, or *deep,* as when it results from stimulation of receptors in the skeletal muscles, fascia, tendons, and joints.

Visceral pain results from stimulation of receptors located in the viscera. Impulses are conducted from these receptors to the cord primarily by sensory fibers in sympathetic nerves and only rarely in parasympathetic nerves.

The cerebrum does not always interpret the source of pain accurately. Sometimes it erroneously refers the pain to a surface area instead of to the region in which the stimulated receptors actually are located. This phenomenon is called *referred pain.* It occurs only as a

Table 32.   Receptors

Sensations	Receptors
Touch	Meissner's corpuscles Merkel's disks Basketlike arrangements around bases of hairs
Pressure	Vater-Pacinian corpuscles
Heat	Corpuscles of Ruffini
Cold	Krause end bulbs
Pain	Naked nerve fibers
Proprioception	Neuromuscular spindles Neurotendinous spindles Ruffini endings in joint capsules

result of stimulation of pain receptors located in deep structures (skeletal muscles and viscera, for example), never from stimulation of skin receptors. In other words, deep somatic pain and visceral pain may be referred but not superficial somatic pain.

According to one theory, pain originating in the viscera and other deep structures is interpreted as coming from the skin area whose sensory fibers enter the same segment of the spinal cord as the sensory fibers from the deep structure. For example, sensory fibers from the heart enter the first to fourth thoracic segments. Pain originating in the heart, therefore, is referred to the skin areas whose sensory fibers also enter those cord segments, that is, to the region over the heart and on the inner surface of the left arm. Several other theories have also been advanced to explain referred pain.

EYE

Anatomy

Coats of eyeball. Approximately five-sixths of the eyeball lies recessed in the orbit, protected by this bony socket. Only its small anterior surface is exposed. Three layers of tissues or coats compose the eyeball. From the outside in they are the sclera, the chorioid,* and the retina. Both the sclera and the chorioid coats consist of an anterior and a posterior portion. Tough white fibrous tissue fashions the *sclera*.

---

*The spelling *chorioid* is preferred as etymologically preferable to the widely used choroid.

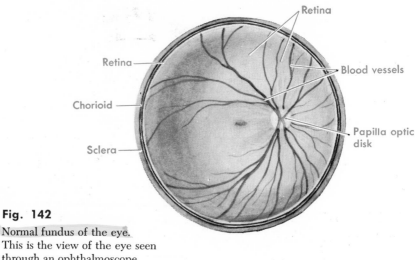

Retina

Retina

Blood vessels

Chorioid

Papilla optic
disk

Sclera

Fig. 142

Normal fundus of the eye.
This is the view of the eye seen
through an ophthalmoscope.

Deep within the anterior part of the sclera at its junction with the
cornea lies a ring-shaped venous sinus, the *canal of Schlemm.* The
anterior portion of the sclera is called the *cornea* and lies over the
colored part of the eye (iris). The cornea is transparent, whereas the
rest of the sclera is white and opaque, a fact which explains why the
visible anterior surface of the sclera is usually spoken of as the "whites"
of the eyes. No blood vessels are found in the cornea, in the aqueous
and vitreous humors, or in the lens.

The middle or *chorioid coat* of the eye contains a great many blood
vessels and a large amount of pigment. Its anterior portion is modified
into three separate structures: the ciliary body, the suspensory ligament, and the iris. The *ciliary body* is formed by a thickening of the
chorioid and fits like a collar into the area between the anterior margin
of the retina and the posterior margin of the iris. The small *ciliary
muscle,* composed of both radial and circular smooth muscle fibers,
lies in the anterior part of the ciliary body. Attached to the ciliary body
is the *suspensory ligament* which blends with the elastic capsule of
the *lens* and holds it suspended in place.

The *iris* or colored part of the eye consists of circular and radial
smooth muscle fibers arranged so as to form a doughnut-shaped structure, that is, round with a hole in the middle called the *pupil.* The iris
attaches to the ciliary body.

The *retina* is the incomplete innermost coat of the eyeball—incomplete in that it has no anterior portion. It consists mainly of nervous
tissue and contains three layers of neurons. Named in order from the
chorioid coat inward, they are photoreceptor neurons, bipolar neurons,
and ganglion neurons. The beginning of the dendrites of the photoreceptor neurons have been given names descriptive of their shapes. Because some look like tiny rods and others like cones, they are called

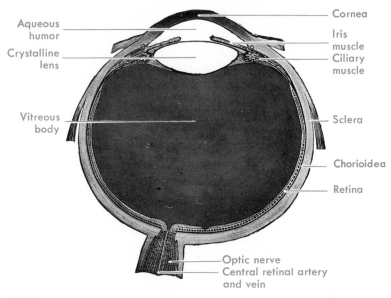

Aqueous humor
Crystalline lens
Vitreous body
Cornea
Iris muscle
Ciliary muscle
Sclera
Chorioidea
Retina
Optic nerve
Central retinal artery and vein

Fig. 143

Diagram of a horizontal section through the right eyeball. (From Pitzman: Fundamentals of anatomy, St. Louis, The C. V. Mosby Co.)

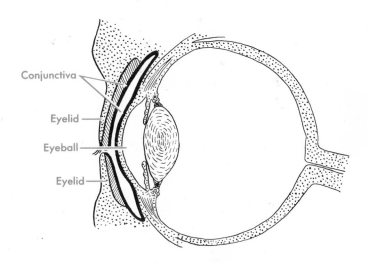

Conjunctiva
Eyelid
Eyeball
Eyelid

Fig. 144

Longitudinal section through the eyeball and lids. The heavy black line indicates the location of the conjunctiva. Note that it is a continuous sheet of membrane lining both lids and covering the surface of the eyeball.

269

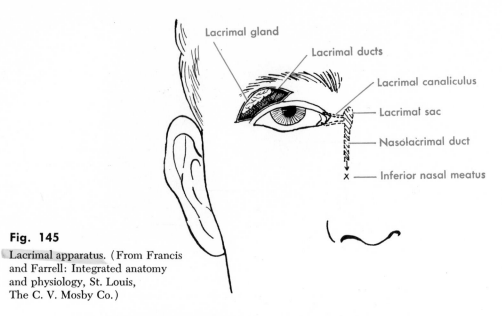

Fig. 145

Lacrimal apparatus. (From Francis
and Farrell: Integrated anatomy
and physiology, St. Louis,
The C. V. Mosby Co.)

respectively *rods* and *cones.* They constitute our visual receptors, structures highly specialized for stimulation by light rays (discussed on p.
277). They differ as to numbers, distribution, and function. The estimated number of cones is 7,000,000 and of rods, somewhere between
10 and 20 times as many. Cones are most densely concentrated in the
fovea centralis, a small depression in the center of a yellowish area
the *macula lutea* found near the center of the retina; they become less

Table 33. Coats of the eyeball

Location	Posterior portion	Anterior portion	Characteristics
Outer coat (sclera)	Sclera proper	Cornea	Protective fibrous coat; cornea transparent; rest of coat white and opaque
Middle coat (chorioid)	Chorioid proper	Ciliary body; suspensory ligament; iris (pupil is hole in iris); lens suspended in suspensory ligament	Vascular, pigmented coat
Inner coat (retina)	Retina	No anterior portion	Nervous tissue; consists of receptors for second cranial nerve; macula lutea yellowish area near center of retina; fovea centralis depression in macula

and less dense from the fovea outward. Rods, on the other hand, are absent entirely from the fovea and macula and increase in density toward the periphery of the retina. How these anatomical facts relate to rod and cone functions is revealed on p. 278.

All the axons of ganglion neurons extend back to a small circular area in the posterior part of the eyeball known as the *optic disk* or papilla. This part of the sclera contains perforations through which the fibers emerge from the eyeball as the *optic nerves.* The optic disk is also called the *blind spot* because light rays striking this area cannot be seen since it contains no rods or cones, only nerve fibers.

Table 33 is a summary of the coats of the eye in outline form.

Cavities and humors of the eye. The eyeball is not a solid sphere but contains a large interior cavity which is divided into two cavities, anterior and posterior. The *posterior cavity* is considerably larger than the anterior since it occupies all the space posterior to the lens, suspensory ligament, and ciliary body. It contains *vitreous humor*, a substance with a consistency comparable to soft gelatin. This semisolid material helps maintain sufficient intraocular pressure to prevent the eyeball from collapsing. (An obliterated artery, the hyaloid canal, runs through the vitreous humor between the lens and optic disk.) The *anterior cavity* of the eye has two subdivisions known as the *anterior* and *posterior chambers.* The entire anterior cavity lies in front of the lens, the posterior chamber being the space directly posterior to the iris, but anterior to the lens, whereas the anterior chamber is the small space anterior to the iris but posterior to the cornea. *Aqueous humor* fills both chambers of the anterior cavity. This substance is clear and watery and often leaks out when the eye is injured.

Still not established is the mechanism by which aqueous humor forms. Presumably both passive filtration from blood in eye capillaries and active transport mechanisms play a part. After circulating from the posterior to the anterior chamber, the fluid is absorbed into venous blood by way of the canal of Schlemm. Perhaps some absorption by

Table 34. Summary of the cavities of the eye

Cavity	Divisions	Location	Contents
Anterior	Anterior chamber	Anterior to iris and posterior to cornea	Aqueous humor
	Posterior chamber	Posterior to iris and anterior to lens	Aqueous humor
Posterior	None	Posterior to lens	Vitreous humor

other channels also occurs. Many theories about *glaucoma* (an eye disease in which intraocular pressure is higher than normal) postulate imbalance between the formation and absorption of aqueous humor. Either excess formation or, more often, decreased absorption is seen as an immediate cause of this condition, but underlying causes are unknown.

Muscles of the eye. Eye muscles are of two types: extrinsic and intrinsic. Extrinsic muscles are those which attach to the outside of the eyeball and to the bones of the orbit. These muscles move the eyeball in any desired direction and are, of course, voluntary muscles. Four of them are straight muscles and two are oblique. Their names describe their positions on the eyeball. They are the superior, inferior, mesial, and lateral rectus muscles and superior and inferior oblique muscles.

Intrinsic eye muscles are found within the eye. They are the iris and the ciliary muscles. These muscles are involuntary. Of interest is the fact that the eye is the only organ in the body in which both voluntary and involuntary muscles are found. The iris regulates the size of the pupil, whereas the ciliary muscle controls the shape of the lens. Contraction of the ciliary muscle pulls the ciliary body forward

Table 35. Summary of eye muscles

	Extrinsic muscles	*Intrinsic muscles*
Names	Superior rectus Inferior rectus Lateral rectus Mesial rectus Superior oblique Inferior oblique	Iris Ciliary muscle
Kind of muscle	Voluntary (striated, skeletal)	Involuntary (smooth, visceral)
Location	Attached to eyeball and bones of orbit	Modified anterior portion of choroid coat of eyeball; iris doughnut-shaped, sphincter muscle; pupil, hole in center of iris
Functions	Eye movements	Iris regulates size of pupil, therefore, amount of light entering eye; ciliary muscle controls shape of lens (accommodation), therefore, its refractive power
Innervation	Somatic fibers of third, fourth, and sixth cranial nerves	Autonomic fibers of third and fourth cranial nerves

and thereby releases the usual backward pull on the suspensory ligament in which the lens is suspended. When the suspensory ligament is thus relaxed, the elastic lens bulges or becomes more convex, an accommodation which is necessary for near vision (p. 276). The essential facts about eye muscles are summarized in Table 35.

Accessory structures of the eye. These structures are the eyebrows and lashes, eyelids, and lacrimal apparatus.

The *eyebrows* and *lashes* serve a cosmetic purpose and give some protection against the entrance of foreign objects into the eyes. Small glands located at the base of the lashes secrete a lubricating fluid. They are of interest because they frequently become infected, forming a *stye.*

The eyelids or palpebrae consist mainly of voluntary muscle and skin, with a border of thick connective tissue at the free edge of each lid known as the tarsal plate. One can feel the tarsal plate as a ridge when turning back the lid to remove a foreign object. Mucous membrane called conjunctiva lines each lid and continues over the surface of the eyeball, where it is modified to given transparency. Inflammation of the conjunctiva (conjunctivitis) is a fairly common infection; it is often called pinkeye because it produces a pinkish discoloration of the eye's surface.

The opening between the eyelids bears the technical name of palpebral fissure. The height of this fissure determines the apparent size of the eyes. In other words, if the lids are habitually held widely opened, the eyes appear large. Keeping the lids only partially open, on the other hand, gives the illusion of small eyes. Actually, there is very little difference in size between eyeballs of different adults. The upper and lower lids join, forming an angle or corner known as a *canthus,* the inner canthus being the mesial corner of the eye and the outer canthus the lateral corner.

The *lacrimal apparatus* consists of the structures which secrete tears and drain them from the surface of the eyeball. They are the lacrimal glands, lacrimal ducts, lacrimal sacs, and nasolacrimal ducts. The *lacrimal glands,* comparable in size and shape to a small almond, are located in a depression of the frontal bone at the upper outer margin of each orbit. Approximately a dozen small ducts lead from each gland, draining the tears onto the conjunctiva at the upper outer corner of the eye. The *lacrimal canals* are small channels, one above, the other below each *caruncle* (small red body at inner canthus); they empty into the lacrimal sacs. The openings into the canals are called *punctae* and can be seen as two small dots at the inner canthus of the eye. The *lacrimal sacs* are located in a groove in the lacrimal bone. The *nasolacrimal ducts* are small tubes which extend from the lacrimal sac into the inferior meatus of the nose. All the tear ducts are lined with mucous membrane, an extension of the mucosa which lines the nose. When this membrane becomes inflamed and swollen, as in a cold, for example, the nasolacriminal ducts become plugged, causing the tears to overflow from the eyes ("watering" eyes) instead of draining into the nose as they do normally.

Physiology of vision

In order for vision to occur, the following conditions must be fulfilled: an image must be formed on the retina to stimulate its receptors (rods and cones), and the resulting nerve impulses must be conducted to the visual areas of the cerebral cortex.

Formation of the retinal image. Four processes focus light rays so that they form a clear image on the retina: *refraction* of the light rays, *accommodation* of the lens, *constriction* of the pupil, and *convergence* of the eyes.

Refraction of light rays. Refraction means the deflection or bending of light rays. It is produced by light rays passing obliquely from one transparent medium into another of different optical density, and the more convex the surface of the medium, the greater is its refractive power. The refracting media of the eye are the cornea, aqueous humor, lens, and vitreous humor. Light rays are bent, or refracted at the anterior surface of the cornea as they pass from the rarer air into the denser cornea, at the anterior surface of the lens as they pass from the aqueous humor into the denser lens, and at the posterior surface of the lens as they pass from the lens into the rarer vitreous humor.

When an individual goes to a doctor for an eye examination, the doctor does what he calls a "refraction." In other words, by various specially designed methods, he measures the refractory or light-bending power of that person's eyes.

In a normal (emmetropic) eye when it is relaxed, the four refracting media together bend light rays sufficiently to bring to a focus on the retina the parallel rays reflected from an object 20 or more feet away. Of course a normal eye can also focus objects located much nearer than twenty feet from the eye. This is accomplished by a mechanism known as accommodation (discussed on pp. 275 and 276). Many eyes, however, show *errors of refraction;* that is, they are not able to focus the rays on the retina under the stated conditions. Some common errors of refraction are *nearsightedness* (myopia), *farsightedness* (hypermetropia), and *astigmatism.*

The nearsighted eye sees distant objects as blurred images because it focuses rays from the object at a point in front of the retina (Fig. 146). According to one theory, this occurs because the eyeball is too

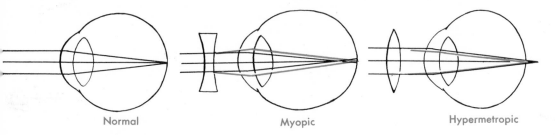

Normal   Myopic   Hypermetropic

Fig. 146

Errors of refraction. Rays from a distant object are focused by the
nearsighted (myopic) eye at a point in front of the retina; glasses with
concave lenses bring the rays to a focus on the retina. The
farsighted (hypermetropic) eye focuses light rays at a theoretical
point behind the retina; a convex lens corrects this condition.
Dotted lines show corrected refraction by glasses.

long and the distance too great from the lens to the retina in the
myopic eye. Concave glasses, by lessening refraction, can give clear
distant vision to nearsighted individuals. Presumably opposite conditions exist in the farsighted eye.

Astigmatism is a more complicated condition in which the curvature of the cornea is uneven, causing horizontal and vertical rays to be
focused at two different points on the retina. Instead of the curvature
of the cornea being a section of a sphere, it is more like that of a tea-
spoon with horizontal and vertical arcs uneven. Suitable glasses correct the refraction of such an eye.

Visual acuity or the ability to distinguish form and outline clearly
is indicated by a fraction which compares the distance at which an
individual sees an object (usually letters of a definite size and shape)
clearly with the distance at which the normal eye would see the object. Thus, if he sees clearly at 20 feet an object which the normal
eye would be able to see clearly at 20 feet, his visual acuity is said to
be 20/20 or normal, but if he sees an object clearly at 20 feet which
the normal eye sees clearly at 30 feet, then his visual acuity is 20/30
or two thirds of normal.

As people grow older, they become farsighted due to the lenses
losing their elasticity and therefore their ability to bulge and to accommodate for near vision. This condition is called *presbyopia.*

Accommodation of the lens. Accommodation for near vision necessitates three changes: increase in the curvature of the lens, constriction
of the pupils, and convergence of the two eyes. Light rays from objects 20 or more feet away are practically parallel. The normal eye,
as previously noted, refracts such rays sufficiently to focus them clearly
on the retina. But light rays from nearer objects are divergent rather
than parallel. So obviously they must be bent more acutely to bring
them to a focus on the retina. Accommodation of the lens or in other
words an increase in its curvature takes place to achieve this greater

refraction. (It is a physical fact that the greater the convexity of a lens, the greater is its refractive power.) Most observers accept Helmholtz' theory about the mechanism that produces accommodation of the lens. According to his theory, the ciliary muscle contracts, pulling the ciliary body and chorioid forward toward the lens. This releases the tension on the suspensory ligament and therefore on the lens which, being plastic, immediately bulges. For near vision, then, the ciliary muscle is contracted, and the lens is bulging, whereas for far vision the ciliary muscle is relaxed and the lens is comparatively flat. Continual use of the eyes for near work produces eyestrain because of the prolonged contraction of the ciliary muscle. Some of the strain can be avoided by looking into the distance at intervals while doing close work.

Constriction of the pupil. The muscles of the iris play an important part in the formation of clear retinal images. Part of the accommodation mechanism consists of contraction of the circular fibers of the iris which constricts the pupil. This prevents divergent rays from the object from entering the eye through the periphery of the cornea and lens. Such peripheral rays could not be brought to a focus on the retina (due to spherical abberration of the lens) and therefore would cause a blurred image. Constriction of the pupil for near vision is called the *near reflex* of the pupil and occurs simultaneously with accommodation of the lens in near vision. The pupil constricts also in bright light (*photopupil reflex or pupillary light reflex*) to protect the retina from too intense or too sudden stimulation.

Convergence. Single binocular vision (seeing only one object instead of two when both eyes are used) occurs when light rays from an object fall on corresponding points of the two retinas. The foveas and all points lying equidistant and in the same direction from the foveas are corresponding points. Whenever the eyeballs move in unison, either with the visual axes parallel (for far objects) or converging upon a common point (for near objects), light rays strike corresponding points of the two retinas. Convergence is the movement of the two eyeballs inward so that their visual axes come together or converge at the object viewed. The nearer the object, the greater is the degree of convergence necessary to maintain single vision. A simple procedure serves to demonstrate the fact that single binocular vision results from stimulation of corresponding points of the two retinas. Gently press one eyeball out of line while viewing an object. Instead of one object, two will be seen. In order to achieve unified movement of the two eyeballs, a functional balance between the antagonistic extrinsic muscles must exist. If, for example, the right internal rectus muscle should contract more forcefully than its antagonist, the right ex-

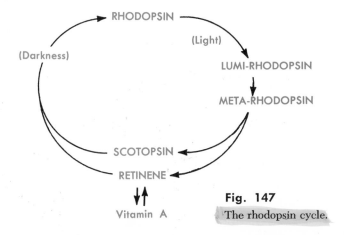

RHODOPSIN

(Light)

(Darkness)

LUMI-RHODOPSIN

META-RHODOPSIN

SCOTOPSIN

RETINENE

Vitamin A

Fig. 147

The rhodopsin cycle.

ternal rectus, the right eye would be pulled in toward the nose instead of its visual axis being held parallel to that of the left eye in distant vision or converged upon the same point in near vision. Light rays from an object would then fall on noncorresponding points of the two retinas, and the object would be seen double (diplopia). Sometimes the individual can overcome the deviation of the visual axes by muscular effort (extra innervation of the weak muscle) and thereby achieve single vision, but only at the expense of muscular and nervous strain. The condition in which the imbalance of the eye muscles can be overcome by extra innervation of the weak muscle is called *heterophoria* (*esophoria* if the internal rectus is stronger and pulls the eye nasalward and *exophoria* if the external rectus is stronger and pulls the eye temporalward). *Strabismus* (cross-eye or squint) is an exaggerated esophoria which cannot be overcome by neuromuscular effort. An individual with strabismus usually does not have double vision, as would be expected, because he learns to suppress one of the images.

Stimulation of the retina. Rods are known to contain *rhodopsin* (visual purple), a pigmented compound. As shown in Fig. 147, it forms by a protein scotopsin combining with retinene, a derivative of vitamin A. Rhodopsin is highly light-sensitive, so that when light rays strike a rod, its rhodopsin rapidly breaks down, also shown in Fig. 147. And in some way this chemical change initiates impulse conduction by the rod. Then if the rod is exposed to darkness for a short time, rhodopsin reforms from the scotopsin and retinene and is ready to function again. *Cones* also contain photosensitive chemicals. Just what they are, however, is not established. (Recent work suggests that there may be three major substances. Iodopsin, chlorolabe, and erythrolabe are the names given them.) Presumably the cone compounds are less sensitive to light than rhodopsin. Brighter light seems necessary for their breakdown. Cones, therefore, are considered to be the receptors responsible for daylight and color vision. Rods, on the other hand, are believed to

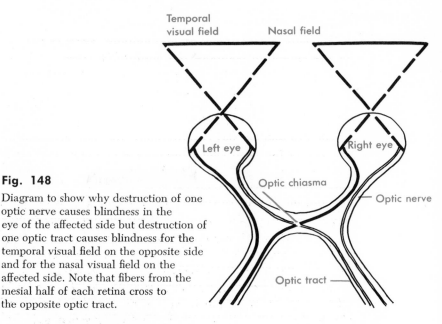

Fig. 148

Diagram to show why destruction of one optic nerve causes blindness in the eye of the affected side but destruction of one optic tract causes blindness for the temporal visual field on the opposite side and for the nasal visual field on the affected side. Note that fibers from the mesial half of each retina cross to the opposite optic tract.

be the receptors for night vision because their rhodopsin quickly becomes almost depleted in bright light due to its rapid breakdown but slow regeneration. This explains why you cannot see for a little while after you go from a bright light to darkness. But when rhodopsin has had time to reform, the rods again start functioning and dark adaptation has occurred. Or as we say, we "can see in the dark once we get used to it." Night blindness occurs in marked vitamin A deficiency. Why? Fig. 147 contains a clue. (Retinene is a derivative of vitamin A.) The fovea contains the greatest concentration of cones and is, therefore, the point of clearest vision in good light. For this reason when we want to seen an object clearly in the daytime, we look directly at it so as to focus the image on the fovea. But in dim light or darkness we see an object better if we look slightly to the side of it, thereby focusing the image nearer the periphery of the retina where rods are more plentiful.

Conduction to visual area. Fibers which conduct impulses from the rods and cones reach the visual cortex in the occipital lobes via the optic nerves, optic chiasma, optic tracts, and optic radiations. Those fibers which originate in the medial half of each retina cross over in the optic chiasma and continue through the optic tract and radiation on the opposite side. This anatomical arrangement explains certain peculiar visual abnormalities seen occasionally with brain tumors or other intracranial lesions (Fig. 148).

The ears, auditory nerves, and auditory areas of the temporal lobes of the cerebrum compose the auditory apparatus. Each ear consists of three parts: external ear, middle ear, and inner ear.

External ear

The external ear has two divisions: the flap or modified trumpet on the side of the head called the *auricle* or *pinna* and the tube leading from the auricle into the temporal bone and named the *external auditory canal* or *meatus*. This canal is about 1¼ inches long and takes, in general, an inward, forward, and downward direction, although the first portion of the tube slants upward and then curves downward. Because of this curve in the auditory canal, the auricle should be pulled up and back to straighten the tube when dropping medications into the ear. Modified sweat glands in the auditory canal secrete *cerumen* (waxlike substance) which occasionally becomes impacted and may cause pain and deafness. The *tympanic membrane* stretches across the inner end of the auditory canal, separating it from the middle ear.

Middle ear

The middle ear (tympanic cavity), a tiny epithelial-lined cavity hollowed out of the temporal bone, contains the three auditory ossicles: the malleus, incus, and stapes. The names of these very small bones describe their shapes (hammer, anvil, and stirrups). The "handle" of the malleus is attached to the inner surface of the tympanic membrane, whereas the "head" attaches to the incus, which, in turn, attaches to the stapes. There are several openings into the middle ear cavity: one from the external auditory meatus, covered over with the tympanic

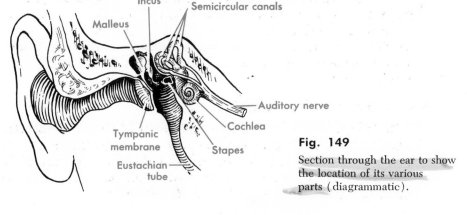

Fig. 149

Section through the ear to show the location of its various parts (diagrammatic).

membrane; two into the internal ear, the fenestra ovalis (oval window), into which the stapes fits, and the fenestra rotunda (round window), which is covered by a membrane; and one into the eustachian tube.

Posteriorly, the middle ear cavity is continuous with a number of mastoid cells in the temporal bone. The clinical importance of these openings is that they provide routes for infection to travel. Head colds, for example, especially in children, may lead to middle ear or mastoid infections via the nasopharynx-eustachian tube-middle ear-mastoid path.

The *eustachian tube,* a collapsible fibrocartilaginous tube lined with mucosa, leads from the middle ear cavity downward, forward, and inward to the nasopharynx (the part of the throat behind the nose).

In the preceding paragraph we called attention to the disadvantage of this anatomical connection between the nasopharynx and middle ear. But the eustachian tube also serves a useful function. It makes possible equalization of pressure against inner and outer surfaces of the tympanic membrane and therefore prevents membrane rupture and the discomfort that marked pressure differences produce. The way the eustachian tube equalizes tympanic membrane pressures is this. When one swallows or yawns, air spreads rapidly through the open tube. Atmospheric pressure then presses against the inner surface of the tympanic membrane. And since atmospheric pressure is continually exerted against its outer surface, the pressures are equal. You might test this mechanism sometime when you are ascending or descending in an airplane—start chewing gum to increase your swallowing and observe whether this relieves the discomfort in your ears.

Inner ear

The inner ear is also called the labyrinth because of its complicated shape. It consists of two main parts, a bony labyrinth and inside this a membranous labyrinth. The bony labyrinth consists of three parts: vestibule, cochlea, and semicircular canals. The membranous labyrinth consists of the utricle, saccule, cochlear duct, and membranous semicircular canals.

Vestibule, utricle, and saccule

The vestibule constitutes the central section of the bony labyrinth. Into it open both the oval and round windows from the middle ear as well as the three semicircular canals of the inner ear. The membranous utricle and saccule are suspended within the vestibule and are separated from its bony walls by fluid (perilymph).

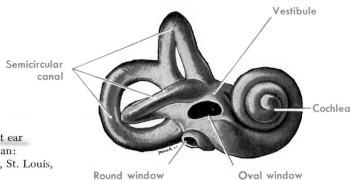

Semicircular
canal

Vestibule

Cochlea

Fig. 150

Bony labyrinth of the right ear
lateral view. (From Pitzman:
Fundamentals of anatomy, St. Louis,
The C. V. Mosby Co.)

Round window   Oval window

Fibers of the vestibular nerve (branch of eighth cranial nerve) end
around hair cells in a special structure within the utricle and saccule
known as the *macula acustica*. Scattered among the hairs in the macula
are *otoliths,* small particles of calcium carbonate. Changing the position of the head causes the otoliths to pull on the hair cells, and this
stimulation evokes *righting reflexes,* muscular responses to restore the
body and its parts to their normal position when they have been placed
in an abnormal one. (Impulses from proprioceptors and from the eyes
also activate righting reflexes. And interruption of the vestibular or
visual or proprioceptive impulses which initiate these reflexes may
cause disturbances of equilibrium, nausea, vomiting, and other symptoms.)

Cochlea and cochlear duct

The word cochlea, which means snail, describes the outer appearance of this part of the bony labyrinth. When sectioned, the cochlea
resembles a tube wound spirally around a cone-shaped core of bone,
the *modiolus*. The modiolus houses the spiral ganglion which consists
of cell bodies of the first sensory neurons in the auditory relay. Inside
the cochlea lies the membranous *cochlear duct*. This structure is
shaped like a tube but is a triangular rather than a round tube. It
forms a kind of shelf across the inside of the bony cochlea, dividing
it into upper and lower sections all along its winding course (Fig. 151).
The upper section, above the cochlea duct, that is, is called the *scala
vestibuli,* whereas the lower section below the cochlea duct is the
scala tympani. The roof of the cochlear duct is known as *Reissner's
membrane* or the vestibular membrane. *Basilar membrane* is the name
given the floor of the cochlear duct; it is supported by bony and fibrous
projections from the wall of the cochlea. Perilymph fills the scala
vestibuli and tympani and endolymph the cochlear duct.

The hearing sense organ, the *organ of Corti,* rests on the basilar
membrane throughout the whole length of the cochlear duct. It consists of supporting cells plus the important *hair cells* (so called because
of their numerous cilia) which project into the endolymph and are
topped by the gelatinous *tectorial membrane.* Dendrites of the sensory

281

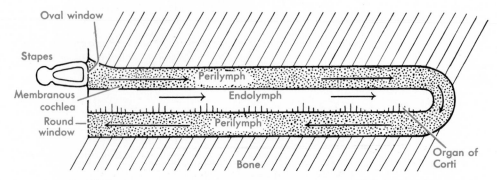

Fig. 151

Diagram of the bony and membranous cochlea, uncoiled. Note the end organ of Corti projecting into the endolymph contained in the membranous cochlea. The perilymph indicated above the endolymph occupies the scala vestibuli; that in the lower compartment lies in the scala tympani (see also Fig. 152) (Modified from Williams: Textbook of anatomy and physiology, Philadelphia, W. B. Saunders Co.)

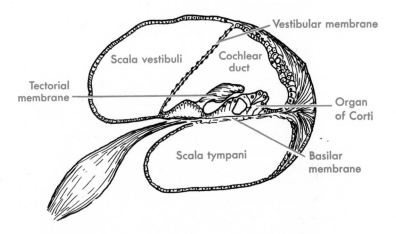

Fig. 152

Section through one of the coils of the cochlea; perilymph fills the scala vestibuli and scala tympani; endolymph fills the cochlear duct (membranous cochlea). A part of the spiral ganglion is shown (bulging stemlike structure at left of diagram).
(Modified from Rasmussen.)

neurons whose cells lie in the spiral ganglion in the modiolus have their beginnings around the bases of the hair cells. Axons of these neurons extend in the cochlear branch of the eighth cranial nerve to the brain-stem.

Semicircular canals

Three semicircular canals, each in a plane approximately at right angles to the others, are found in each temporal bone. Within the bony semicircular canals and separated from them by perilymph are the membranous semicircular canals. Each contains endolymph and connects with the utricle, one of the membranous sacs inside the bony vestibule. Near its junction with the utricle the canal enlarges into an ampulla. Some of the receptors for the vestibular branch of the eighth cranial nerve lie in each ampulla. Like all receptors for both vestibular and auditory branches of this nerve, these receptors, too, are hair cells in a supporting structure. Here in the ampulla, the cells and supporting structure together are named the *crista ampullaris,* whereas in the utricle and saccule they are called the macula acustica and in the cochlear duct, the organ of Corti. Sitting atop the crista is a gelatinous structure called the *cupula.*

The crista is thought to serve as the end organ for sensations of head movements and the macula in the utricle as the end organ for sensations of head positions. Hence both the crista and the macula of the utricle function to give the sense of equilibrium. But the macula in the saccule according to Ham, is "probably related in some way to the sense of hearing" and not to the sense of equilibrium.*

Hearing

Hearing results from stimulation of the auditory area of the cerebral cortex (temporal lobe, Fig. 123). Before reaching this area of the brain, however, sound waves must be projected through air, bone, and fluid to stimulate nerve endings and set up impulse conduction over nerve fibers.

Sound waves in the air enter the external auditory meatus, probably without much aid from the pinna in collecting and reflecting them because of its smallness in man. At the inner end of the meatus they strike against the tympanic membrane, setting it in vibration. Here, bone conduction of sound waves begins. Because auditory ossicles are connected —malleus to incus and incus to stapes—this is a chain reaction. Vibrations of the tympanic membrane move the malleus (whose handle at-

---

*From Ham, Arthur W., and Leeson, Thomas S.: Histology, ed. 4, Philadelphia, 1961, J. B. Lippincott Co., p. 913.

283

taches to the membrane), which moves the incus, which moves the stapes against the oval window into which it fits so precisely. At this point fluid conduction of sound waves begins. When the stapes moves against the oval window, pressure is exerted inward into the perilymph in the scala vestibuli of the cochlea. This starts a "ripple" in the perilymph which is transmitted through Reissner's membrane (the roof of the cochlear duct) to endolymph inside the duct and thence to the floor of the duct (the basilar membrane), and then finally to perilymph in the scala tympani where the ripple expends itself against the round window. It is the movement of the endolymph that stimulates receptors of the organ of Corti and initiates nerve impulse conduction along the spiral ganglion neurons and thence by way of the cochlear division of the eighth cranial nerve to the brainstem.

Before reaching the auditory area of the temporal lobe, impulses pass through "relay stations" in nuclei in the medulla, pons, midbrain, and thalamus.

Equilibrium

In addition to hearing, the inner ear aids in the maintenance of equilibrium by making possible sensations of position and movements of the head.

OLFACTORY SENSE ORGANS

The receptors for the fibers of the olfactory (first) cranial nerves lie in the mucosa of the upper part of the nasal cavity. Their location here explains the necessity for sniffing or drawing air forcefully up into the nose in order to smell delicate odors. They are ciliated cells and are relatively simple compared with the complex visual and auditory receptors. Whereas the olfactory receptors are extremely sensitive, that is, are stimulated by even very slight odors, they are also easily fatigued—a fact which explains why odors which are at first very noticeable are not sensed at all after a short time.

GUSTATORY SENSE ORGANS

The receptors for the taste nerve fibers (glossopalatine branch of the facial [seventh] cranial nerve and of the glossopharyngeal [ninth] cranial nerve) are known as *taste buds* or taste corpuscles. They are located in the papillae of the tongue. Not all taste receptors are stimulated by the same kinds of substances. Four different tastes are recognized, each resulting from stimulation of a different set of taste buds—for sweet, sour, bitter, and salt substances. All the other flavors experienced are a result of fusion of two or more of the four tastes named, as sugar in lemon juice and as a result of stimulation of the olfactory receptors. In other words, the myriads of tastes recognized are not tastes alone but tastes plus odors. For this reason a cold which interferes with the stimulation of the olfactory receptors by odors from foods in the mouth markedly dull one's taste sensations.

The four kinds of taste corpuscles are not evenly distributed over the tongue. Most of those sensitive to bitter are located at the back of the tongue, those sensitive to sweet at the tip, and those sensitive to sour and to salt along the sides and tip. If a patient takes a bitter medicine by placing it on the tip of the tongue and swallowing it quickly with water, he will experience less of the bitter taste than if he places it on the back of the tongue where there is a concentration of taste buds sensitive to bitter.

Outline summary

The sense organs

1. General remarks—millions of receptors constitute the sense organs; for classification, location, and function of receptors see Table 32, p. 267
2. Somatic pain—results from stimulation of pain receptors (nociceptors) in skin or in deep structures, skeletal muscles, tendons, or joints
3. Visceral pain—reults from stimulation of pain receptors in viscera by pressure or chemical stimuli: conducted almost exclusively by sensory fibers in sympathetic nerves
4. Referred pain—pain interpreted as coming from a skin area when it actually originates in a deep structure

Eye

1. Anatomy
   a. coats of eyeball—summarized in Table 33, p. 270
   b. cavities and humors of eye—summarized in Table 34, p. 271
   c. muscles of eye (Table 35, p. 272)
      1. extrinsic—attach to outside of eyeball and to bones of orbit; voluntary muscles; move eyeball in desired direc-

tions; four straight (rectus) muscles —superior, inferior, lateral, and mesial; two oblique muscles—superior and inferior
      2. intrinsic—within eyeball; named iris and ciliary muscles; involuntary; iris regulates size of pupil; ciliary muscle controls shape of lens, making possible accommodation for near and far objects
   d. accessory structures of eye—eyebrows and lashes, protective and cosmetic; eyelids or palpebrae are lined with mucous membrane which continues over surface of eyeball; called conjunctiva; opening between lids is palpebral fissure; corners where upper and lower lids join called canthus, mesial and lateral; lacrimal apparatus—lacrimal glands, ducts, sacs, and nasolacrimal ducts
2. Physiology of vision—fulfillment of following conditions results in conscious experience known as vision
   a. formation of an image on retina; accomplished by the following:
      1. refraction or bending of light rays as they pass through eye

285

2. accommodation or bulging of lens if object viewed lies nearer than twenty feet from eye
3. constriction of pupil; occurs simultaneously with accommodation for near objects and also in bright light
4. convergence of eyes for near objects so light rays from an object fall on corresponding points of two retinas; necessary for single binocular vision
   b. stimulation of retina by light rays producing photochemical change in rods and cones
   c. conduction to visual area by fibers in optic nerves, optic chiasma, and optic tracts to occipital lobe cortex

Auditory apparatus

1. Anatomy
   a. external ear—consists of auricle or pinna and external auditory canal
   b. middle ear, tympanic cavity—separated from external ear by tympanic membrane; contains auditory ossicles and openings from eustachian tube, mastoid sinuses, external and internal ears; eustachian tube, collapsible tube, lined with mucosa, extending from nasopharynx to middle ear; equalizes pressure on both sides of eardrum; open when yawning or swallowing
   c. inner ear or labyrinth—consists of bony and membranous portions, latter contained within former; bony labyrinth has three divisions—cochlea, vestibule, and semicircular canals; membranous cochlear duct contains receptors for cochlear or auditory branch of eighth cranial nerve (makes possible hearing); utricle and membranous semicircular canals contain receptors for vestibular branch of eighth cranial nerve (important in maintenance of equilibrium)
2. Physiology of ear
   a. hearing—result of stimulation of auditory area of temporal lobes by impulses over auditory nerves, which are stimulated by sound waves being projected through air, bone, and fluid before reaching auditory receptors (organ of Corti)

b. equilibrium—stimulation of receptors in semicircular canals and utricle initiates righting reflexes essential for balance

Olfactory sense organs

Receptors for first cranial nerve located in nasal mucosa high along septum; very sensitive but easily fatigued

Gustatory sense organs

Receptors for seventh and ninth cranial nerves, called taste corpuscles or taste buds; located in papillae of tongue; four different kinds—those sensitive to sweet, salt, sour, and bitter; all other tastes result from fusion of two or more of these tastes or from olfactory stimulation

Review questions
Sense organs

1. What two general functions do sense organs perform?
2. Explain briefly the principle of specificity of receptors.
3. Describe briefly one theory about the mechanism of referred pain.
4. Explain briefly the mechanism for accommodation for near vision.
5. Define briefly the term refraction. Name the refractory media of the eye.
6. Concave glasses are prescribed for near-sighted vision. Upon what principle is this based?
7. What is the name of the receptors for vision in dim light? For bright light?
8. Distinguish between exteroceptors, proprioceptors, and visceroceptors.
9. Describe the main features of middle ear structure.
10. Name the parts of the bony and membranous labyrinths and describe the relationship of membranous labyrinth parts to those of the bony labyrinth.
11. In what ear structure(s) is the hearing sense organ located? The equilibrium sense organs?

Maintaining the metabolism of the body

Chapter IX

The circulatory system

Functions

Blood cells
Erythrocytes
Leukocytes
Platelets

Blood groups

Blood plasma
Definition
Composition

Blood clotting
Purpose
Mechanism
Factors that oppose
Factors that hasten
Pharmaceutical preparations
that retard clotting
Clinical methods of hastening
clotting

Heart
Description
Covering
Structure
Physiology

Blood vessels
Kinds
Structure
Functions
Names of main blood vessels
Fetal circulation

Circulation
Definitions
Functions of circulation
mechanisms
Principles of circulation

Blood pressure measurement

**Blood pressure related to
bleeding**

Velocity of blood

Pulse
Definition
Cause
Pulse wave
Where pulse can be felt
Venous pulse

Lymphatic system
Definition
Lymph and tissue fluid
Lymphatics
Lymph circulation
Lymph nodes
Spleen

FUNCTIONS

Transportation is the primary function of the circulatory system. Its secondary functions—the functions to which it contributes—are every function of every cell and every function of the body as a whole. This is a sweeping statement and is therefore suspect, but we shall try to support it with substantial evidence as this and the remaining chapters of the book unfold. For now, just a few examples: the circulatory system transports food and oxygen to all cells so plays a vital part in cellular metabolism and in all cellular functions. It transports water and electrolytes so makes vital contributions to the maintenance of homeostasis —homeostasis of fluid and of pH and even of body temperature. It transports hormones and enzymes so takes part in the control and integration of countless functions. It transports antibodies so contributes heavily to the body's defense against microorganisms. Our discussion in this chapter will center around the following main topics: blood, heart, blood vessels, circulation, and lymphatic system.

BLOOD

Blood is one of the body's three major fluids (interstitial fluid and intracellular fluid are the other two). Water, solutes, and cells compose the blood. We shall discuss blood cells first and then blood plasma, the fluid portion of blood, in which solutes are dissolved.

Blood cells
Kinds

Three main kinds of blood cells are recognized: red cells (erythrocytes), white cells (leukocytes), and platelets (thrombocytes). Leukocytes are further divided as shown in the following summary of the kinds of blood cells:

Erythrocytes or red blood cells
Leukocytes or white blood cells
   Granular leukocytes: neutrophils, eosinophils, and basophils
   Nongranular leukocytes: lymphocytes and monocytes
Platelets (thrombocytes)

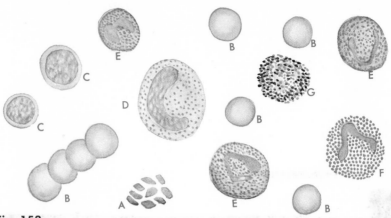

Fig. 153

Human blood cells.

  A. Platelets

  B. Red blood cells (erythrocytes)

  C to G. White blood cells (leukocytes)

  C. Lymphocytes

  D. Monocytes

  E. Neutrophils

  F. Eosinophils

  G. Basophils

From 65 to 75% of white blood cells are type E (neutrophils).

In another method of classifying blood cells, they are divided into two main types according to origin:

  Myeloid cells (formed in myeloid tissue, that is, in red bone marrow)

    Erythrocytes

    Granular leukocytes: neutrophils, eosinophils, and basophils

    Platelets

  Lymphoid cells (or lymphatic cells; formed mainly in lymphatic tissue, namely, lymph nodes, thymus, and spleen)

    Lymphocytes

    Monocytes

Erythrocytes

Appearance and size. Facts about normal red cell size and shape hold more than academic interest. Because they so often become abnormal in anemia and certain other diseases, these characteristics are also clinically important. Red cells are extremely small; more than 3000 of them could be placed side by side in 1 inch since they measure only about 7 microns in diameter. A normal mature red cell has no nucleus. Just before the cell reaches maturity and enters the blood stream from the bone marrow, the nucleus is extruded, and the cell becomes caved in on both sides—biconcave disks is the usual description of red cell shape.

Structure and functions. Red blood cell functions, the transport of oxygen and carbon dioxide, illustrate the familiar principle that structure determines function. Packed within one tiny red cell are an esti-

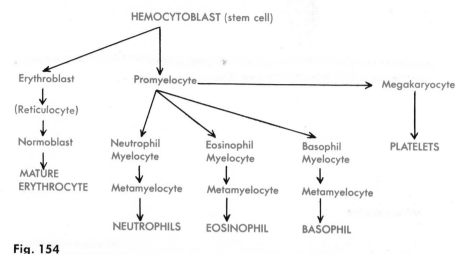

Fig. 154

Stages of development of red blood cells (erythrocytes), granular leukocytes, and platelets in red bone marrow. Under ordinary conditions when the need for red cells is not greater than normal, most erythroblasts develop directly into normoblasts without going through the reticulocyte stage.

mated 200 million to 300 million molecules of the complex compound *hemoglobin*. One hemoglobin molecule consists of a protein molecule (globin) combined with four molecules of a pigmented compound (heme). Because each molecule of heme contains 1 atom of iron, 1 hemoglobin molecule contains 4 iron atoms. And this is the structural fact that enables 1 hemoglobin molecule to unite with 4 oxygen molecules to form oxyhemoglobin (a reversible reaction). Hemoglobin can also combine with carbon dioxide to form carboxyhemoglobin (also reversible). But in this reaction the structure of the globin part of the hemoglobin molecule rather than of its heme part makes the combining possible. Further discussion of oxygen and carbon dioxide transport appears in Chapter X.

Formation (erythropoiesis). Erythrocytes are formed in the red bone marrow* from nucleated cells known as hemocytoblasts or stem cells. The main stages of red cell development (Fig. 154) are as follows: hemocytoblast, erythroblast, normoblast, and erythrocyte (mature red cell). But, curiously, when for some reason the body needs for red cell production to be speeded up greatly, another stage, reticulocytes, occurs between the erythroblast and normoblast stages. Hemoglobin synthesis starts during the erythroblast stage. Extrusion of the nucleus

---

*Locations of red bone marrow are given on p. 87. Before birth, the liver and spleen produce red blood cells, but by birth and from that time on only the red bone marrow performs this function. An exception to this principle is that the liver and spleen are thought to again produce red cells under some markedly abnormal conditions. With increased age comes decreased marrow productivity, a fact that may partially account for the anemia so common in old age.

occurs sometimes from erythroblasts (to form reticulocytes) but more often from normoblasts (to form mature red cells).

Frequently a physician needs information about the rate of erythropoiesis to help him make a diagnosis or prescribe treatment. A *reticulocyte count* gives this information. For example, a lower than normal reticulocyte count is one of the signs of anemia due to decreased red cell production. A higher than normal reticulocyte count, on the other hand, indicates accelerated red cell production such as may occur following treatment of anemia.

Destruction. The life span of a red blood cell circulating in the blood stream is now believed to be about 120 days, based on studies using radioactive substances (isotopes) to "tag" red cells. Apparently as red cells grow older, their membranes become increasingly fragile and eventually rupture, causing the cell to break apart or fragment within the capillaries. Following this, reticuloendothelial cells in the liver, spleen, and bone marrow phagocytose the red cell fragments and break down their hemoglobin to yield an iron-containing pigment (hemosiderin) and bile pigments (bilirubin and biliverdin). Eventually the bone marrow uses most of the iron over again for new red cell synthesis, and the liver excretes the bile pigments in the bile.

Erythrocyte homeostatic mechanism. Red cells are formed and destroyed at a breathtaking rate. Millions are destroyed while millions of others are formed every second of every day of our lives! Obviously some kind of homeostatic mechanism operates to balance the number of cells formed against the number destroyed, since, in health, the number of red cells remains relatively constant at about 4½ to 5½ million per cubic millimeter of blood. The exact mechanism responsible for this constancy is not known. It is known, however, that the rate of red cell production speeds up very soon after tissue hypoxia develops for any reason. The stimulus for starting the mechansim, in other words, appears to be be tissue hypoxia. Whether or not it acts as a direct stimulant of the bone marrow is not known. It may produce this stimulation indirectly by causing secretion of a substance (erythropoietin) which, in turn, stimulates the bone marrow (Fig. 155). Still unknown is the source of erythropoietin; the kidneys and pituitary gland have both been suggested as possible sources.

Note that for the red blood cell homeostatic mechanism to succeed in maintaining a normal number of red cells, the bone marrow must function adequately. To do this the blood must supply it with adequate amounts of several substances with which to form the new red cells—iron and amino acids, for example, and also copper, vitamin B compounds, and possibly cobalt to serve as catalysts. In addition, the gastric mucosa must provide some unidentified intrinsic factor necessary

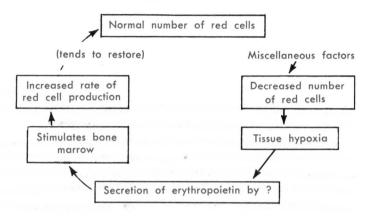

Fig. 155

Postulated red blood cell homeostatic mechanisms. Hypoxia may stimulate bone marrow directly instead of indirectly by erythropoietin as shown.

for absorption of vitamin B_{12} (called extrinsic factor because of its external source in foods; also called antianemic principle). The chain of reactions necessary for normal red cell production might be summarized as follows:

normal gastric mucosa
supplies
intrinsic factor
which
promotes vitamin B_{12} absorption
which
stimulates bone marrow
to produce
normal number of mature red blood cells

Failure to maintain homeostasis of red blood cells may result from interference at some point in the foregoing chain of reactions. For example, pernicious anemia develops when the gastric mucosa fails to produce sufficient intrinsic factor. Inadequate absorption of vitamin B_{12} then follows, and the bone marrow, deprived of its stimulation, produces fewer but larger red cells than normal. Many of these cells are immature with overly fragile membranes, a fact which leads to their more rapid destruction.

A clinical example of failure of red cell homeostasis, seen in recent years, is anemia due to bone marrow injury by x-ray or gamma ray radiations.

Other factors may also cause marrow damage. To help diagnose this condition, a sample of marrow is removed from the sternum by means of a sternal puncture and is studied microscopically for abnormalities. When damaged marrow can no longer keep red cell production apace with destruction, red cell homeostasis is not maintained. The red cell count falls below normal, and the individual has anemia.

Can you deduce other ways anemia might develop other than by a decrease in the rate of red cell production? It does sometimes happen that an individual becomes anemic even though his bone marrow produces red cells at a normal rate or faster. How?*

The number of red blood cells is determined by the *"red count"* or is estimated by the hematocrit. The *hematocrit* is the percentage of red cells in whole blood. For example, a hematocrit of 47 means that in every 100 milliliters of whole blood there are 47 milliliters of blood cells and 53 milliliters of fluid (plasma). Normally, the average hematocrit for a man is about 47 ($\pm$ 7, normal range) and for a woman about 42 ($\pm$ 5).

Leukocytes

Appearance and size. Consult Fig. 153. Note particularly the differences in color of the cytoplasmic granules and in the shapes of the nuclei of the granular leukocytes. Neutrophils take their name from the fact that they stain with neutral dyes. And because their nuclei have two to five or more lobes, neutrophils are also called *polymorphonuclear leukocytes* or, to avoid that tongue twister, simply "polymorphs." Eosinophils stain with acid dyes; their nuclei have two oval lobes. Basophils stain with basic dyes; their nuclei are roughly S-shaped.

Lymphocytes and monocytes do not contain granules in their cytoplasm, a characteristic indicated by the classification of these cells as nongranular leukocytes.

Functions. White blood cells constitute part of the important defense mechanisms of the body. Most of them carry on *phagocytosis,* a process in which they ingest and digest microorganisms and other foreign particles. Neutrophils and monocytes are most actively phagocytic, whereas eosinophils are only moderately so. All leukocytes are motile cells, a characteristic that enables them to move out of capillaries by squeezing through the intercellular spaces of the capillary wall (a process called *diapedesis*) and to migrate by ameboid movement toward injurious particles that may have invaded the tissues. Neutrophils and lymphocytes are highly motile, whereas eosinophils are sluggishly so.

You may recall that reticuloendothelial cells (p. 63) also perform the function of phagocytosis. In general, however, they do this work within more localized areas than white cells which can be transported by the blood to any part of the body. One more point—white blood

---

*When red cells are being destroyed faster than bone marrow can replace them even by increasing its red-cell production as much as possible.

cells carry on their function of phagocytosis in the tissues. Where do red cells perform their functions?

Uncertainty prevails about lymphocyte functions. Some investigators believe that they form antibodies. Others, on the basis of the fine structure of lymphocyte cytoplasm, believe that this is highly improbable* but think it probable that small lymphocytes may carry antibodies on their cell surfaces.

Formation. All three types of granular leukocytes originate, as do erythrocytes, in myeloid tissue, whereas nongranular leukocytes derive from lymphatic tissue—mainly in the lymph nodes and spleen.

Myeloid tissue (bone marrow) and lymphatic tissue together constitute the hemopoietic or blood cell-forming tissues of the body. Red bone marrow is myeloid tissue that is actually producing blood cells; its red color comes from the red cells it contains. Yellow marrow, on the other hand, is yellow because it stores considerable fat. It is not active in the business of blood cell formation as long as it remains yellow. Sometimes, however, it becomes active and red in color when an extreme and prolonged need for red cell production occurs.

Granular leukocytes, like erythrocytes, pass through several recognized stages before becoming mature cells: hemocytoblast (or myeloblast), promyelocyte, myelocyte, metamyelocyte, and mature leukocyte (Fig. 154, p. 291).

Destruction and life span. The life span of white blood cells is not known. It is conjectured that lymphocytes live the shortest time, probably less than twenty-four hours and monocytes the longest time. Granular leukocytes are thought to live perhaps three days or less or possibly as long as about twelve days. Some of them at least are probably destroyed by phagocytosis. Many lymphocytes leave the body in the feces; many others may degenerate in the lymphatic tissue where they are formed.

Numbers. A cubic millimeter of blood normally contains about 5000 to 9000 leukocytes, with definite percentages of each type (Table 36). The latter varies in certain abnormal conditions and, therefore, has clinical significance. In acute appendicitis, for example, the percentage of neutrophils as well as the total white count increases. In fact this characteristic finding may be the deciding point for surgery.

The procedure in which the different types of leukocytes are counted and their percentage of the total white count is computed is known as a *differential count*. In other words, a differential count is a percentage count of white cells. Table 36 lists the different kinds of white cells

---

*Ham, Arthur W., and Leeson, Thomas S.: Histology, ed. 4, Philadelphia, 1961, J. B. Lippincott Co., pp. 187-189.

Table 36. White blood cells

Class	Differential count*	
	Normal range (%)	Typical normal (%)
Those with nongranular cytoplasm and regular nucleus		
Lymphocytes (large and small)	20 to 25	25
Monocytes	3 to 8	6
Those with granular cytoplasm and irregular nuclei—leukocytes		
Eosinophils (acid staining)	2 to 5	3
Basophils (basic staining)	½ to 1	1
Neutrophils (neutral staining)	65 to 75	65
Total		100

*In any differential count the sum of the percentages of the different kinds of leukocytes must, of course, total 100%.

Table 37. Blood cells

Cells	Number	Function	Formation (hemopoiesis)	Destruction
Red blood cells (erythrocytes)	4½ to 5½ million per c.mm. (total of approximately 25 trillion in body)	Transport oxygen and carbon dioxide	Red marrow of bones (myeloid tissue)	By fragmentation in circulating blood and by macrophages of spleen, liver, and red bone marrow; thought to live about 120 days in blood stream
White blood cells (leukocytes)	5 to 9 thousand per c.mm.	Defense against microorganisms and other injurious factors—by phagocytosis	Granular leukocytes in red marrow; nongranular leukocytes in lymphatic tissue	Not known definitely; probably some destroyed by phagocytosis and some by microorganisms
Platelets (thrombocytes)	250,000 to 450,000 per c.mm.; wide variation with different counting methods	Initiate blood clotting	Red marrow	Unknown

and a normal differential count. A decrease in the number of white blood cells is *leukopenia*; an increase in the number of white cells is *leukocytosis*. (*Leukemia* is a malignant disease characterized by a marked increase in the number of white blood cells).

Platelets

Appearance and size. Platelets are small fragments of cells.

Functions. These important little blood cells help set in operation the blood-clotting mechanism (p. 300).

Formation and life span. Platelets are formed in the red bone marrow presumably by fragmentation of very large cells known as megakaryocytes (Fig. 154). Their life span is not known definitely but is thought to be only a few days. In Table 37 is given a summary of the basic facts about blood cells.

Blood types (or blood groups)

The term blood type refers to the type of antigens* present on or in red blood cell membranes. Most common are those known as factors A and B and the Rh factor. Many other factors have also been identified, but they are less important clinically and are too complex to discuss here. Since blood types are named according to the antigens present on red cells, the main blood types are the following:

1. *type* A—A factor antigen on red cells.
2. *type* B—B factor antigen on red cells.
3. *type* AB—both A and B factor antigens on red cells.
4. *type* O—neither A nor B antigen factor on red cells.
5. *Rh positive*—Rh factor antigen on red cells, with or without A or B factors.
6. *Rh negative*—Rh factor antigen absent from red cells.

Blood plasma may or may not contain antibodies which can react with red cell antigens A, B, and Rh. An important principle about this is that plasma never contains antibodies against the antigens present on its own red blood cells—for obvious reasons—if it did, the antibody would react with the antigen and thereby destroy the red cells. But (and this is an equally important principle) plasma does contain antibodies against the main antigens *not* present on its red cells. Applying these two principles: plasma of type A blood contains b antibodies but does not contain a antibodies (small letters distinguish antibodies from antigens designated by capital letters). Type B blood contains a antibodies but not b antibodies. Rh negative blood contains Rh anti-

---

*Antigen—substance capable of stimulating formation of antibodies which can react with the antigen, for example, to agglutinate or clump it or to dissolve it.

bodies (but no Rh factor on its red cells). Suppose you have type AB blood, Rh positive. Which antigens would be present on your red blood cell membranes? What antibodies would be present in your blood plasma?*

Practical use is made of knowledge about blood types in the typing and cross matching of blood before transfusions. Type O blood is referred to as *universal donor* blood. Not only can it be transfused safely into a person whose blood is also type O, but it can also be given as well to one who has type A, B, or AB blood. Why? Because type O blood cells contain neither A nor B antigens to react with either or both types of antibodies which might be present in the recipient's blood; therefore, the type O donor blood cells will not be agglutinated (clumped) or hemolyzed by the recipient's blood. *Universal recipient* blood because it contains neither a nor b antibodies and supposedly cannot agglutinate any donor's red cells. What type, therefore, is universal recipient blood? A? B? AB? Or O?

Blood plasma

Plasma is the liquid part of blood or whole blood minus its cells. It can be prepared simply by letting blood removed from the body stand for some time after a chemical has been added to it to prevent clotting. Blood cells, being heavier than water, sink to the bottom of the container and clear, straw-colored plasma lies above them. A more rapid way of forming plasma is to centrifuge whole blood, a very rapid whirling process which hurls cells to the bottom of the tube.

Composition

Plasma is approximately 90% water and 10% solutes. These may be classified in several ways.

According to size of solute particles

1. *crystalloids*—particles less than 1 millimicron in diameter, for example, mineral salts.
2. *colloids*—particles 1 to about 100 millimicrons in diameter, for example, proteins—albumin, globulins, and fibrinogen.

According to whether or not solute ionizes

1. *electrolytes*—molecules ionize in solution, for example, the mineral salts and proteins in blood are electrolytes. Because salt molecules dissociate very rapidly to yield positive ions (cations)

---

*Type AB blood—antigens A and B and Rh factor all present on red cells; no a or b or Rh antibodies in plasma.

and negative ions (anions), almost all the salt in blood is present as ions rather than as molecules. Proteins, on the other hand, ionize to a much lesser extent so that relatively more protein molecules and fewer protein ions are present in blood.
2. *nonelectrolytes*—molecules do not ionize, for example, lipids, glucose, and various metabolic wastes exist as molecules in blood, not as ions.

According to function

1. *nutrients*—glucose, amino acids, and fats.
2. *metabolic wastes*—urea, uric acid, creatinine, and lactic acid.
3. *respiratory gases*—oxygen and carbon dioxide.
4. *regulatory substances*—hormones, enzymes, and mineral salts.
5. *protective substances*—antibodies.

Blood clotting

Consult Fig. 159, p. 302.

Purpose

The purpose of blood clotting is obvious—to plug up ruptured vessels and prevent excessive loss of the body's vital fluid.

Mechanism

Because of the function of clotting, the mechanism for producing it must be swift and sure when needed, as when a vessel is cut or ruptured. But equally important it needs to be prevented from happening when it is not needed because clots can plug up vessels that must stay open if cells are to receive blood's life-sustaining cargo of oxygen. Essentially, clotting is a mechanism whereby the soluble blood protein fibrinogen is changed into the insoluble protein fibrin. The nature of this mechanism has long been and still is the subject of numerous investigations and theories.

In fact, it is one of the most if not the most complex, confused fields in physiology. To try to find our way through this maze, a good method seems to be to think of the clotting mechanism as consisting of three major stages and to discuss each of these in turn. These stages are as follows:

1. Thromboplastin formation
2. Thrombin formation
3. Fibrin formation

Thromboplastin formation. This first stage of blood clotting consists of a number of imperfectly understood chemical reactions. They result

299

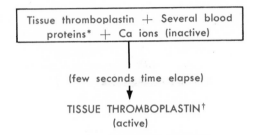

Tissue thromboplastin + Several blood
proteins* + Ca ions (inactive)

(few seconds time elapse)

TISSUE THROMBOPLASTIN†
(active)

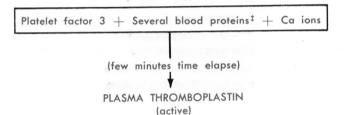

Platelet factor 3 + Several blood proteins‡ + Ca ions

(few minutes time elapse)

PLASMA THROMBOPLASTIN
(active)

°Factor VII (or preconvertin), factor V (or proaccelerin), and Stuart factor; all three of these blood proteins are of the globulin type.

†Also called prothrombinase.

‡The most important ones are thought to be antihemophilic factor (AHF)—absent in hemophilia A, plasma thromboplastic component (PTC)—absent in hemophilia B, plasma thromboplastic antecedent (PTA), Hageman factor, and Stuart factor; all of these blood proteins are globulins.

Fig. 156

Stage 1 in blood clotting, the formation of tissue and plasma thromboplastins. Platelet factor 3 is released from platelets which disintegrate on contact with wettable ("rough") surface.

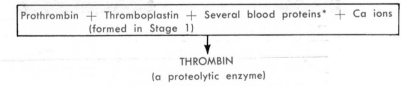

Prothrombin + Thromboplastin + Several blood proteins* + Ca ions
(formed in Stage 1)

THROMBIN
(a proteolytic enzyme)

°Factor V or proaccelerin, factor VII or proconvertin, and Stuart factor; all of these are globulin proteins.

Fig. 157

Step 2 of blood clotting, the formation of thrombin. Prothrombin is one of the globulin blood proteins. Liver cells synthesize prothrombin, and vitamin K is a necessary catalyst for this synthesis.

in the formation of active thromboplastin (prothrombinase) from two sources, tissues (near clotting area) and platelets. The trigger that sets off these reactions, though not completely clear, is known to involve contact of blood with wettable surfaces (surfaces that are not perfectly smooth, that are rough). Active tissue thromboplastin apparently is formed within a few seconds time. In Fig. 156 is given an abbreviated description of this reaction.

When platelets contact a wettable surface, they tend to disintegrate, releasing granules of a substance known as *platelet factor 3* (or as platelet thromboplastic factor, a phospholipid of the cephalin group). Platelet factor 3 then reacts with several blood proteins and calcium ions to form active plasma thromboplastin in about 3 to 6 minutes time (Fig. 156).

Thrombin formation. One of the complex globulin proteins in blood is *prothrombin.* Prothrombin combines with thromboplastin (formed in stage 1) and several blood proteins and calcium ions to form thrombin (Fig. 157). Vitamin K catalyzes prothrombin synthesis by liver cells. Although a balanced diet includes foods that contain vitamin K, synthesis of it in the body also occurs—not by body cells but by certain bacteria normally present in the intestines (except for a time in newborn infants). But even though foods and synthesis supply ample amounts of this vitamin, a person still may have a vitamin K deficiency. Explanation of this paradox lies in the fact of inadequate absorption of vitamin K in the presence of too little bile in the intestine. Vitamin K is fat-soluble so that its absorption requires bile. And, therefore, patients whose bile ducts become obstructed or whose liver is too severely diseased to produce adequate amounts of bile cannot absorb enough vitamin K for normal prothrombin synthesis. As a result their blood does not clot normally. They have a bleeding tendency. As a preoperative safeguard, they are generally given some kind of vitamin K preparation.

Fibrin formation. Another blood protein synthesized by liver cells and involved in blood clotting is *fibrinogen.* Its molecules are long, fiberlike, and large—they have a molecular weight of over 400,000. The enzyme thrombin, formed in stage 2, catalyzes the formation of the gel fibrin from the sol fibrinogen (Fig. 158). Fibrin appears as an

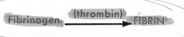

Fig. 158

Stage 3 of blood clotting, the formation of fibrin.
Fibrinogen is one of the blood proteins. Liver cells synthesize fibrinogen as well as prothrombin.

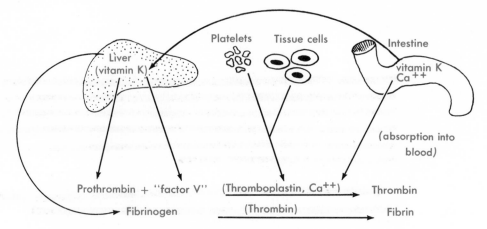

Fig. 159

Diagram to show where substances that take part in blood clotting come from. Note that vitamin K catalyzes liver synthesis of prothrombin and that both injured platelets and tissue cells release thromboplastin.

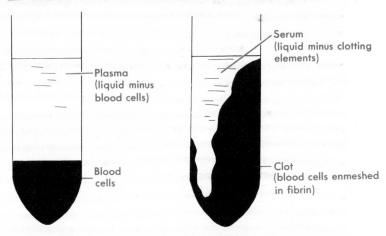

Fig. 160

Diagram to show the difference between blood plasma and blood serum. Plasma is whole blood minus cells; serum is whole blood minus the clotting elements. Plasma is prepared by centrifuging blood; serum by clotting blood.

entangled network of fine threads. Red cells catch in this entanglement, producing the red color of clotted blood. The pale yellowish liquid left after a clot forms is *blood serum*. Serum should not be confused with plasma, which is whole blood minus the cells (Figs. 158 to 160).

Factors that oppose blood clotting

Although blood clotting probably goes on continuously and concurrently with clot dissolution (fibrinolysis), several factors do operate to oppose clot formation and enlargement in intact vessels. For one thing, the normal endothelial lining of blood vessels is a smooth nonwettable surface. Therefore platelets do not readily adhere to it and disintegrate to release thromboplastin. For another thing, blood contains some substances that tend to prevent clotting—*antithrombins*, for example, that inactivate thrombin and make it unable to catalyze stage 3, fibrin formation. *Heparin* is one substance that acts as an antithrombin. Its normal concentration in blood, however, is too low to have much effect in keeping blood fluid. Where it comes from is not definitely known. Mast cells are known to contain considerable amounts of heparin though they may not themselves synthesize it but only store it. It was first prepared from liver—hence its name—but various other organs also contain heparin.

Factors that hasten clotting

Two conditions particularly favor thrombus formation: a rough spot in the endothelium (blood vessel lining) and abnormally slow blood flow. Atherosclerosis, for example, is associated with an increased tendency toward thrombosis because of endothelial rough spots in the form of plaques of accumulated lipid material. Immobility, on the other hand, slows blood flow—one reason for the importance attached to the practice of moving bed patients frequently. Presumably sluggish blood flow allows thromboplastin to accumulate sufficiently to reach a concentration adequate for clotting.

Once started, a clot tends to grow. Platelets enmeshed in the fibrin threads disintegrate, releasing more thromboplastin which, in turn, causes more clotting, which enmeshes more platelets, and so on, in a vicious circle. Clot-retarding substances, available in recent years, have proved valuable for retarding this process.

Pharmaceutical preparations that retard clotting

The anticoagulant *Dicumarol* has become well known because of its clinical value in lessening thrombus and embolus formation. It is thought to decrease prothrombin synthesis, perhaps by blocking vitamin K action (Fig. 159). Commercial preparations of heparin are also used as anticoagulants. These are useful to prevent clotting in the body or outside of it. Blood to be used for transfusions is usually treated with a citrate compound. The latter combines with calcium ions. Therefore, citrate prevents coagulation by blocking formation of what substance? (If you are not sure, see Fig. 159 for the answer.)

Clot dissolution

Fibrinolysis is the physiological mechanism that dissolves clots. Newer evidence indicates that the two opposing processes of clot formation and fibrinolysis go on continuously. Doctor George Fulton of

Boston University has presented one bit of dramatic evidence. He took micromovies which show tiny blood vessels rupturing under apparently normal circumstances and clots forming to plug them. An enzyme, *fibrinolysin*, is known to be present in blood and to be able to hydrolyze and thereby dissolve fibrin. Many other factors, however, presumably also take part in clot dissolution—for instance, substances that activate profibrinolysin, the inactive form of fibrinolysin. Streptokinase, an enzyme from certain streptococci, can act this way and so cause clot dissolution and even hemorrhage.

Clinical methods of hastening blood clotting

In case of excessive bleeding, it is often necessary to speed up the blood-clotting mechanism. The principle involved is apparent—to increase any of the substances essential for clotting. Practically, this is accomplished in the following ways:

1. By stimulating the platelets and tissues to liberate more thromboplastin by bringing them in contact with unsmooth surfaces, such as gauze, or by applying heat, or by gently squeezing the tissues around the ruptured vessel.
2. By applying purified thrombin (in the form of sprays or impregnated gelatin sponges which can be left in a wound).
3. By applying fibrin foam, films, etc.

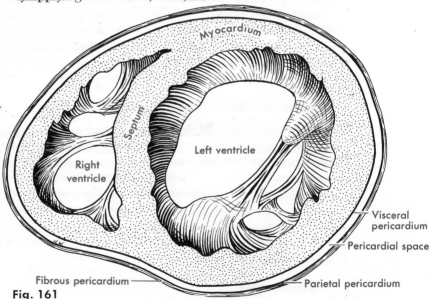

Fig. 161

Diagram of a cross-section view of the heart and its coverings showing the location of the visceral and parietal layers of the serous pericardium, the pericardial space, and the fibrous pericardium.

HEART

Description

The human heart is a four-chambered muscular organ, shaped and sized roughly like a man's closed fist. It lies in the mediastinum, with approximately two thirds of its mass to the left of the midline of the body and one third to the right. Its lower border, which forms a blunt point known as the *apex*, lies on the diaphragm, pointing toward the left. To count the apical beat, one must place a stethoscope directly over the apex, that is, in the space between the fifth and sixth ribs (fifth intercostal space) on a line with the midpoint of the left clavicle. The upper border of the heart, or its base, lies just below the second rib. The boundaries, which, of course, indicate its size, have considerable clinical importance since a marked increase in heart size accompanies certain types of heart disease. Therefore when diagnosing heart disorders, the doctor charts the boundaries of the heart.

Covering

Structure

The heart has its own special covering, a loose-fitting inextensible sac called the *pericardium*. The pericardium consists of two parts: a fibrous portion and a serous portion. The sac itself is made of tough white fibrous tissue but is lined with smooth, moist serous membrane—the parietal layer of the serous pericardium. The same kind of membrane covers the entire outer surface of the heart. This covering layer is known as the visceral layer of the serous pericardium or as the *epicardium*. The fibrous sac attaches to the large blood vessels emerging from the top of the heart but not to the heart itself; therefore it fits loosely around the heart with a slight space between the visceral layer adhering to the heart and the parietal layer adhering to the inside of the fibrous sac. This space is called the *pericardial space*; it contains a few drops of lubricating fluid secreted by the serous membrane and is called *pericardial fluid*.

The structure of the pericardium can be summarized in outline form as follows:

1. *fibrous pericardium*—loose-fitting sac around the heart.
2. *serous pericardium*—consisting of two layers.
   (a) *parietal layer*—lining inside of the fibrous pericardium.
   (b) *visceral layer (epicardium)*—adhering to outside of heart; between visceral and parietal layers is a potential space, the pericardial space, which contains a few drops of pericardial fluid.

Function

The fibrous pericardial sac with its smooth, well-lubricated lining provides protection against friction. The heart moves easily in this loose-fitting jacket with no danger of irritation from friction between the two surfaces so long as the serous pericardium remains normal. If, however, it becomes inflamed (pericarditis) and too much pericardial fluid or fibrin or pus develops in the pericardial space, the visceral and parietal layers may adhere to each other in spots, interfering with the normal contractions of the heart. In such cases it sometimes becomes necessary to remove the fibrous pericardium with its lining of parietal serous membrane in order for the heart to continue functioning. This operation, a spectacular procedure, is called a *pericardectomy*.

Structure

Heart wall

Three distinct layers of tissue make up the heart wall. The bulk of the wall consists of specially constructed muscle tissue known as cardiac muscle or the *myocardium*. Covering the myocardium on the outside and adherent to it is the visceral *pericardium* (or *epicardium*) already described. Lining the interior of the myocardial wall is a delicate layer of endothelial* tissue known as the *endocardium*. On its inner surface the myocardium is raised into ridgelike projections, the papillary muscles.

Cavities

The interior of the heart is divided into four chambers, two upper and two lower. The upper cavities are named *atria*† and the lower ones *ventricles*. Of these, the ventricles are considerably larger and thicker walled than the atria because they carry a heavier pumping burden than the atria. Also, the left ventricle has thicker walls than the right because it has to pump blood through all the vessels of the body, except those to and from the lungs, whereas the right ventricle sends blood only through the lungs.

---

*Endothelial tissue resembles simple squamous epithelial tissue in that it consists of a single layer of flat cells. It differs from epithelial tissue in that it arises from the mesoderm layer of the embryo, whereas epithelial tissue arises from the ectoderm.

†The atria are sometimes called auricles. Strictly speaking, the latter term means the earlike flaps protruding from the atria, although the two terms are often used synonymously.

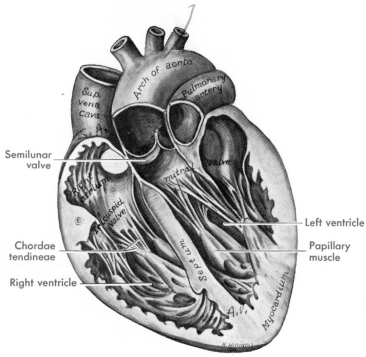

Labels on figure: Arch of aorta, Sup. vena cava, Pulmonary artery, Semilunar valve, mitral valve, tricuspid valve, Chordae tendineae, Right ventricle, Septum, Left ventricle, Papillary muscle, Myocardium

Fig. 162

Frontal section of the heart to show
the main structural features of its interior.

Valves and openings

The heart valves are mechanical devices which permit the flow of
blood in one direction only. Four sets of valves are of importance to
the normal functioning of the heart. Two of these, the cuspid valves,
are located in the heart, guarding the openings between the atria and
ventricles (atrioventricular orifices); the other two, the semilunar
valves, are located inside the pulmonary artery and the great aorta
just as they arise from the right and left ventricles, respectively. The
cuspid valve guarding the right atrioventricular orifice consists of three
flaps of endocardium anchored to the papillary muscles of the right
ventricle by several cordlike structures called *chordae tendineae.* Because this valve has three flaps, it is appropriately named the *tricuspid
valve.* The valve which guards the left atrioventricular orifice is similar in structure to the tricuspid except that it has only two flaps and
is, therefore, called the *bicuspid,* or more commonly the *mitral valve.*
(An easy way to remember which valve is on the right and which on
the left is to remember that the names whose first letters come nearest together in the alphabet go together—thus, L and M for *left* side,
*mitral valve, and R and T for *right* side, *tricuspid.)* The construction
of both cuspid valves allows blood to flow from the atria into the ventricles but prevents it from flowing back up into the atria from the
ventricles. Ventricular contraction forces the blood in the ventricles

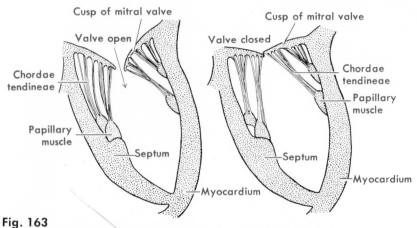

Fig. 163

Action of the cuspid (atrioventricular) valves. When the valves are open, blood passes freely from the atria to the ventricles, A; filling of the ventricles closes the valves, B, and prevents a backflow of blood into the atria when the ventricles contract.

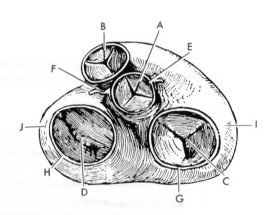

Fig. 164

Diagram to show the appearance of the heart valves when closed and viewed from above: A, aortic semilunar; B, pulmonary semilunar; C, tricuspid, and, D, mitral valves; E and F, coronary arteries; G and H, walls of atria; and I and J, walls of ventricles. (From Stewart: Physiology.)

hard against the cuspid valves, closing them and thereby ensuring the movement of the blood upward into the pulmonary artery and aorta as the ventricles contract.

The *semilunar valves* consist of half-moon-shaped flaps growing out from the lining of the pulmonary artery and great aorta. When these valves are closed, blood fills the spaces between the flaps and the vessel wall, giving each flap the appearance of a tiny filled bucket. Inflowing blood smooths the flaps against the blood vessel wall, collapsing the buckets and thereby opening the valves.

Like the cuspid valves, the semilunar valves, by preventing backflow of blood, cause it to flow forward in places where there would otherwise be considerable backflow. Whereas the cuspid valves prevent blood from flowing back up into the atria from the ventricles, the semilunar valves prevent it from flowing back down into the ventricles from the aorta and pulmonary artery. Any one of the four valves may lose its ability to close tightly. Such a condition is known as *valvular insufficiency* or, because it permits blood to "leak" back into the part of the heart from which it came, "leakage of the heart." *Mitral stenosis* is an abnormality in which the left atrioventricular orifice becomes narrowed by scar tissue which forms as a result of disease and therefore hinders the passage of blood from the left atrium to the left ventricle.

Blood supply

Myocardial cells receive blood by way of two small vessels, the right and left coronary arteries. Since the openings into these vitally important vessels lie behind flaps of the aortic semilunar valve, they come off of the aorta at its very beginning and are its first branches. Both right and left coronary arteries have two main branches, as shown in Table 38.

Table 38

Left coronary artery	Right coronary artery
1. Anterior descending artery—supplies branches to the left and right ventricles 2. Circumflex artery—supplies branches to left atrium and left ventricle	1. Posterior descending artery—supplies branches to both left and right ventricles 2. Marginal artery—supplies branches to right atrium and right ventricle

Note that each ventricle receives blood from both major branches of its respective coronary artery and from the descending branch of the opposite coronary artery, whereas each atrium receives blood from only one source. More specifically, the left ventricle receives blood from the anterior descending and circumflex branches of the left coronary artery and from the posterior descending branch of the right coronary artery. The left atrium, on the other hand, receives blood only from the left circumflex artery. This structural fact seems appropriate in relation to function. The ventricles do more work than the atria and therefore need more blood.

Another fact about the heart's own blood supply—and one of life and death importance—is the fact that only a few anastomoses exist between the larger branches of the coronary arteries. An *anastomosis* consists of one or more branches from the proximal part of an artery to a more distal part of itself or of another artery. Thus, anastomoses provide detour routes which arterial blood can travel if the main route becomes obstructed. They provide the means for collateral circulation to a part. This explains why the scarcity of anastomoses between larger coronary arteries looms as so large a threat to life. If, for example, a blood clot plugs one of the larger coronary artery branches, as it frequently does in coronary thrombosis or embolism, too little or no blood can reach some of the heart muscle cells. In other words, they become ischemic. Deprived of oxygen, they cannot contract normally and soon die (myocardial infarction). A brighter part of the picture, however, is another anatomical fact: many anastomoses do exist between very small arterial vessels in the heart, and these anastomoses can, if given time, grow and provide collateral circulation to ischemic areas. In recent years surgical procedures have been devised to aid this process.*

Conduction system of the heart

Four structures—the sinoatrial node, atrioventricular node, atrioventricular bundle, and Purkinje fibers—compose the conduction system of the heart. Each of these structures consists of cardiac muscle modified enough in structure to differ in function from ordinary cardiac muscle. The main specialty of ordinary cardiac muscle is contraction. In this it is like all muscle, and like all muscle ordinary cardiac muscle can also conduct impulses. But conduction alone is the specialty of the modified cardiac muscle that composes the conduction system structures.

Sinoatrial node. The sinoatrial node (SA node, Keith-Flack node, or pacemaker) is a small mass of modified cardiac muscle fibers located at the junction of the superior vena cava and the right atrium and is abundantly supplied with both sympathetic and parasympathetic fibers. Normally, the SA node, stimulated by impulses over these fibers, initiates each heartbeat—hence its designation as the pacemaker.

Atrioventricular node. The atrioventricular node (AV node or node of Tawara) is a small mass of special cardiac muscle tissue in the lower part of the interatrial septum.

Atrioventricular bundle and Purkinje fibers. The atrioventricular bundle (bundle of His) is a bundle of special cardiac muscle fibers which originate in the AV node and which extend by two branches about halfway down the two sides of the interventricular septum where they continue as the Purkinje fibers. The latter extend out to the papillary muscles and lateral walls of the ventricles.

Impulse conduction through the heart normally starts in the SA node, spreads through atrial muscle fibers in all directions, causing atrial contraction. When impulses reach the AV node, it relays them by way of the AV node, bundle of His, and Purkinje fibers to the

*Beck, C. S.: Operations for coronary disease, Am. J. Nursing 9:1076, 1954.

Fig. 165

Model of the atrioventricular node and bundle of His, two of the important neuromuscular structures of the heart. (From Howell: A textbook of physiology, Philadelphia, W. B. Saunders Co.)

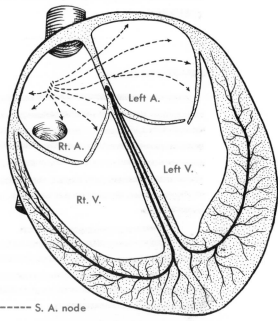

Fig. 166

Diagram to show the location of the sinoatrial and atrioventricular nodes of the heart. Fibers from the atrioventricular node which lie in the interventricular septum are known as the bundle of His and those which extend out to the myocardium as Purkinje fibers.

Left A.

Rt. A.

Left V.

Rt. V.

- - - - - S. A. node

———— A. V. node, bundle of His, and Purkinje fibers

ventricles, causing their contraction. Impulse conduction generates tiny electrical currents in the heart which spread through surrounding tissues to the surface of the body where they can be recorded by the electrocardiograph.

Nerve supply

Both divisions of the autonomic nervous system send fibers to the heart. Sympathetic fibers (contained in the middle, superior, and inferior cardiac nerves) and parasympathetic fibers (in branches of the vagus) combine to form *cardiac plexuses* located close to the arch of

311

the aorta. From the cardiac plexuses fibers accompany the right and left coronary arteries to enter the heart. Here most of the fibers terminate in the SA node, but some end in the AV node and in the atrial myocardium. Sympathetic nerves to the heart are also called accelerator nerves. Vagus fibers to the heart are inhibitory.

Physiology

Function

The function of the heart is to pump blood in sufficient amounts to meet the varying needs of the cells of the body for the substances it transports. Mechanisms which accomplish this function of pumping different volumes of blood per minute under different conditions are discussed on p.345.

The cardiac cycle

The term cardiac cycle means a complete heartbeat consisting of contraction (systole) and relaxation (diastole) of both atria plus contraction and relaxation of both ventricles. The two atria contract simultaneously; then as they relax, the two ventricles contract and relax, instead of the entire heart contracting as a unit; this gives a kind of milking action to the movements of the heart. The atria remain relaxed during part of the ventricular relaxation and then start the cycle over again. In Table 39 are described the events occurring during the cycle. Note the following facts:

1. The contracting force of the atria completes the emptying of blood out of the atria into the ventricles. Cuspid valves are necessarily open during this phase, the ventricles relaxed, filling with blood, and the semilunar valves closed so that blood does not flow on out into the pulmonary artery or aorta.

2. The atria relax, and blood enters them from the veins during the first part of their diastole and starts draining out into the ventricles during the latter part of it; the cuspid valves are closed during the first part of the diastole (while the ventricles are contracting, squeezing blood through the open semilunar valves into the pulmonary artery and aorta) but open as the ventricles relax, the semilunars close, and the ventricles start to fill with blood from the atria. About what per cent of the time are the atria relaxed or resting? The ventricles? Consult Table 39 to find your answers.

Heart sounds during cycle. The heart makes certain typical sounds during each cycle which are described as sounding like lub-dup through a stethoscope. The first or systolic sound is believed due to the contraction of the ventricles and to vibrations of the closing cuspid

Table 39. The cardiac cycle (in tenths of seconds—0.8 second for complete cycle)

Seconds	0.1	0.2	0.3	0.4	0.5	0.6	0.7	0.8
Atria	Contract— blood squeezed into ventricles	Relax Blood enters from venae cavae and pulmonary veins and drains into ventricles						
Cuspid valves	Open	Closed		Open				
Ventricles	Relaxed— filling with blood from atria	Contract Blood emptying into pulmonary artery and aorta		Relax Filling with blood from atria				
Semilunar valves	Closed	Open		Closed				

valves. It is longer and lower than the second or diastolic sound, which is thought to be caused by vibrations of the closing semilunar valves. Both of these sounds have clinical significance since they give information about the valves of the heart. Any variation from normal in the sounds indicates imperfect functioning of the valves. *Heart murmurs* are one type of abnormal sound frequently heard and may signify incomplete closing of the valves (valvular insufficiency) or stenosis of them.

BLOOD VESSELS

Kinds

There are three kinds of blood vessels: arteries, veins, and capillaries. By definition an *artery* is a vessel which carries blood away from the heart. All arteries except the pulmonary artery and its branches carry oxygenated blood. Small arteries are called *arterioles*.

A *vein*, on the other hand, is a vessel which carries blood toward the heart; all of the veins except the pulmonary contain deoxygenated blood. Small veins are called *venules*. Both arteries and veins are macroscopic structures. *Capillaries* are microscopic vessels which carry blood from small arteries to small veins—that is, from arterioles to venules. They represented the "missing link" in the proof of circulation for many years—from the time William Harvey first declared that blood circulated from the heart through arteries to veins and back to

313

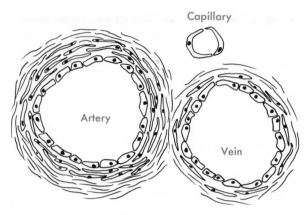

Fig. 167

Diagram to show contrast in diameter and thickness of walls of artery, vein, and capillary. Capillaries are microscopic vessels.
Note that the capillary wall consists of only a single layer of flat endothelial cells—a structural fact that suits them well for their vital function, the rapid exchange of substances between blood and tissue cells. (For an electron micrograph view of an arteriole, see Fig. 25.)

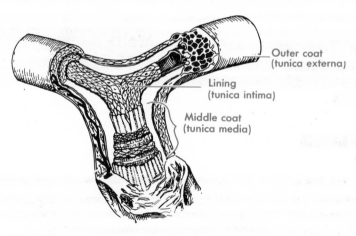

Outer coat (tunica externa)

Lining (tunica intima)

Middle coat (tunica media)

Fig. 168

Cutaway view of arterial wall showing three coats. Outer coat consists of fibrous tissue chiefly, middle coat consists of elastic, fibrous, and smooth muscle tissue, and inner coat consists of endothelial lining cells. (Modified from Kahn: Man in structure and function, New York, Alfred A. Knopf.)

Table 40. Structure of the blood vessels

	Arteries	Veins	Capillaries
Coats	Lining (tunica intima) of endothelium Middle coat (tunica media) of smooth muscle, elastic, and some white fibrous tissues; this coat permits constriction and dilatation Outer coat (tunica adventia or externa) of white fibrous tissue; causes artery to stand open instead of collapsing when cut (see Fig. 168)	Same three coats but thinner and fewer elastic fibers; veins collapse when cut; semilunar valves present at intervals	Only lining coat present; therefore walls only one-cell thick

Blood supply Endothelial lining cells supplied by blood flowing through vessels; exchange of oxygen, etc., between cells of middle coat and blood by diffusion; outer coat supplied by tiny vessels known as the *vasa vasorum* or "vessels of the vessels"

Nerve supply Smooth muscle cells of middle coat innervated by autonomic fibers

Abnormalities *Arteriosclerosis*—hardening of walls of arteries
    Aneurysm—saclike dilatation of an artery wall
    Varicose veins—stretching of walls, particularly around semilunar valves
    Phlebitis—inflammation of a vein; "milk leg" is phlebitis of femoral vein of women after childbirth

the heart until the time that microscopes made it possible to find these connecting vessels between arteries and veins. Many people rejected Harvey's theory of circulation on the basis that there was no possible way for blood to get from arteries to veins. The discovery of the capillaries formed the final proof that the blood actually does circulate from the heart into arteries to arterioles, to capillaries, to venules, to veins, and back to the heart.

Structure

See Table 40 (above) for structure of the blood vessels.

Functions

The capillaries, though seemingly the most insignificant of the three kinds of blood vessels because of their diminutive size, nevertheless are the most important vessels functionally. Since the prime function of blood is to transport essential materials to and from the cells and since the actual delivery and collection of these substances take place in the capillaries, the capillaries may be regarded as the most important blood vessels functionally. The arteries serve merely as "distributors" carrying the blood to the capillaries, the veins as "collectors" returning it from them, and the heart as a "pump," keeping it moving through this circuit of vessels. In short, the entire circulatory mechanism pivots around this one essential, that of keeping the capillaries supplied with an amount of blood adequate to the changing needs of the cells. All the factors governing circulation operate to this one end.

Although capillaries are very tiny (on the average only 1 millimeter long or about 1/25 inch), they are so numerous as to be incomprehensible. Someone has calculated that if these microscopic tubes were joined end to end, they would extend 62,000 miles, in spite of the fact that it takes twenty-five of them to reach a single inch! According to one estimate, one square inch of muscle tissue contains over a million and a half of these important little vessels. None of the billions of cells composing the body lie very far removed from a capillary. The reason for this lavish distribution of capillaries is of course apparent in view of their function of keeping the cells supplied with needed materials and rid of injurious wastes.

Next we shall discuss briefly the main arteries and veins and then consider circulation, that is, blood flow through the heart and blood vessels.

Names of main blood vessels

Arteries

Locate the arteries, as named in Table 41 (see also Figs. 169 to 172) in which are listed the main arteries. The names of blood vessels and the relation of the vessels to each other are more easily learned from diagrams than from descriptions.

Table 41. Main arteries

Artery	Branches (only the largest ones named)
Ascending aorta	Coronary arteries (two, to myocardium)
Aortic arch	Innominate artery Left subclavian Left common carotid
Innominate artery	Right subclavian Right common carotid
Subclavian (right and left)	Vertebral° Axillary (continuation of subclavian)
Axillary	Brachial (continuation of axillary)

°For footnote see next page.

Table 41. Main arteries—cont'd

Artery	*Branches (only the largest ones named)*
Brachial	Radial Ulnar
Radial and ulnar	Palmar arches (superficial and deep arterial arches in hand formed by anastomosis of branches of radial and ulnar arteries; numerous branches to hand and fingers)
Common carotid (right and left)	Internal carotid (brain, eye, forehead, and nose)* External carotid (thyroid, tongue, tonsils, ear, etc.)
Descending thoracic aorta	Visceral branches to pericardium, bronchi, esophagus, mediastinum Parietal branches to chest muscles, mammary glands, and diaphragm

Descending abdominal aorta	Visceral branches
	  1. Celiac axis (or artery) which branches into gastric, hepatic, and splenic arteries (stomach, liver, and spleen)
	  2. Right and left suprarenal arteries (suprarenal glands)
	  3. Superior mesenteric artery (small intestine)
	  4. Right and left renal arteries (kidneys)
	  5. Right and left spermatic (or ovarian) arteries (testes or ovaries)
	  6. Inferior mesenteric artery (large intestine)
	Parietal branches to lower surface of diaphragm, muscles and skin of back, spinal cord, and meninges
	Right and left common iliac arteries—abdominal aorta terminates in these vessels in an inverted Y formation

Right and left common iliac arteries	Internal iliac or hypogastric (pelvic wall and viscera) External iliac (to leg)
External iliac (right and left)	Femoral (continuation of external iliac after it leaves abdominal cavity)
Femoral	Popliteal (continuation of femoral)
Popliteal	Anterior tibial Posterior tibial
Anterior and posterior tibial	Plantar arch (arterial arch in sole of foot formed by anastomosis of terminal branches of anterior and posterior tibial arteries; small arteries lead from arch to toes)

*The right and left vertebral arteries extend from their origin as branches of the subclavian arteries up the neck, through foramina in the transverse processes of the cervical vertebrae, and through the foramen magnum into the cranial cavity and unite on the undersurface of the brainstem to form the *basilar artery,* which shortly branches into the right and left *posterior cerebral arteries.* The internal carotid arteries enter the cranial cavity in the midpart of the cranial floor, where they become known as the *anterior cerebral arteries.* Small vessels, the *communicating arteries,* join the anterior and posterior cerebral arteries in such a way as to form an arterial circle (the *circle of Willis*) at the base of the brain, a good example of arterial anastomosis (Fig. 172).

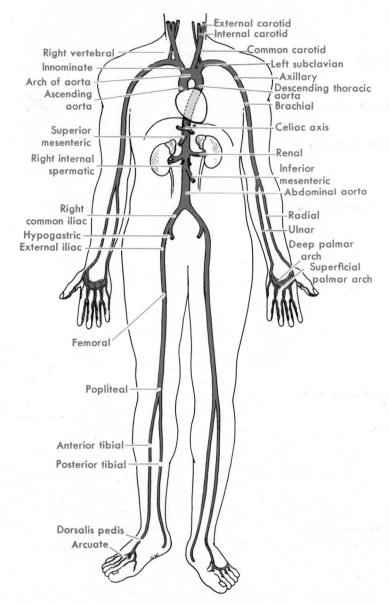

External carotid
Internal carotid
Right vertebral
Innominate
Arch of aorta
Ascending aorta
Superior mesenteric
Right internal spermatic
Right common iliac
Hypogastric
External iliac
Femoral
Popliteal
Anterior tibial
Posterior tibial
Dorsalis pedis
Arcuate
Common carotid
Left subclavian
Axillary
Descending thoracic aorta
Brachial
Celiac axis
Renal
Inferior mesenteric
Abdominal aorta
Radial
Ulnar
Deep palmar arch
Superficial palmar arch

Fig. 169

Main arteries of the body.

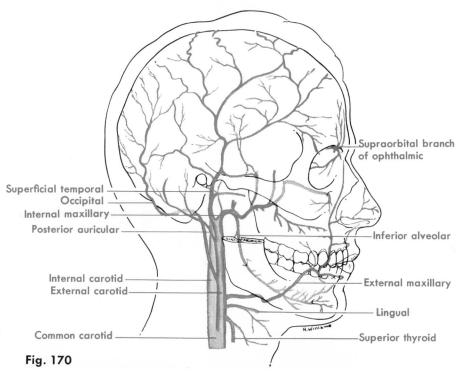

Fig. 170

Main arteries of the face and head. Superficial vessels are shown in brighter color than deep vessels. (From Francis and Farrell: Integrated anatomy and physiology, St. Louis, The C. V. Mosby Co.)

As you learn the names of the main arteries, keep in mind that these are only the major pipelines distributing blood from the heart to the various organs and that in each organ the main artery resembles a tree trunk in that it gives off numerous branches which continue to branch and rebranch, forming ever smaller vessels (arterioles) which also branch, forming microscopic vessels, the capillaries. In other words, any artery eventually ramifies into capillaries. A few arteries open into other branches of the same or other arteries. Such a communication is termed an *arterial anastomosis*. Anastomoses, we have already noted, fulfill an important protective function in that they provide detour routes for blood to travel in the event of obstruction of a main artery. Examples of arterial anastomoses are the circle of Willis at the base of the brain and the palmar and plantar arches. Other examples are found around several joints as well as in other locations.

Veins

Several facts should be borne in mind while learning the names of veins.

1. Veins are the ultimate extensions of capillaries just as capillaries are the eventual extensions of arteries. Whereas arteries branch into vessels of decreasing size to form arterioles and eventually capillaries,

319

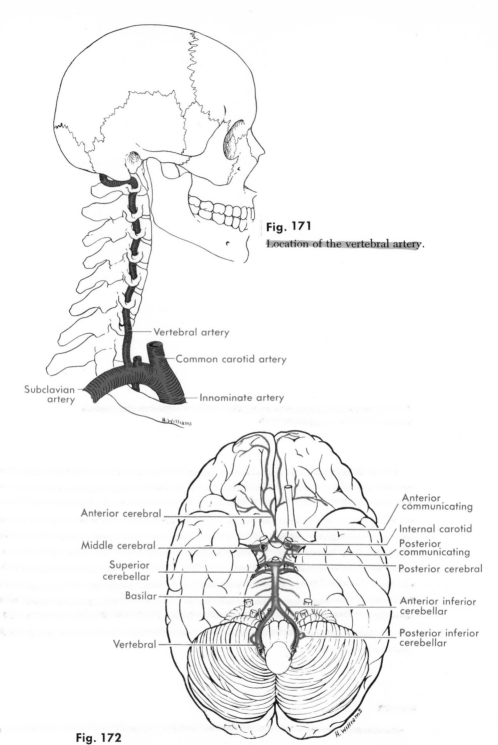

Fig. 171

Location of the vertebral artery.

Vertebral artery

Common carotid artery

Subclavian artery

Innominate artery

Anterior cerebral

Middle cerebral

Superior cerebellar

Basilar

Vertebral

Anterior communicating

Internal carotid

Posterior communicating

Posterior cerebral

Anterior inferior cerebellar

Posterior inferior cerebellar

Fig. 172

Arteries at the base of the brain, including the circle of Willis composed of the two anterior cerebral arteries joined by the communicating arteries to the two posterior cerebral arteries. (From Francis and Farrell: Integrated anatomy and physiology, St. Louis, The C. V. Mosby Co.)

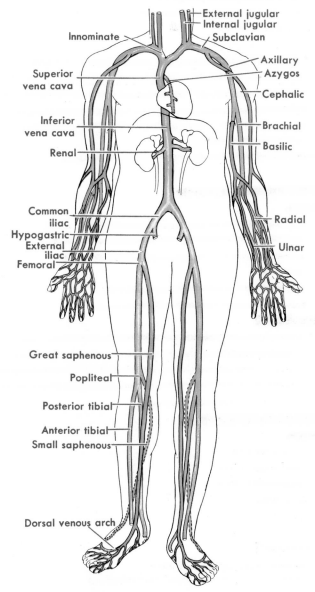

External jugular
Internal jugular
Subclavian
Innominate
Axillary
Azygos
Superior vena cava
Cephalic
Inferior vena cava
Brachial
Renal
Basilic
Common iliac
Radial
Hypogastric
External iliac
Femoral
Ulnar
Great saphenous
Popliteal
Posterior tibial
Anterior tibial
Small saphenous
Dorsal venous arch

Fig. 173
Main veins of the body.

capillaries unite into vessels of increasing size to form venules and eventually veins.

2. Many of the main arteries have corresponding veins bearing the same name and located alongside or near the arteries. These veins, like the arteries, lie in deep, well-protected areas, for the most part close along the bones. Example: femoral artery and femoral vein, both located along the femur bone.

3. Veins found in the deep parts of the body are called *deep veins* in contradistinction to *superficial veins* which lie near the surface. These latter are the veins that can be seen through the skin.

4. The large veins of the cranial cavity, formed by the dura mater, are not called veins but *sinuses;* they should not be confused with the bony sinuses of the skull.

The following list identifies the major veins. Locate each one as named on Figs. 173 to 177.

Veins of upper extremities (Fig. 174)

    Deep

        Palmar (volar) arch (also superficial)

        Radial (partially deep, partially superficial)

        Ulnar (partially deep, partially superficial)

        Brachial

        Axillary (continuation of brachial)

        Subclavian (continuation of axillary)

    Superficial

        Veins of hand form dorsal and venous arches which together with complicated network of superficial veins of lower arm finally pour their blood into two large veins—cephalic (thumb side) and basilic (little finger side); these two veins empty into the deep axillary vein

Veins of lower extremities (Figs. 175 and 176)

    Deep

        Plantar arch

        Anterior tibial

        Posterior tibial

        Popliteal

        Femoral

        External iliac

    Superficial

        Dorsal venous arch of foot

        Great (or internal or long) saphenous

        Small (or external or short) saphenous

      (Great saphenous terminates in femoral vein in groin; small saphenous terminates in popliteal vein)

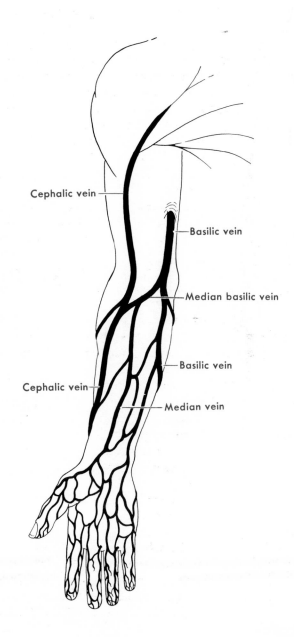

Cephalic vein

Basilic vein

Median basilic vein

Basilic vein

Cephalic vein

Median vein

Fig. 174

Main superficial veins of the upper
extremity, anterior view.

323

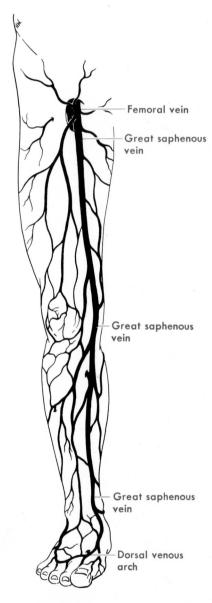

- Femoral vein
- Great saphenous vein
- Great saphenous vein
- Great saphenous vein
- Dorsal venous arch

Fig. 175

Main superficial veins of the lower extremity, anterior view.

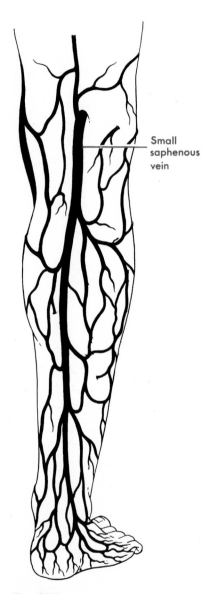

- Small saphenous vein

Fig. 176

Main superficial veins of the lower extremity, posterior view.

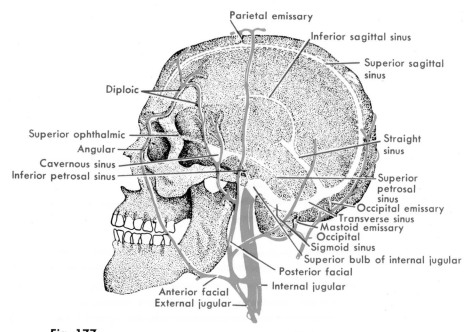

Parietal emissary

Inferior sagittal sinus

Superior sagittal sinus

Diploic

Superior ophthalmic

Angular

Cavernous sinus

Inferior petrosal sinus

Straight sinus

Superior petrosal sinus

Occipital emissary

Transverse sinus

Mastoid emissary

Occipital

Sigmoid sinus

Superior bulb of internal jugular

Posterior facial

Internal jugular

Anterior facial

External jugular

Fig. 177

Veins of head; note connections between superficial and deep veins.
(From Quiring: Collateral circulation, Philadelphia, Lea & Febiger.)

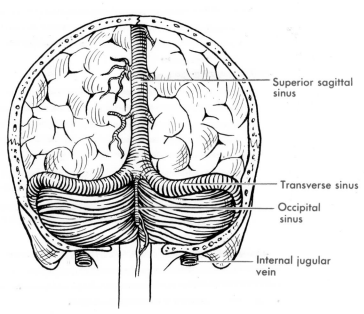

Superior sagittal sinus

Transverse sinus

Occipital sinus

Internal jugular vein

Fig. 178

Blood sinuses of the skull.

Veins of head and neck (Fig. 177)
  Deep (in cranial cavity)
    Longitudinal (or sagittal) sinus
    Inferior sagittal and straight sinus
    Numerous small sinuses
    Right and left transverse (or lateral) sinuses
    Internal jugular veins, right and left (in neck); continuations
      of transverse sinuses
    Innominate veins, right and left; formed by union of subclavian
      and internal jugulars
  Superficial
    External jugulars, right and left (in neck); receive blood from
      small superficial veins of face, scalp, and neck; terminate in
      subclavian veins (small emissary veins connect veins of scalp
      and face with blood sinuses of cranial cavity, a fact of clinical
      interest as a possible avenue for infections to enter cranial
      cavity)

Veins of abdominal organs (Fig. 173)
  Spermatic (or ovarian)
  Renal   Drain into inferior
  Hepatic   vena cava
  Suprarenal

    The left spermatic and left suprarenal veins usually drain into left
      renal vein instead of into inferior vena cava; for return of blood
      from abdominal digestive organs, see discussion of portal circu-
      lation, p. 327; also Fig. 179.

Veins of thoracic organs
    Several small veins, such as the bronchial, esophageal, pericardial,
      etc., return blood from chest organs (except lungs) directly into
      superior vena cava or into azygos vein; azygos vein lies to right
      of spinal column and extends from inferior vena cava (at level
      of the first or second lumbar vertebra) to terminal part of supe-
      rior vena cava; hemiazygos vein lies to left of spinal column,
      extending from lumbar level of inferior vena cava through dia-
      phragm to terminate in azygos vein; an accessory hemiazygos
      vein connects some of superior intercostal veins with azygos or
      hemiazygos vein.

    Correlations. Middle ear infections sometimes cause infection of the
transverse sinuses with the formation of a thrombus; in such cases the
internal jugular vein may be ligated to prevent the development of a
fatal cardiac or pulmonary embolism.

    Intravenous injections are most often given into the median basilic
vein at the bend of the elbow. Blood which is to be used for various

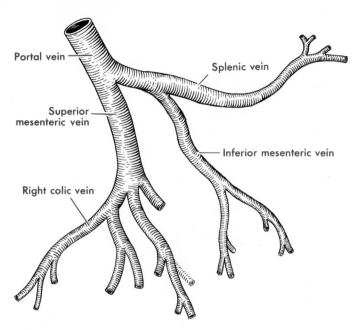

Fig. 179

Diagram to show the main veins forming the portal system.

laboratory tests is also usually removed from this vein. In an infant, however, the longitudinal sinus is more often punctured (through the anterior fontanel) because the superficial arm veins are too tiny for the insertion of a needle.

Portal circulation

Veins from the spleen, stomach, pancreas, and intestines do not pour their blood directly into the inferior vena cava as do the veins from other abdominal organs. Instead they send their blood to the liver by means of the portal vein. Here the blood mingles with the arterial blood in the capillaries and is eventually drained from the liver by the hepatic veins which join the inferior vena cava. The reason for this detouring of the blood through the liver before it returns to the heart will be discussed in the chapter on digestion. Fig. 179 shows the plan of the portal system. The portal vein is formed by the union of the splenic and superior mesenteric veins, but blood from the gastric, pancreatic, and inferior mesenteric veins drains into the splenic vein before it merges with the superior mesenteric vein.

If either portal circulation or venous return from the liver is interfered with (as they often are in certain types of liver or heart disease), then venous drainage from most of the other abdominal organs is necessarily obstructed also. The accompanying increased capillary pressure accounts at least in part for the occurrence of ascites ("dropsy" of abdominal cavity) under these conditions.

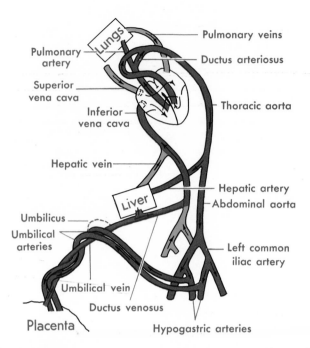

Pulmonary veins
Ductus arteriosus
Pulmonary artery
Lungs
Superior vena cava
Thoracic aorta
Inferior vena cava
Hepatic vein
Hepatic artery
Liver
Abdominal aorta
Umbilicus
Umbilical arteries
Left common iliac artery
Umbilical vein
Ductus venosus
Placenta
Hypogastric arteries

Fig. 180

Scheme to show the plan of fetal circulation. Note the following essential features: (1) two umbilical arteries, extensions of the hypogastric or internal iliac arteries which carry blood to (2) the placenta which is attached to the uterine walls; (3) the umbilical vein which returns blood, rich in oxygen and food, from the placenta; (4) the ductus venosus, a small vessel which connects the umbilical vein with the inferior vena cava; (5) the foramen ovale, and opening in the septum between the right and left atria; and (6) the ductus arteriosus, a small vessel which connects the pulmonary artery with the thoracic aorta.

Fetal circulation

Circulation in the body before birth necessarily differs from circulation after birth for two main reasons—because fetal blood secures oxygen and food from maternal blood instead of from its own lungs and digestive organs respectively. Obviously, then, there must be additional blood vessels in the fetus to carry the fetal blood into close approximation with the maternal blood and to return it to the fetal body. These structures are the two *umbilical arteries,* the *umbilical vein,* and the *ductus venosus.* Also there must be some structure to function as the lungs and digestive organs do postnatally—that is, a place where an interchange of gases, foods, and wastes between the fetal and maternal blood can take place. This structure is the *placenta.* The exchange of substances occurs without any actual mixing of maternal and fetal bloods since each flows in its own capillaries.

In addition to the placenta and umbilical vessels, three structures located within the fetus' own body play an important part in fetal circulation. One of them (ductus venosus) serves as a detour by which most of the blood returning from the placenta bypasses the fetal liver. The other two (foramen ovale and ductus arteriosus) provide detours by which blood bypasses the lungs. A brief description of each of the six structures necessary for fetal circulation follows.

1. *Two umbilical arteries* are extensions of the internal iliac (hypogastric) arteries and carry fetal blood to the placenta.

2. *Placenta* is a structure attached to uterine wall; exchange of oxygen and other substances between maternal and fetal blood takes place in the placenta.

3. *Umbilical vein* returns oxygenated blood from placenta, enters the fetal body through the umbilicus, extends up to undersurface of the liver where it gives off two or three branches to the liver, and then continues on as the ductus venosus. Two umbilical arteries and umbilical vein together constitute the *umbilical cord* and are shed at birth along with the placenta.

4. *Ductus venosus* is a continuation of the umbilical vein along the undersurface of the liver and drains into the inferior vena cava. Most of the blood returning from the placenta bypasses the liver. Only a relatively small amount enters the liver by way of the branches from the umbilical vein into the liver.

5. *Foramen ovale* is an opening in the septum between the right and left atria. A valve at the opening of the inferior vena cava into the right atrium directs most of the blood through the foramen ovale into the left atrium so that it bypasses the fetal lungs. A small per cent of the blood leaves the right atrium for the right ventricle and pulmonary artery. But even most of this does not flow on into the lungs. Still another detour, the ductus arteriosus, diverts it.

6. *Ductus arteriosus* is a small vessel connecting the pulmonary artery with the descending thoracic aorta. It therefore enables another portion of the blood to detour into the systemic circulation without going through the lungs.

Almost all fetal blood is a mixture of oxygenated and deoxygenated blood. Examine Fig. 180 carefully to determine why this is so. What happens to the oxygenated blood returned from the placenta via the umbilical vein?

Since the six structures that serve fetal circulation are no longer needed after birth, several changes take place. As soon as the umbilical cord is cut, the two umbilical arteries, the placenta, and the umbilical vein obviously no longer function. The placenta is shed from the mother's body as the afterbirth with part of the umbilical vessels attached. The sections of these vessels remaining in the infant's body eventually become fibrous cords which remain throughout life. (The umbilical vein becomes the round ligament of the liver.) The ductus venosus, no longer needed to bypass blood around the liver, eventually becomes the ligamentum venosum of the liver. The foramen ovale normally becomes functionally closed soon after a newborn baby takes his first breath and full circulation through his lungs becomes established. Complete structural closure, however, requires longer. According to Gray, the foramen ovale "gradually decreases in size during the first month but a small opening usually persists until the last third of the first year and often later."* Eventually the foramen ovale becomes a mere depression (fossa ovalis) in the wall of the right atrial septum. About the ductus ateriosus, Gray writes that it "begins to contract immediately after respiration is established, and its lumen slowly becomes obliterated."* Eventually it also turns into a fibrous cord.

CIRCULATION

Definitions

The term circulation of blood, suggests its meaning, namely, blood flow through vessels arranged to form a circuit or circular pattern. Blood flow from the heart (left ventricle) through all blood vessels except those of the lungs and back to the heart (to the right atrium) is spoken of as *systemic circulation*. The left ventricle pumps blood into the ascending aorta. From here it flows into arteries that carry it into the various tissues and organs of the body. Within each structure blood moves from arteries to arterioles to capillaries. Here, the vital two-way exchange of substances occurs between blood and cells. Blood flows next out of each organ by way of its venules and then its veins to drain eventually into the inferior or superior vena cava. These two great veins of the body return venous blood to the heart to the right atrium to complete systemic circulation. But the blood has not quite come full circle back to its starting point, the left ventricle. To do this and start on its way again, it must first flow through another circuit, the *pulmonary circulation*. Venous blood moves from the right atrium to the right ventricle to the pulmonary artery to lung arterioles and capillaries. Here exchange of gases between blood and air takes place, converting venous blood to arterial blood. This oxygenated blood then flows on through lung venules into four pulmonary veins and returns to the left atrium of the heart. From the left atrium it enters the left ventricle to be pumped again through the systemic circulation.

---

*From Goss, Charles M. (editor): Gray's anatomy of the human body, ed. 27, Philadelphia, 1959, Lea & Febiger, p. 579.

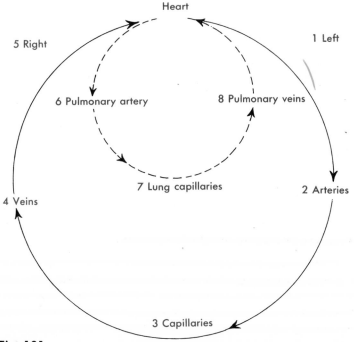

Fig. 181

Scheme to show the relation of systemic and pulmonary circulation. As indicated by the numbers, blood circulates from the left side of the heart to arteries, to capillaries, to veins, to the right side of the heart, to the lungs, and back to the left side of the heart, thereby completing a circuit. Refer to this diagram when tracing the circulation of blood to or from any part of the body. Where would arterioles and venules fit into this diagram?

How to trace the circulation of blood. In order to enumerate the vessels through which blood flows in reaching a designated part of the body or in returning to the heart from a part, one must remember the following:

1. That blood always flows in this direction—from *left ventricle* of heart to *arteries,* to *capillaries* of each body part, to *veins,* to *right atrium, right ventricle, pulmonary artery, lung capillaries, pulmonary veins, left atrium,* and back to left ventricle. (Fig. 181.)
2. That when blood is in capillaries of abdominal digestive organs, it must flow through portal system before returning to heart.
3. Names of main arteries and veins of body.

For example, if one were to trace the circulation of glucose instilled into the rectum to the cells of the right little finger, the vessels through which it would pass after absorption from the intestinal mucosa into capillaries would be as follows: *capillaries* into venules of large intestine into inferior mesenteric *vein,* splenic vein, portal vein, capillaries of liver, hepatic veins, inferior vena cava, *right atrium* of heart, *right ventricle, pulmonary artery, lung capillaries, pulmonary veins, left atrium, left ventricle, ascending aorta,* aortic arch, innominate artery, right subclavian artery, right axillary artery, right brachial artery, right ulnar artery, arteries of palmar arch, arterioles, and *capillaries* of right little finger.

Note: The structures italicized show the direction of blood flow as described in point 1 above and illustrated in Fig. 181. Follow this course of circulation on Figs. 179, 173, and 169 as you study it. Try to answer Question 37 of the review questions at the end of this chapter, using the plan outlined. For circulation to various parts of body, see Fig. 193, p. 348.

Functions of circulation mechanisms

Circulation is, of course, a vital function. It constitutes the only means by which cells can receive materials needed for energy and growth and can have their wastes removed. Not only is circulation necessary, but circulation of different volumes of blood per minute is also essential for healthy survival. More active cells need more blood per minute than less active cells. The reason underlying this principle is obvious. The more work cells do, the more energy they use and the more substances they need to supply this energy. Only arterial blood can deliver these energy-suppliers (oxygen and foods). So the more active any part of the body is, the greater the volume of blood circulated to it per minute must be. And this requires that circulating mechanisms accomplish two functions: maintain circulation (keep blood flowing, that is) and vary circulation (cause a larger volume of blood to circulate per minute when activity increases and a smaller volume when activity decreases).

To achieve these two ends, a great many factors must operate together. Incidentally, this is an important physiological principle that you have no doubt observed by now—that every body function depends upon many other functions. A constellation of separate processes or mechanisms act as a single integrated mechanism. Together they perform some one large function. For example, many mechanisms together accomplish the large function we call circulation. To try to make the complexities of circulation mechanisms a little more understandable, we shall use a question and answer method for our discussion of the principles of circulation.

Principles of circulation

Why does blood circulate? What makes it keep moving over and over again as long as life lasts, from the left heart through the systemic vessels to the right heart, to the lungs, and back to the left heart?

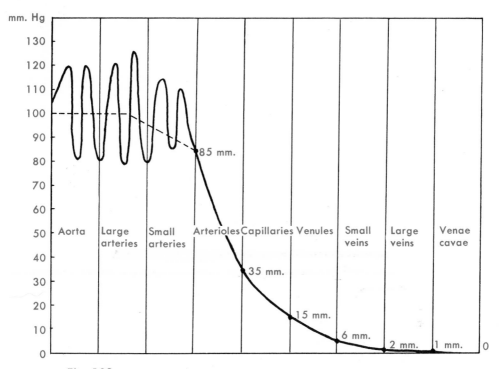

Fig. 182

Blood pressure gradient. Dotted line indicates average or mean systolic pressure in arteries.

Answer: Blood flows for the same reason that any fluid flows—whether it be water in a river or in a garden hose or in hospital tubing or blood in vessels. A fluid flows because a pressure gradient exists between different parts of its bed. This primary fluid flow principle derives from Newton's first and second laws of motion. In essence, these laws state the following principles:

1. That a fluid does not flow when its pressure is the same in all parts of it.
2. That a fluid flows only when its pressure is higher in one area than in another, and it flows always from the higher pressure area toward the lower pressure area.

In brief, then, the answer to our first question about circulation is that blood circulates because a blood pressure gradient exists within the circulatory system.

What is blood pressure gradient?

Answer: Blood pressure gradient is blood pressure difference. For example, if blood pressure in the aorta averages 100 mm. Hg and pressure in a vein is 5 mm. Hg, a blood pressure gradient of 95 mm. Hg exists between the two areas. A blood pressure gradient might be thought of a blood pressure hill down which blood flows. The symbol $(P_1 - P_2)$ is often used to stand for a pressure gradient, with P_1 the symbol for the higher pressure and P_2 the symbol for the lower pressure.

Suppose for instance that the average capillary pressure in the capillaries of your arm muscles is 25 mm. Hg and the average pressure in the arterioles from which these capillaries branch is 60 mm. Hg. Which is P_1? P_2? What is the blood pressure gradient? In which direction would blood necessarily flow?

The blood pressure gradient for systemic circulation taken as a whole is about 100 mm. Hg since aortic pressure averages about 100 mm. Hg and pressure in the venae cavae at their junction with the right atrium approximates 0.

What factors determine arterial blood pressure?

Answer: The primary determinant is the volume of blood in the arteries. A direct relation exists between arterial blood volume and arterial pressure. This means that an increase in arterial blood volume tends to increase arterial pressure, and conversely a decrease in arterial volume tends to decrease arterial pressure. Many factors together indirectly determine arterial pressure through their influence on arterial volume. Two of the most important are cardiac minute output (CMO) and peripheral resistance. A change in either tends to change the volume of blood entering the arteries and thereby to change the blood pressure in the same direction. More specifically, anything which increases cardiac minute output tends to increase arterial blood volume and thereby to increase arterial blood pressure. Anything which decreases cardiac minute output tends to decrease arterial blood volume and pressure. Anything which increases peripheral resistance

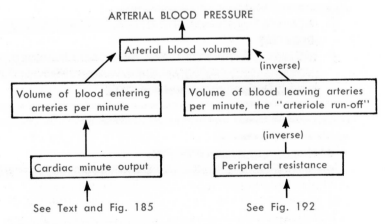

Fig. 183

Factors that determine arterial blood pressure.

tends to increase arterial blood volume and pressure, and anything which decreases peripheral resistance tends to decrease arterial volume and pressure. Now let us examine these terms cardiac minute output and peripheral resistance a little further.

Cardiac minute output means what you would guess—the volume of blood pumped out of the left ventricle into the aorta each minute. How big this volume is, of course, depends both upon the number of heart contractions per minute and upon the amount of blood pumped per contraction. Contraction of the heart is called *systole;* therefore the volume of blood pumped by one contraction is known as *systolic discharge. Stroke volume* means the same thing, the amount of blood pumped by one stroke (contraction) of the ventricle. Stroke volume reflects the force or strength of ventricular contraction—the stronger the contraction the greater the stroke volume tends to be. Cardiac minute output can be computed by the following simple equation:

$$\text{Stroke volume} \times \text{Heart rate} = \text{CMO}$$

From this equation we can derive the following principles. Anything which changes either the rate of the heartbeat or its stroke volume tends to change cardiac minute output, arterial blood volume, and blood pressure in the same direction. In other words, anything which makes the heart beat faster or anything which makes it beat stronger, increasing its stroke volume, tends to increase cardiac minute output and, therefore, arterial blood volume and pressure. Conversely, anything which causes the heart to beat more slowly or more weakly tends to decrease cardiac minute output, arterial volume, and blood pressure. But do not overlook the word *tend* in the preceding sentences. A change in heart rate or in stroke volume does not always change the heart's output, or the amount of blood in the arteries, or the blood pressure. To see whether this is true, do the following simple arithmetic, using the formula just given for computing CMO. Assume a normal rate and stroke volume of 72 beats per minute and 70 milliliters respectively. Next suppose the rate drops to 60 and the stroke volume increases to 100. Does the decrease in heart rate actually cause a decrease in cardiac minute output in this case? Clearly not—the cardiac minute output increases. Do you think it is valid, however, to say that a slower rate *tends* to decrease the heart's minute output? By itself, without any change in any other factor, would not a slowing of the heartbeat cause cardiac minute volume, arterial volume, and blood pressure to fall?

Peripheral resistance, another factor that helps determine arterial blood pressure, is resistance to blood flow imposed by the force of friction between blood and the walls of its vessels. Friction develops partly because of a characteristic of blood—its viscosity or stickiness—and partly from the small diameter of arterioles and capillaries. Peripheral resistance helps determine arterial pressure by controlling the rate of "arteriole runoff," the amount of blood that runs out of the arteries into the arterioles. The greater the resistance is, the less the arteriole runoff tends to be. And, therefore, the more blood left in the arteries, the higher arterial pressure tends to be.

Summarized our answer to the third question, arterial blood pressure is determined directly by arterial blood volume which is determined by many factors but especially by the heart's output and peripheral resistance.

What factors regulate the stroke volume of the heart?

Answer: The main regulator of the strength of the heartbeat and therefore of its stroke volume is now believed to be the ratio of sympathetic-parasympathetic stimulation of the heart. An increase in sympathetic stimulation tends to make the heart contract more forcefully and to increase its stroke volume. On the other hand, an increase in parasympathetic stimulation tends to produce opposite results—weaker contraction and smaller stroke volume.

Many years ago Starling described a principle later made famous as Starling's law of the heart. In this principle he stated the factor he had observed as the main regulator of heartbeat strength in experiments performed on denervated animal hearts. He wrote, "the energy set free at each contraction of the heart is a simple function of the length of the fibers composing its muscular walls." Interpreted, this means that within limits, the longer or more stretched the heart fibers at the beginning of contraction, the stronger will be their contraction.

The factor determining how stretched the animal hearts were at the beginning of contractions was, as you might deduce, the amount of blood in the hearts at the end of diastole. The more blood returned to the hearts per minute, the more stretched were their fibers, the stronger were their contractions, and the larger was the volume of blood they ejected with each contraction. If, however, too much blood stretched the hearts too far, beyond a certain critical point, they seemed to lose their elasticity. They then contracted less vigorously—much as a rubber band, stretched too much, rebounds with less force.

Starling's law of the heart is valid under experimental conditions. But under physiological conditions a neural factor dominates over his mechanical factor in controlling heartbeat strength. Under physiological conditions the ratio of sympathetic-parasympathetic impulses is the main regulator of the strength of the heartbeat.

What factors regulate the heart rate?

Answer: Pressoreflexes constitute the dominant heart rate control

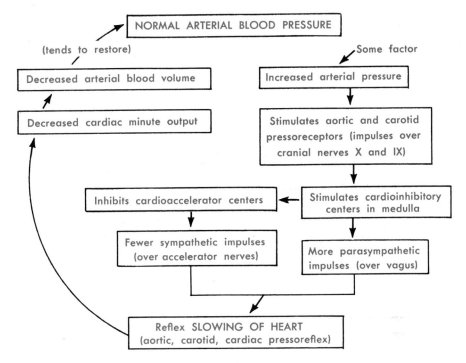

Fig. 184

The aortic and carotid cardiac pressoreflexes, a mechanism that tends to maintain or restore homeostasis of arterial blood pressure by regulating the rate of the heartbeat. Note that by this mechanism an increase in arterial blood pressure leads to reflex slowing of the heart and tends to lower blood pressure. The converse is also true; a decrease in blood pressure leads to reflex acceleration of the heart and tends to raise the pressure upward toward normal.

mechanism, although various other factors also influence heart rate.

The cardiac pressoreflexes. Pressoreceptors (Fig. 184) are located in the aortic arch, the carotid sinus.* Sensory fibers extend from the aortic arch pressoreceptors via the aortic depressor nerve (branch of vagus) to the cardioinhibitory center in the medulla. From the cardioinhibitory center efferent impulses are transmitted to the heart (SA node mainly) by parasympathetic fibers in the vagus. Carotid sinus pressoreceptors have their dendrites in the sinus nerve (branch of ninth

---

*The carotid sinus is a small dilatation of the vessels where the common carotid artery bifurcates to form the internal and external carotids. The sinus is located under the sternocleidomastoid muscle at the level of the upper margin of the thyroid cartilage. Just external to the carotid sinus is a small structure, the carotid body, which contains many chemoreceptors. Like the carotid sinus pressoreceptors, the chemoreceptors are receptors for a branch of the glossopharyngeal nerve, but unlike the pressoreceptors, they are sensitive to excess blood carbon dioxide or to deficient blood oxygen instead of to changes in blood pressure.

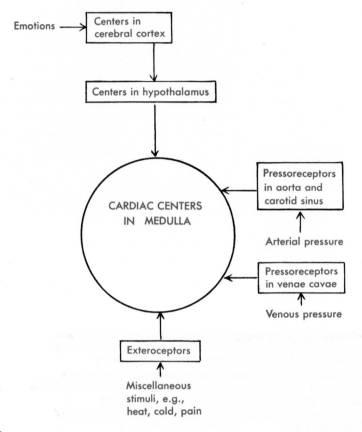

Fig. 185

Scheme to show some of the many parts of the heart rate control mechanism.
Impulses from various receptors are conducted by sensory fibers which terminate in synapses
with neurons in cardiac centers. Motor fibers from the centers relay impulses to sympathetic
and parasympathetic neurons which transmit them to the heart. Also streaming into the cardiac
centers are impulses from the hypothalamus, presumably part of the pathway by which
emotions influence heart rate.

cranial nerve) and their cell bodies in two ganglia* lodged in the temporal bone; their axons extend into the medulla where they synapse with neurons of the cardioinhibitory and vasomotor centers.

If blood pressure within the aorta or carotid sinus increases suddenly, it stimulates the aortic or carotid pressoreceptors. This leads to stimulation of the cardioinhibitory center and reciprocal inhibition of the accelerator center, which in turn leads to more impulses per second over the vagus and fewer impulses over the cardioaccelerator nerves to the heart and tends to cause reflex slowing of the heart.

---

*Petrous and jugular ganglia.

On the other hand, a decrease in aortic or carotid blood pressure usually initiates reflex acceleration of the heart. The lower blood pressure stimulates pressoreceptors less strongly. Hence the cardioinhibitory center receives fewer stimulating impulses and the cardioaccelerator center fewer inhibitory impulses—net result, the heart beats faster.

Pressoreceptors located in the right atrium of the heart respond to changes in right atrial pressure. An increase in this pressure results in reflex acceleration of the heart, and a decrease in right atrial pressure produces reflex slowing.

Almost fifty years ago the noted physiologist Bainbridge demonstrated reflex heart acceleration in dogs following injection of saline solution or blood intravenously but did not establish the mechanism involved. But since then some have postulated that this Bainbridge reflex (accelerated heart beat following increased venous return) is initiated by stimulation of pressoreceptors in the vena cava or right atrium. Others deny that such a reflex exists at all.

Miscellaneous factors that influence heart rate. Included in this category are such important factors as emotions, exercise, hormones, blood temperature, and stimulation of various exteroceptors. Anxiety, fear, and anger often make the heart beat faster. Grief, in contrast, tends to slow it. Presumably, emotions produce changes in the heart rate through the influence of impulses from the cerebrum via the hypothalamus to cardiac centers in the medulla and cord. In exercise, the heart normally accelerates. The mechanism is not definitely known. But it is thought to include impulses from the cerebrum through the hypothalamus to cardiac centers. Epinephrine is the hormone most noted as a cardiac accelerator. Increased blood temperature or stimulation of skin heat receptors tend to increase the heart rate, and decreased blood temperature or stimulation of skin cold receptors tend to slow it. Sudden intense stimulation of pain receptors also tends to decrease the heart rate. In Fig. 185 are summarized the major factors controlling the rate of the heartbeat.

What factors determine peripheral resistance?

Answer: Peripheral resistance, as already noted, exists mainly because of blood viscosity and the small diameter of arterioles.

What determines blood viscosity?

Answer: Viscosity is defined by Stedman as "a condition of more or less adhesion of the molecules of a fluid to each other, so that it flows with difficulty."* Blood viscosity is due in part to the blood proteins but mainly to the red cells. An increase in either blood protein or red

---

*From Stedman's Medical Dictionary, ed. 20, Philadelphia, 1961, Williams & Wilkins Co.

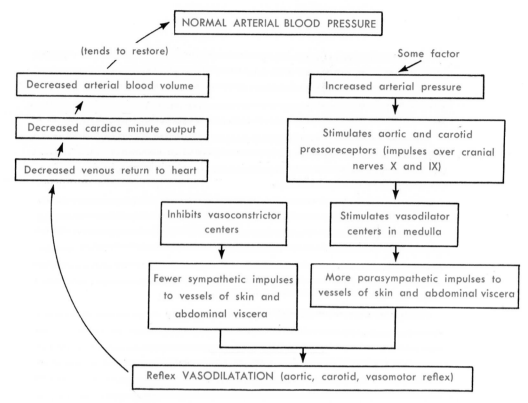

Fig. 186

The aortic and carotid vasomotor pressoreflexes, a mechanism
that operates simultaneously with the aortic and carotid
cardiac pressoreflexes to maintain or restore homeostasis of
arterial blood pressure (see Fig. 184). An increase in arterial
blood pressure leads to both reflex dilatation of many blood
vessels and reflex slowing of the heart. Both of these changes
tend to lower the blood pressure to normal.

blood cell concentrations tends to increase viscosity, and a decrease in
either tends to decrease it. Under normal circumstances blood viscosity
changes very little. But under certain abnormal conditions, such as
marked anemia or hemorrhage, a decrease in blood viscosity may be
the crucial factor lowering peripheral resistance and arterial pressure
even to the point of circulatory failure.

   What factors regulate arteriole diameter?

   Answer: Factors that control arteriole diameter might be said to
constitute the vasomotor control mechanism. Like most physiological
mechanisms, it consists of many parts (Fig. 188).

   For the sake of discussion we shall classify these as pressoreflexes,
chemoreflexes, the medullary ischemic reflex, and control by higher
brain centers.

Vasomotor pressoreflexes (Fig. 186). A sudden increase in arterial blood pressure stimulates aortic and carotid pressoreceptors—the same ones that initiate cardiac reflexes. Not only does this lead to stimulation of cardioinhibitory centers but also to stimulation of vasodilator centers and reciprocal inhibition of vasoconstrictor centers. (Together these centers constitute the *vasomotor centers*.) As a result more impulses per second go out over parasympathetic fibers and fewer over sympathetic fibers, producing widespread dilatation of arterioles and of venules of the "blood reservoirs." Since sympathetic vasoconstrictor impulses predominate at normal arterial pressures, inhibition of these is considered the major mechanism of vasodilatation.

The main *blood reservoirs* are the venous plexuses and sinuses in the skin and abdominal organs (especially in the liver and spleen). In other words, blood reservoirs are the venous networks of most of the body, with the exception of those of the skeletal muscles, heart, and brain. The term reservoir is apt, since these veins serve as storage depots for blood that can be released and returned to the heart for a "shifting"

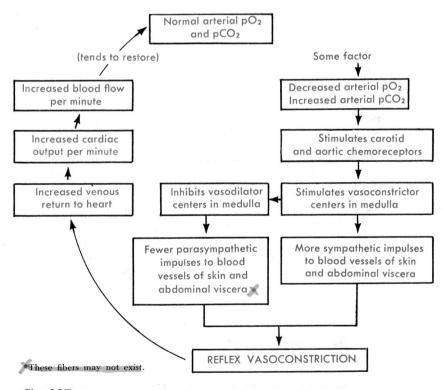

*These fibers may not exist.

Fig. 187

Vasomotor chemoreflex.

to heart and skeletal muscles when increased activity demands. The mechanism which accomplishes this is as follows.

A decrease in arterial pressure initiates constriction of arterioles, venules, and veins in blood reservoir organs, notably the skin, liver, and spleen. Fewer impulses go from aortic and carotid pressoreceptors to the vasodilator centers, thereby depressing them and reciprocally stimulating the vasoconstrictor centers. More impulses, therefore, are sent out from the vasoconstrictor centers via sympathetic fibers to smooth muscle of arterioles, venules, and veins in blood reservoirs causing their constriction. This squeezes more blood out of them, increasing the amount of venous return to the heart. Eventually this extra blood is redistributed to more active structures such as skeletal muscles and heart because their arterioles become dilated due largely to operation of a local mechanism (p. 344). Thus the vasoconstrictor pressoreflex and the local vasodilating mechanism together serve as an important device for shifting blood from reservoirs to structures which need it more. It is an especially valuable mechanism during exercise.

Vasomotor chemoreflexes (Fig. 187). Chemoreceptors located in the

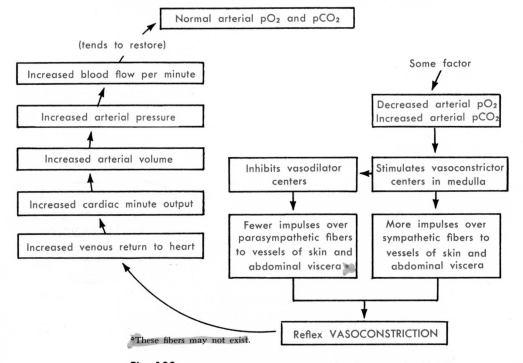

Fig. 188

The *medullary ischemic reflex*, a mechanism that tends to maintain or restore homeostasis of blood pO_2 and pCO_2.

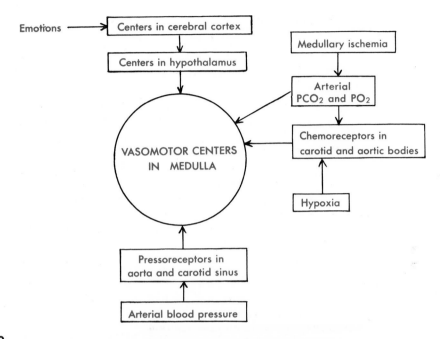

Fig. 189

Scheme to show some of the many parts of the vasomotor control mechanism.
Impulses from chemoreceptors and pressoreceptors are conducted by sensory fibers which
terminate in synapses with neurons in vasomotor centers. Motor fibers from the centers relay
impulses to sympathetic and parasympathetic neurons which transmit them to smooth muscle
in blood vessels, causing them to constrict or dilate. Also streaming into the vasomotor
centers are impulses from the hypothalamus, presumably part of the pathway by which emotions
influence blood pressure.

aortic and carotid bodies are particularly sensitive to a deficiency of
blood oxygen (hypoxia) and somewhat less sensitive to excess blood
carbon dioxide (hypercapnia) and to decreased arterial blood pH.
When one or more of these conditions stimulates the chemoreceptors,
their fibers transmit more impulses to the vasoconstrictor center, and
vasoconstriction of arterioles and venous reservoirs soon follows.

The medullary ischemic reflex (Fig. 188). The medullary ischemic
reflex mechanism is said to exert the most powerful control of all on
small blood vessels. Both oxygen lack and carbon dioxide excess accompany ischemia (inadequate blood supply), but, presumably, it is
the latter, the hypercapnea, that intensely and directly stimulates the
vasoconstrictor center to bring about marked arteriole and venous reservoir constriction.

Vasomotor control by higher brain centers (Fig. 189). Impulses
from centers in the cerebral cortex and in the hypothalamus are be-

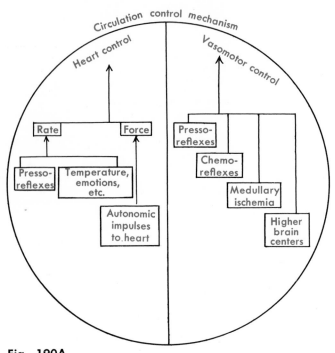

Fig. 190A

Scheme to show some of the many parts of
the complex circulation control mechanism.

lieved to be transmitted to the vasomotor centers and to thereby help
control vasoconstriction and dilatation. One evidence supporting this
view, for example, is the fact that vasoconstriction and a rise in arterial blood pressure characteristically accompany emotions of intense
fear or anger. Also, laboratory experiments on animals in which stimulation of the posterior or lateral parts of the hypothalamus leads to
vasoconstriction support the belief that higher brain centers influence
the vasomotor centers in the medulla.

Local control of arterioles

Some kind of local mechanism is known to operate to produce vasodilatation in localized areas. Although the mechanism is not clear, it is
known to function in time of increased tissue activity. It also operates
in ischemic tissues, serving as a homeostatic mechanism which tends to
restore normal blood flow. It probably accounts for the increased blood
flow into skeletal muscles during exercise. Norepinephrine, histamine,
lactic acid, and other locally produced substances have been suggested
as the stimuli which activate the local vasodilator mechanism. Local
vasodilation is also referred to as *reactive hyperemia*.

What factors determine the volume of blood flow per minute? Or,

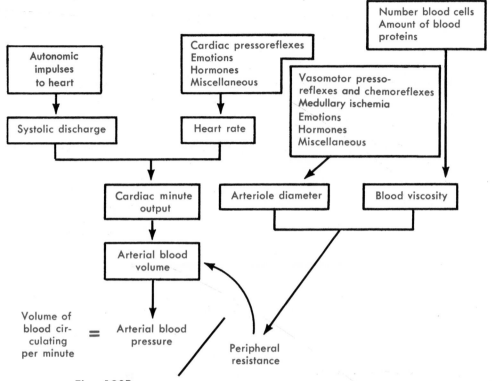

Fig. 190B

Another scheme to show some of the many parts of the complex circulation control mechanism. Note that the volume of blood circulating through the body per minute is determined mainly by arterial blood pressure and peripheral resistance but that a great many factors act together to regulate these two factors.

stated differently, what makes circulation increase or decrease from time to time?

Answer: The answer to this question lies within the answers to our first eight questions about circulation. In most abbreviated form it might be stated this way: the amount of blood flowing through the body per minute is determined by both the blood pressure gradient and peripheral resistance.

A nineteenth century physiologist and physicist, Poiseuille, described the relationship between these three factors—pressure gradient, resistance, and volume of fluid flow per minute—with a mathematical equation known as *Poiseuille's law*. Because the systemic blood pressure gradient normally about equals the mean or average arterial blood pressure (p. 345, answer to second question), we can write Poiseuille's law as applied to circulation in the simplest terms as follows: the volume

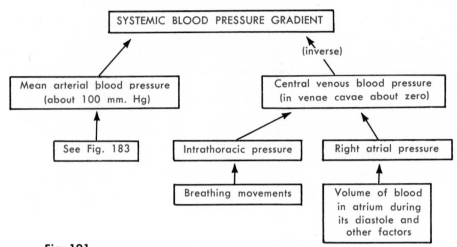

Fig. 191

Factors that determine the systemic blood pressure gradient.

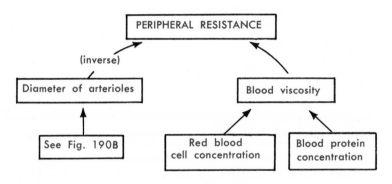

Fig. 192

The main determinants of peripheral resistance.

of blood circulated per minute is directly related to arterial pressure and inversely related to resistance or:

$$\text{Volume blood circulated per minute} = \frac{\text{Arterial pressure}}{\text{Resistance}}$$

The preceding statement and equation need qualifying with regard to the influence of peripheral resistance on circulation. For instance, according to the equation, an increase in peripheral resistance would tend to decrease blood flow. But increased peripheral resistance has a secondary action that acts against its primary action. It tends to decrease arteriole runoff and thereby tends to increase arterial pressure and increase circulation. So to say unequivocally what the effect of an increased peripheral resistance will be on circulation is impossible. The clinical condition arteriosclerosis with hypertension (high blood pressure) illustrates this point. Both peripheral resistance and arterial pressure are increased in this condition. As a result, circulation may decrease if resistance increases more than arterial pressure. If arterial pressure increases proportionately to resistance, it may remain normal.

Special factors influencing venous return to the heart

Two special factors that promote the return of venous blood to the heart are respirations and skeletal muscle contractions. Both produce their facilitating effect on venous return by increasing the pressure gradient between peripheral veins and venae cavae.

The process of breathing increases the pressure gradient between peripheral and central veins by both increasing peripheral venous pressure and decreasing central venous pressure. Each time the diaphragm contracts, enlarging the thoracic cavity and compressing the abdominal cavity, the pressure in the thoracic cavity and therefore in the thoracic portion of the vena cava and in the atria decreases, whereas that in the abdominal cavity and the abdominal veins increases. Deeper respirations intensify these effects and therefore tend to increase venous return to the heart more than do normal respirations. This is part of the reason why the principle is true that increased respirations and increased circulation tend to go hand in hand.

Skeletal muscle contractions operate in the following way to promote venous return: as each skeletal muscle contracts, it squeezes the soft veins scattered through its interior, thereby milking the blood in them upward or toward the heart. And it is prevented from falling back as the muscle relaxes by the closing of the semilunar valves present in veins. Their flaps catch the blood as gravity pulls backward on it (Fig. 194). The net effect of skeletal muscle contraction and venous valvular action, therefore is to move venous blood toward the heart, to increase the venous return.

The value of skeletal muscle contractions in moving blood through veins is illustrated by a common experience. Who has not noticed how much more uncomfortable and tiring standing still is than walking? After several minutes of standing quietly, the feet and legs feel "full" and swollen. Blood has accumulated in the veins because the skeletal muscles are not contracting and squeezing it upward. The repeated contractions of the muscles when walking, on the other hand, keep the blood moving in the veins and prevent the discomfort of distended veins.

347

ARTERIAL SUPPLY—FROM LEFT VENTRICLE BODY PART VENOUS DRAINAGE—INTO RIGHT ATRIUM OF HEART

Arterial Supply—from left ventricle	Body Part	Venous Drainage—into right atrium of heart
Ascending aorta → Coronary	Heart muscle	Coronary → Coronary sinus → Right atrium
Same → Aortic arch → Left common carotid → External carotid → Various branches	Head and neck (exclusive of brain)	External jugular → Subclavian → Innominate → Superior vena cava
Same → Same → Internal carotid → Circle of Willis	Brain	Longitudinal sinus → Transverse sinus → Internal jugular → Same → Same
Same → Same → Innominate		
Right common carotid → Same → Same	Other cranial sinuses	Same → Same
Same → Same → Subclavian → Vertebral → Basilar	Same	Same → Same
Same → Same → Axillary → Brachial → Ulnar; radial → Superficial volar arch; Deep volar arch → Hand	Hand	Superficial and deep volar venous arches → Radial or ulnar → Brachial → Axillary → Same
		Cephalic or basilic → Axillary → Subclavian → Same
Same → Thoracic aorta → Pericardial	Pericardium	Pericardial → Same
Same → Same → Bronchial	Bronchi, lungs	Bronchial → Azygos → Same
Same → Same → Esophageal	Esophagus	Esophageal → Azygos → Same
Same → Same → Intercostal	Skin and muscles of chest wall, pleurae, spinal cord, spine	Intercostal → Azygos → Same
Same → Same → Superior phrenic	Upper surface of diaphragm	Superior phrenic → Same
Same → Same → Abdominal aorta → Inferior phrenic	Undersurface of diaphragm	Inferior phrenic → Inferior vena cava → Same
Same → Same → Celiac → (1) Left gastric	Stomach, esophagus	Gastric → Portal → Liver → Hepatic → Same

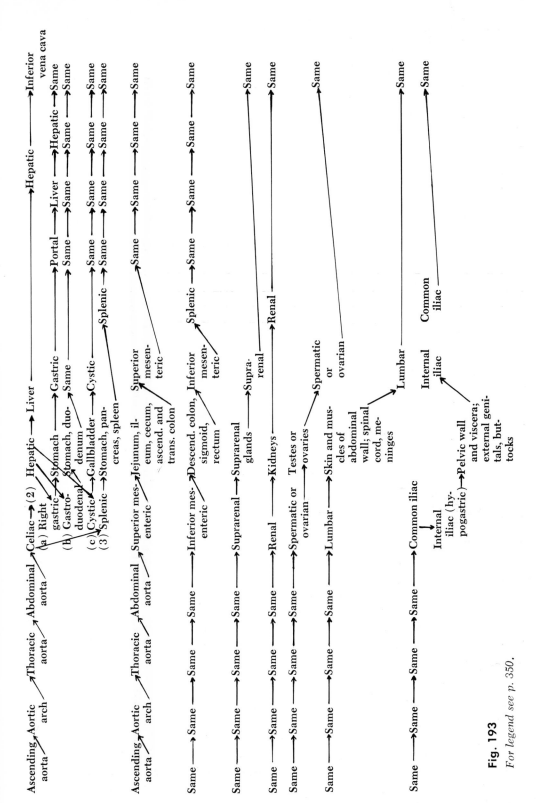

Fig. 193

For legend see p. 350.

349

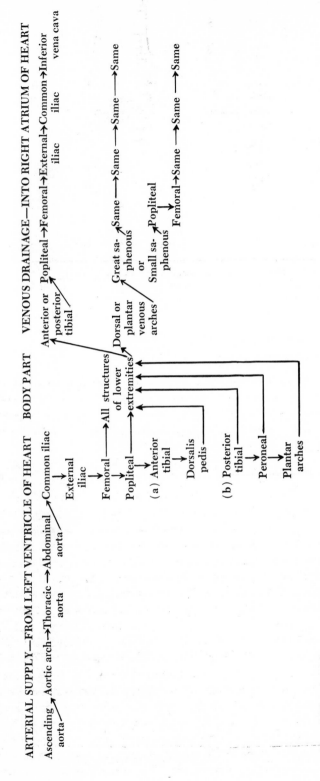

Fig. 193—cont'd

Summary of circulation. To use this chart, find body part to which circulation is to be traced in middle column; arteries supplying blood to the part are listed to the left of the part; veins draining blood away from it are listed to the right of the part. (From Mosby's comprehensive review of nursing, St. Louis, The C. V. Mosby Co.)

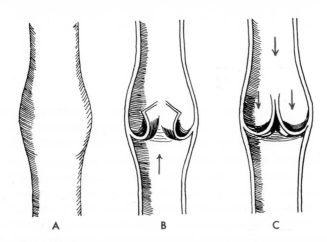

Fig. 194

Diagram showing the action of venous valves: **A,** external view of vein showing dilation at site of the valve; **B,** interior of vein with the valve in open position; **C,** interior of vein with the valve in closed position. (Jane Hopp after Sir Arthur Keith; from Francis and Farrell: Integrated anatomy and physiology, St. Louis, The C. V. Mosby Co.)

HOW ARTERIAL BLOOD PRESSURE IS MEASURED CLINICALLY

Blood pressure is measured with the aid of an apparatus known as a sphygmomanometer which makes it possible to measure the amount of air pressure equal to the blood pressure in an artery. The measurement is made in terms of how many millimeters high the air pressure raises a column of mercury in a glass tube.

The sphygmomanometer consists of a rubber cuff attached by a rubber tube to a compressible bulb and by another tube to a column of mercury which is marked off in millimeters. The cuff is wrapped around the arm over the brachial artery, and air is pumped into the cuff by means of the bulb. In this way air pressure is exerted against the outside of the artery. Air is added until the air pressure exceeds the blood pressure within the artery, or in other words until it compresses the artery. At this time no pulse can be heard through a stethoscope placed over the brachial artery at the bend of the elbow along the inner margin of the biceps muscle. By slowly releasing the air in the cuff, the air pressure is decreased until it approximately equals the blood pressure within the artery. At this point the vessel opens slightly and a small spurt of blood comes through, producing the first sound, one with a rather sharp, taplike quality. This is followed by increasingly louder sounds which suddenly change, becoming more muffled, then disappearing altogether. The nurse must train herself to hear these different sounds and to read the column of mercury at the same time since the first taplike sound represents the *systolic blood pressure,* that is, the force with which the blood is pushing against the artery walls when the ventricles are contracting. The lowest point at which the sounds can be heard, just before they disappear, is approximately equal to the *diastolic pressure* or the force of the blood when the ventricles are relaxed. Systolic pressure gives valuable information about the force of the left ventricular contraction, and diastolic pressure gives valuable information about the resistance of the blood vessels. Clinically, diastolic pressure is considered more important than systolic pressure because it indicates the pressure or strain to which blood vessel walls are constantly subjected and also reflects the condition of the peripheral vessels since diastolic pressure rises or falls with the peripheral resistance.

Blood in the average adult's arteries exerts a pressure equal to that required to raise a column of mercury about 120 mm. (or a column of water over 5 feet) high in a glass tube during systole of the ventricles and 80 mm. high during their diastole. For the sake of brevity, this is expressed as a blood pressure of 120 over 80 (120/80). The first or upper figure represents systolic pressure and the second diastolic pressure. From the figures just given we observe that blood pressure fluctuates considerably during each heartbeat. During ventricular systole the force is great enough to raise the mercury column 40 mm. higher than during ventricular diastole. This difference between systolic and diastolic pressure is called *pulse pressure.* It characteristically increases in arteriosclerosis due mainly to increased systolic pressure. Pulse pressure increases even more markedly in aortic valve insufficiency due both to a rise in systolic and a fall in diastolic pressure.

RELATION OF BLOOD PRESSURE TO ARTERIAL AND VENOUS BLEEDING

Because blood exerts a comparatively high pressure in arteries and a very low pressure in veins, it gushes forth with considerable force from a cut artery but seeps in a slow, steady stream from a vein. As we have just seen, each ventricular contraction raises arterial blood pressure to the systolic level, and each ventricular relaxation lowers it to the diastolic level. As the ventricles contract, then, the blood spurts forth forcefully due to increased pressure in the artery, but as the ventricles relax, the flow ebbs to almost nothing due to the fall in pressure. In other words, blood escapes from an artery in spurts because of the alternate raising and lowering of arterial blood pressure but flows slowly and steadily from a vein because of the low, practically constant pressure. A uniform instead of a pulsating pressure exists in the capillaries and veins because the arterial walls, being elastic continue to squeeze the blood forward while the ventricles are in diastole, thereby causing it to enter the capillaries under a steady pressure.

VELOCITY OF BLOOD

The speed with which blood flows (that is, distance per minute) through its vessels is governed in part by the physical principle that when a liquid flows from an area of one cross-section size to an area of larger size, its velocity will be slower in the area with the larger cross section. For example, a narrow river whose bed widens flows more slowly through the wider section than through the narrow. In terms of blood vascular system, the total cross-section area of all arterioles together is greater than that of the arteries; therefore, blood flows more slowly through arterioles than through arteries. Likewise, the total cross-section area of all capillaries together is greater than that of all arterioles and, therefore, capillary flow is slower than arteriole. Venule cross-section area, on the other hand, is smaller than capillary cross-section area; therefore, the blood velocity increases in venules and again in veins, which have a still smaller cross-section area. In short, the most rapid blood flow takes place in arteries and the slowest in capillaries.

PULSE

Definition

Pulse is defined as the alternate expansion and recoil of an artery.

Cause

Two factors are responsible for the existence of a pulse which can be felt:

1. Intermittent injections of blood from the heart into the aorta, which alternately increase and decrease the pressure in that vessel; if blood poured steadily out of the heart into the aorta, the pressure there would remain constant and there would be no pulse.
2. The elasticity of the arterial walls, which makes it possible for them to expand with each injection of blood and then recoil; if the vessels were fashioned from rigid material such as glass, there would still be an alternate raising and lowering of pressure within them with each systole and diastole of the ventricles, but the walls could not expand and recoil and, therefore, no pulse could be felt.

Pulse wave

Each ventricular systole starts a new pulse which proceeds as a wave of expansion throughout the arteries and is known as the pulse wave. It gradually lessens as it travels, disappearing entirely in the capillaries.

353

The pulse felt in the radial artery at the wrist does not coincide with the contraction of the ventricles but rather follows each contraction by an appreciable interval (the length of time required for the pulse wave to travel from the aorta to the radial artery). The farther from the heart the pulse is taken, therefore, the longer that interval is.

Any nurse has only to think of the number of times she has counted pulses to become aware of the diagnostic importance of the pulse. It reveals important information about the cardiovascular system, about heart action, blood vessels, and circulation.

Where the pulse can be felt

In general, the pulse can be felt wherever an artery lies near the surface and over a bone or other firm background. Some of the specific locations where the pulse is most easily felt are as follows:

1. *radial artery*—at wrist.
2. *temporal artery*—in front of ear or above and to outer side of eye.
3. *common carotid artery*—along anterior edge of sternocleidomastoid muscle at level of lower margin of thyroid cartilage.
4. *facial artery*—at lower margin of lower jaw bone on a line with corners of mouth and in a groove in mandible about one third of way forward from angle.
5. *brachial artery*—at bend of elbow along inner margin of biceps muscle.
6. *femoral artery*—in middle of groin where artery passes over pelvic bone.
7. *popliteal artery*—in popliteal space behind knee.

Note: The so-called pressure points or points at which pressure may be applied to stop arterial bleeding are roughly related to the points where the pulse may be felt in that they both are found where an artery lies near the surface and near a bone which can act as a firm background for pressure. There are six important pressure points:

1. *temporal artery*—in front of ear.
2. *facial artery*—same place as pulse is taken.
3. *common carotid artery*—point where pulse is taken, with pressure back against spinal column.
4. *subclavian artery*—behind mesial third of clavicle, pressing against first rib.
5. *brachial artery*—few inches above elbow on inside of arm, pressing against humerus.
6. *femoral artery*—where pulse is taken.

In trying to stop arterial bleeding by pressure, one must always remember to apply the pressure at the pressure point which lies between the bleeding part and the heart, since the blood flows from the heart through the arteries to the part. Pressure between the heart and bleeding point, therefore, cuts off the source of the blood flow.

Venous pulse

A pulse exists in the large veins only, particularly in those near the heart, due to changes in venous blood pressure brought about by alternate contraction and relaxation of the atria of the heart. Venous pulse does not have as great clinical signficance as arterial pulse and is only rarely recorded.

LYMPHATIC SYSTEM

Definition

The lymphatic system is actually part of the circulatory system since it consists of a moving fluid (lymph and tissue fluid) derived from the blood and a group of vessels (lymphatics) which return the lymph to the blood.

Lymph and interstitial fluid (tissue fluid)

Definition

Lymph is the clear watery-appearing fluid found in the lymphatic vessels, whereas interstitial fluid is located intercellularly in the microscopic spaces between cells. In some tissues it is part of a semifluid ground substance; in others it is the bound water in a gelatinous ground substance. Interstitial fluid and blood together constitute the extracellular fluid or, in the words of Walter Cannon, the internal environment of the body—the fluid environment of cells in contrast to the atmosphere or external environment of the body. Both lymph and tissue fluid closely resemble blood plasma in composition, the main difference being that they contain a lower percentage of proteins than does plasma. (The term lymph is frequently used to mean both the fluid in the lymphatics and that in the tissue spaces.)

Lymphatics

Formation and distribution

Lymphatic vessels originate as microscopic blind-end vessels called *lymphatic capillaries.* These tiny vessels are located in the intercellular spaces and are widely distributed throughout the body. As twigs of a tree join to form branches and branches join to form larger branches, and large branches join to form the tree trunk, so do lymphatic capillaries merge, forming slightly larger lymphatics that join

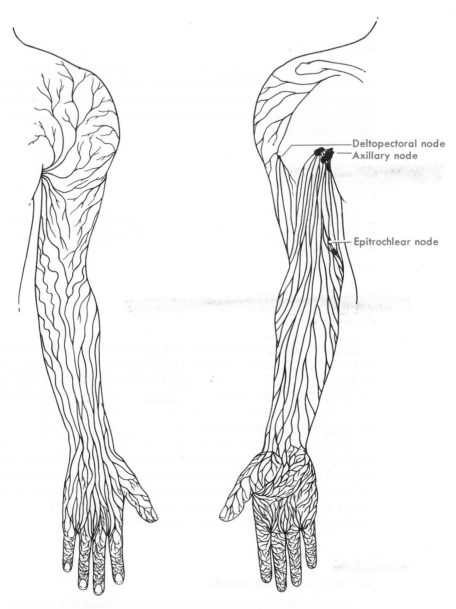

Fig. 195

Superficial lymphatics of the
upper extremity, posterior surface.

Fig. 196

Superficial lymphatics of the
upper extremity, anterior surface.

(After Sappey; from Francis and Farrell: Integrated anatomy and physiology,
St. Louis, The C. V. Mosby Co.)

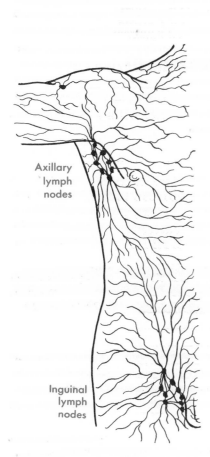

Fig. 197

Distribution of the superficial lymphatics and lymph nodes of the front of the trunk.

Axillary lymph nodes

Inguinal lymph nodes

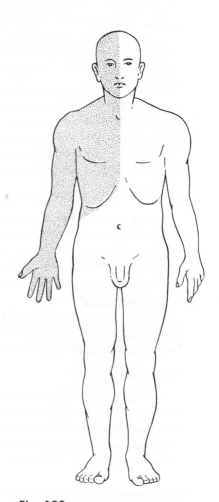

Fig. 198

Lymph drainage. The right lymphatic duct drains lymph from the part of the body indicated by the stippled area. Lymph from all the rest of the body enters the general circulation by way of the thoracic duct.

357

other lymphatics to form still larger vessels, which merge to form the main lymphatic trunks: the *right lymphatic ducts* and the *thoracic duct.* Lymph from the entire body, except the upper right quadrant (Fig. 198), drains eventually into the thoracic duct, which drains into the left subclavian vein at the point where it joins the left internal jugular vein. Lymph from the upper right quadrant of the body empties into the right lymphatic duct (or more commonly into three collecting ducts) and thence into the right subclavian vein. Since most of the lymph of the body returns to the blood stream by way of the thoracic duct, this vessel is considerably larger than the other main lymph channels, the right lymphatic ducts, but is much smaller than the large veins, which it resembles in structure. It has a diameter about the size of a goose quill and a length of from 15 to 18 inches. It originates as a dilated structure, the *cisterna chyli,* in the lumbar region of the abdominal cavity and ascends by a flexuous course to the root of the neck where it joins the subclavian vein as just described. The presence of semilunar valves at frequent intervals along the duct gives it a somewhat varicose appearance.

Structure of the lymphatics

Lymphatics resemble veins in structure with these exceptions: (1) lymphatics are thinner-walled, (2) they contain more valves, and (3) they contain lymph nodes (or glands) located at certain intervals along their course. Lymphatics originating in the villi of the small intestine are called *lacteals,* whereas the milky fluid found in them after digestion is *chyle.*

Function of the lymphatics. The function of lymphatics is the return of water and proteins from the interstitial fluid to blood from which they came. Proteins can return to blood only via lymphatics.

Lymph circulation

Water and solutes continually filter out of capillary blood into the interstitial fluid. To balance this outflow, fluid continually re-enters blood from the interstitial fluid. Some osmoses back into the capillaries, and a much smaller amount enters lymphatic capillaries by a method not yet clearly understood. For more details about fluid exchange between blood and interstitial fluid, see Chapter XV. From lymphatic capillaries, lymph flows through progressively larger lymphatic vessels to eventually re-enter blood at the junction of the internal jugular and subclavian veins (Fig. 199).

Although there is no pump connected with the lymphatic vessels to force lymph onward as the heart does blood, still lymph moves slowly and steadily along in its vessels, notwithstanding the fact that most of the flow is uphill. What mechanisms establishes the pressure gradient required by the basic law of fluid flow? Two of the same mechanisms that contribute to the blood pressure gradient also establish a lymph pressure gradient. These are breathing movements and skeletal muscle contractions.

The mechanism of inspiration, due to the descent of the diaphragm, causes intraabdominal pressure to increase as intrathoracic pressure decreases. And this causes pressure to increase in the abdominal portion of the thoracic duct and to decrease in the thoracic portion. In other words the process of inspiring establishes a pressure gradient in the thoracic duct which causes lymph to flow upward through it into the left subclavian vein.

In addition contracting skeletal muscles exert pressure on the lymphatics to push the lymph forward because valves within the lymphatics prevent backflow.

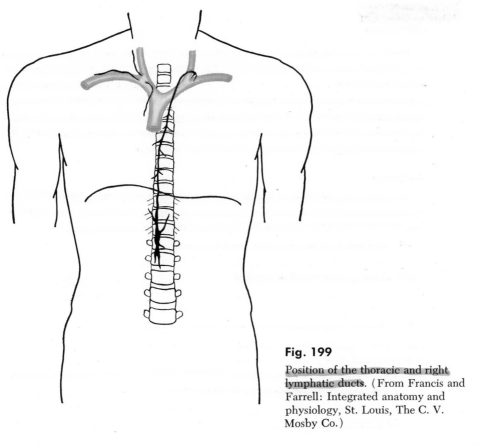

Fig. 199

Position of the thoracic and right lymphatic ducts. (From Francis and Farrell: Integrated anatomy and physiology, St. Louis, The C. V. Mosby Co.)

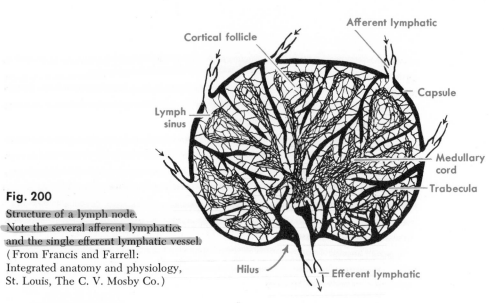

Fig. 200

Structure of a lymph node.
Note the several afferent lymphatics
and the single efferent lymphatic vessel.
(From Francis and Farrell:
Integrated anatomy and physiology,
St. Louis, The C. V. Mosby Co.)

Lymph nodes

Structure

Lymph nodes or glands, as they are often called, are oval or bean-shaped structures. Some are as small as a pinhead and others as large as a Lima bean. As shown in Fig. 200, lymph moves into the nodes via several afferent lymphatic vessels. Here it moves slowly through sinus channels lined with phagocytic reticuloendothelial cells and emerges usually by one efferent vessel. Lymphatic tissue, densely packed with lymphocytes, composes the substance of the node.

Location

With the exception of comparatively few single nodes, most of the lymph nodes are arranged in groups or clusters in certain areas. The group locations of greatest clinical importance are as follows:
1. *submental and submaxillary groups* in the floor of the mouth —lymph from the nose, lips, and teeth drains through these nodes.
2. *superficial cervical glands* in the neck along the sternocleidomastoid muscle—these nodes drain lymph from the head (which has already passed through other nodes) and neck.
3. *superficial cubital or supratrochlear nodes* located just above the bend of the elbow—lymph from the forearm passes through these nodes.
4. *axillary nodes*—(20 to 30 large nodes clustered deep within the under arm and upper chest regions)—lymph from the arm and upper part of the thoracic wall, including the breast, drains through these nodes.

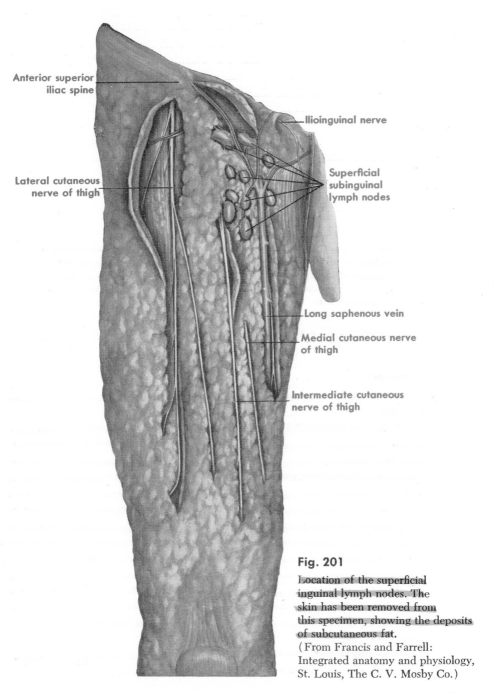

Anterior superior
iliac spine

Ilioinguinal nerve

Superficial
subinguinal
lymph nodes

Lateral cutaneous
nerve of thigh

Long saphenous vein

Medial cutaneous nerve
of thigh

Intermediate cutaneous
nerve of thigh

Fig. 201

Location of the superficial
inguinal lymph nodes. The
skin has been removed from
this specimen, showing the deposits
of subcutaneous fat.
(From Francis and Farrell:
Integrated anatomy and physiology,
St. Louis, The C. V. Mosby Co.)

361

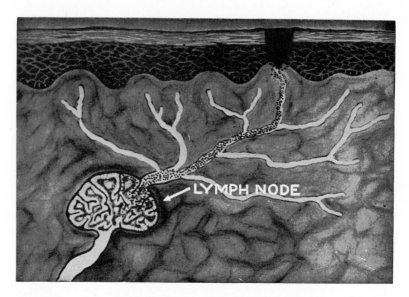

LYMPH NODE

Fig. 202

Diagram to show how lymph nodes prevent the spread of bacteria by
filtering out and destroying many of the bacteria which are brought
to the nodes from the tissues by way of afferent lymphatics. In the
above diagram, bacteria are represented by black dots; lymphatics, by
white channels. (Courtesy Erpi Classroom Films, Inc., New York City.)

5. *inguinal nodes* in the groin—lymph from the leg and external
genitals drains through these.

Functions

Lymph nodes perform two unrelated functions, defense and hemopoiesis:

1. *The defense functions of lymph nodes: filtration and phagocytosis.* The structure of the sinus channels within lymph nodes slows the
lymph flow through them, giving the reticuloendothelial cells that line
the channels time to remove microorganisms and other injurious particles—cancer cells and soot, for example—from the lymph and phagocytose them. Sometimes, however, such hordes of microorganisms enter
the nodes that the phagocytes cannot destroy enough of them to prevent their injuring the node. An infection of the node, adenitis, then
results. Also, because cancer cells often break away from a malignant
tumor and enter lymphatics, they travel to the lymph nodes where they
may set up new growths. This may leave too few channels for lymph
from the arm to return to the blood, with the result that fluid accumulates in the interstitial spaces, causing the arm to become markedly
swollen.

2. *Hemopoiesis.* The lymphatic tissue of lymph nodes forms lymphocytes and monocytes, the nongranular white blood cells.

Location

The spleen is located in the left hypochondrium directly below the diaphragm, above the left kidney and descending colon, and behind the fundus of the stomach.

Structure

The spleen is roughly ovoid in shape, and its size varies greatly in different individuals and in the same individual at different times. For example, it hypertrophies during infectious diseases and atrophies in old age. Within the spleen are numerous areas of lymphatic tissue and many venous sinuses.

Functions

The spleen has long puzzled physiologists who have ascribed many and sundry functions to it. According to present-day knowledge, it performs the following functions:

1. **Defense.** The spleen's reticuloendothelial cells, like all such cells, carry on phagocytosis; therefore, the spleen plays a part in the body's defense against microorganisms.

2. **Red blood cell destruction.** The spleen's reticuloendothelial cells also phagocytose fragments of old worn-out red blood cells.

3. **Blood reservoir.** The pulp of the spleen and its venous sinuses store considerable blood; its normal volume of about 350 milliliters is said to decrease about 200 milliliters in less than a minute's time following sympathetic stimulation that produces marked constriction of its smooth capsule.

4. *Hemopoiesis.* Nongranular leukocytes, that is, monocytes and lymphocytes, are formed in the spleen, as are red blood cells before birth; after birth the spleen is said to again form some red cells in extreme hemolytic anemia.

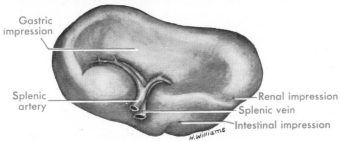

Fig. 203

Spleen, medial aspect. (From Francis and Farrell: Integrated anatomy and physiology, St. Louis, The C. V. Mosby Co.)

5. An interesting hypothesis about the spleen is that sometimes it removes too many blood platelets from circulation, causing a platelet deficiency *(thrombocytopenia)* and consequent tiny capillary hemorrhages; surgical removal of the spleen has been tried on some patients with thrombocytopenia; some surgeons report cures following this treatment.

Outline summary

The circulatory system

Functions

1. Primary function—transportation of various substances to and from body cells
2. Secondary functions—contributes to all bodily functions, for example:
   a. cellular metabolism
   b. homeostasis of pH
   c. homeostasis of temperature
   d. defense against microorganisms

Blood cells

1. Kinds—red blood cells (erythrocytes), white blood cells (leukocytes), platelets (thrombocytes)
2. Red blood cells
   a. size and appearance—biconcave disks about 7 microns in diameter
   b. structure and function—millions of molecules of hemoglobin inside each red cell make possible red cell functions of oxygen and carbon dioxide transport
   c. formation (erythropoiesis)—by myeloid tissue (red bone marrow); see Fig. 154 for stages of red cell development
   d. destruction—by fragmentation in capillaries; reticuloendothelial cells phagocytose red cell fragments and break down hemoglobin to yield iron containing pigment and bile pigments; bone marrow reuses most of iron for new red cell synthesis; liver excretes bile pigments; life span of red cells about 120 days according to studies made with radioactive isotopes
   e. homeostasis of red blood cells—stimulus thought to be tissue hypoxia; for description of mechanisms see Fig. 155. Clinical applications discussed on p. 292:

pernicious anemia, vitamin B_{12}, bone marrow damage, reticulocyte count, red count, hematocrit, and sternal punctures
3. White blood cells
   a. appearance and size—vary; some relatively large cells (monocytes, for example) and some small cells (small lymphocytes, for example); nuclei vary from spherical to S-shaped to lobulated; cytoplasm of neutrophils, eosinophils, and basophils contain granules which take neutral, acid, and basic stains, respectively
   b. functions—defense or protection since carry on phagocytosis and lymphocytes may form antibodies
   c. formation—in myeloid tissue (red bone marrow) for granular leukocytes; nongranular leukocytes (lymphocytes and monocytes) in lymphatic tissue, that is, mainly in lymph nodes and spleen
   d. destruction and life span—some destroyed by phagocytosis; life span unknown
   e. numbers—about 5000 to 10,000 leukocytes per cubic millimeter of blood; differential count on p. 296
4. Platelets
   a. appearance and size—platelets are small fragments of cells
   b. functions—disintegrating platelets release factor which combines with blood proteins and calcium ions to form plasma thromboplastin which initiates blood clotting
   c. formation and life span—formed in red bone marrow by fragmentation of large

cells (megakaryocytes, Fig. 154); life span not known, probably only few days

Blood types (or blood groups)

1. Names—indicate type of antigen on or in red cell membranes
2. Plasma does not contain antibodies against antigens present on its red cells but does contain antibodies against other major blood cell antigens not present on its red cells
3. Universal donor: type O; universal recipient: type AB

Blood plasma

1. Definition—liquid part of blood or whole blood minus its cells
2. Composition—about 90% water and 10% solutes; most solutes crystalloids but some colloids; most solutes electrolytes, but some nonelectrolytes; solutes include foods, wastes, gases, hormones, enzymes, vitamins, and antibodies

Blood clotting

1. Purpose—to plug up ruptured vessels and thus prevent fatal hemorrhage
2. Mechanism
   a. stage 1—thromboplastin formation; see Figs. 156 and 159
   b. stage 2—thrombin formation; see Figs. 157 and 159
   c. stage 3—fibrin formation; see Figs. 158 and 159
3. Factors that oppose clotting
   a. smooth endothelium that lines blood vessels prevents platelet adherence and consequent disintegration; some platelet disintegration continuously despite this preventive
   b. blood normally contains certain anticoagulants, for example, antithrombins, substances which inactivate thrombin so that it cannot catalyze fibrin formation
4. Factors that hasten clotting
   a. endothelial "rough" spots (e.g., lipoid plagues in atherosclerosis)
   b. sluggish blood flow
5. Pharmaceutical preparations that retard clotting—commercial heparin, Dicumarol, citrates (for transfusion blood)
6. Clinical methods of hastening blood clotting
   a. apply rough surfaces to wound to stimulate platelets and tissues to liberate more thromboplastin

b. apply purified thrombin
c. apply fibrin foam, film, etc.

Heart
Description

Four-chambered muscular organ; lies in mediastinum with apex on diaphragm, two thirds of its bulk to left of midline of body and one third to right; apical beat may be counted by placing stethoscope in fifth intercostal space on line with left midclavicular point

Covering

1. Structure—loose-fitting, inextensible sac (fibrous pericardium) around heart, lined with serous pericardium (parietal layer) which also covers outer surface of heart (visceral layer or epicardium); small space between parietal and visceral layers of serous pericardium contains a few drops of pericardial fluid
2. Function—protection against friction

Structure

1. Heart wall—myocardium, name of muscular wall; endocardium, lining; pericardium, covering
2. Cavities
   a. upper two—atria
   b. lower two—ventricles
3. Valves and openings
   a. openings between atria and ventricles—atrioventricular orifices, guarded by cuspid valves, tricuspid on right and mitral or bicuspid on left; valves consist of three parts: flap, chordae tendineae, and papillary muscle
   b. opening from right ventricle into pulmonary artery guarded by semilunar valves
   c. opening from left ventricle into great aorta guarded by semilunar valves
4. Blood supply—from coronary arteries; branch from ascending aorta behind semilunar valves
   a. left ventricle receives blood via both major branches of left coronary artery and from one branch of right coronary artery
   b. right ventricle receives blood via both major branches of right coronary artery and from one branch of left coronary artery
   c. each atrium receives blood only from

365

one branch of its respective coronary artery

d. usually only a few anastomoses between larger branches of coronary arteries; so that occlusion of one of these produces areas of myocardial infarction; if not fatal, anastomoses between smaller vessels grow and provide collateral circulation

5. Conduction system of the heart
    a. sinoatrial node (pacemaker of heart)—small mass of modified cardiac muscle at junction of superior vena cava and right atrium; numerous sympathetic and parasympathetic fibers terminate here, initiating each heartbeat
    b. atrioventricular node—small mass of modified cardiac muscle in septum between the two atria
    c. atrioventricular bundle (bundle of His)—special cardiac muscle fibers originating in AV node and extending down interventricular septum
    d. Purkinje fibers—extension of bundle of His fibers out into walls of ventricles

6. Nerve supply—sympathetic fibers (in cardiac nerves) and parasympathetic fibers (in vagus) form cardiac plexuses; fibers from plexuses terminate mainly in SA node; sympathetic fibers tend to accelerate and strengthen heartbeat; vagal fibers slow it

Physiology

1. Function—maintains blood flow and varies rate of flow according to energy needs of cells

2. Cardiac cycle
    a. nature—consists of systole and diastole of atria and of ventricles; atria contract and as they relax, ventricles contract
    b. time required for cycle—about four fifths of second or from 70 to 80 times per minute
    c. events of cycle
        1. atria contracted—cuspid valves open; ventricles relaxed; semilunar valves closed
        2. atria relaxed—cuspid valves closed during first part of atrial diastole while ventricles are contracted and then open as ventricles relax; semi-

lunar valves open during ventricular contraction
    d. heart sounds during cycle—lub due to contraction of ventricles and closure of cuspid valves; dup due to closure of semilunar valves

Blood vessels
Kinds

1. Arteries—vessels which carry blood away from heart; all except pulmonary artery carry oxygenated blood
2. Veins—vessels which carry blood toward heart; all except pulmonary veins carry deoxygenated blood
3. Capillaries—microscopic vessels which carry blood from small arteries (arterioles) to small veins (venules)

Structure—see Table 40, p. 315
Functions

1. Arteries and arterioles—carry blood away from heart to capillaries
2. Capillaries—deliver materials to cells (by way of tissue fluid) and collect substances from them; vital function of entire circulatory system
3. Veins and venules—carry blood from capillaries back to heart

Names of main blood vessels

1. Systemic circulation
    a. arteries—see p. 316 and Fig. 169
    b. veins—see pp. 322 to 327 and Fig. 173
2. Portal circulation—see p. 327 and Fig. 179
3. Fetal circulation—see p. 328 and Fig. 180

Circulation
Definitions

1. Circulation—blood flow through a circuit of vessels
2. Systemic circulation—blood flow from left ventricle into arorta, other arteries, arterioles, capillaries, venules, and veins to right atrium of heart
3. Pulmonary circulation—blood flow from right ventricle to pulmonary artery to lung arterioles, capillaries, and venules, to pulmonary veins, to left atrium

Functions of circulation mechanisms

1. Maintain circulation

2. Vary circulation; increase blood flow per minute when activity increases and decrease blood flow when activity decreases

Principles of circulation

1. Blood circulates because a blood pressure gradient exists within its vessels; systemic blood pressure gradient (mean arterial pressure minus central venous pressure) equals about 100 mm. Hg
2. Arterial blood pressure determined primarily by the volume of blood in the arteries; other factors remaining constant, the greater the arterial blood volume, the greater the arterial blood pressure
3. Arterial blood volume is determined mainly by cardiac minute output and peripheral resistance — directly related to cardiac output and inversely related to resistance
4. Cardiac minute output determined by the heart's rate of contraction and its systolic discharge and directly related to both factors
5. The heart's systolic discharge regulated mainly by ratio of sympathetic-parasympathetic impulses
6. The heart rate regulated by pressoreflexes and by many miscellaneous factors; increased arterial pressure in aorta or carotid sinus tends to produce reflex slowing of the heart, whereas increased right atrial pressure tends to produce reflex cardiac acceleration
7. Peripheral resistance determined mainly by blood viscosity and by arteriole diameter; in general, the less the blood viscosity, the less the peripheral resistance but the smaller the diameter of arterioles the greater the peripheral resistance
8. Blood viscosity determined by the concentration of blood proteins and of blood cells and directly related to both
9. Arteriole diameter regulated mainly by pressoreflexes and chemoreflexes in general, an increase in arterial pressure produces reflex dilatation of arterioles, whereas hypoxia and hypercapnea cause constriction of arterioles in the blood reservoir organs but dilatation of them in local structures, notably in skeletal muscles, heart, and brain

10. The volume of blood circulating per minute determined by the blood pressure gradient and peripheral resistance; according to Poiseuille's law is directly related to the pressure gradient and inversely related to peripheral resistance
11. Respirations and skeletal muscle contractions tend to increase venous return to the heart

How arterial blood pressure is measured

By sphygmomanometer; systolic pressure normally about 120 mm. Hg and diastolic pressure about 80 mm. Hg

Relation of blood pressure to arterial and venous bleeding

1. Arterial bleeding in spurts due to difference in amounts of systolic and diastolic pressures
2. Venous bleeding—slow and steady due to low, practically constant venous pressure

Velocity of blood

Speed with which blood flows; most rapid in arteries and slowest in capillaries

Pulse

1. Definition—alternate expansion and recoil of artery
2. Cause—intermittent injections of blood from heart into aorta with each ventricular contraction; pulse can be felt because of elasticity of arterial walls
3. Pulse wave—pulse starts at beginning of aorta and proceeds as a wave of expansion throughout arteries
4. Where pulse can be felt — radial, temporal, common carotid, facial, brachial, femoral, and popliteal arteries; where near surface and over firm background, such as bone; pressure points, points where bleeding can be stopped by pressure, roughly related to places where pulse can be felt
5. Venous pulse—in large veins only; due to changes in venous pressure brought about by alternate contraction and relaxation of atria

Lymphatic system
Definition
Part of circulatory system—consists of lymph, tissue fluid, lymphatics, and lymph nodes

Lymph and interstitial fluid (tissue fluid)
1. Definition
   a. lymph—clear, watery fluid found in lymphatic vessels
   b. interstitial fluid (tissue fluid)—clear liquid in tissue spaces

Lymphatics
1. Formation and distribution—start as capillaries in tissue spaces; widely distributed throughout body; two or more main lymphatic ducts—thoracic duct, which drains into left subclavian vein at junction of internal jugular and subclavian, and one or more right lymphatic ducts which drain into right subclavian vein
2. Structure—similar to veins except thinner walled; contain more valves and contain lymph nodes located at intervals

Lymph circulation
1. Water and solutes from capillary blood to interstitial fluid, to lymphatics, to blood at junction of internal jugular and subclavian veins

Lymph nodes
1. Structure—lymphatic tissue, separated into compartments by fibrous partitions; afferent lymphatics enter each node and efferent lymphatics leave each node
2. Location—usually in clusters (see pp. 360 to 362)
3. Functions
   a. filter out injurious substances and phagocytose them; defense mechanisms
   b. formation of lymphocytes and monocytes; hemopoiesis

Spleen
1. Location—left hypochondrium
2. Structure—similar to lymph nodes, ovoid in shape; size varies; contains numerous venous blood spaces that serve as blood reservoir
3. Functions
   a. hemopoiesis of nongranular leukocytes (monocytes and lymphocytes) and of red cells before birth
   b. protection by phagocytosis by reticuloendothelial cells and possibly antibody formation by lymphocytes
   c. blood reservoir
   d. hypothesis that spleen sometimes removes too many thrombocytes from blood, causing platelet deficiency that leads to pinpoint capillary hemorrhages

Review questions
The circulatory system
1. Name the three kinds of blood cells.
2. Compare different kinds of blood cells as to (1) appearance and size, (2) functions, (3) formation, destruction, and life span, and (4) number per cubic millimeter of blood.
3. State a rule of thumb for estimating blood volume. About how much blood is there in your body?
4. What is normal pH range for blood?
5. Differentiate between blood plasma and blood serum.
6. Briefly describe the chemical composition of blood.
7. Explain the blood clotting mechanism; show the main parts of the mechanism by diagram.
8. On what principles do the mechanisms that oppose blood clotting operate?
9. Why and how does a vitamin K deficiency affect blood clotting?
10. Explain some principles and methods by which blood clotting may be hastened.
11. Describe the structure of the heart and its location. Where should a stethoscope be placed to listen to the apical beat?
12. Describe the pericardium, differentiating between the fibrous and serous portions.
13. Exactly where is pericardial fluid found? Explain its function.
14. Describe the heart's own blood supply. Explain the structural reason why occlusion of a large coronary artery branch has serious consequences.
15. Explain the innervation of the heart; include a description of sensory and motor nerves to the heart and cardiac centers.
16. Name and describe the special neuromuscular structures of the heart, including their location and function, and impulse conduction through the heart.

17. Compare arteries, veins, and capillaries as to structure and functions.
18. Differentiate between systemic, pulmonary, and portal circulation.
19. Explain the differences between fetal and postnatal circulation and the functional reasons for them.
20. Explain the heart control mechanism; include control of both rate and force. Devise a diagram to indicate the different parts of the mechanism.
21. Explain the vasomotor mechanism. Devise a diagram to indicate its various parts.
22. Explain reactive hyperemia and one theory about the mechanism producing it.
23. State in your own words the basic principle of fluid flow.
24. State in your own words Poiseuille's law. Give an example of increased circulation to illustrate application of this law. Give an example of decreased circulation to illustrate application of this law.
25. What mechanisms control arterial blood pressure? Cite an example of the operation of one or more of these mechanisms to increase arterial pressure; to decrease it.
26. What mechanisms control peripheral resistance? Cite an example of the operation of one or more parts of this mechanism to increase resistance; to decrease it.
27. What two factors determine blood viscosity? What does viscosity mean? Give an example of a condition in which blood viscosity decreases. Explain its effect on circulation.
28. What effect, if any, would a respiratory stimulant drug have on circulation. Explain why it would or would not affect circulation.
29. Describe and explain the effects of exercise on circulation.
30. Explain the principles of the clinical method used to measure blood pressure.
31. Explain why a pulse can be felt in certain vessels. In which vessels is there a palpable pulse?
32. Specify places where pulse can be felt.
33. What and where is lymph? Describe its circulation.
34. Compare lymphatics and lymph nodes as to structure and location and function.
35. Describe the location and function of the spleen. What functions is it thought to perform?
36. If cancer cells from a breast cancer were to enter the lymphatics of the breast, where do you think they might lodge and start new growths? Explain, using your knowledge of the anatomy of the lymphatic and circulatory systems.
37. Starting with the left ventricle of the heart, list the vessels through which blood would flow in reaching (1) the small intestine, (2) the large intestine, (3) the liver (two ways), (4) the spleen, (5) the stomach, (6) the kidneys, (7) the suprarenal glands, (8) the ovaries or testes, (9) the anterior part of the base of the brain, and (10) the little finger of the right hand. List the vessels through which the blood returns from these parts to the right atrium of the heart (see Figs. 169, 173, and 181).
38. Name and explain the action of the heart; its valves.
39. Trace the flow of blood through the heart.
40. Give two reasons why blood is considered a protective agent against infection.
41. Describe one or more mechanisms that probably operate to return circulation to normal a short time after exercise ceases.
42. Give the general location of the following veins: longitudinal sinus, internal jugular vein, innominate vein, portal vein, great saphenous vein, inferior vena cava, and basilic vein.
43. Define the following terms briefly:

adenitis	leukopenia
anemia	lymphocyte
aneurysm	monocyte
arteriosclerosis	myocardium
basophils	neutrophil
blood pressure	pH
diastole	phagocytosis
differential count	phlebitis
embolus	plasma
endocardium	peripheral resistance
eosinophil	pulse pressure
erythrocyte	sphygmomanometer
heart block	thrombocyte
hemophilia	thrombus
leukemia	systole
leukocyte	

Chapter X

The respiratory system

FUNCTIONS AND IMPORTANCE

The respiratory system consists of those organs which make it possible for blood to exchange gases with air. They are the nose, pharynx, larynx, trachea, bronchi, and lungs. This group of organs constitute the lifeline of the body. If anything interferes with the functioning of this anatomical lifeline, death ensues in a very short time. The exchange of gases between the blood and air is known as respiration, but actually it is only one phase of respiration. The transportation of gases between the lungs and tissues constitutes another phase, and the exchange of gases between the blood and tissues still another. The first phase is a function of the respiratory system; the second and third phases, of the circulatory system. The first and second phases are vital only because they make possible the third phase. The all-important requisite is that the cells receive oxygen and rid themselves of carbon dioxide or, in other words, that they "breathe." Because most of the billions of cells composing the human body are far removed from the air, the only way they can carry on this essential exchange of gases is through the medium of structures that are able to bring about an exchange of gases between the air and the transportation agent of the body. The respiratory organs are such structures and are, therefore, of vital importance.

ORGANS

Nose

Structure

The nose consists of an internal and an external portion. The external portion, that is, the part which protrudes from the face, is considerably smaller than the internal portion, which lies over the roof of the mouth. The interior of the nose is hollow and is separated by a partition, the *septum*, into a right and a left cavity. The palatine bones, which form both the floor of the nose and the roof of the mouth, separate the nasal cavities from the mouth cavity. Sometimes the palatine bones fail to unite completely, producing a condition known as *cleft palate* (Fig. 286). When this abnormality exists, the mouth is only partially separated from the nasal cavity, and difficulties arise in swallowing.

371

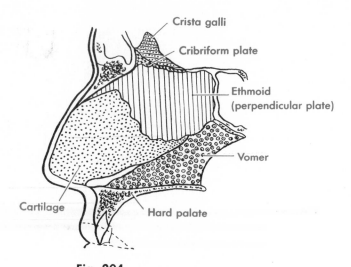

Crista galli

Cribriform plate

Ethmoid
(perpendicular plate)

Vomer

Cartilage

Hard palate

Fig. 204

Diagram showing the formation of the nasal
septum by the perpendicular plate of the ethmoid,
the vomer bone, and cartilage.

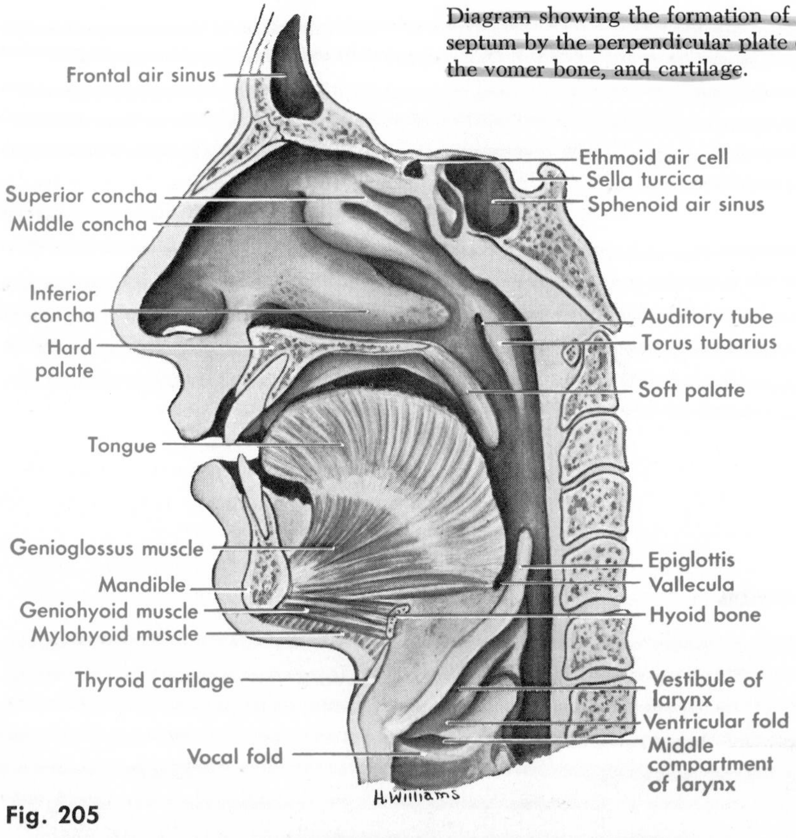

Frontal air sinus

Ethmoid air cell
Sella turcica
Sphenoid air sinus

Superior concha
Middle concha

Inferior
concha

Auditory tube
Torus tubarius

Hard
palate

Soft palate

Tongue

Genioglossus muscle

Epiglottis
Vallecula

Mandible

Geniohyoid muscle

Hyoid bone

Mylohyoid muscle

Thyroid cartilage

Vestibule of
larynx
Ventricular fold

Vocal fold

Middle
compartment
of larynx

H.Williams

Fig. 205

Sagittal section through the face and neck. The nasal septum has been
removed, exposing the lateral wall of the nasal cavity. Note position
of the conchae (turbinates). (From Francis and Farrell: Integrated
anatomy and physiology, St. Louis, The C. V. Mosby Co.)

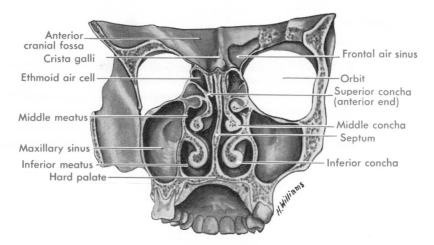

Anterior cranial fossa
Crista galli
Ethmoid air cell
Middle meatus
Maxillary sinus
Inferior meatus
Hard palate
Frontal air sinus
Orbit
Superior concha (anterior end)
Middle concha
Septum
Inferior concha

H. Williams

Fig. 206

Frontal section through the nose. Note irregularly shaped passageways formed in nasal cavity by the conchae. Posterior wall of right frontal sinus removed. (From Francis and Farrell: Integrated anatomy and physiology, St. Louis, The C. V. Mosby Co.)

Each nasal cavity is divided into three passageways (superior, middle, and inferior meati) by the projection of the turbinates (conchae) from the lateral walls of the internal nose (Figs. 205 and 206). The superior and middle turbinates are processes of the ethmoid bone, while the inferior turbinates are separate bones.

The external openings into the nasal cavities (nostrils) have the technical name of *anterior nares*. The posterior nares (or choanae) are openings from the internal nose into the nasopharynx.

Ciliated mucous membrane lines the nose and the rest of the respiratory tract down as far as the smaller bronchioles.

Four pairs of sinuses drain into the nose. These paranasal sinuses are the frontal, maxillary, ethmoidal, and sphenoidal. They drain as follows:

1. Into the middle meatus (passageway below middle turbinate)—frontal, maxillary, and anterior ethmoidal sinuses.
2. Into the superior meatus—posterior ethmoidal sinuses.
3. Into the space above the superior turbinates (sphenoethmoidal recess)—sphenoid sinuses.

Functions

The nose serves as a passageway for air going to and from the lungs, filtering it of impurities and warming, moistening, and chemically examining it for substances which might prove irritating to the mucous lining of the respiratory tract; it serves as the organ of smell, since olfactory receptors are located in the nasal mucosa, and it aids in phonation.

373

Structure

Another name for the pharynx is the throat. It is a tubelike structure about 5 inches long which extends from the base of the skull to the esophagus and lies just anterior to the cervical vertebrae. It is made of muscle, is lined with mucous membrane, and has three parts: one located behind the nose, the *nasopharynx;* one behind the mouth, the *oropharynx;* and another behind the larynx, the *laryngopharynx.*

Seven openings are found in the pharynx (Fig. 205):

1. Two from the eustachian tubes into the nasopharynx.
2. Two posterior nares into the nasopharynx.
3. The opening from the mouth, known as the *fauces,* into the oropharynx.
4. The opening into the larynx from the laryngopharynx.
5. The opening into the esophagus from the laryngopharynx.

The *adenoids* or pharyngeal tonsils are located in the nasopharynx, on its posterior wall opposite the posterior nares. If the adenoids become enlarged, they fill the space behind the posterior nares, making it difficult or impossible for air to travel from the nose into the throat. When this happens, the individual keeps his mouth open to breathe and is described as having an "adenoidy" appearance.

Two pairs of organs are found in the oropharynx: the faucial or *palatine tonsils,* located behind and below the pillars of the fauces, and the *lingual tonsils,* located at the base of the tongue. The palatine tonsils are the ones most commonly removed by a tonsillectomy although the lingual ones are sometimes removed also.

Functions

The pharynx serves as a hallway for the respiratory and digestive tracts, since both air and food must pass through this structure before reaching the appropriate tubes, and it plays an important part in phonation; for example, only by the pharynx changing its shape can the different vowel sounds be formed.

Location

The larynx or voice box lies at the upper end of the trachea and just below the pharynx. It might be described as a kind of vestibule opening into the trachea from the pharynx.

Structure

The larynx consists of nine pieces of cartilage so joined that they make a boxlike structure. Three of them are prominent enough to warrant mention:

1. The largest cartilage and the one which gives the characteristic

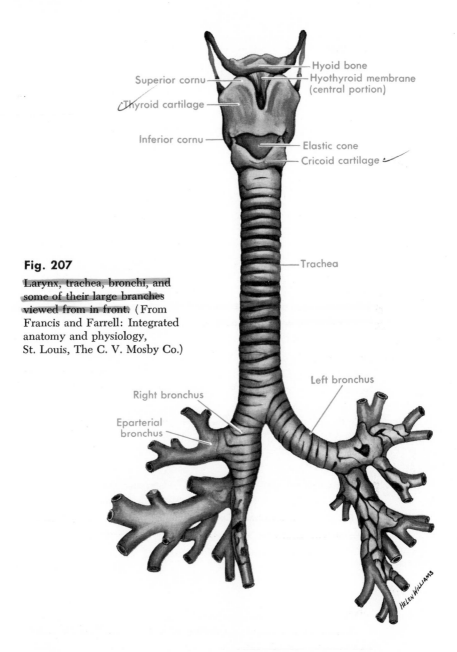

Superior cornu

Thyroid cartilage

Inferior cornu

Hyoid bone

Hyothyroid membrane
(central portion)

Elastic cone

Cricoid cartilage

Trachea

Fig. 207

Larynx, trachea, bronchi, and
some of their large branches
viewed from in front. (From
Francis and Farrell: Integrated
anatomy and physiology,
St. Louis, The C. V. Mosby Co.)

Left bronchus

Right bronchus

Eparterial
bronchus

HELEN WILLIAMS

triangular shape to the anterior wall of the larynx is called the *thyroid
cartilage* or, by lay people, the Adam's apple. This cartilage is usually larger in men than in women and has less of a fat pad lying over
it, two facts which make it protrude more noticeably in the male neck.

2. A small cartilage, attached alone one edge to the thyroid cartilage, but free on its other borders, giving it a hingelike action, is
named the *epiglottis* or the lid cartilage because during the swallowing

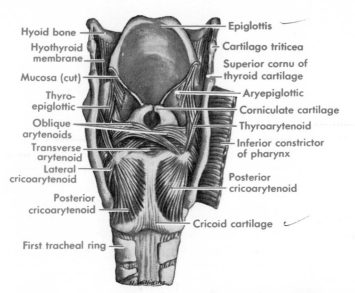

Fig. 208

Posterior view of the larynx showing many of the muscles which function to alter the shape of the larynx. (From Francis and Farrell: Integrated anatomy and physiology, St. Louis, The C. V. Mosby Co.)

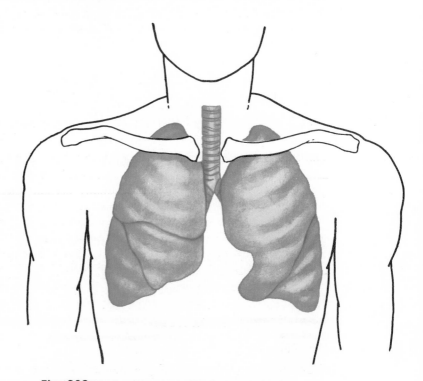

Fig. 209

Lungs and trachea in position. (From Francis and Farrell: Integrated anatomy and physiology, St. Louis, The C. V. Mosby Co.)

act it forms a kind of lid over the opening into the larynx. When the epiglottis fails to close, food or liquids enter the larynx instead of the esophagus, and we say we have "swallowed down our Sunday throat."

3. The *cricoid* or signet ring cartilage, so called because its shape resembles a signet ring (turned so the signet forms part of the posterior wall of the larynx), is the most inferiorly placed of the nine cartilages.

The mucous membrane lining of the larynx forms two horizontal folds known as the *false vocal cords*. The *true vocal* cords are fibrous bands stretched across the hollow interior of the larynx. The space between the true vocal cords (or vocal folds) is called the *glottis*.

Function

The function of the larynx is voice production, the pitch of which is determined by the length and tension of the vocal cords; short tense cords produce high notes and long relaxed cords low notes. Several other structures aid the larynx in voice production by acting as sounding boards or resonating chambers. Thus, the size and shape of the nose, mouth, pharynx, and bony sinuses help to determine the quality of the voice.

Trachea

Structure

lung tube

Smooth muscle, in which are embedded C-shaped rings of cartilage at regular intervals, fashions the walls of the trachea or windpipe. The cartilaginous rings are incomplete on the posterior surface. They give firmness to the wall, tending to prevent it from collapsing and shutting off the vital airway. Occasionally certain conditions, such as diphtheria or cervical adenitis, may obstruct the trachea, making emergency measures to open it necessary. Two methods are used. Either an incision is made into the trachea (tracheotomy) and a double metal tube inserted through the opening in the neck, or the tube is inserted by way of the mouth and larynx (intubation).

The trachea is about 4½ inches long and extends from the larynx to the bronchi. It is cylindrical in shape with a diameter of approximately 1 inch. *(11 C.M.)*

Function

The trachea performs a simple but vital function—it furnishes part of the open passageway through which air can reach the lungs from the outside. Obstruction of this airway for even a few minutes causes death from asphyxiation. *minutes for child to die from obstructed trachea.*

377

Bronchi

Structure

The trachea divides at its lower end into two *primary bronchi*, of which the right bronchus is slightly larger and more vertical than the left, a fact which explains why aspirated foreign objects frequently lodge in the right bronchus. In structure the bronchi resemble the trachea, their walls containing the same type of cartilaginous rings and the same ciliated mucous lining.

Each primary bronchus enters the lung on its respective side and immediately divides into smaller branches called *secondary bronchi*. The secondary bronchi continue to branch, forming small *bronchioles*. The trachea and the two primary bronchi and their many branches resemble an inverted tree trunk with its branches and are, therefore, spoken of as the bronchial tree. The bronchioles subdivide into smaller and smaller tubes, eventually terminating in microscopic branches which divide into *alveolar ducts*, which terminate in several alveolar sacs, the walls of which consist of numerous *alveoli*. The structure of an alveolar duct with its branching alveolar sacs can be likened to a bunch of grapes—the stem represents the alveolar duct, each cluster of grapes represents an alveolar sac, and each grape represents an alveolus.

The structure of the secondary bronchi and bronchioles shows some modification of the primary bronchial structure. The cartilaginous rings become irregular and disappear entirely in the smaller bronchioles. By the time the branches of the bronchial tree have dwindled sufficiently to form the alveoli, only the internal surface layer of cells remains. In other words, the walls of the alveoli consist of a single layer of simple, squamous epithelial tissue, a structural feature of importance in the performance of their function.

Function

The tubes composing the bronchial tree perform the same function as the trachea—that of furnishing a passageway by which air can reach the interior of the lung. The alveoli, enveloped as they are by a network of capillaries, provide spaces where a gaseous exchange between the air and the blood can occur. Someone has observed that "the lung passages all serve the alveoli" just as "the circulatory system serves the capillaries." Certain diseases may block the passage of air through the bronchioles or through the alveoli. For example, in pneumonia the alveoli become inflamed, and the accompanying wastes plug up these minute air spaces, making the affected part of the lung solid. Whether the victim survives depends largely upon the extent of the solidification.

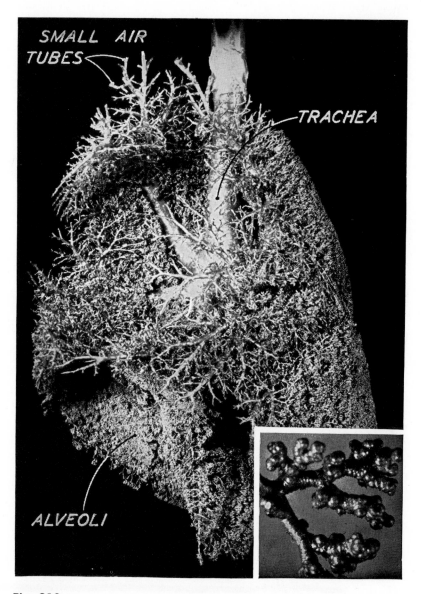

Fig. 210

Metal cast of air spaces of the lungs of a dog. The inset (lower right) shows a cast of clusters of alveoli at the terminations of tiny air tubes. The magnification of the inset is about eleven times the actual size. (From Carlson and Johnson: The machinery of the body, Chicago, The University of Chicago Press.)

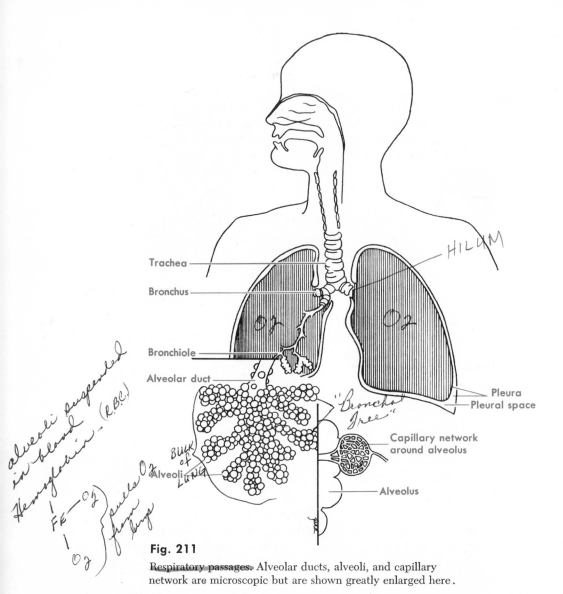

Trachea

Bronchus

Bronchiole

Alveolar duct

HILUM (handwritten)

O_2 (handwritten) O_2 (handwritten)

Pleura
Pleural space

"Bronchial Tree" (handwritten)

Capillary network
around alveolus

BULK of LUNG (handwritten)

Alveoli

Alveolus

alveoli suspended in blood (handwritten)
Hemoglobin — (R.B.C.) (handwritten)
FE—O_2 (handwritten)
O_2 (handwritten)
fuels O_2 from lungs (handwritten)

Fig. 211

Respiratory passages. Alveolar ducts, alveoli, and capillary
network are microscopic but are shown greatly enlarged here.

Lungs

Structure

The lungs are cone-shaped organs, large enough to fill the pleural
portion of the thoracic cavity completely. They extend from the diaphragm to a point slightly above the clavicles and lie against the ribs
both anteriorly and posteriorly. The medial surface of each lung is
roughly concave to allow room for the mediastinal structures and for
the heart, but concavity is greater on the left than on the right because
of the position of the heart. The primary bronchi and pulmonary
blood vessels (bound together by connective tissue to form what is

known as the *root* of the lung) enter each lung through a slit on its medial surface called the *hilum*. *– knotch on mesial side*

The broad inferior surface of the lung, which rests on the diaphragm, constitutes the *base*, whereas the pointed upper margin is the *apex*.

The left lung is partially divided by fissures into two *lobes* (upper and lower) and the right lung into three lobes (superior, middle, and inferior). Internally each lung consists of millions of microscopic alveoli with their related ducts and bronchioles and bronchi, as described in the paragraph on the bronchi.

Visceral pleura covers the outer surfaces of the lungs and adheres to them much as the skin of an apple adheres to the apple.

Function

The lungs provide a place where an exchange of gases can take place between blood and air. Lung structure makes possible this function. Because an open airway branches into millions of thin-walled alveoli, enveloped by networks of capillaries, large amounts of oxygen can be quickly loaded into blood and large amounts of carbon dioxide quickly unloaded from it.

THORAX

Definition

The thorax is the chest.

Structure

As described on p. 18, the thoracic cavity has three divisions, separated from each other by partitions of pleura. The part of the cavity occupied by the lungs is the pleural division; the space between the lungs, occupied by the esophagus, trachea, large blood vessels, etc. is the mediastinum; and the part occupied by the heart and its enveloping sac is the pericardial portion.

The parietal layer of the pleura lines the entire thoracic cavity, meaning the internal surface of the ribs, the superior surface of the diaphragm, and the mediastinum. A separate pleural sac thus encases each lung. Since the outer surface of each lung is covered by the visceral layer of the pleura, the visceral pleura lies against the parietal pleura, separated only by a potential space (pleural space) which contains just enough pleural fluid for lubrication. Thus, when the lungs inflate with air, the smooth, moist visceral pleura coheres to the smooth, moist parietal pleura. Friction is thereby avoided and respirations are painless. In pleurisy, on the other hand, the pleura is inflamed and respirations become painful.

The elliptical shape of the ribs and their angle of attachment to

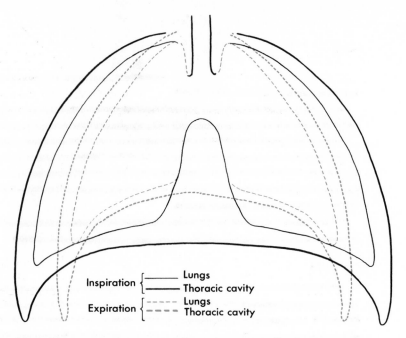

Fig. 212

Changes in size of the thorax and lungs during inspiration and expiration. This drawing was made from x-ray photographs taken separately of inspiration and expiration. The solid lines show the marked enlargement of the thorax and lungs due to contraction and descent of the diaphragm and elevation of rib cage; the broken lines indicate the decreased size of the thorax and lungs with diaphragm relaxation and depression of the rib cage.

the spine have functional significance. Lifting up the chest raises the ribs so they no longer slant downward from the spine, and because of their elliptical shape, this enlarges both depth (from front to back) and width of the thorax. (If this does not sound convincing to you, examine a skeleton to see why it is so.)

RESPIRATIONS

Kinds of respiration

There are two kinds of respiration: external or "lung breathing" and internal or "cell breathing." Lung breathing is important only because it makes possible cell breathing. It is the necessary preliminary to cell breathing. Obviously, blood must receive oxygen from air in order to continue delivering it to cells, and it is this—the continual supply of oxygen to cells—that is essential for life.

Mechanism of respiration

Air moves in and out of the lungs for the same basic reason that blood flows in vessels—because of a pressure gradient—a gas pressure

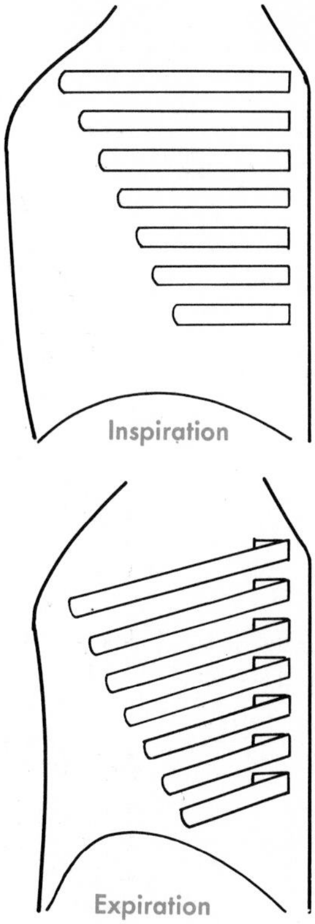

Fig. 213

Diagram to show greater anteroposterior diameter of the thorax when the elliptical rib cage is elevated.

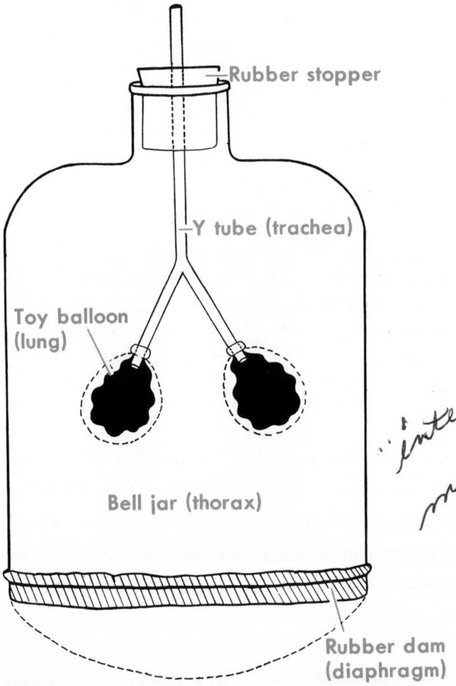

Inspiration

Expiration

Rubber stopper

Y tube (trachea)

Toy balloon (lung)

Bell jar (thorax)

"intercostals" muscles for respiration

Rubber dam (diaphragm)

Fig. 214

Device for showing the effects of diaphragm action on the air content of the lungs. A glass bell jar serves as the thorax, an inverted Y tube in a rubber stopper as the trachea and bronchi, two toy balloons as the lungs, and a piece of rubber dam as the diaphragm. Pulling down on the rubber diaphragm enlarges the glass thorax lengthwise and causes air to push down into the balloon lungs. Releasing the pull on the rubber diaphragm decreases the size of the glass thorax and squeezes air out of the balloons. This simple experiment demonstrates several important facts about human breathing: that the lungs are passive organs in breathing; that inspiration results from an enlargement of the thorax which is accomplished primarily by the contraction of the diaphragm; that expiration results from a decrease in the size of the thorax brought about by relaxation of the diaphragm.

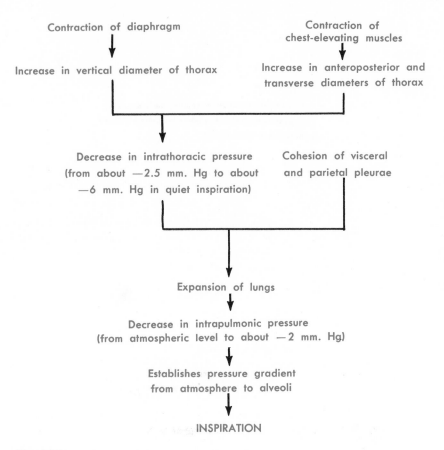

Fig. 215

The mechanism of inspiration.

gradient in the case of air movement and a blood pressure gradient in the case of blood flow. When atmospheric pressure is greater than pressure within the lung, air flows down this gas pressure gradient, that is, from the atmosphere into the lungs. Inspiration occurs, in other words. And when pressure in the lungs is greater than atmospheric pressure, air again moves down a gas pressure gradient. But now, this means that it moves in the opposite direction. This time air moves outward from the lungs into the air. The respiratory mechanism, therefore, must somehow establish these two gas pressure gradients—one in which intrapulmonic pressure (pressure within the lungs) is lower than atmospheric pressure to produce inspiration and one in which it is higher than atmospheric pressure to produce expiration. These pressure gradients are established by changes in the size of the thoracic cavity, which, in turn, is produced by contraction and relaxation of respiratory muscles. When the diaphragm contracts, for example, it descends, and this enlarges the vertical length of the thorax. Other muscles may also contract at the same time, elevating the sternum and

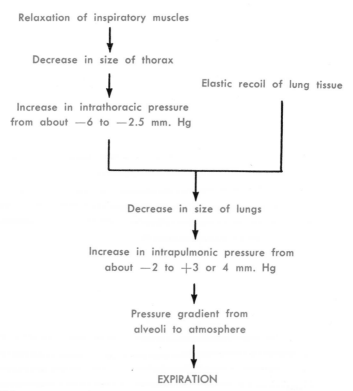

Relaxation of inspiratory muscles

↓

Decrease in size of thorax

↓

Elastic recoil of lung tissue

Increase in intrathoracic pressure
from about −6 to −2.5 mm. Hg

↓

Decrease in size of lungs

↓

Increase in intrapulmonic pressure from
about −2 to +3 or 4 mm. Hg

↓

Pressure gradient from
alveoli to atmosphere

↓

EXPIRATION

Fig. 216

The mechanism of expiration.

ribs and enlarging the thorax from front to back and from side to side. The increase in size of the thorax causes intrapleural (intrathoracic) pressure to decrease. At the end of an expiration and before the beginning of the next inspiration, intrathoracic pressure is about 2.5 mm. Hg less than atmospheric pressure, or in other words it is −2.5 mm. Hg. During quiet inspiration intrathoracic pressure decreases further to −6 mm. Hg; that is, it becomes more negative than it was at the beginning of inspiration. This decrease in intrathoracic pressure and the cohesion of the lungs to the inner wall of the thorax together bring about the expansion of the lungs and a decrease in their inside or intrapulmonic pressure. It decreases from atmospheric level to a subatmospheric level, namely to −2 mm. Hg. With this, the gas pressure gradient necessary for causing air to move into the lungs is established. Figs. 215 and 216 show the mechanism of inspiration and of expiration in the form of a diagram.

   To apply some of the information just discussed about the respiratory mechanism, let us suppose that a surgeon makes an incision through the chest wall into the pleural space, as he would in doing one of the dramatic, modern "open chest" operations. Air would then be present in the thoracic cavity, a condition known as *pneumothorax.*

385

What change, if any, do you think would take place in respirations? Intrathoracic pressure would, of course, immediately increase from its normal subatmospheric level to atmospheric level. More pressure than normal would, therefore, be exerted upon the outer surface of the lung and would cause its collapse. It could even collapse the other lung. This is because the mediastinum is a mobile rather than a rigid partition between the two pleural sacs; this anatomical fact allows the increased pressure in the open chest side to push the heart and other mediastinal structures over toward the intact side where they exert pressure on the other lung. Pneumothorax results in many respiratory and circulatory changes. They are of great importance in determining medical and nursing care but lie beyond the scope of this book.

Amount of air exchanged in breathing

Poiseuille's law (p. 345) applies to the flow of gases as well as of liquids. This means that the volume of air inspired is directly related to the gas pressure gradient between the atmosphere and the lung alveoli and is inversely related to the resistance opposing air flow. In general, the deeper the inspiration, the lower is the intrapulmonic pressure, the greater is the pressure gradient from atmosphere to alveoli, and the larger is the volume of air inspired. Obstruction of the airway has the opposite effect. For example, if the tongue falls back into the throat, as it may do in an unconscious patient, this obviously increases resistance and slows air flow. It may even prevent any air at all from moving down into the alveoli.

An apparatus called a *spirometer* is used to measure the amount of air exchanged in breathing. The amount of air exhaled normally after a normal inspiration is termed *tidal air*. The average individual has a tidal air of approximately 500 milliliters (about 1 pint). A forcible expiration after a normal inspiration represents the *supplemental air* (or *expiratory reserve volume*). *Complemental air* (or *inspiratory reserve volume*) is the amount which can be forcibly inspired over and above a normal inspiration; it is measured by having the individual exhale normally after a forced inspiration. Both supplemental and complemental air average about 1500 milliliters. No matter how forcefully an individual exhales, he cannot squeeze all the air out of his lungs. Some of it remains trapped in the alveoli; this amount of air which cannot be forcibly expired is known as *residual air* and amounts to about 1000 milliliters. If, after death, the thoracic cavity is opened and the lungs are collapsed by atmospheric pressure, a small amount of air still remains in the alveoli (*minimal air*); its presence can be demonstrated by placing a small piece of lung in water. It will float due to the

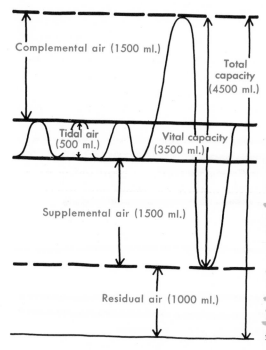

Complemental air (1500 ml.)

Total capacity (4500 ml.)

Tidal air (500 ml.)

Vital capacity (3500 ml.)

Supplemental air (1500 ml.)

Residual air (1000 ml.)

Fig. 217

During normal, quiet respirations about 500 ml. of air (tidal air) is exchanged between the atmosphere and lungs. With a forcible inspiration, about 1500 ml. more air can be inhaled (complemental air). After a normal inspiration, approximately 1500 ml. of air can be forcibly expired (supplemental air). Vital capacity is the amount of air which can be forcibly expired after a maximum inspiration and indicates, therefore, the largest amount of air which can be exchanged during respiration. Residual air is that which remains trapped in the alveoli.

presence of the minimal air, whereas any other soft tissue will sink. Because of this property, the lungs of an animal are known as the "lights" in slaughterhouses. The demonstration of minimal air in the lungs sometimes has legal importance in proving whether or not a child has lived at all or was born dead. If he has once filled his lungs with air, minimal air can be demonstrated at autopsy by the simple method described. *(4500 ml)*

The term *vital capacity* means the approximate volume of the lungs, as determined by measuring the largest possible expiration after the largest possible inspiration. It equals the sum of the tidal air, plus the complemental air, plus the supplemental air. Vital capacity depends upon the size of the thoracic cavity which, in turn, depends upon the size of the rib cage, upon posture, and upon various other factors. For example, if the lungs contain more blood than normal, alveolar air space is encroached upon, and vital capacity accordingly decreases. This becomes a very important factor in congestive heart disease and probably explains also the smaller vital capacity in normal individuals in the supine position. Excess fluid in the pleural or abdominal cavities also decreases vital capacity, as does the disease emphysema. In the latter condition, alveolar walls become stretched, that is, lose their elasticity, and are unable to collapse normally for expiration. This leads to a great increase in the amount of residual air—so much so, in fact, that the chest occupies the inspiratory position even at rest. Excessive muscular effort is necessary, therefore, for inspiration, and because of the loss of elasticity of lung tissue, greater effort is required, too, for expiration.

Types of breathing

Respirations, when normal, are of either of two types or a combination of both: abdominal or costal. *Abdominal breathing*, sometimes called diaphragmatic or deep breathing, is characterized by an outward movement of the abdominal wall due to the contraction and descent of the diaphragm. *Costal*, shallow, or chest *breathing* is characterized by an upward, outward movement of the chest due to contraction of the external intercostals and other chest-elevating muscles. Normal quiet breathing of either the abdominal or costal type is known as *eupnea*.

There are various types of abnormal respirations, a few of which will be described. *Apnea* is a temporary cessation of respirations. *Dyspnea* is difficult or labored breathing. *Orthopnea* is inability to breathe in the horizontal position. *Cheyne-Stokes* ⁽²⁻³⁰˙ ᵍᵖᵐ⁾ respirations are characterized by a period of dyspnea followed by a period of apnea. The latter type of respiration often precedes death.

SOME PRINCIPLES ABOUT GASES

Before discussing the physiology of respirations, we need to understand the following principles.

1. *Dalton's law* (or the law of partial pressures). The term *partial pressure* means that pressure exerted by any one gas in a mixture of gases or in a liquid. The partial pressure of a gas in a mixture of gases is directly related to the concentration of that gas in the mixture and to the total pressure of the mixture. Suppose we apply this principle to compute the partial pressure of oxygen in the atmosphere. The concentration of oxygen in the atmosphere is 20.96% and the total pressure of the atmosphere is 760 mm. Hg under standard conditions. Therefore:

$$\text{Atmospheric } pO_2 = 20.96\% \times 760 = 159.2 \text{ mm. Hg}$$

The symbol used to designate partial pressure is a small letter p preceding the chemical symbol for the gas. Examples: alveolar air pO_2 is about 100 mm. Hg; arterial blood pO_2 is also about 100 mm. Hg; venous blood pO_2 is about 37 mm. Hg. The word *tension* is often used as a synonym for the term partial pressure—oxygen tension means the same thing as pO_2.

2. The partial pressure of a gas in a liquid is directly related to the amount of that gas dissolved in the liquid, which, in turn, is deter-

mined by the partial pressure of the gas in the environment of the liquid. Gas molecules diffuse into a liquid from its environment and dissolved in the liquid until the partial pressure of the gas in solution becomes equal to its partial pressure in the environment of the liquid. For example, alveolar air constitutes the environment of blood moving through pulmonary capillaries. Standing between the blood and the air are only the very thin alveolar and capillary membranes, and both of these are highly permeable to oxygen and carbon dioxide. By the time blood leaves the pulmonary capillaries as arterial blood, diffusion and approximate equilibration of oxygen and carbon dioxide across the membranes has occurred. Arterial blood pO_2 and pCO_2, therefore, usually equal or very nearly equal alveolar pO_2 and pCO_2.

How blood transports respiratory gases

Blood transports oxygen and carbon dioxide as solutes and as parts of molecules of certain chemical compounds. Immediately upon entering the blood both oxygen and carbon dioxide dissolve in the plasma. But, because fluids can hold only small amounts of gas in solution, most of the oxygen and carbon dioxide rapidly form a chemical union with some other blood constituent. In this way comparatively large volumes of the gases can be transported. For example, every 100 milliliters of arterial blood contains about 20 milliliters of oxygen instead of a mere 0.5 milliliter which is all that can stay in solution in that amount of blood. About 19 milliliters of oxygen combines chemically with the hemoglobin present in 100 milliliters of blood to form oxyhemoglobin. Since each gram of hemoglobin can unite with about 1.3 milliliters of oxygen, the exact amount of oxygen in blood depends in large part upon the amount of hemoglobin present—15 grams of hemoglobin per 100 milliliters of blood is a typical normal blood hemoglobin content. With this amount of hemoglobin, 100 milliliters of arterial blood, when 100% saturated with oxygen, contains the following:

$$\begin{cases} 19.5 \text{ milliliters oxygen as oxyhemoglobin } (15 \times 1.3 \text{ milliliters}) \\ 0.5 \text{ milliliters oxygen in solution in plasma} \\ 20.0 \text{ milliliters total oxygen content} \end{cases}$$

Perhaps a more common way of expressing blood oxygen content is in terms of volume per cent. Normal arterial blood, for example, contains about 20 vol.% O_2 (meaning 20 milliliters of oxygen in each 100 milliliters of blood).

Blood that contains more hemoglobin can, of course, transport more oxygen and that which contains less hemoglobin can transport less

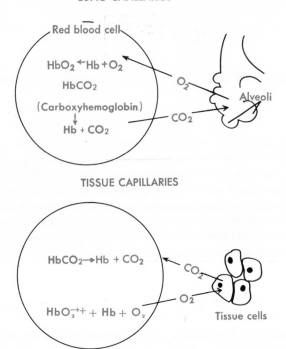

LUNG CAPILLARIES

Red blood cell

$HbO_2 \leftarrow Hb + O_2$

$HbCO_2$

(Carboxyhemoglobin)

$Hb + CO_2$

O_2

CO_2

Alveoli

TISSUE CAPILLARIES

$HbCO_2 \rightarrow Hb + CO_2$

$HbO_2^- + + Hb + O_2$

CO_2

O_2

Tissue cells

Fig. 218

Diagram showing main facts about oxygen and carbon dioxide transport. In *lung capillaries* oxygen pressure increases and carbon dioxide pressure decreases—conditions that accelerate both oxygen association with hemoglobin and carbon dioxide dissociation from carboxyhemoglobin. In *tissue capillaries* oxygen pressure decreases and carbon dioxide pressure increases—conditions that accelerate both oxygen dissociation from oxyhemoglobin and carbon dioxide association with hemoglobin.

oxygen. Hence, hemoglobin deficiency anemia decreases oxygen transport and may be responsible for marked cellular hypoxia (inadequate oxygen supply).

In order to combine with hemoglobin, oxygen must, of course, diffuse from plasma into the red cells where millions of hemoglobin molecules are located. Several factors influence the rate at which hemoglobin combines with oxygen in lung capillaries. For instance, an increasing blood pO_2 and a decreasing pCO_2 both accelerate hemoglobin association with oxygen.

$$Hb + O_2 \xrightarrow[\text{(Decreasing } pCO_2)]{\text{(Increasing } pO_2)} HbO_2$$

Decreasing pO_2 and increasing pCO_2, on the other hand, accelerate oxygen dissociation from oxyhemoglobin. Oxygen associates with hemoglobin rapidly—so rapidly, in fact, that about 97% of the blood's hemoglobin has united with oxygen by the time the blood leaves the lung capillaries to return to the heart. In other words, the average *oxygen saturation* of arterial blood is about 97%.

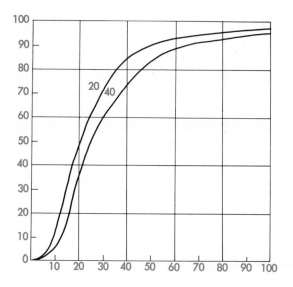

Fig. 219

Oxygen association curves of human blood showing that the per cent of hemoglobin associated with oxygen depends upon both the oxygen and carbon dioxide pressures of the blood. *Vertical coodinate:* $\%O_2$ saturation (% of hemoglobin combined with oxygen) *Horizontal coordinate:* pO_2 in mm. Hg pressure. *Numbers on curves:* pCO_2 in mm. Hg pressure. *Interpretation:* when blood pO_2 is 40 and pCO_2 is also 40, almost 75% of the hemoglobin is combined with O_2 (that is, blood has about a 75% O_2 saturation). *Questions:* What is $\%O_2$, saturation with blood pO_2, 40 and pCO_2, 20? Is it true that the less CO_2 dissolved in blood, the greater its O_2 saturation can be?

Carbon dioxide is carried in the blood in several ways, the most important of which are described briefly as follows:

1. A small amount dissolves in plasma and is transported as a solute (dissolved carbon dioxide produces pCO_2 of blood).

2. More than one half of the carbon dioxide is carried in the plasma as bicarbonate ions.*

---

*As a preliminary to sodium bicarbonate formation from carbon dioxide, a phenomenon known as the chloride shift occurs. Part of the CO_2 which diffuses into red cells combines with water because of the catalytic action of the enzyme, carbonic anhydrase.

$$CO_2 + H_2O \xrightarrow{\text{(Carbonic anhydrase)}} H_2CO_3 \longrightarrow H^+ + HCO_3^-$$

HCO_3 ions then diffuse out of the red cell into the plasma, while Cl ions from the plasma diffuse into the red cell to take their place. The advantage of this arrangement is that it helps maintain the normal alkaline pH of the blood. When venous blood, with its high $NaHCO_3$ content, reaches the lungs, these reactions reverse and CO_2 is released into the alveolar air. Only about 10% of venous CO_2 is normally eliminated, the other 90% being retained. Whole venous blood has a pCO_2 of about 45 mm. and whole arterial blood has a pCO_2 of about 40 mm. This level of pCO_2 in arterial blood is essential for continued activation of the respiratory center and, therefore, for continued respirations. If blood pCO_2 falls to around 19 to 24 mm., respirations cease.

3. Somewhat less than one third of blood carbon dioxide unites with the NH_2 group of certain proteins to form carbamino compounds. Most of these are formed and transported in the red cells since hemoglobin is the main protein to combine with carbon dioxide; the compound formed is referred to as carboxyhemoglobin. Carbon dioxide association with hemoglobin is accelerated by an increasing pCO_2 and a decreasing pO_2 and is slowed by the opposite conditions.

Exchange of gases between alveolar air and venous blood

The exchange of gases between alveolar air and venous blood occurs in lung capillaries, across the alveolar-capillary membrane. Oxygen enters blood from the alveolar air because the pO_2 of alveolar air is greater than the pO_2 of venous blood. Another way of saying this is that oxygen diffuses "down" its pressure gradient. Simultaneously, carbon dioxide molecules exit from the blood by diffusing down the carbon dioxide pressure gradient out into the alveolar air. The pCO_2 of venous blood is much higher than the pCO_2 of alveolar air. This two-way exchange of gases between alveolar air and venous blood converts venous blood to arterial blood.

Table 42. Oxygen and carbon dioxide pressure gradients

	Atmosphere	Alveolar air	Arterial blood	Venous blood
pO_2	160*	100	100	37
pCO_2	0.3	40	40	46

*All figures indicate approximate mm. Hg pressure under usual conditions.

How much oxygen diffuses into blood each minute depends upon several factors, notably upon these three: (1) the oxygen pressure gradient between alveolar air and venous blood (alveolar pO_2-venous blood pO_2), (2) the total functional surface area of the alveolar-capillary membrane, and (3) the respiratory minute volume (respiratory rate per minute times volume of air inspired per respiration). All three of these factors bear a direct relation to oxygen diffusion. Anything that decreases alveolar pO_2, for instance, tends to decrease the alveolar-venous oxygen pressure gradient and therefore tends to decrease the amount of oxygen entering the blood. Application: alveolar air pO_2 decreases as altitude increases, and therefore less oxygen enters the blood at high altitudes.

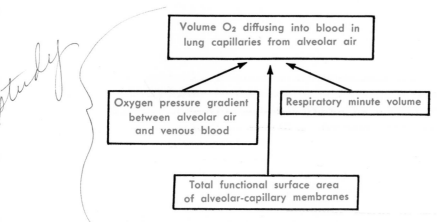

Fig. 220

Factors determining volume of oxygen entering lung capillary blood. An increase in any of the factors tends to increase oxygenation of blood; a decrease in one of them tends to decrease blood oxygenation.

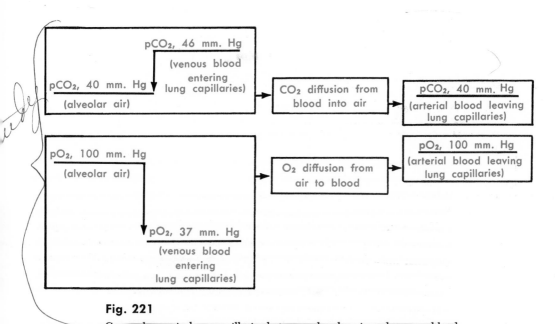

Fig. 221

Gas exchange in lung capillaries between alveolar air and venous blood. The CO_2 pressure gradient between alveolar air and venous blood causes outward diffusion of CO_2 from lung capillary blood and lowers blood pCO_2 from its venous level to its arterial level. The O_2 pressure gradient between alveolar air and venous blood causes inward diffusion of O_2 into lung capillary blood and raises blood pO_2 from its venous level up to its arterial level.

Anything that decreases the total functional surface area of the alveolar-capillary membrane also tends to decrease oxygen diffusion into the blood (by functional surface area is meant that which is freely permeable to oxygen). Application: in emphysema, this total functional area decreases and is one of the factors responsible for poor blood oxygenation in this condition.

Anything that decreases the respiratory minute volume also tends to decrease blood oxygenation. Application: morphine slows respirations and therefore decreases the respiratory minute volume and tends to lessen the amount of oxygen entering the blood. In Fig. 220 are shown the main factors influencing blood oxygenation.

We have stated the principle that structure determines functions several times. You may find it interesting to note the application of this principle to gas exchange in the lungs. Several structural facts facilitate the uptake of oxygen by blood in lung capillaries: the fact that the walls of the alveoli and of the capillaries together form a very thin barrier for the gases to cross (estimated at not more than 0.004 millimeter thick); the fact that both alveolar and capillary surfaces are extremely large; the fact that the lung capillaries accommodate a large amount of blood at one time (about 900 milliliters); the fact that the blood is distributed through the capillaries in a layer so thin (equal only to the diameter of one red corpuscle) that each corpuscle comes in close proximity to alveolar air.

Exchange of gases between arterial blood and cells

The exchange of gases between arterial blood and cells takes place because of the principle already noted that gases move down a gas pressure gradient. More specifically, in the tissue capillaries oxygen diffuses out of arterial blood because the oxygen pressure gradient favors its outward diffusion. Arterial blood pO_2 is about 100 mm. Hg, interstitial fluid pO_2 is considerably lower, and intracellular fluid pO_2 is still lower. Although interstitial fluid and intracellular fluid pO_2 are not definitely established, they are thought to vary considerably—perhaps from around 60 mm. Hg down to about 1 mm. Hg. As activity increases in any structure, its cells necessarily utilize oxygen more rapidly. This decreases intracellular and interstitial pO_2 which, in turn, tends to increase the oxygen pressure gradient between blood and tissues and to accelerate oxygen diffusion out of the tissue capillaries. In this way, the rate of oxygen utilization by cells automatically tends to regulate the rate of oxygen delivery to cells. As dissolved oxygen diffuses out of arterial blood, blood pO_2 decreases, and this accelerates oxyhemoglobin dissociation to release more oxygen into the plasma for diffusion out to cells, as indicated in the following equation.

$$Hb + O_2 \underset{(\text{Increasing pCO}_2)}{\overset{(\text{Decreasing pO}_2)}{\longleftarrow}} HbO_2$$

Because of oxygen release to tissues from tissue capillary blood, pO_2, oxygen saturation, and total oxygen content are all less in venous blood than in arterial blood as shown in Table 43.

Table 43. Blood oxygen

	Venous blood	Arterial blood
pO_2	37 mm. Hg	100 mm. Hg
Oxygen saturation	75%	97%
Oxygen content	15 ml. O_2 per 100 ml. blood	20 ml. O_2 per 100 ml. blood°

°Oxygen utilization by tissues $(20-5) = 5$ ml. O_2 per 100 ml. blood circulated per minute.

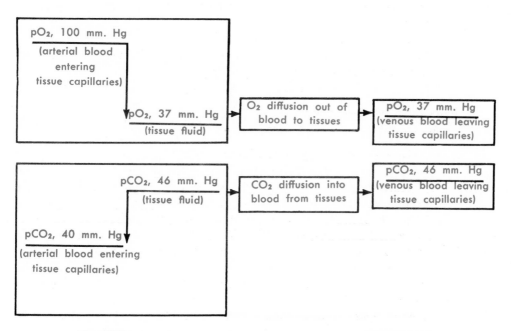

Fig. 222

Gas exchange in tissue capillaries between arterial blood and cells. Oxygen and carbon dioxide pressure gradients between arterial blood entering tissue capillaries and tissue fluid cause outward diffusion of oxygen from blood and inward diffusion of carbon dioxide into blood.

395

Carbon dioxide exchange between tissues and blood takes place in the opposite direction from oxygen exchange. Catabolism produces large amounts of carbon dioxide inside cells. Hence, intracellular and interstitial pCO_2 are higher than arterial blood pCO_2. This means that the carbon dioxide pressure gradient causes diffusion of carbon dioxide from the tissues into the blood flowing along through tissue capillaries. Consequently the pCO_2 of blood increases to the venous level of about 46 mm. Hg. This increasing pCO_2 and decreasing pO_2 together produce two effects—they favor both oxygen dissociation from hemoglobin and carbon dioxide association with hemoglobin to form carboxyhemoglobin.

Control of respirations

The mechanism for controlling respiration has many parts. A brief description of its main features follows.

1. *The pCO_2, pO_2, and pH of arterial blood* all influence respirations. The pCO_2 influences respiratory centers in the medulla directly and indirectly via its action on chemoreceptors. The normal range for arterial pCO_2 is about 38 to 40 mm. Hg. When it increases even slightly above this, it stimulates the inspiratory centers (clusters of neurons located bilaterally in the medulla). Faster breathing results, with a greater volume of air moving in and out of the lungs per minute. Decreased arterial pCO_2 produces the opposite effects, inhibiting medullary respiratory centers and slowing respirations. In fact, breathing stops entirely for a few moments (apnea) when arterial pCO_2 drops moderately—to about 35 mm. Hg, for example.

Arterial blood pCO_2, in addition to acting on respiratory centers directly, also influences them indirectly via its effect on carotid and aortic chemoreceptors. Moderate increases in arterial pCO_2 stimulate these receptors, and this leads to stimulation of inspiratory centers and faster breathing. Conversely, decreased arterial pCO_2 results in reflex slowing of respirations. There has been much debate over the question of which is the more important regulator of respirations—arterial pCO_2 acting directly on respiratory centers or reflexly on them via the chemoreceptors. The majority seems to favor the view that the direct influence of arterial pCO_2 on respiratory centers is primary.

The role of *arterial blood pO_2* in controlling respirations is not entirely clear. Presumably it is minor so long as it stays above a certain level. Neurons of the respiratory centers, like all body cells, require adequate amounts of oxygen in order to function optimally. Consequently if they become hypoxic, they are depressed, that is, send fewer impulses to respiratory muscles, and respirations decrease or

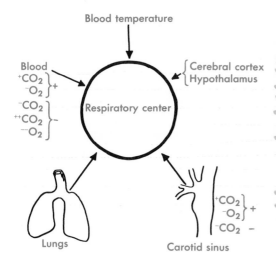

Blood temperature

Blood
$^+CO_2$
$-O_2$ } +

$-CO_2$
$^{++}CO_2$ } -
$-O_2$

Respiratory center

{ Cerebral cortex
Hypothalamus

Lungs

$^+CO_2$
$-O_2$ } +

$-CO_2$ -

Carotid sinus

Fig. 223

Respiratory control mechanism. Scheme to show the main factors which influence the respiratory center and thereby control respirations. A moderate increase in blood CO_2 or a moderate decrease in blood oxygen stimulates respirations by the carotid reflex and by direct action on the nerve cells of the respiratory center. Either a marked excess or a deficiency of blood CO_2 depresses the center, as does marked oxygen lack. Impulses from the lungs, the cerebral cortex, and the hypothalamus may either stimulate or inhibit respirations. Increased blood temperature stimulates respirations and lowered temperature depresses respirations.

fail entirely. This principle has important clinical significance. For example, the respiratory centers cannot respond to stimulation by an increasing blood CO_2 if at the same time blood pO_2 falls below a critical level—a fact of especial importance during anesthesia and in strenuous exercise.

However, a decrease in arterial blood pO_2 to a point above the critical level stimulates chemoreceptors in the carotid and aortic bodies and causes reflex stimulation of the inspiratory center. This constitutes an emergency respiratory control mechanism. It does not help regulate respirations under normal conditions because normally arterial blood pO_2 remains above the level necessary to stimulate the chemoreceptors.

A decrease in *arterial blood pH* (increase in acid) has a stimulating effect on carotid and aortic chemoreceptors and on respiratory centers and therefore tends to increase respirations.

2. *Arterial blood pressure* helps control respirations through the respiratory pressoreflex mechanism. A sudden rise in arterial pressure, by acting on aortic and carotid pressoreceptors, results in reflex slowing of respirations. And a sudden drop in arterial pressure brings about a reflex increase in rate and depth of respirations. The pressoreflex mechanism is probably not of great importance in the control of respirations. It is, however, as you will recall, of major importance in the control of circulation.

3. The *Hering-Breuer reflexes* help control respirations—particularly their depth and rhythmicity. They are believed to regulate the normal depth of respirations (extent of lung expansion) and therefore the volume of tidal air in the following way. Presumably when the tidal volume of air has been inspired, the lungs are expanded enough to stimulate its internal pressoreceptors. They send inhibitory impulses to the inspiratory center, relaxation of inspiratory muscles occurs, and

397

expiration follows—the Hering-Breuer expiratory reflex. Then when the tidal volume of air has been expired, the lungs are sufficiently deflated to inhibit the lung pressoreceptors and allow inspiration to start again —the Hering-Breuer inspiratory reflex.

4. The *pneumotaxic center* in the upper part of the pons is postulated to function mainly to maintain rhythmicity of respirations. Whenever the inspiratory center is stimulated, it sends impulses to the pneumotaxic center as well as to inspiratory muscles. The pneumotaxic center, after a moment's delay, stimulates the expiratory center which then feeds back inhibitory impulses to the inspiratory center. Inspiration, therefore, ends and expiration starts. Lung deflation soon initiates the Hering-Breuer inspiratory reflex, and inspiration starts again. In short, the pneumotaxic center and Hering-Breuer reflexes together constitute an automatic device for producing rhythmic respirations.

5. The *cerebral cortex* helps control respirations. Impulses to the respiratory center from the motor area of the cerebrum may either increase or decrease the rate and strength of respirations. In other words, an individual may voluntarily speed up or slow down his breathing rate. This voluntary control of respirations, however, has certain limitations. For example, one may will to stop breathing and do so for a few minutes. Holding the breath results, however, in an increase in the carbon dioxide content of the blood since it is not being removed by respirations. Carbon dioxide is a powerful respiratory stimulant. So that when arterial blood pCO_2 increases to a certain level, it stimulates the inspiratory center both directly and reflexly to send motor impulses to the respiratory muscles, and breathing is resumed even though the individual may still will contrarily. This knowledge that the carbon dioxide content of the blood is a more powerful regulator of respirations than cerebal impulses is of practical value when dealing with a child who holds his breath to force the granting of his wishes. The best treatment is to ignore such behavior, knowing that respirations will start again as soon as the amount of carbon dioxide in the blood becomes sufficiently concentrated.

6. Miscellaneous factors also influence respirations. Among these are blood temperature and sensory impulses from skin thermal receptors and from superficial or deep pain receptors.

   (a) *sudden painful stimulation*—such painful stimulation produces a reflex apnea, but continued painful stimuli causes faster and deeper respirations.

   (b) *sudden cold stimuli*—sudden cold stimuli applied to the skin cause temporary apnea.

   (c) *afferent impulses*—afferent impulses initiated by stretching the anal sphincter produce reflex acceleration and deepening of respirations. Use has sometimes been made of this mechanism as an emergency measure to stimulate respirations during surgery.

(d) *stimulation of the pharynx or larynx*—stimulation of the pharynx or larynx by irritating chemicals or by touch causes a temporary apnea. This is the choking reflex, a valuable protective device. It operates, for example, to prevent aspiration of food or liquids during swallowing.

Control of respirations during exercise

Respirations increase greatly during strenuous exercise. The mechanism which accomplishes this, however, is not the one which produces more moderate increases in breathing. A number of studies have shown that arterial blood pCO_2, pO_2, and pH do not change enough during exercise to produce the degree of hyperpnea (faster, deeper respirations) observed. Venous blood pCO_2, however, is known to increase with strenuous muscle exertion. Just recently Dr. Krahl and Dr. Armstrong of the University of Maryland School of Medicine, reported finding chemoreceptors in the walls of the pulmonary artery—a strategic location for them to be acted on by changes in venous blood.[*] It may be, they suggest, that the higher venous pCO_2 present during exercise acts as a stimulant to these receptors and helps bring about the characteristic faster, deeper breathing.

---

[*]Breathing regulated by blood composition, Science Newsletter **82:56**, 1962.

Outline summary

The respiratory system

Functions and importance

Exchange of gases between blood and air; of vital importance

Organs

Nose

1. Structure
   a. portions—internal, in skull, above roof of mouth; external, protruding from face
   b. cavities
      1. divisions—right and left
      2. meati—superior, middle, and lower; named for turbinate located above each meatus
   3. openings—to exterior, anterior nares; to nasopharynx, posterior nares
   4. turbinates (conchae)—superior and middle, processes of ethmoid bone; inferior turbinates separate bones; divide internal nasal cavities into three passageways or meati
   5. floor—formed by palatine bones which also act as roof of mouth

c. lining—ciliated mucous membrane
d. sinuses draining into nose (or paranasal sinuses)—frontal, maxillary (or antrum of Highmore), sphenoidal, and ethmoidal
2. Functions
   a. serves as passageway for incoming and outgoing air, filtering, warming, moistening, and chemically examining it
   b. organ of smell because olfactory receptors located in nasal mucosa
   c. aids in phonation

Pharynx

1. Structure—made of muscle with mucous lining
   a. divisions—nasopharynx, behind nose; oropharynx, behind mouth; laryngopharynx, behind larynx
   b. openings—four in nasopharynx: two auditory tubes and two posterior nares; one in oropharynx: fauces from mouth; and two in laryngopharynx: into esophagus and into larynx
   c. organs in pharynx—adenoids or pharyngeal tonsils in nasopharynx; palatine and lingual tonsils in oropharynx
2. Functions—serves both respiratory and digestive tracts as passageway for air and food; aids in phonation

Larynx

1. Location—at upper end of trachea, just below pharynx
2. Structure
   a. cartilages—nine pieces arranged in boxlike formation; thyroid is largest of cartilages, known as "Adam's apple"; epiglottis is "lid" cartilage; cricoid is "signet ring" cartilage
   b. vocal cords—false cords are folds of mucous lining; true cords are fibroelastic bands stretched across hollow interior of larynx; glottis is opening between true vocal cords
   c. lining—ciliated mucous membrane
   d. sexual differences—male larynx larger, covered with less fat, and therefore more prominent than female larynx
3. Function—expired air causes true vocal cords to vibrate, producing voice; pitch determined by length and tension of cords

Trachea

1. Structure
   a. walls—smooth muscle; contain C-shaped rings of cartilage at intervals, which keep the tube open at all times; lining —ciliated mucous membrane
   b. extent—from larynx to bronchi; about 4½ inches long
2. Function—furnishes open passageway for air going to and from lungs

Bronchi

1. Structure—formed by division of trachea into two tubes; right bronchus slightly larger and more vertical than left; same structure as trachea; each primary bronchus branches as soon as enters lung into secondary bronchi which branch into bronchioles, which branch into microscopic alveolar ducts, which terminate in cluster of blind sacs called alveoli; trachea and two primary bronchi and all their branches compose the "bronchial tree"; alveolar walls composed of single layer of cells
2. Function—bronchi and their many branching tubes furnish passageway for air going to and from lungs; alveoli provide large, thin-walled surface area where blood and air can exchange gases

Lungs

1. Structure
   a. size, shape, location—large enough to fill pleural divisions of thoracic cavity; cone-shaped; extend from base, on diaphragm, to apex, located slightly above clavicle
   b. divisions—three lobes in right lung, two in left; root of lung consists of primary bronchus and pulmonary artery and veins, bound together by connective tissue; hilum is vertical slit on mesial surface of lung through which root structures enter lung; base is broad, inferior surface of lung; apex is pointed upper margin
   c. covering—visceral layer of pleura
2. Function — furnish place where large amounts of air and blood can come in close enough contact for rapid exchange of gases to occur

Thorax
Definition
The chest

Structure
1. Has three divisions
   a. pleural portion—contains lungs
   b. mediastinum—area between two lungs; contains esophagus, trachea, great blood vessels, etc.
   c. pericardial portion—space occupied by heart and pericardial sac
2. Lining
   a. Parietal layer of pleura lines entire chest cavity and covers superior surface of diaphragm; forms separate sac encasing each lung; separated from visceral pleura, covering lungs, only by potential space, the pleural space, which contains few drops of pleural fluid
3. Shape of ribs and angle of their attachment to spine—such that elevation of the rib cage enlarges two dimensions of the thorax, its width and depth from front to back

Respirations
Kinds of respiration
1. External or lung breathing
2. Internal or cell breathing

Mechanism of respiration
1. Contraction of diaphragm and chest elevating muscles enlarges thorax, thereby decreases intrathoracic pressure, which causes expansion of lungs which decreases intrapulmonic pressure to subatmospheric level, which establishes gas pressure gradient which causes air to move into the lungs
2. Relaxation of inspiratory muscles produces opposite effects; see Fig. 216.

Amount of air exchanged in breathing
1. Directly related to gas pressure gradient between atmosphere and lung alveoli and inversely related to resistance opposing air flow
   a. measured by apparatus called a spirometer
   b. tidal air—average amount expired after normal inspiration; approximately 1 pint
   c. supplemental air—amount which can be forcibly expired after normal inspiration
   d. complemental air—amount which can be forcibly inspired after normal inspiration; measured by having individual expire normally after forced inspiration
   e. residual air—that which cannot be forcibly expired from lungs
   f. minimal air—that which can never be removed from alveoli, even when lungs subjected to atmospheric pressure
   g. vital capacity—approximate capacity of lungs (limited by size of thoracic cavity and various other factors, such as amount of blood in lungs and condition of alveoli); air which can be forcibly expired after forcible inspiration represents vital capacity
2. Types of breathing
   a. normal (eupnea)
      1. abdominal (also called deep or diaphragmatic breathing)—characterized by outward movement of abdominal wall due to contraction and descent of diaphragm
      2. costal (also called shallow or chest breathing) — characterized by upward, outward movement of chest due to contraction of chest-elevating muscles
   b. abnormal
      1. apnea—temporary cessation of respirations
      2. dyspnea—difficult or painful respirations
      3. orthopnea—inability to breathe in horizontal position
      4. Cheyne-Stokes—alternate periods of dyspnea and apnea

Some principles about gases

1. Dalton's law—partial pressure of a gas in a mixture of gases is directly related to the concentration of that gas in the mixture and to the total pressure of the mixture
2. Partial pressure of a gas in a liquid is directly related to amount of gas dissolved in liquid; becomes equal to partial pres-

sure of that gas in the environment of the liquid

How blood transports respiratory gases

1. Oxygen
   a. about 0.5 milliliter transported as a *solute*, that is, dissolved in 100 milliliters blood
   b. about 19.5 milliliters O_2 per 100 milliliters blood transported as *oxyhemoglobin* in red blood cells
   c. about 20 milliliters *total O_2 — content* per 100 milliliters blood (100 per cent saturation of 15 grams hemoglobin)
2. Carbon dioxide
   a. small amount dissolves in plasma and transported as true *solute*
   b. more than half of CO_2 transported as *bicarbonate ion* in plasma
   c. somewhat less than one third of CO_2 transported in red blood cells as *carboxyhemoglobin*

Exchange of gases between alveolar air and venous blood

1. Where it occurs—in lung capillaries; across alveolar-capillary membrane
2. What exchange consists of—oxygen diffuses out of alveolar air into venous blood; carbon dioxide diffuses in opposite direction
3. Why it occurs—oxygen pressure gradient causes inward diffusion of oxygen; carbon dioxide pressure gradient causes outward diffusion of carbon dioxide

	Alveolar air	Venous blood
pO_2	100 mm. Hg	37 mm. Hg
pCO_2	40 mm. Hg	46 mm. Hg

4. Results of gas exchange
   a. pO_2 of blood increases to arterial blood level
   b. pCO_2 of blood decreases to arterial blood level
   c. Oxygen association with hemoglobin to form oxyhemoglobin and carbon dioxide dissociation from carboxyhemoglobin both accelerated by the increasing pO_2 and decreasing pCO_2

Exchange of gases between arterial blood and cells

1. Where it occurs—tissue capillaries
2. What the exchange consists of—oxygen diffuses out of arterial blood into interstitial fluid and on into cells, whereas carbon dioxide diffuses in opposite direction
3. Why it occurs—O_2 pressure gradient causes outward diffusion of O_2; CO_2 pressure gradient causes inward diffusion of CO_2

	Arterial blood	Interstitial fluid
pO_2	100 mm. Hg	60 (?) mm. Hg down to 1 (?) mm. Hg
pCO_2	46 mm. Hg	50 (?) mm. Hg

4. Results of oxygen diffusion out of blood and carbon dioxide diffusion into blood
   a. pO_2 blood decreases as oxygen moves out of tissue capillaries; arterial pO_2, 100 mm. Hg becomes venous pO_2, 40 mm. Hg (figures vary)
   b. pCO_2 blood increases; arterial pCO_2, 40 mm. Hg becomes venous pCO_2, 46 mm. Hg (figures vary)
   c. oxygen dissociation from hemoglobin and carbon dioxide association with hemoglobin to form carboxyhemoglobin both accelerated by decreasing pO_2 and increasing pCO_2

Control of external respirations—Fig. 223

1. Respiratory centers—inspiratory and expiratory centers in medulla; pneumotaxic center in pons
2. Control of respiratory centers
   a. carbon dioxide is major regulator of respirations; increased blood carbon dioxide content, up to a certain level, stimulates respirations and above this level depresses respirations; decreased blood carbon dioxide decreases respirations
   b. oxygen content of blood influences respiratory center — decreased blood O_2, down to a certain level, stimulates respirations and below this critical level depresses them; O_2 control of respira-

tions nonoperative under normal conditions

c. Hering-Breuer mechanism helps control rhythmicity of respirations; increased alveolar pressure inhibits inspiration and starts expiration; decreased alveolar pressure stimulates inspiration and ends expiration

d. miscellaneous factors influence respiratory center—for example, body temperature, pain, emotions, etc.

Review questions

The respiratory system

1. What anatomical feature favors the spread of the common cold through the respiratory passages and into the middle ear and mastoid sinus?
2. How are the turbinates arranged in the nose? What are they?
3. What organs are found in the nasopharynx?
4. What tubes open into the nasopharynx?
5. Make a diagram showing the termination of a bronchiole in an alveolar duct with alveoli.
6. What kind of membrane lines the respiratory system?
7. What is the serous covering of the lungs called? Where else, besides covering the lungs, is this same membrane found?
8. The pharynx is common to what two systems?
9. Are the lungs active or passive organs during breathing? Explain.
10. What is the main inspiratory muscle?
11. How is inspiration accomplished? Expiration?

12. If an opening is made into the pleural cavity from the exterior, what happens? Why?
13. What is the pleural space? What does it contain?
14. What substance found in blood is the natural chemical stimulant for the respiratory center?
15. Compare mechanisms which achieve internal and external respiration.
16. Respirations increase during exercise. Explain the mechanisms involved.
17. What is the voice box? Of what is it composed? What is the Adam's apple?
18. What is the epiglottis? What is its function?
19. What are the true vocal cords? Where are they? What name is given to the opening between the cords?
20. Name the three divisions of the thorax and their contents.
21. Compare the mechanisms which accelerate respiration with those which accelerate circulation during exercise.
22. Make a generalization about the effect of a moderate increase in the amount of blood CO_2 on circulation and respiration. What advantage can you see in this effect?
23. Make a generalization about the effect of a moderate decrease in blood O_2 on circulation and respiration.
24. Define the following terms briefly:

alveolus	pO_2
apnea	pleurisy
asphyxia	residual air
complemental air	respiration
cyanosis	spirometer
dyspnea	supplemental air
minimal air	thorax
orthopnea	tidal air
pCO_2	vital capacity

Chapter XI

The digestive system

Functions and importance

Organs of digestive system
Walls of organs
Mouth
Tongue
Salivary glands
Teeth
Pharynx
Esophagus
Stomach
Small intestine
Large intestine
Liver
Gallbladder
Pancreas
Vermiform appendix

Digestion
Definition
Purpose
Kinds
Control of digestive gland
    secretion

Absorption
Definition
How accomplished

Metabolism
Meaning
Ways in which foods are
    metabolized
Carbohydrate metabolism
Blood glucose homeostatic
    mechanisms
Fat metabolism
Protein metabolism
Metabolism of vitamins,
    mineral salts, and water
Metabolic rates

Heat regulation of the body
Heat production
Heat loss
Thermostatic control of heat
    produced and lost
Correlations

FUNCTIONS AND IMPORTANCE

The organs of the digestive system together perform a vital function—that of preparing food for absorption and for use by the millions of body cells. Most food when eaten is in a form which cannot reach the cells (because it cannot pass through the intestinal mucosa into the blood stream) nor could it be used by the cells even if it could reach them. It must, therefore, be modified as to both chemical composition and physical state. This process of altering the chemical and physical composition of food so that it can be absorbed and utilized by body cells is known as digestion and is the function of the digestive system. Part of the digestive system, the large intestine, serves also as an organ of elimination, ridding the body of the wastes resulting from the digestive process.

ORGANS OF THE DIGESTIVE SYSTEM

The main organs of this system form a tube all the way through the ventral cavities of the body. It is open at both ends. This tube is usually referred to as the *alimentary canal* (or tract) or the *gastrointestinal* or GI tract. The following organs form the gastrointestinal tract: mouth, pharynx, esophagus, stomach, and intestines. Several accessory organs are located in the main digestive organs or open into them. They are the teeth, tongue, salivary glands, pancreas, liver, gallbladder, and vermiform appendix.

Walls of organs

Coats composing walls. The alimentary canal is essentially a tube whose walls are fashioned of four layers of tissues: a mucous lining, a submucous coat of connective tissue in which are embedded the main blood vessels of the tract, a muscular coat, and a fibroserous coat.

Modifications of coats. Although the same four tissue coats form the various organs of the alimentary tract, their structure varies in different organs. Some of these modifications are listed in Table 44.

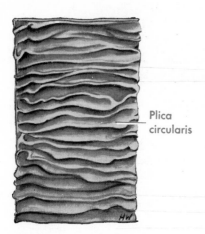

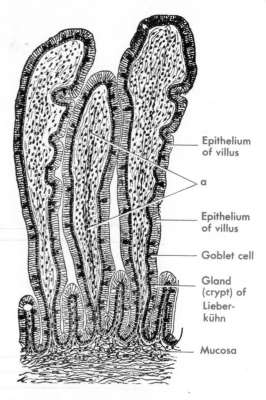

Epithelium
of villus

a

Epithelium
of villus

Goblet cell

Gland
(crypt) of
Lieber-
kühn

Mucosa

Plica
circularis

Fig. 224
Section of the jejunum showing the
circular folds (valvulae connivents or
plica circularis). (From Francis and
Farrell: Integrated anatomy and physiology,
St. Louis, The C. V. Mosby Co.)

Fig. 225
Section through the intestinal mucosa showing
the villi: a, lacteal or lymphatic vessel.
(From Brash and Jamieson: Cunningham's
textbook of anatomy, London, Oxford
University Press.)

The parietal peritoneum, which lines the posterior wall of the abdominal cavity, projects from the lumbar region into the abdominal
cavity in a double fold, shaped like a plaited fan. It is named the
mesentery (Fig. 226). The loose outer edge of this great fan measures
approximately 20 feet, whereas its attached posterior border has a
length of from only 6 to 8 inches. Most of the small intestine is attached to its outer edge. The mesentery, then, may be defined as a
fan-shaped double fold of parietal peritoneum by which the small intestine is anchored to the posterior abdominal wall. It should not be
confused with the *greater omentum*,* an apron-shaped double fold of
peritoneum which is attached, at its upper border, to the first part of
the duodenum, the lower edge of the stomach, and the transverse
colon and hangs down loosely over the intestines. In case of a localized

*The *lesser omentum* is a fold of peritoneum which attaches the liver to the
lesser curvature of the stomach and beginning of the duodenum.

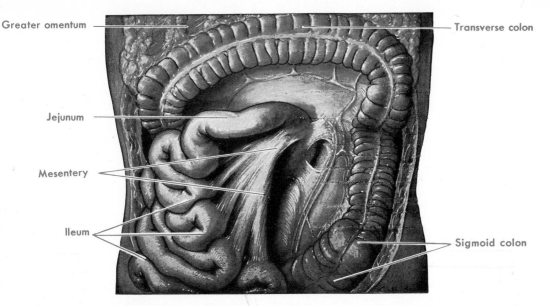

Greater omentum — ⎯⎯⎯⎯⎯⎯ Transverse colon

Jejunum —

Mesentery —

Ileum —

⎯⎯⎯ Sigmoid colon

Fig. 226

Mesentery as seen when the intestine is pulled aside. (From Callander: Surgical anatomy, Philadelphia, W. B. Saunders Co.)

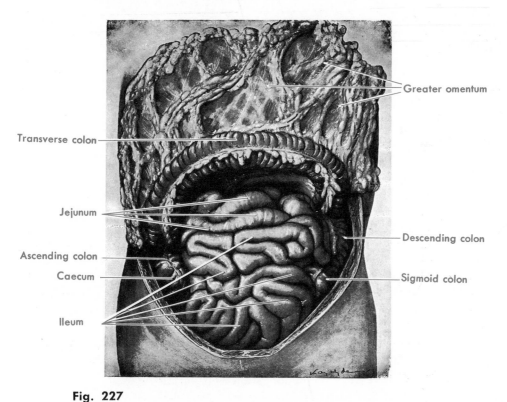

Greater omentum

Transverse colon—

Jejunum —

Ascending colon —

Caecum —

Ileum —

—Descending colon

—Sigmoid colon

Fig. 227

Abdominal viscera. Note appearance of the omentum. It has been lifted up to reveal the viscera. (From Callander: Surgical anatomy, Philadelphia, W. B. Saunders Co.)

407

Table 44. Modifications of coats of digestive tract

Organ	Mucous coat	Muscle coat	Fibroserous coat
Esophagus		Two layers—an inner one of circular fibers and an outer one of longitudinal fibers; striated muscle in upper part and smooth in lower part of esophagus and in rest of tract	Outer coat fibrous; serous around part of esophagus in thoracic cavity
Stomach	Arranged in temporary longitudinal folds called *rugae;* allow for distention (Fig. 229) Contains microscopic gastric and hydrochloric acid glands	Has three layers instead of usual two, circular, longitudinal, and oblique fibers; two sphincters—cardia at entrance of stomach and pylorus at its exit formed by circular fibers	Outer coat visceral peritoneum; hangs in double fold from lower edge of stomach over intestines, forming apronlike structure, greater *omentum,* or "lace apron" (Fig. 227)
Small intestine	Contains permanent circular folds, *valvulae conniventes* (or plica circularis) (Fig. 224) Microscopic fingerlike projections, the *villi* (Fig. 225) Microscopic intestinal glands (of Lieberkühn) Microscopic duodenal (or Brunner's) glands Clusters of lymph nodes, *Peyer's patches* Numerous single lymph nodes, called solitary nodes	Two layers—an inner one of circular fibers and an outer one of longitudinal fibers	Outer coat visceral peritoneum
Large intestine	Solitary nodes Intestinal glands	Incomplete outer longitudinal coat; present only in three tapelike strips; shirr large intestine into small sacs (haustra) (Fig. 231); internal anal sphincter formed by circular smooth fibers and external anal sphincter by striated fibers	Outer coat visceral peritoneum

abdominal inflammation, such as appendicitis, the omentum envelops the inflamed area, walling it off from the rest of the abdomen. Spotty deposits of fat accumulate in the omentum, giving it a lacy appearance (Fig. 227).

Mouth (or buccal cavity)

The following structures form the buccal cavity: the cheeks—side walls, the tongue and its muscles—floor, and the hard and soft palates—roof. Of these, only the palates will be discussed here. The *hard palate* consists of the two palatine bones and parts of the two superior maxillary bones. The *soft palate*, which forms a partition between the mouth and nasopharynx, is fashioned of muscle arranged in the shape of an arch. The opening in the arch leads from the mouth into the oropharynx and is named the *fauces*, whereas the two vertical side portions of the arch are appropriately termed the pillars of the fauces. Suspended from the midpoint of the posterior border of the arch is a small cone-shaped process, the *uvula*. The entire buccal cavity, like the rest of the digestive tract, is lined with mucous membrane.

The tongue, teeth, and salivary glands are accessory organs of the mouth.

Tongue

Skeletal muscle covered with mucous membrane composes the tongue. Several muscles which originate on skull bones insert into the tongue. The rough elevations on the tongue's surface are called *papillae.* They contain the taste buds. Three types, filliform, fungiform, and vallate, can be observed. The filliform papillae are numerous threadlike structures distributed over the anterior two thirds of the tongue; fungiform papillae are knoblike elevations most numerous near the edges of the tongue; vallate papillae form an inverted V at the posterior part of the tongue. The *frenum* (or frenulum) is a fold of mucous membrane in the midline of the undersurface of the tongue which helps to anchor the tongue to the floor of the mouth. If the frenum is too short for freedom of tongue movements, the individual is said to be tongue-tied, and his speech is faulty.

Salivary glands   *(produce saliva → ptyalin)*

See Table 45 for information on the names, location, and duct openings of the salivary glands.

409

Table 45. Salivary glands

Name of gland	Location	Duct openings
Parotid	Below and in front of ear	On inside of cheek, opposite upper second molar tooth; known as Stensen's duct
Submaxillary	Posterior part of floor of mouth	Floor of mouth, at sides of frenum; known as Wharton's duct
Sublingual	Anterior part of floor of mouth, under tongue	Several ducts open into floor of mouth

Mumps is an acute infection of the parotid glands characterized by swelling of the glands. The act of opening the mouth causes pain because it squeezes that part of the gland which projects between the temporomandibular joint and the mastoid process. When a dentist fills a tooth, he places rolls of absorbent cotton over the openings of the salivary ducts to prevent saliva from entering the cavity.

Teeth

7 weeks embryonic development

erupt - 6-7 mon post natal

The so-called baby teeth or the set which appears first and is later shed are technically known as the *deciduous teeth*, whereas the set which replaces these are the *permanent teeth*. The names and numbers of teeth present in both sets are given in Table 46.

The first deciduous tooth erupts usually at the age of about 6 months. The rest follow at the rate of one or more a month until all twenty have appeared. There is, however, great individual variation in the ages of dentition (tooth eruption). Deciduous teeth are shed generally between the ages of 6 and 13 years. The third molars (wisdom teeth) are the last to appear, erupting usually sometime after 17 years of age.

Table 46. Dentition

Name of tooth	Number per jaw	
	Deciduous set	Permanent set
Central incisors	2	2
Lateral incisors	2	2
Cuspids (canines)	2	2
Premolars (bicuspids)	0	4
Molars (tricuspids)	4	6
Total per jaw	10	16
Total per set	20	32

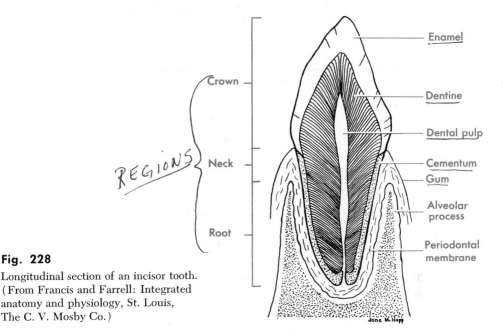

Fig. 228

Longitudinal section of an incisor tooth. (From Francis and Farrell: Integrated anatomy and physiology, St. Louis, The C. V. Mosby Co.)

Correlations

Intact enamel resists bacterial attack, but once it is broken, the softer dentine decays. Pyorrhea is an inflammation of the gums (gingiva) and periodontal membrane (Fig. 228).

Pharynx

For a discussion of the pharynx, see pp. 348 and 349.

Esophagus

The esophagus, a collapsible tube about 10 inches long, extends from the pharynx to the stomach, piercing the diaphragm in its descent from the thoracic to the abdominal cavity. It lies posterior to the trachea and heart.

Unlike the trachea, the esophagus is a collapsible tube, its muscle walls lacking the cartilaginous rings found in the trachea (Table 44).

Stomach

Size, shape, and position

The alimentary tube dilates, just below the diaphragm, into an elongated pouchlike structure, the stomach (see Fig. 229), the size of which varies according to several factors, notably sex and the amount

411

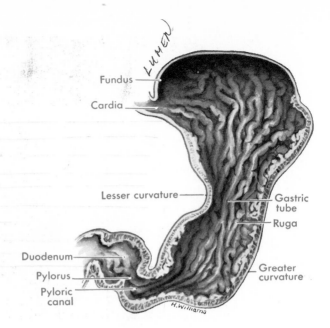

Fig. 229

Frontal section of the stomach. (From Francis and Farrell: Integrated
anatomy and physiology, St. Louis, The C. V. Mosby Co.)

of distention. The female stomach is usually more slender and smaller
in general than the male stomach. For some time after a meal, the
stomach is enlarged due to distention of its walls, but as food leaves,
the walls partially collapse, leaving the organ about the size of a large
sausage.

The stomach lies in the upper part of the abdominal cavity under
the liver and diaphragm, with approximately five sixths of its mass to
the left of the median line. In other words, it is described as lying in
the epigastrium and left hypochondrium (Fig. 230). Its position, however, alters frequently. For example, with each inspiration it is pushed
downward and with each expiration upward. When it is greatly distended from an unusually large meal, its size interferes with the descent of the diaphragm on inspiration, producing the familiar feeling
of dyspnea which accompanies overeating. In this state the stomach
also pushes upward against the heart, giving rise to the sensation that
the heart is being crowded.

Divisions

The *fundus,* the *body,* and the *pylorus* are the three divisions of
the stomach. The fundus is the enlarged portion to the left and above
the opening of the esophagus into the stomach. The body is the central part of the stomach, and the pylorus is its lower portion (Fig. 229).

Curves

The upper right border of the stomach presents what is known as
the *lesser curvature* and the lower left border the *greater curvature.*

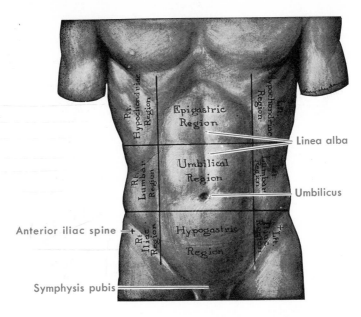

Fig. 230

Regions of the abdominal wall. (From Callander: Surgical anatomy, Philadelphia, W. B. Saunders Co.)

Sphincter muscles

Sphincter muscles guard both stomach openings. A sphincter muscle consists of circular fibers so arranged that there is an opening in the center of them (like the hole in a doughnut) when they are relaxed and no opening when they are contracted. The *cardiac sphincter* guards the opening of the esophagus into the stomach and the *pyloric sphincter* the opening from the pyloric portion of the stomach into the first part of the small intestine (duodenum). This latter muscle is of clinical importance because *pylorospasm* is a fairly common condition in babies. The pyloric fibers do not relax normally to allow food to leave the stomach, and the baby vomits his food instead of digesting and absorbing it. The condition is relieved by administering a drug which relaxes smooth muscle. Another abnormality of the pyloric sphincter is pyloric stenosis, an obstructive narrowing of its opening.

Coats

See Table 44 for information on coats of the stomach.

Glands

Numerous microscopic tubular glands are embedded in the gastric mucosa. Those in the mucosa that lines the fundus and body of the stomach secrete most of the gastric juice, a fluid composed of mucus, enzymes, and hydrochloric acid. *Epithelial cells* that form the surface of the gastric mucosa (next to the lumen of the stomach) secrete mucus. *Parietal cells* secrete hydrochloric acid, and *chief cells* (or

413

zymogen cells) secrete the enzymes of the gastric juice. In pernicious anemia, the gastric mucosa atrophies with the result that hydrochloric acid and a mysterious substance known as the intrinsic factor are not produced. Achlorhydria, therefore, is a finding in pernicious anemia. Absence of the intrinsic factor produces anemia because without it vitamin B_{12} cannot be absorbed, and without vitamin B_{12} the red bone marrow is not sufficiently stimulated to produce enough normal red blood cells.

Functions

The stomach carries on the following functions:

1. It serves as a reservoir, storing food until it can be partially digested and moved further along the gastrointestinal tract.

2. It secretes gastric juice, one of the juices whose enzymes digest food.

3. Through contractions of its muscular coat, it churns the food, breaking it into small particles and mixing them well with the gastric juice. In due time it moves the gastric contents on into the duodenum.

4. It secretes the intrinsic factor just mentioned.

5. It carries on a limited amount of absorption—of some water, alcohol, and certain drugs.

Small intestine

Size and position

The small intestine is a tube measuring approximately 1 inch in diameter and 20 feet in length. Its coiled loops fill most of the abdominal cavity.

Divisions

The small intestine consists of three divisions: the duodenum, the jejunum, and the ileum. The *duodenum** is the upper most division and is the part to which the pyloric end of the stomach attaches. It is about 10 inches long and is shaped roughly like the letter **C**. The duodenum becomes *jejunum* at the point where the tube turns abruptly forward and downward. The jejunal portion continues for approximately the next 8 feet, where it becomes *ileum*, but without any clear line of demarcation between the two divisions. The ileum is about 12 feet long.

---

*Derivation of the word duodenum may interest you. It comes from words which means 12 fingerbreadths, a distance of about 11 inches, the approximate length of the duodenum.

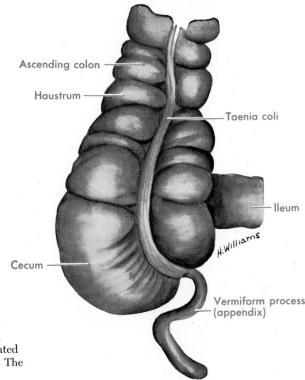

Fig. 231

Cecum and appendix. Note the
haustra, that is, the sacculations,
characteristic of the large intestine,
particularly of the transverse colon.
(From Francis and Farrell: Integrated
anatomy and physiology, St. Louis, The
C. V. Mosby Co.)

In the figure, labels read:
Ascending colon — Haustrum — Taenia coli — Ileum — Cecum — Vermiform process (appendix) — H. Williams

Coats

See Table 44 for information on the coats of the small intestine.

Functions

The small intestine carries on three main functions, as follows:

1. It completes the digestion of foods. The digestive intestinal juice contains mucus and many digestive enzymes. The glands of Lieber-kühn secrete the digestive enzymes, whereas the glands of Brunner and innumerable goblet cells secrete the mucus.

2. It absorbs the end products of digestion into blood and lymph.

3. It secretes hormones—for example, some which help control the secretion of pancreatic juice, bile, and intestinal juice.

Large intestine (or colon)

Size

This part of the alimentary canal bears the name *large intestine* because its diameter is noticeably larger than the diameter of the small intestine; its length, however, is much less, being about 5 or 6 feet. Its average diameter is approximately 2½ inches but decreases toward the lower end of the tube.

415

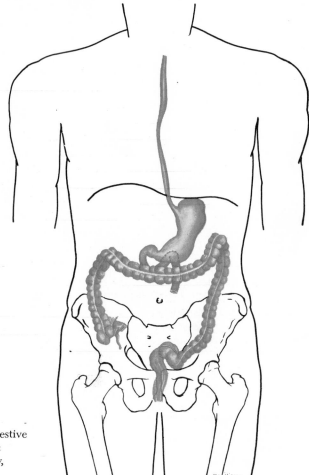

Fig. 232

Normal position of some of the digestive
organs. (From Francis and Farrell:
Integrated anatomy and physiology,
St. Louis, The C. V. Mosby Co.)

Divisions

The divisions of the large intestine are as follows.

Cecum. The first 2 or 3 inches of the large intestine are named the
cecum. It is located in the lower right quadrant of the abdomen (Figs.
230 and 232).

Colon. The colon is divided into the following portions:

1. *ascending*—lies in the vertical position, on the right side of the
   abdomen, extending up to the lower border of the liver; the
   ileum joins the large intestine at the junction of the cecum and
   ascending colon, the place of attachment resembling the letter **T**
   in formation (Fig. 231); the ileocecal valve guards the opening
   of the ileum into the large intestine, permitting material to pass
   from the former into the latter but not in the reverse direction.

2. *transverse*—passes horizonally across the abdomen, below the
   liver and stomach and above the small intestine.

3. *descending*—lies in the vertical position, on the left side of the abdomen, extending from a point below the stomach to the level of the iliac crest.
4. *sigmoid*—the downward course of the large intestine below the iliac crest; describes an S-shaped curve; the lower part of the curve, which joins the rectum, bends toward the left, the anatomical reason for placing a patient on the left side when giving an enema; in this position gravity aids the flow of the water from the rectum into the sigmoid flexure.

Rectum. The last seven or eight inches of the intestinal tube is called the rectum. The terminal inch of the rectum is called the *anal canal;* its mucous lining is arranged in numerous vertical folds known as *rectal columns,* each of which contains an artery and a vein. *Hemorrhoids* (or piles) are enlargements of the veins in the anal canal. The opening of the canal to the exterior is guarded by two sphincter muscles—an internal one of smooth muscle and an external one of striated muscle; the opening itself is called the *anus.* The general direction of the rectum is up, in, and back.

Coats

See Table 44 for information on the coats of the large intestine.

Functions

The main functions of the large intestine are absorption of water and elimination of the wastes of digestion.

Liver

Location and size

The liver is the largest gland in the body. It weighs between 3 and 4 pounds, lies immediately under the diaphragm, and occupies most of the right hypochondrium and part of the epigastrium.

Lobes

The falciform ligament divides the liver into two main lobes, right and left, with the right lobe having three parts designated as the right lobe proper, the caudate lobe (a small four-sided area on the posterior surface), and the quadrate lobe (an approximately oblong section on the undersurface). Each lobe is divided into numerous lobules by small blood vessels and by fibrous strands which form a supporting framework (the capsule of Glisson) for them. The capsule of Glisson is an extension of the heavy connective tissue capsule that envelops the entire liver. The hepatic lobules, the anatomical units of the liver, are tiny hexagonal or pentagonal cylinders about 2 millimeters high and 1 millimeter in diameter. A small branch of the hepatic vein extends through the center of each lobule. Around this central (intralobular) vein, in columns radiating outward, are arranged the hepatic cells. Three separate sets of tiny tubes—branches of the hepatic artery, of the portal vein (interlobular veins), and of the hepatic duct (interlobular bile ducts)—are arranged around each lobule. From these, irregular branches (sinusoids) of the interlobular veins extend between the radiating columns of hepatic cells to join the central vein. Branches of the interlobular bile ducts also run between each two rows of hepatic cells.

Ducts

The small bile ducts within the liver join to form two larger ducts which emerge from the undersurface of the organ as the right and left hepatic ducts but which immediately join to form one *hepatic duct*. The hepatic duct merges with the *cystic duct* from the gallbladder, forming the *common bile duct* (Fig. 233) which opens into the duodenum in a small raised area, called the *papilla* of *Vater*, or duodenal papilla. This papilla is located 3 to 4 inches below the pyloric opening from the stomach.

Functions

The liver is one of the most vital organs of the body. Although its cells are merely microscopic dots in size, they do so many things at once as to seem incredible—or perhaps miraculous would be a better word. Because of the diversity of its activities, a single liver cell might be likened to a *factory* (it makes many chemical compounds), a *warehouse* (it stores such valuables as glycogen, iron, and certain vitamins), a *waste disposal plant* (it excretes bile pigments, urea, and various detoxication products), and a *power plant* (its catabolism produces considerable heat).

Here, in brief are the liver's main functions:

1. It secretes about a pint of bile a day. Bile contains bile salts which facilitate fat digestion and absorption and various waste products.

2. The liver plays an essential role in the metabolism of all three kinds of foods.

    (a) For its special part in carbohydrate metabolism, the liver carries on three processes: glycogenesis, glycogenolysis, and gluconeogenesis (p. 437). Briefly, by these processes, the liver tends to maintain homeostasis of blood sugar—helped, as we shall see, by various other processes.

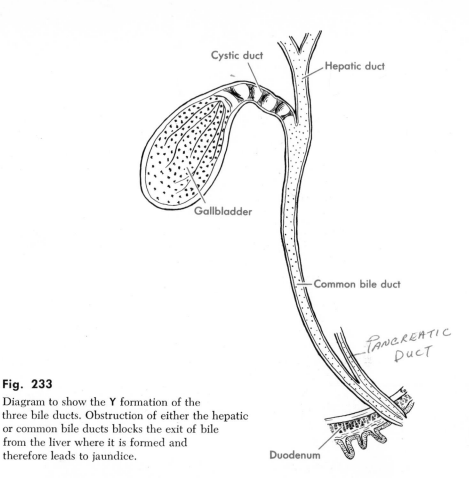

Fig. 233

Diagram to show the **Y** formation of the
three bile ducts. Obstruction of either the hepatic
or common bile ducts blocks the exit of bile
from the liver where it is formed and
therefore leads to jaundice.

(b) Liver cells, more than any others, carry out the first step in both
protein and fat catabolism.

(c) Liver cells perform an essential part of protein anabolism by
synthesizing various blood proteins such as prothrombin and fibrinogen, albumins, and many globulins. This function alone
stamps the liver as one of the highly essential workers for bodily
welfare and survival. Consider these three vital functions of the
blood proteins synthesized by the liver: (1) prothrombin and
fibrinogen are, as you already know, essential for blood clotting,
(2) all blood proteins contribute to blood osmotic pressure and
therefore are important for maintaining water balance, and (3)
all blood proteins contribute to blood viscosity and therefore
are essential for normal circulation.

Gallbladder

Size, shape, and location

The gallbladder is a pear-shaped sac from 3 to 4 inches long and an
inch or more wide. It lies on the undersurface of the liver and is attached to this organ by areolar tissue.

419

Structure

Smooth muscle composes the walls of the gallbladder. The mucosal lining is arranged in rugae, similar in structure and function to those of the stomach.

Functions

The gallbladder concentrates and stores the bile which enters it by way of the hepatic and cystic ducts. Then later, when digestion is going on in the stomach and intestines, the gallbladder contracts, ejecting the concentrated bile into the duodenum.

Correlations

Inflammation of the lining of the gallbladder is called *cholecystitis*. The operation which removes the gallbladder is a cholecystectomy. *Jaundice*, a yellow discoloration of the skin and mucosa, results whenever obstruction of the hepatic or common bile ducts occurs. Bile is thereby denied its normal exit through the intestinal contents and is absorbed into the blood instead, causing the yellow skin coloring. The stool of such patients is clay colored due to the absence of normal bile pigments.

Pancreas

Size, shape, and location

The pancreas is roughly fish-shaped. It lies behind the stomach, with its head and neck in the C-shaped curve of the duodenum, its body extending horizontally across the posterior abdominal wall, and its tail touching the spleen. According to an old anatomical witticism, the "romance of the abdomen" is the pancreas lying "in the arms of the duodenum."

This gland varies in size according to sex and individuals, being larger in men than in women. Usually it has a length of from 6 to 9 inches, a width of from 1 to 1½ inches, and a thickness of from ½ to 1 inch. It weighs about 3 ounces.

Structure

The pancreas is classified as a compound tubuloacinar gland. The word compound tells us that the gland has a duct and that the duct has branches. The term tubuloacinar, on the other hand, tells us that some of the secreting units of the pancreas resemble tiny tubes and some tiny grapes in shape. Secreting cells constitute the walls of these tubular and acinar units. These are exocrine glands since they release their secretion into the microscopic duct within each unit. These tiny

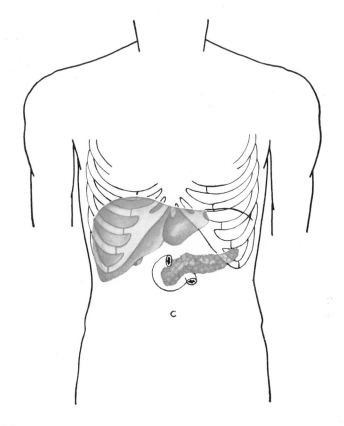

Fig. 234

Normal position of the liver and pancreas. (From Francis and Farrell: Integrated anatomy and physiology, St. Louis, The C. V. Mosby Co.)

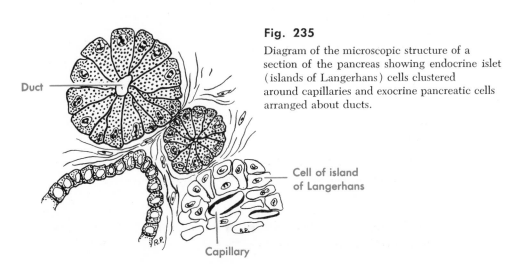

Fig. 235

Diagram of the microscopic structure of a section of the pancreas showing endocrine islet (islands of Langerhans) cells clustered around capillaries and exocrine pancreatic cells arranged about ducts.

Duct

Cell of island of Langerhans

Capillary

ducts unite to form larger ducts which eventually join the main pancreatic duct, the *duct of Wirsung*, which extends throughout the length of the gland from its tail to its head. It empties into the duodenum at the same point as the common bile duct, that is, at the duodenal papilla. (An accessory duct, the *duct of Santorini*, is frequently found extending from the head of the pancreas into the duodenum, about an inch above the duodenal papilla.)

In between the tubuloacinar units of the pancreas, like so many little islands isolated from one another and from the ducts of the pancreas, lie clusters of cells called *islets* or *islands of Langerhans*. Special staining techniques have revealed that three kinds of cells—alpha, beta, and delta—composed the islands of Langerhans. They are secreting cells, but their secretion passes into blood capillaries rather than into ducts. Thus the pancreas is a dual gland—an exocrine or duct gland because of the tubuloacinar units and an endocrine or ductless gland because of the islands of Langerhans.

Functions

1. The tubuloacinar units of the pancreas secrete the enzymes found in pancreatic juice; hence the pancreas plays an important part in the function of digestion (p. 428).

2. Beta cells of the pancreas secrete *insulin*, a hormone of major importance in carbohydrate metabolism (p. 437).

3. Alpha cells, as indicated by considerable evidence, secrete *glucagon*, another hormone involved in carbohydrate metabolism (p. 438).

Vermiform appendix

Size, shape, and location

The appendix is a blind tube branching from the lower portion of the cecum (Fig. 231). As its name suggests, it resembles a large angle worm in size and shape, although its size varies greatly in different individuals.

Structure

The structure of the appendix is similar to that of the rest of the intestine. Its mucous lining frequently becomes inflamed, a condition well known as *appendicitis*.

DIGESTION

Definition

Digestion is the sum of all the changes food undergoes in the alimentary canal.

Purpose

The purpose of digestion as suggested in the dictionary definition is "the conversion of food into assimilable matter." Digestion is necessary because foods, as eaten, are too complex in physical and chemical composition to pass through the intestinal mucosa into the blood or for cells to utilize them for energy and tissue building. In other words, digestion is the necessary preliminary to both absorption and metabolism of foods.

Kinds of digestion

Since both the physical and chemical composition of ingested food makes its absorption impossible, two kinds of digestive changes are necessary, *mechanical and chemical*.

Mechanical digestion. Mechanical digestion consists of all those movements of the alimentary tract which bring about the following:

1. Change the physical state of ingested food from comparatively large, solid pieces into minute dissolved particles, thereby facilitating chemical digestion.
2. Propel the food forward along the alimentary tract, finally eliminating the digestive wastes from the body.
3. Churn the intestinal contents in such a way that it becomes well mixed with the digestive juices and that all parts of it come in contact with the surface of the intestinal mucosa, thereby facilitating absorption.

A list of definitions of the different processes involved in mechanical digestion, together with the organs which accomplish them, are given in Table 47. Swallowing, the movement of food out of the stomach, and defecation are considered in more detail below.

Swallowing consists of three steps: movement of the food through the mouth into the pharynx, through the pharynx into the esophagus, and through the esophagus into the stomach. The first act only is voluntary, that is, can be controlled by the will. The other two actions are reflexes which occur automatically after food enters the pharynx. Stimulation of the mucosa of the back of the mouth, pharynx, or laryngeal region initiates the second step by producing contractions of the muscular pharyngeal walls. Consequently paralysis of the sensory nerves to the mucosa of the back of the mouth, pharynx, or laryngeal region by a drug such as Novocain makes swallowing impossible. Since the pharynx serves both the digestive and respiratory systems, it has connections with the parts of the digestive tract above and below it (mouth and esophagus) and with the parts of the respiratory tract above and below (nasal cavity and larynx). When food enters the pharynx and its walls contract, theoretically its contents could be squeezed in any of these four directions, that is, back up into the nose

423

Table 47. Processes in mechanics of digestion

Organ	Mechanical process	Nature of process
Mouth (teeth and tongue)	Mastication	Chewing movements—reduce size of food particles and mix them with saliva
	Deglutition	Swallowing—movement of food from mouth to stomach
Pharynx	Deglutition	
Esophagus	Deglutition Peristalsis	Wormlike movements which squeeze food downward in tract; constricted ring forms first in one section, then next, and so on, causing waves of contraction to spread throughout canal
Stomach	Churning	Forward and backward movement of gastric contents; peristalsis propels it forward; closed pyloric sphincter deflects it backward
	Peristalsis	Moves material through stomach and at intervals into duodenum
Small intestine	Churning (rhythmic segmentation) Peristalsis	A forward and backward movement within segment of intestine; purpose is to mix food and digestive juices thoroughly and to bring all digested food in contact with intestinal mucosa to facilitate absorption; purpose of peristalsis, on the other hand, is to propel intestinal contents along digestive tract
Large intestine Colon	Haustral churning Peristalsis	Churning movements within haustral sacs
Descending colon	Mass peristalsis	Entire contents moved into sigmoid colon and rectum; usually occurs after a meal
Rectum	Defecation	Emptying of rectum, so-called bowel movement

or mouth or downward into the larynx or esophagus. That it takes only one of these routes (into the esophagus) is due to the fact that the openings into the other organs become blocked off during swallowing. Elevation of the tongue (so that it presses against the roof of the mouth) bars entry into the mouth, elevation of the soft palate obstructs the passageway into the nose, and elevation of the larynx closes over the opening into this organ. As the larynx moves upward, the base of the tongue pushes the epiglottis downward over the laryngeal opening like a lid. Because solids or liquids entering the larynx and lower respiratory tract may bring on fatal consequences (either from asphyxiation or infection), an additional mechanism is provided to prevent such an occurrence. Stimulation of the mucosa of the back of the mouth, pharynx, and laryngeal region produces not only the second phase of the swallowing act but also momentary inhibition of respirations. Obviously prevention of inspiration during swallowing greatly lessens the danger of foods entering the respiratory tract.

Stimulation of the esophageal mucosa by material entering it from the pharynx initiates the reflex of esophageal peristalsis. Liquids and well-chewed foods are precipitated down the esophagus to the cardiac sphincter by the force of pharyngeal contraction and by gravity. They are then moved through the sphincter into the stomach by means of esophageal peristalsis. The latter is responsible for propelling large solid particles throughout the length of the esophagus.

Emptying of the stomach after a meal requires a considerable period of time (about 1 to 4 hours for the average meal). Many theories have been proposed about the mechanism regulating gastric emptying. It is now known that as small amounts of gastric contents become liquefied they are ejected bit by bit every 20 seconds or so into the duodenum until a certain amount has accumulated there. From then on the emptying process slows down due to operation of a mechanism known as the *enterogastric reflex*. Both nerve impulses and a hormone initiate this reflex. Fats and sugars present in the small intestine, for example, stimulate the intestinal mucosa to release a hormone (called enterogastrone) into the blood stream. When it circulates to the stomach wall, it has an inhibitory effect on gastric muscle, decreasing its peristalsis (the enterogastric reflex) and thereby slowing down stomach emptying. Proteins and acid, on the other hand, initiate the enterogastric reflex by stimulating vagal nerve receptors in the intestinal mucosa.

Defecation is a reflex brought about by stimulation of receptors in the rectal mucosa. Recent distension of the rectum constitutes the usual stimulus. Normally the rectum is empty until mass peristalsis moves fecal matter out of the colon into the rectum. This produces the desire to defecate, increases colonic peristalsis, and initiates reflex relaxation of the internal sphincter of the anus. Voluntary straining efforts and relaxation of the external anal sphincter may then follow as a result of the desire to defecate. And together these several responses bring about defecation. Note that this is a reflex partly under voluntary control. If it is voluntarily inhibited, rectal receptors soon become depressed and the urge to defecate is usually not re-experienced until about twenty-four hours later, when mass peristalsis again takes place. During the interim water is absorbed from the fecal mass, producing a hardened or constipated stool.

Chemical digestion. Chemical digestion consists of all the changes in chemical composition which foods undergo in their travel through the alimentary canal. These changes result from the hydrolysis of foods (*hydrolysis* is a chemical process in which a compound unites with water and then splits into simpler compounds). Numerous enzymes* present in the various digestive juices catalyze the hydrolysis of foods.

Although six kinds of chemical substances are eaten (carbohydrates,

---

*As previously noted, in order for body activities to be integrated or unified so as to achieve their over-all function of survival, control of the body's numerous activities is imperative. Two general types of mechanisms—chemical and nervous—constitute the control mechanisms. Chemical mechanisms involve four kinds of substances: enzymes, vitamins, hormones, and miscellaneous substances (for example, carbon dioxide).

Definition: The term enzyme means literally "in yeast"; it was derived from the fact that these substances were first discovered in yeast cells. Enzymes are usually defined simply as "organic catalysts"; that is, they are organic compounds, and they accelerate chemical reactions without appearing in the final products of the reaction. Enzymes are vital substances. Without them the chemical reactions necessary for life could not take place. So important are they that someone has even defined life as the "orderly functioning of hundreds of enzymes."

Chemical structure: Enzymes are proteins. Frequently their molecules also contain a nonprotein part called the *prosthetic group* of the enzyme molecule (if this group readily detaches from the rest of the molecule, it is spoken of as the *coenzyme*). Some prosthetic groups contain inorganic ions (Ca^{++}, Mg^{++}, Mn^{++}, etc.). Many of them contain vitamins. In fact, every vitamin of known function constitutes part of a prosthetic group of some enzyme. Nicotinic acid, thiamine, riboflavin, and other B complex vitamins, for example, function in this way.

Classification and naming: Two of the systems used for naming enzymes are as follows: the suffix *ase* is used either with the root name of the substance whose chemical reaction is catalyzed (the substrate chemical, that is) or with the word which describes the kind of chemical reaction catalyzed. Thus, according to the first method, sucrase is an enzyme which catalyzes a chemical reaction in which sucrose takes part; according to the second method, sucrase might also be called hydrolase because it hydrolyzes sucrose. Enzymes investigated before these methods of nomenclature were adopted still are called by older names, such as ptyalin, pepsin, trypsin, etc.

Classified according to the kind of chemical reactions catalyzed, enzymes fall into several groups:

1. *oxidation-reduction enzymes*—known as oxidases, hydrogenases, and dehydrogenases; energy release for muscular contraction and all physiological work depends upon these enzymes
2. *hydrolyzing enzymes* or hydrolases—digestive enzymes belong to this group; these are generally named after the substrate acted upon—for example, lipase, sucrase, maltase, etc.

Continued on next page.

proteins, fats, vitamins, mineral salts, and water); only the first three named have to be chemically digested in order to be absorbed.

In order for enzymes to perform their digestive functions, the reaction of the digestive juice which contains them must be controlled. Saliva, for example, is normally neutral or slightly acid in reaction. Its main enzyme, ptyalin, is gradually inactivated by marked acidity such as occurs in gastric juice. In contrast, pepsin, an enzyme in gastric juice is inactive unless sufficient hydrochloric acid is present; therefore,

---

3. *phosphorylating enzymes*—these add or remove phosphate groups; known as phosphorylases or phosphatases
4. *enzymes which add or remove carbon dioxide*—known as carboxylases or decarboxylases
5. *enzymes which rearrange atoms within a molecule*—known as mutases or isomerases
6. *hydrases*—enzymes which add water to a molecule without splitting it, as hydrolases do

Enzymes are also classified as intracellular or extracellular, depending upon whether they act within cells or outside of them in the surrounding medium. Most enzymes act intracellularly in the body, an important exception being the digestive enzymes.

Properties: In general, the same as protein properties, since enzymes are proteins. For example, they form colloidal solutes in water and are precipitated or coagulated by various agents, such as high temperatures and salts of heavy metals. Hence these agents inactivate enzymes. Other important enzyme properties are as follows.

1. Most enzymes are *specific in their action*, that is, act only on a specific substrate. This is attributed to a "key-in-a-lock" kind of action, the configuration of the enzyme molecule fitting the configuration of some part of the substrate molecule.

2. Enzymes *function optimally at a specific pH* and become inactive if this deviates beyond narrow limits.

3. A *variety of physical and chemical agents inactivate or inhibit enzyme action:* for example, x-rays and radium rays (this presumably accounts for some of the ill effects of excessive radiation), certain antibiotic drugs, unfavorable pH, etc.

4. *Most enzymes catalyze a chemical reaction in both directions,* the direction and rate of the reaction being governed by the law of mass action. An accumulation of a product slows the reaction and tends to reverse it. A practical application of this fact is the slowing of digestion when absorption is interferred with and the products of digestion accumulate.

5. *Enzymes are continually being destroyed in the body,* therefore have to be continually synthesized, even though they are not used up in the reactions they catalyze.

6. *Many enzymes are synthesized in an inactive form* which must be activated by some other substance before the enzyme can function. The kinases are such enzyme activators. Thrombokinase (thromboplastin), for example, converts inactive prothrombin into active thrombin; enterokinase changes inactive trypsinogen into active trypsin, etc.

427

Table 48. Chemical digestion

Digestive juices and enzymes	Food enzyme digests (or hydrolyzes)	Resulting product
Saliva Ptyalin	Starch (a polysaccharide or complex sugar)	Maltose (a disaccharide or double sugar)
Gastric juice Pepsin, plus hydrochloric acid Lipase (of little importance)	Proteins, including casein Emulsified fats (butter, cream, etc.)	Proteoses and peptones (partially digested proteins) *Fatty acids and glycerol**
Bile contains no enzymes	Large fat droplets (unemulsified fats)	Small fat droplets or emulsified fats
Pancreatic juice Protease (trypsin)† Lipase (steapsin) Amylase (amylopsin)	Proteins (either intact or partially digested) Bile-emulsified fats Starch	Proteoses, peptides, and *amino acids* *Fatty acids and glycerol* Maltose
Intestinal juice (succus entericus) Peptidases ~~EPYPSIN~~ Sucrase Lactase Maltase	Peptides Sucrose (cane sugar) Lactose (milk sugar) Maltose (malt sugar)	*Amino acids* *Glucose and fructose*‡ (simple sugars or monosaccharides) *Glucose and galactose* (simple sugars) *Glucose* (grape sugar)

*Substances in italics are end products of digestion or, in other words, completely digested foods ready for absorption.
†Secreted in inactive form (trypsinogen); activated by enterokinase, an enzyme in the intestinal juice.
‡Glucose is also called dextrose; fructose is called levulose.

in diseases characterized by gastric hypoacidity (pernicious anemia, for example) hydrochloric acid is given orally before meals.

Carbohydrate digestion. Carbohydrates are saccharide compounds. This means that their molecules contain one or more saccharide groups ($C_6H_{10}O_5$). Polysaccharides, notably starches, contain many of these groups, disaccharides (sucrose, lactose, and maltose) contain two of them, and monosaccharides (glucose, fructose, and galactose) contain only one. Polysaccharides are hydrolyzed to disaccharides by enzymes known as *amylases* found in saliva and pancreatic juice (salivary amylase was formerly called ptyalin and pancreatic amylase was known as amylopsin). Disaccharides are hydrolyzed to monosaccharides by the intestinal juice enzymes sucrase, lactase, and maltase.

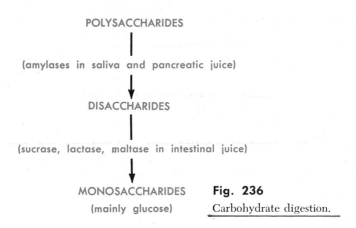

POLYSACCHARIDES

(amylases in saliva and pancreatic juice)

DISACCHARIDES

(sucrase, lactase, maltase in intestinal juice)

MONOSACCHARIDES **Fig. 236**
(mainly glucose)   Carbohydrate digestion.

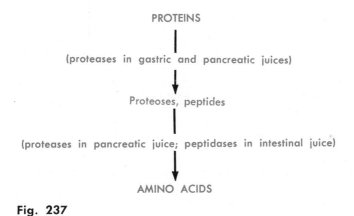

PROTEINS

(proteases in gastric and pancreatic juices)

Proteoses, peptides

(proteases in pancreatic juice; peptidases in intestinal juice)

AMINO ACIDS

Fig. 237
Protein digestion.

FATS (triglycerides)

(lipase in pancreatic juice)

FATTY ACIDS and GLYCEROL

Fig. 238
Fat digestion by lipase; facilitated first by emulsion by bile.

429

Protein digestion. Protein compounds have very large molecules made up of amino acids. Enzymes called *proteases* catalyze the hydrolysis of proteins into intermediate compounds, for example, proteoses and peptides, and finally into amino acids. The main proteases are pepsin in gastric juice, trypsin in pancreatic juice, and peptidases in intestinal juice.

Fat digestion. Because fats are insoluble in water, they must be emulsified, that is, dispersed as very small droplets before they can be digested. Bile emulsifies fats in the small intestine. This facilitates fat digestion by providing a greater contact area between fat molecules and pancreatic lipase, the main fat-digesting enzyme (pancreatic lipase was formerly known as steapsin). For a summary of the actions of each digestive juice, see Table 48.

Residues of digestion. Certain components of food resist digestion and are eliminated from the intestines in the feces. These *residues of digestion* are cellulose from carbohydrates, undigested connective tissue and toxins from meat proteins, and undigested fats. In addition to these wastes, feces consists of bacteria, pigments, water, and mucus.

Control of digestive gland secretion

Digestive glands secrete when food is present in the alimentary tract or when it is seen, smelled, or imagined. Complicated reflex and chemical (hormonal) mechanisms control the flow of digestive juices in such a way that they appear in proper amounts when and for as long as needed.

Saliva. As far as is known, only reflex mechanisms control the secretion of saliva. Chemical, mechanical, olfactory, and visual stimuli initiate afferent impulses to centers in the brain stem which send out efferent impulses to salivary glands, stimulating them. Chemical and mechanical stimuli come from the presence of food in the mouth, and olfactory and visual stimuli come from the smell and sight of food.

Gastric secretion. Stimulation of gastric juice secretion occurs in three phases controlled by reflex and chemical mechanisms. Because stimuli which activate these mechanisms arise in the head, stomach, and intestines, the three phases are known as the cephalic, gastric, and intestinal phases, respectively.

The *cephalic phase* is also spoken of as the reflex phase and as the psychic phase because a reflex mechanism controls gastric juice secretion at this time and psychic factors activate the mechanism. For example, the sight or smell or taste of food that is pleasing to an individual stimulates various head receptors and thereby initiates reflex stimulation of the gastric glands. Parasympathetic fibers in branches of the vagus nerve conduct the stimulating efferent impulses to the glands.

Table 49.   Actions of some digestive hormones summarized

Hormone	Source	Action
Gastrin	Formed by gastric mucosa in presence of partially digested proteins	Stimulates gastric secretion
Secretin	Formed by action of hydrochloric acid on prosecretin (chemical normally present in intestinal mucosa)	Stimulates pancreatic secretion Stimulates secretion of bile by liver May stimulate secretion of intestinal juice
Cholecystokinin	Formed by intestinal mucosa in presence of fats	Stimulates ejection of bile from gallbladder

During the *gastric phase* of gastric juice secretion, the following chemical control mechanism dominates. Substances (such as meat extractives and products of protein digestion) in foods that have reached the pyloric portion of the stomach stimulate its mucosa to release a hormone called *gastrin* into the blood in stomach capillaries. When it circulates to the gastric glands, it greatly accelerates their secretion of gastric juice which has a high pepsin and hydrochloric acid content (see Table 49). Hence, this seems to be a device for ensuring that when food is in the stomach there will be enough enzymes there to digest it.

The *intestinal phase* of gastric juice secretion is less clearly understood than the other two. A chemical control mechanism, however, is believed to operate. And it is known, too, that the hormone *enterogastrone* (released by intestinal mucosa when fat is in the intestine) causes a lessening of both gastric secretion and motility.

Pancreatic secretion. Chemical control of pancreatic secretion has been established, and reflex control is postulated. Chemical control ensures continued pancreatic secretion while food is in the duodenum. The presence in the small intestine of hydrochloric acid, protein and fat digestion products, and other substances causes the intestinal mucosa to release a hormone, *secretin,* into the blood which when circulated to the pancreas causes it to increase the volume of its secretion. Secretin was the first hormone discovered, a fact of historical significance since it initiated the broad concept of hormonal control of body activities. Another hormone, *pancreozymin,* has also been shown to be released by the intestinal mucosa in response to the presence in the intestine of hydrochloric acid and other substances. Pancreozymin increases the concentration of enzymes in the pancreatic juice.

Secretion of bile. Chemical mechanisms dominate the control of bile. Secretin, the same hormone that stimulates pancreatic activity, stimulates the liver to secrete bile. The ejection of bile, however, from the gallbladder into the duodenum is largely controlled by another hormone, *cholecystokinin,* which is formed by the intestinal mucosa when fats are present in the duodenum.

Intestinal secretion. Knowledge concerning the regulation of the secretion of *intestinal juice* is still somewhat obscure. It is thought that the intestinal mucosa, stimulated by hydrochloric acid and food products, releases into the blood a hormone, *enterocrinin,* which brings about increased intestinal juice secretion. Presumably neural mechanisms also help control the secretion of this digestive juice.

ABSORPTION

Definition

The passage of substances (notably digested foods, water, salts, and vitamins) through the intestinal mucosa into the blood or lymph.

How accomplished

Absorption is not entirely a passive process explainable on the basis of the physical laws of diffusion, filtration, and osmosis alone. Investigation has shown that these phenomena play a part in absorption but that they are aided by an active transport mechanism. These are not clearly understood processes carried on by epithelial cells of the intestinal mucosa. They move substances in the opposite direction from that expected according to the laws of osmosis and diffusion.

The mechanism postulated for glucose absorption (Fig. 239, C) consists of these steps:

1. Glucose moves into cells of the intestinal mucosa presumably by means of an active transport mechanism.

2. Inside the mucosal cells phosphorylation of the glucose molecule occurs immediately, presumably by the following reaction:

$$\text{Glucose} + \text{ATP} \xrightarrow{\text{(Glucokinase)}} \text{Glucose-6-phosphate} + \text{ADP}$$

3. Glucose-6-phosphate diffuses across the mucosal cell, and near its surface adjacent to a blood capillary, the preceding equation is reversed, but by another enzyme, phosphatase. Glucose then moves out of the cell into the blood.

That an active transport mechanism operates for the absorption of amino acids is a conclusion supported by considerable evidence. But a definite description of the mechanism is still lacking. And the mechanism for fat absorption is also not clear although it too is thought to involve some kind of active transport. It is known, however, that some fatty acids and glycerol enter intestinal mucosal cells and there recombine to form neutral fats which then move out of the cells into

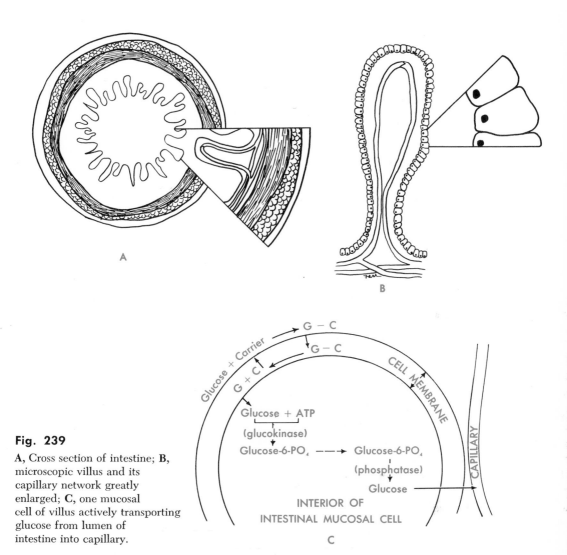

Fig. 239

A, Cross section of intestine; B, microscopic villus and its capillary network greatly enlarged; C, one mucosal cell of villus actively transporting glucose from lumen of intestine into capillary.

Glucose + Carrier

G + C

G – C

G – C

CELL MEMBRANE

CAPILLARY

Glucose + ATP
(glucokinase)

Glucose-6-PO₄ ---→ Glucose-6-PO₄

(phosphatase)

Glucose

INTERIOR OF
INTESTINAL MUCOSAL CELL

C

lymphatic capillaries (lacteals) in the intestinal villi. In addition, some fatty acids are absorbed as such into blood capillaries, and some neutral fats are absorbed without first being hydrolyzed to fatty acids and glycerol.

Active transport mechanisms seem to be available also for water and salt absorption. And apparently some sort of mechanism exists for preventing absorption of certain substances. Magnesium sulfate (Epsom salts), for example, is not absorbed from the intestine even though its molecules are smaller than glucose molecules which can diffuse through the intestinal mucosa. In fact, it is this nonabsorbability of magnesium sulfate that makes it an effective cathartic. (Since magnesium sulfates do not diffuse freely through the intestinal mucosa, do you think their presence in intestinal fluid would create an osmotic

Table 50. Food absorption

Form absorbed	Structures into which absorbed	Circulation
Protein—as amino acids Perhaps minute quantities of some whole proteins are absorbed—in allergic reactions, for example	Blood in intestinal capillaries	Portal vein, liver, hepatic vein, inferior vena cava to heart, etc.
Carbohydrates—as simple sugars	Same as amino acids	Same as amino acids

Fats
  Glycerol
 	
  Fatty acids combine with bile salts to form water-soluble substance
  Some finely emulsified undigested fats are absorbed
	Lymph in intestinal lacteals
	Lymph in intestinal lacteals
	Small fraction enters intestinal blood capillaries
		During absorption, that is, while in epithelial cells of intestinal mucosa, glycerol and fatty acids recombine to form microscopic particles of fats (chylomicrons); lymphatics carry them by way of thoracic duct to left subclavian vein, superior vena cava, heart, etc.
		Some fats transported by blood in form of phospholipids or cholesterol esters

pressure gradient between the intestinal fluid and blood? If so, what effect would this have on water movement between these two fluids? Reread pp. 39 to 40 if you need help in answering these questions.)

Note that after absorption food does not pass directly into the general circulation. Instead it is first carried via the portal system to the liver. During intestinal absorption, blood entering the liver via the portal vein contains greater concentrations of glucose, amino acids, and fats than does blood leaving the liver via the hepatic vein for the systemic circulation. Clearly the excess of these food substances, over and above the normal blood levels, has remained behind in the liver.

What the liver does with them is part of the story of metabolism, our next topic for discussion.

METABOLISM
Meaning

The history of foods in the body resolves itself into three major periods. Listed in the order of occurrence, they are as follows:

1. *period of digestion*—which occurs in the alimentary canal.
2. *period of absorption*—which takes place through the intestinal mucosa into the blood and lymph.

3. *period of metabolism*—which occurs after absorption and according to the broadest interpretation of the word consists of (a) circulation of digested, absorbed foods, (b) chemical changes in the foods, brought about by the cells of the body, and (c) elimination of waste products formed during the chemical changes in the foods.

Metabolism might be defined, then, as all the changes that occur in foods after they are digested and absorbed, that is, their circulation, the changes in their chemical composition, and their elimination from the body. Usually, however, the term metabolism is used to mean the chemical changes absorbed foods undergo within the body cells, or more simply, metabolism is the body's utilization of foods. Digestion and absorption are merely preliminary steps or preparations for this third food process, metabolism.

Ways in which foods metabolized

Foods consist of six kinds of chemical compounds: carbohydrates, proteins, fats, vitamins, inorganic salts (or minerals), and water. The body utilizes or metabolizes these substances in two general ways—catabolizes them to make their stored energy available for cellular work and anabolizes them to build protoplasm, enzymes, hormones, and other complex compounds.

Only recently has research been able to unlock some of the secrets of anabolism. Brilliant work by many investigators has disclosed some of the actual events that take place inside cells as they build the small, simple molecules of foods up into the large, complex molecules of enzymes and hosts of other compounds. A full description of this does not seem appropriate in a book of this kind. But if you enjoy reading exciting though not easy material, by all means read the articles named in the footnote.* And for a brief description of anabolism, see p. 448 of this chapter. Anabolism is one of the most important kinds of work that cells do. Such vital functions as cell growth and repair and reproduction, for example, are achieved through the process of anabolism.

The relationship between anabolism and catabolism is worth noting. Anabolism depends upon catabolism. Catabolism must occur in order that anabolism may occur. Why? Because catabolism provides the energy for the work of anabolism. Energy is stored in ATP molecules during catabolism and is released from them during anabolism.

---

*Allfrey, V. G., and Mirsky, A. E.: How cells make molecules, Scient. Am. **205**:74, 1961, and Hurwitz, J., and Furth, J. J.: Messenger RNA, Scient. Am. **206**:41, 1962.

Carbohydrate metabolism

Carbohydrate catabolism was described in some detail on pp. 43 to 48. Reread these pages carefully if you are not sure of the answers to the following questions:

What over-all *chemical* change occurs in glycolysis? In the citric acid cycle?

What *energy* change occurs in glycolysis? In the citric acid cycle?

Where do glycolysis and the citric acid cycle occur?

All body cells catabolize carbohydrates. This process, as we have seen, provides cells with energy for doing their work—the work which

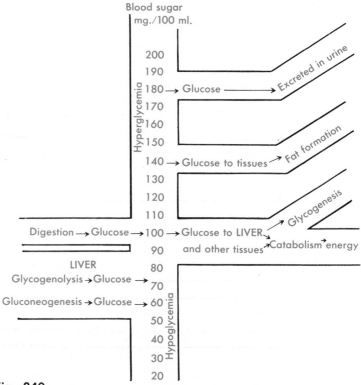

Fig. 240

When blood glucose starts to decrease toward lower normal, liver cells increase the rate at which they convert glycogen, amino acids, and fats to glucose (glycogenolysis and gluconeogenesis) and release it into blood. But when blood glucose increases, liver cells increase the rate at which they remove glucose molecules from blood and convert them to glycogen for storage (glycogenesis). At still higher levels, glucose leaves blood for tissue cells to be anabolized into adipose tissue and at still higher levels is excreted in the urine.

they do for themselves, such as anabolism and active transport of substances through their membranes, and the specialized work which they do for the body as a whole, such as contraction by muscle cells, conduction by nerve cells, secretion by gland cells, etc. In addition, catabolism also produces heat energy. In fact it is the body's only means of producing heat. Carbohydrate catabolism consists basically of two processes, glycolysis and the citric acid cycle, discussed on pp. 43 to 44. In addition, it frequently includes another process called glycogenolysis which we shall discuss in this chapter (p. 438).

Body cells also anabolize carbohydrates, as well as catabolize them. Two types of carbohydrate anabolism are glycogenesis and gluconeogenesis.

We shall now discuss the processes of carbohydrate metabolism not considered earlier, glycogenesis, glycogenolysis, and gluconeogenesis.

Glycogenesis

Glycogenesis as defined by Stedman is "the formation of glycogen from glucose or from monosaccharides such as fructose or galactose."[*] Glycogenesis takes place inside cells when they do not need to catabolize all of the glucose which enters them for energy. Since glycogenesis is an intracellular process, glucose must, of course, move from the extracellular fluid through the cell membrane into the intracellular fluid. That an active transport is involved in moving glucose into cells is known. And it is also known that the hormone insulin accelerates this process and the potassium and phosphate ions are transported into cells simultaneously with glucose—though independently it now seems by another mechanism. But there still remain these unknowns—the exact nature of the glucose transport mechanism and the way in which insulin acts to accelerate it. In short, we know *that* glucose is actively transported into cells but not *how;* we know that insulin accelerates glucose transport but not *how.*

When insulin is administered to a patient whose blood glucose is higher than normal (hyperglycemia), it soon decreases—a clinical fact consistent with the concept that insulin in some way accelerates glucose transport into the cell.

Immediately upon reaching the interior of the cell, (or possibly during transport through the cell membrane), glucose reacts with ATP to produce glucose-6-phosphate. An enzyme, glucokinase, catalyzes this reaction.

Glucose-6-phosphate then undergoes three reactions, each catalyzed

---

*From Stedman's medical dictionary, ed. 20, Philadelphia, 1961, Williams & Wilkins Co.

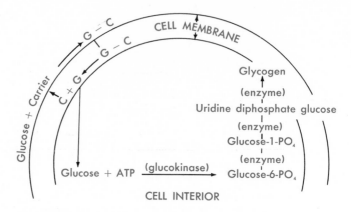

Fig. 241

Glycogenesis.

by a different enzyme, to become glycogen, and the process of glycogenesis is completed (Fig. 241).

Glycogenolysis

Glycogenolysis is "the hydrolysis of glycogen and its conversion into glucose."[*] Thus, the over-all chemical change that occurs in glycogenolysis is the reverse of the over-all chemical change in glycogenesis, but the intermediate chemical reactions are different. An enzyme, phosphorylase, breaks glycogen down to glucose-1-phosphate and another enzyme converts it to glucose-6-phosphate. This much of the process of glycogenolysis is known to take place in muscle and liver cells. But the final step, the formation of glucose from glucose-6-phosphate, occurs in liver cells but not in muscle cells. Liver cells contain the phosphatase enzyme necessary for catalyzing this reaction; muscle cells do not. (Intestinal mucosal cells which absorb glucose from the intestine into the blood also contain this phosphatase; so, too, do kidney tubule cells which absorb glucose from the tubules into blood.) The hormone epinephrine accelerates both liver and muscle glycogenolysis, presumably by activating phosphorylase—one of the reasons blood glucose increases during stress, a time when epinephrine secretion increases. Glucagon, the hormone secreted by alpha cells of the pancreas, is believed to accelerate only liver glycogenolysis.

Gluconeogenesis

Gluconeogenesis is "the formation of glucose or glycogen from substances which are themselves not carbohydrates, such as protein or fat."[*] The process, which occurs in the liver, consists of many complex chemical reactions. Several hormones mainly from the anterior pituitary gland and the adrenal cortex accelerate gluconeogenesis (discussed in paragraph on homeostasis of blood glucose).

---

[*]From Stedman's medical dictionary, ed. 20, Philadelphia, 1961, Williams & Wilkins Co.

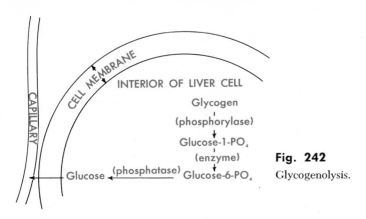

Fig. 242

Glycogenolysis.

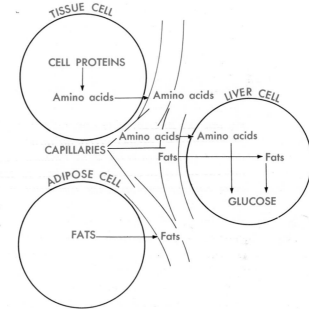

Fig. 243

Liver gluconeogenesis from mobilized tissue proteins and fats.

Blood glucose homeostatic mechanisms

To say that the body maintains homeostasis of blood glucose means that the amount of glucose in the blood normally stays within a narrow range—for example, about 80 to 120 milligrams per 100 milliliters of blood (under fasting conditions, that is, at least 8 hours after eating, using micro-Folin-Wu technique). The main blood glucose homeostatic mechanisms are hormonal devices for controlling the rates of glycogenesis, glycogenolysis, gluconeogenesis, and glucose metabolism by all body cells. We shall call the three control mechanisms to be discussed here the insulin mechanism, the adenohypophyseal-adrenal cortex mechanism, and the sympathetic-adrenal medulla mechanism.

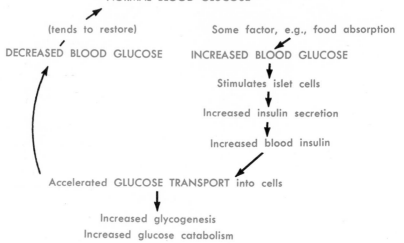

Fig. 244

Insulin mechanism for maintaining homeostasis of blood glucose.

The *insulin mechanism*, as indicated in Fig. 244, is activated by changes in the blood glucose level. Briefly, an increase in blood glucose toward and above the upper normal limits acts as a stimulus to the beta cells of the islands of Langerhans, causing them to accelerate their secretion of insulin. The increased amount of insulin in the blood then acts in some way that is still unknown to speed up glucose transport into cells from the extracellular fluid. As a result, blood glucose tends to decrease back toward normal, whereas cellular utilization of glucose increases. Cells either catalobize the glucose faster for energy, or they anabolize it faster, that is, increase their rate of glycogenesis. This insulin mechanism, as just described, normally operates to maintain homeostasis of blood glucose after meals when glucose is being absorbed into the blood from the digestive tract. It serves to prevent hyperglycemia (abnormally high blood glucose) at such times.

In contrast, when blood glucose decreases, as it does in between the periods of glucose absorption, insulin secretion and glycogenesis also decrease. Glucose transport into cells slows accordingly, and this tends to slow down a further decline in the blood glucose level.

The *adenohypophyseal-adrenal cortex mechanism* for regulating blood glucose is called into play when blood glucose falls toward or below normal—in between meals, for example, after absorption has ceased. Various kinds of physical and emotional stress situations are also postulated to activate this mechanism. It operates in this way. Either a decrease in blood glucose or stress leads to increased secretion of ACTH (adrenocorticotrophic hormone) by the adenohypophysis. ACTH then stimulates the adrenal cortex to speed up its secretion of

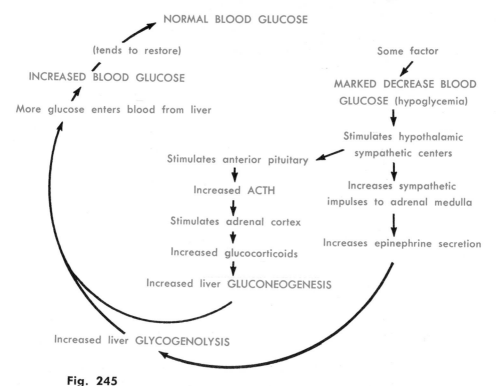

Fig. 245

The adenohypophyseal-adrenal cortex and the sympathetic adrenal medulla mechanisms for restoring homeostasis of blood glucose.

glucocorticoids (hydrocortisone is the main one). And finally, glucocorticoids accelerate gluconeogenesis. Exactly how they do this still remains a question.

The *sympathetic-adrenal medulla mechanism* is activated by a low blood glucose level. This is presumed to excite sympathetic centers in the hypothalamus. Increased epinephrine output by the adrenal medulla quickly follows. Epinephrine, as already mentioned, accelerates liver glycogenolysis and tends thereby to raise the blood glucose content.

The rate of glucose catabolism, that is, of glycolysis, and the citric acid cycle (discussed on pp. 43 to 44) are controlled by the amount of *thyroid hormone* in the blood. An increase in thyroid hormone accelerates glucose catabolism, just as does an increase in insulin. It also may increase gluconeogenesis by accelerating catabolism of tissue proteins. This occurs when inadequate amounts of glucose are available for catabolism to meet the body's energy needs. Hence, when cells are receiving an adequate supply of glucose, an increase in thyroid secretion, for example, tends to decrease blood glucose by speeding up glucose catabolism. But under starvation conditions, an increase in thyroid secretion may tend to increase blood glucose back up toward normal by promoting gluconeogenesis.

In summary, glucose metabolism is regulated mainly by the following hormones:

1. *insulin*—tends to decrease blood glucose.
2. *ACTH, glucocorticoids, and epinephrine*—tend to increase blood glucose.
3. *thyroid hormone*—ordinarily tends to decrease blood glucose.

Also, in summary, three important principles about normal carbohydrate metabolism are these:

1. The *principle of glycogenesis*. During absorption some of the glucose molecules in the portal vein blood (brought directly to the liver from the intestine) enter liver cells for glycogenesis. The resulting glycogen remains stored in liver cells until needed for cellular metabolism. Normally, enough glucose leaves the blood so that no more than about 120 to 140 milligrams of glucose remain in each 100 milliliters of blood leaving the liver by way of the hepatic vein. Muscle cells also store excess glucose as glycogen, as do many other cells to a lesser degree. The total amount of glycogen stored, however, is only enough to supply the body's energy needs for a few hours.

2. The *principle of the "preferred energy fuel."* All body cells catabolize glucose for their needed energy supply when the amount of glucose and the amount of insulin in the blood are adequate. Glucose is the "preferred energy fuel" of human cells—preferred to fat and protein, that is. Therefore, cells get their energy first from glucose —for as long as enough of it continues to enter them—then next from fats and last from proteins.

3. The *principle of glucose storage as fat*. If blood glucose still remains higher than normal after glycogenesis and catabolism and if the blood insulin content is adequate, the excess glucose is converted to fat (mainly by liver cells) and is stored as such in fat depots, in adipose tissue, in other words. Briefly, the process is this. Some of the acetyl coenzyme A formed by glycolysis, instead of being oxidized via the citric acid cycle, is built up into fatty acids which then combine with glycerol to form fats which are stored in the fat depots.

Fat metabolism

Body cells both catabolize and anabolize fats. Fats constitute a more concentrated energy food than carbohydrates. Catabolism of 1 gram of fat yields 9 Calories of heat, catabolism of 1 gram of carbohydrates yields only 4.1 Calories. *Fat catabolism*, like carbohydrate catabolism, consists of two main processes each of which, in turn, consists of a series of chemical reactions. The first process in fat catabolism is called *ketogenesis*, which means the formation of ketone

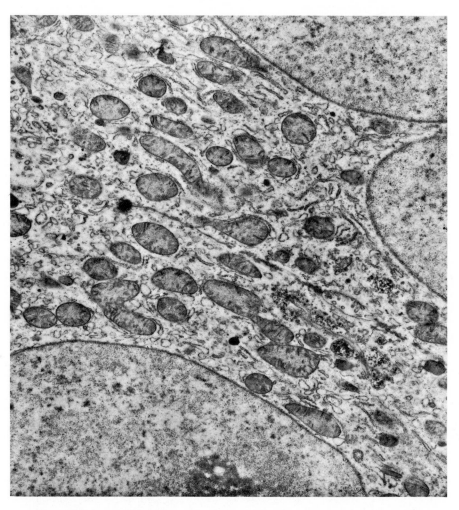

Fig. 246

Electron microphotograph of mouse liver. Numerous mitochondria are visible in the midportion of the photograph. ($\times$25,000.) (Courtesy Western Reserve University Department of Pathology.)

bodies. Liver cells carry on most of the ketogenesis for the body. It consists of the following steps: first, the hydrolysis of fat to form fatty acids and glycerol, next, a series of chemical reactions (known as beta oxidations) by which fatty acids are converted to coenzyme A, and, last, the conversion of acetyl coenzyme A to acetoacetic acid (by a process called condensation). Acetoacetic acid is a ketone body. Some of it undergoes a chemical change to become acetone and beta-hydroxy butyric acid, two other ketone bodies present in extracellular

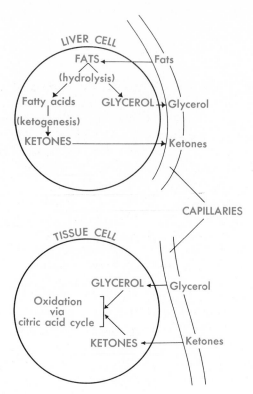

Fig. 247

Fat catabolism consisting of, first, ketogenesis by liver cells and, second, of oxidation by tissue and liver cells.

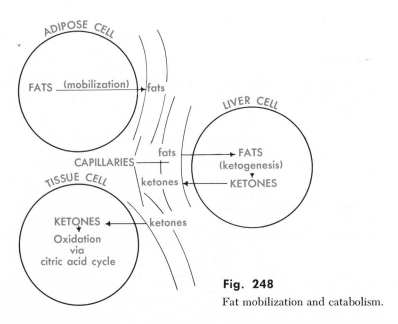

Fig. 248

Fat mobilization and catabolism.

fluid. They are oxidized via the citric acid cycle, the final step of fat catabolism as well as of glucose catabolism. Liver cells oxidize a small portion of the ketone bodies for their own energy needs, but most of them are transported by the blood to other tissue cells for the final step of catabolism. Glycerol is metabolized similarly to glucose.

The release of fats from adipose tissue cells is spoken of as *fat mobilization*. Fat mobilization normally occurs only when too little glucose is entering cells to supply all of their energy needs. This means that it occurs under two circumstances—when blood contains either less glucose than normal (for example, between meals, in the postabsorptive state, and with starvation diets) or when it contains less insulin than normal (diabetes mellitus). Under these conditions, fat mobilization from adipose tissue cells occurs. Liver cells then increase their rate of ketogenesis, and more ketone bodies and glycerol enter tissue cells for catabolism. In fact, ketogenesis may accelerate so much that the cells cannot oxidize the ketone bodies as fast as they are being formed. So they accumulate in the blood and produce a condition called *ketosis.* Frequently then the individual's breath smells of acetone, an easily recognized odor once you have learned to identify it.

Fat anabolism consists of the storage of fats in fat depots and to a lesser degree in liver cells. It also includes the use of fats in the synthesis of protoplasm and various complex compounds. Fats stored in the fat depots constitute the body's largest reserve energy source—too large too often, unfortunately.

Control of fat metabolism

Although a great many factors act simultaneously to control fat metabolism, the following seem most important.

1. The *rate of glucose catabolism* is one of the main regulators of fat metabolism. Because glucose is the cells' preferred energy fuel, carbohydrates have a fat-sparing action. This means that whenever cells

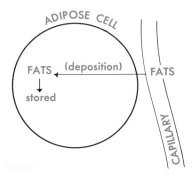

Fig. 249
Fat deposition.

445

are catabolizing glucose fats are being spared; that is, they are not being mobilized out of storage nor are they being catabolized. Instead they are being stored for future use. Adequate glucose catabolism, therefore, tends to increase fat deposition (storage) and to decrease fat mobilization and catabolism.

2. *Insulin helps control fat metabolism* indirectly by its effects on glucose metabolism which, in turn, affects fat metabolism. In general, normal amounts of insulin, together with normal or high amounts of blood glucose, tend to increase fat deposition and to decrease fat mobilization and catabolism. Insulin deficiency, as in diabetes mellitus, produces opposite effects. Fat mobilization and catabolism increase (tending to produce ketosis), and fat deposition decreases. The relation of insulin to fat metabolism is sometimes described by saying that insulin has an antiketogenic effect whereas insulin deficiency has a ketogenic effect. Using the information in this paragraph, can you explain specifically what this means?

3. *Glucocorticoids help control fat metabolism.* Under some conditions, glucocorticoids promote fat deposition—for example, when the blood concentration of glucocorticoids is higher than normal, as in Cushing's syndrome. But paradoxically, glucocorticoids sometimes accelerate fat mobilization instead of deposition. For instance, in starvation when not enough glucose is available for cellular catabolism and in various stress situations, glucocorticoids speed up fat mobilization and increase gluconeogenesis from these mobilized fats. And in diabetes mellitus, also, in which blood glucose is high but cellular glucose is low, glucocorticoids accelerate fat mobilization. But under these circumstances they accelerate liver ketogenesis from the mobilized fats instead of gluconeogenesis. This serves the useful purpose of making ketone bodies available for catabolism when cells need them, that is, when not enough glucose is being transported into cells for them to maintain a high enough rate of catabolism to supply their energy needs.

Protein metabolism

In protein metabolism, anabolism is primary and catabolism is secondary. In carbohydrate and fat metabolism the opposite is true—catabolism is primary and anabolism is secondary. Proteins are primarily tissue-building foods. Carbohydrates and fats are primarily energy-supplying foods. Sometimes protein anabolism results in an increase in the total bulk of the body's protoplasm, as in growth and reproduction. Other times it results merely in the replacement of disintegrating cells, that is, in repair of tissues. Obviously, anabolism of

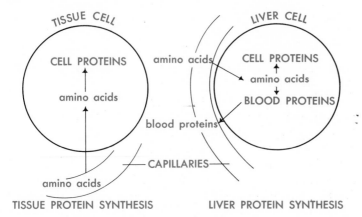

TISSUE PROTEIN SYNTHESIS　　　LIVER PROTEIN SYNTHESIS

Fig. 250

Protein synthesis.

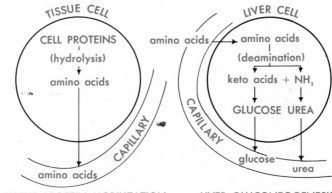

Fig. 251

Protein mobilization.

TISSUE PROTEIN MOBILIZATION　　　LIVER GLUCONEOGENESIS

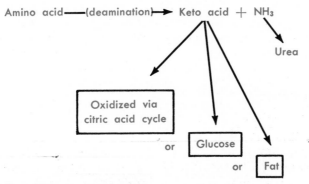

Fig. 252

Protein catabolism. Deamination and glucose and urea formation
occur in liver cells. Oxidation of keto acids takes place in
tissue and liver cells.

proteins for growth is of paramount importance in children, whereas that for repair is more important in adults.

In addition to building tissues from amino acids, the body also utilizes these materials for synthesizing many other protein substances, such as enzymes, hormones, antibodies, and other blood proteins.

According to recent concepts the process of *protein anabolism* occurs in this way. Each gene (a segment of a DNA molecule in a chromosome in a cell nucleus) directs the formation of one specific "transfer RNA" molecule. This molecule diffuses out of the nucleus, attaches to a specific amino acid in the cytoplasm and transfers it to a ribosome ("template RNA" granules; cell's protein factory). Here it places the amino acid in the position where its molecule fits into the molecule of the "template RNA." More transfer RNA molecules, one after the other in rapid sequence, bring more amino acids to the ribosome and fit them into their proper positions. Result? A chain of amino acids joined to each other in a definite sequence or, in other words, synthesis of a specific enzyme or other protein. Thus, each cell's genes determine the structure of its proteins. One authority estimates that human cells synthesize 1000 to 2000 different enzymes:* Liver cells, in addition to synthesizing their own cell proteins, make fibrinogen, albumin, and all other blood proteins except the gamma globulin antibodies.

Protein catabolism, like the catabolism of fats, consists of two processes, the first of which takes place mainly in liver cells and the second of which is the citric acid cycle. The first step in protein catabolism is known as *deamination,* a reaction in which an amino (NH_2) group is split off from an amino acid molecule to form a molecule of ammonia and one of keto acid. Most of the ammonia is converted to urea and is excreted via the urine. The keto acid may be oxidized via the tricarboxylic acid cycle (p. 44) or may be converted to glucose (an example of gluconeogenesis) or to fat. Formerly protein catabolism was believed to occur only when the amount of protein ingested exceeded that needed for anabolism. It is now known to go on continuously, even on protein-deficient diets, although at a greatly reduced rate under the latter condition.

In a normal healthy adult, the amount of nitrogen taken into the body (in protein foods) equals the amount of nitrogen excreted in the urine, feces, and sweat—a fact referred to as *nitrogen balance.* When the amount of protein catabolized exceeds the amount ingested (as evidenced by a larger amount of nitrogen in the urine than in proteins eaten), a condition of negative nitrogen balance exists, indicating catabolism of the tissue proteins. Protein-poor diets, starvation, and

---

*Hurwitz, J., and Furth, J. J.: Messenger RNA, Scient. Am. **206**:41, 1962.

wasting illnesses, for example, produce a negative nitrogen balance. A positive nitrogen balance (urine nitrogen less than nitrogen intake), on the other hand, accompanies any condition in which large amounts of tissue are being synthesized, as during growth, pregnancy, and convalescence from an emaciating illness.

The main facts about protein metabolism are summarized in Figs. 250 to 252. Compare them with Figs. 240 and 247 to 249. Note the important part played by the liver in the metabolism of all three kinds of foods.

Control of protein metabolism

Protein metabolism, like that of carbohydrates and fats, is controlled largely by hormones rather than by the nervous system. Somatotrophic hormone and the male hormone testosterone both have a stimulating effect on protein synthesis or anabolism. For this reason, they are referred to as anabolic hormones. Glucocorticoids (and ACTH), on the

Table 51. Metabolism

Food	Anabolism	Catabolism
Carbohydrates	Temporary excess changed into glycogen by liver cells in presence of insulin; stored in liver and skeletal muscles until needed and then changed back to glucose (Figs. 241, 242) True excess beyond body's energy requirements converted into adipose tissue; stored in various fat depots of body	Oxidized, in presence of insulin, to yield energy (4.1 Calories per gram) and wastes (carbon dioxide and water) $C_6H_{12}O_6 + 6O_2 \longrightarrow$ energy $+ 6CO_2 + 6H_2O$
Fats	Built into adipose tissue; stored in fat depots of body	Fatty acids $\downarrow$ (liver) ketone bodies $\downarrow$ (tissues) energy (9.3 Calories per Gm.) $+ CO_2 + H_2O$ Glycerol $\downarrow$ (liver) glycogen or glucose
Proteins	Temporary excess stored in liver and skeletal muscles Synthesized into new tissues; that is, muscle, nerve, connective, and epithelial	Deaminated by liver forming ammonia (which is converted to urea) and keto acids (which are either oxidized or changed to glucose or fat)

other hand, tend to accelerate mobilization of tissue proteins and therefore are spoken of as catabolic hormones. They are thought to act in some way, still unknown, to speed up the hydrolysis of tissue cell proteins to amino acids, their entry into the blood, and conversion to glucose (gluconeogenesis) by liver cells.

Thyroid hormone is necessary for and tends to promote protein anabolism and, therefore, growth when plenty of carbohydrates and fats are available for energy production. On the other hand, under different conditions, for example, when the amount of thyroid hormone is excessive or when the energy foods are deficient, this hormone may then promote protein mobilization and catabolism.

Some of the facts about metabolism set forth in the preceding paragraphs are summarized in Table 51.

Metabolism of vitamins, mineral salts, and water

Vitamins are substances that were recognized as necessary for life and health before their chemical composition was known. They constitute part of the chemical mechanisms for controlling body activities. All those of known function are components of enzyme molecules; therefore they are necessary for numerous physiological reactions. Without adequate amounts of the various vitamins, normal energy production, growth and development, reproduction, resistance to infection, and health in general are not possible. If the diet is too deficient in vitamins, life itself cannot continue. As their name suggests, vitamins are vital.

Mineral salts are also essential for both health and life. Not only do they function as part of the body's chemical control mechanism, but they also constitute structural components of body tissues. For example, calcium and phosphorus are important ingredients of bones and teeth.

Examples of minerals functioning as control mechanisms are the following. Sodium salts play an important part in the maintenance of the acid-base balance of the body and in the maintenance of water balance. They are essential, too, for normal heart action. Calcium salts help sustain rhythmical heart and intestinal contractions and are necessary for normal skeletal muscular action and normal growth. A number of enzymes contain minerals.

Water is metabolized in the following ways:

1. Water is an important constituent of every cell in the body. It composes well over one half of the cells' substance. When dehydrated slightly, cells lose their power to resist infection and die if they are more completely dehydrated.

2. Water is essential for the accomplishment of all body functions, for example, glandular secretions, digestion, absorption, anabolism, elimination of wastes, heat regulation, respiration, circulation, resistance to disease, etc. All cellular activity, and therefore life itself, depends upon the presence of adequate amounts of water. Materials must be dissolved in order to cross the cell membrane and in order to facilitate chemical reactions between them.

3. Water is important for the dilution of toxic wastes, thereby preventing damage of the kidney cells when they eliminate these toxins.

How important water is to life can be estimated by the fact that life can be maintained for a much longer time without food than without water. Men adrift in the ocean, for example, will live much longer with fresh water and no food than they will with food and no water. For a summary of some of the mechanisms involved in maintaining the water balance of the body, see Chapter XV.

Metabolic rates

Meaning

The term metabolic rate may be defined as the amount of heat produced by the body in a given time and under given circumstances. A synonym for "metabolic rate" might be said to be "rate of heat production." Metabolic rates actually measure catabolic rates because it is impossible to determine the amount of food anabolized, but it is comparatively easy to measure the amount catabolized, that is, oxidized. This is done clinically by the indirect method of measuring the amount of oxygen consumed in a given time and from this computing the number of Calories of heat produced in that time (p. 454).

Ways of expressing

Metabolic rates are expressed in either of two ways:
1. In terms of the number of calories produced in a given time, either per hour or per 24 hours (a large Calorie is the amount of heat used in raising the temperature of 1 liter of water 1° C.; since a Calorie is a unit of heat measurement, it is, therefore, the appropriate unit for expressing the amount of heat indicated by metabolic rates).
2. As normal or as a definite per cent above or below normal.

Basal metabolic rate

The basal metabolic rate (BMR) expresses the amount of heat produced by the body when it is in the waking state but at complete rest, when it is in the postabsorptive state (that is, 12 to 18 hours after

451

the last meal), and when the environmental temperature is just comfortably warm. These three conditions are known as "basal" conditions because under these conditions the heat produced represents the minimum amount generated by body cells when they are as nearly at rest as possible, with only vital processes, such as circulation and respiration, functioning. The basal metabolic rate, then, states the minimum amount of heat the body must produce in a given time (usually 24 hours) in order merely to keep itself alive and awake. If, for example, the basal metabolic rate is 1200 Calories per day, the body catabolizes the amount of food that yields 1200 Calories just to have enough energy for its vital processes.

Factors influencing basal metabolic rate

The basal metabolic rate is not identical for all individuals because of the influence of various factors (Fig. 253), some of which are described in the following paragraphs.

Size. In computing the BMR, size is usually considered the amount of the body's surface area; it is computed from the individual's height and weight. Per square meter of body surface, if other conditions are equal, a large individual has the same basal metabolic rate as a small one, but because a large individual has more square meters of surface area, his basal metabolism is greater than that of a small individual. For example, the BMR for a man in his twenties is about 40 Calories per square meter of body surface per hour (Table 52). A large man with a body surface area of 1.9 square meters would, therefore, have a basal metabolism of 76 Calories per hour, whereas a smaller man with a surface area of perhaps 1.6 square meters would have a basal metabolism of only 64 Calories per hour. The average surface area for American adults is 1.6 square meters for women and 1.8 square meters for men.

Sex. Men oxidize their food approximately 5 to 7 per cent faster than women; therefore, their basal metabolic rates are 5 per cent higher for a given size. A man 5 feet, 6 inches tall, weighing 140 pounds, has a 5 per cent higher basal metabolic rate than a woman of the same height, weight, and age.

Age. That the fires of youth burn more brightly than those of age is a physiological as well as a psychological fact. In general, the younger the individual, the higher is his basal metabolic rate for given size and sex. Exception: the BMR is slightly lower at birth than a few years later; that is to say, the rate increases slightly during the first 3 to 6 years and then starts to decrease and continues to do so throughout life. In Table 52 is given the basal metabolism per hour per square meter of surface area for different age groups.

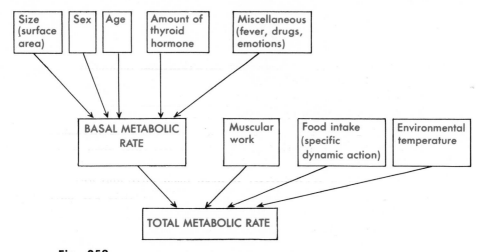

Fig. 253

Factors that determine the basal and total metabolic rates.

Thyroid hormone. Thyroid hormone stimulates basal metabolism. Without a normal amount of this hormone in the blood, a normal basal metabolic rate cannot be maintained. When an excess of thyroid hormone is secreted, foods are catabolized faster, much as coal is burned faster when a furnace draft is open. Deficient thyroid secretion, on the other hand, slows the rate of metabolism.

Fever. Fever increases the basal metabolic rate. According to DuBois, metabolism increases about 13 per cent per degree C. rise in body temperature.*

Drugs. Certain drugs, such as caffeine, Benzedrine, and dinitrophenol, increase the basal metabolic rate.

Other factors. Other factors, such as *sleep, emotions,* and *pregnancy,* also influence basal metabolism. During sleep the basal rate decreases. Emotions and pregnancy increase it.

How basal metabolic rate determined

Originally basal metabolic rates were determined by a method known as direct calorimetry, which was too time consuming and costly for use on large numbers of people. Now, a rapid, inexpensive method, *indirect calorimetry,* is used in practically all hospitals, as well as in many doctors' offices and nutrition laboratories. This method of determining metabolism consists simply of an oxygen tank into which the patient breathes by means of a rubber tube leading to his mouth, his nose being clamped off. He receives oxygen from the tank and expires carbon dioxide into it, the latter being removed by soda lime contained

---

*Bard, Philip: Medical physiology, ed. 11, St. Louis, 1961, The C. V. Mosby Co., p. 483.

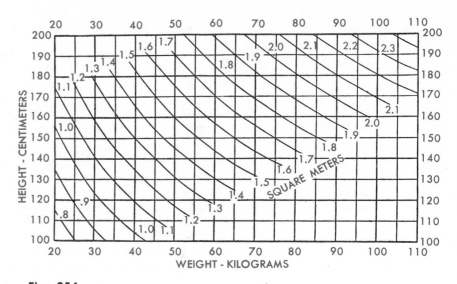

Fig. 254

Chart for determining surface area of man in square meters from weight
in kilograms and height in centimeters according to the following formula:
area (sq. cm.) = wt.$^{0.425}$ x ht.$^{0.725}$ x 7184. (From DuBois and DuBois:
Arch. Int. Med. 17:863, 1916.)

in a tank within the oxygen tank. The amount of oxygen consumed in
a given length of time is measured. Research has shown that for every
liter of oxygen consumed, 4.825 Calories of heat are produced (if a
normal mixed diet has been ingested). Multiplying the amount of
oxygen consumed by 4.825 therefore gives the number of Calories
produced in the given time. From that figure the number produced
in 24 hours can, of course, be readily computed. This number represents the patient's basal metabolic rate per day expressed in Calories.
Usually the basal metabolic rate is expressed as normal or as a definite
per cent above or below normal, the percentage being computed by
comparing the actual basal metabolic rate (in Calories) with what is
known to be an average basal metabolic rate (in Calories) for normal
individuals of the given size, sex, and age. Statistical tables, based
on research, give these normal rates for different sizes, sexes, and
ages. For instance, you can compute the average BMR for a person
of your own size, sex, and age in this way:

1. Start with your weight in kilograms and your height in centimeters. (Convert pounds to kilograms by dividing pounds by 2.2.
Convert inches to approximate centimeters by multiplying inches by
2.5). For example, 110 pounds = 50 kilograms; 5 feet 3 inches = 158
centimeters.

2. Convert your weight and height to square meters, using chart
on this page. For example, weight 50 kilograms and height 158 centimeters = about 1.5 square meters surface area of body.

Table 52. Basal metabolism (Aub-DuBois)

Age (yr.)	Calories per hour per square meter body surface	
	Male	Female
10-12	51.5	50.0
12-14	50.0	46.5
14-16	46.0	43.0
16-18	43.0	40.0
18-20	41.0	38.0
20-30	39.5	37.0
30-40	39.5	36.5
40-50	38.5	36.0
50-60	37.5	35.0
60-70	36.5	34.0

3. Find your age and sex on Table 52 and then multiply the number of Calories per square meter per hour given there by your square meters of surface area and then by 24. For example, average BMR per day for a 25-year-old female, weight 110 pounds and height 5 feet 3 inches $= 1332$ Calories $(37 \times 1.5 \times 24)$.

A quick rule of thumb for estimating a young woman's BMR is to multiply her weight in pounds by twelve.

Total metabolic rate

The *total metabolic rate*, as the term suggests, expresses the total amount of heat produced in the body in a given time (usually 24 hours) under normal conditions. By "normal" conditions are meant times when the body works, eats, and digests food, and, perhaps, adjusts to cold environmental temperatures, in addition to carrying on the minimum vital functions performed under basal conditions. Total metabolic rates, therefore, represent the amount of food the body must burn not only to keep alive and awake but also to do muscular work, digest food, and adjust to cold temperatures. They are, of course, always higher per individual than basal metabolic rates since the total metabolic rate consists of the basal rate plus a variable amount of heat produced by exercise, digestion, etc.

Exercise or muscular work of any kind increases metabolism because the energy used for muscular work is supplied by the catabolism of foods.

The ingestion and digestion of food also involve muscular work and, therefore, increase the rate of metabolism, but in addition, the food itself, in some way not clearly understood, speeds up metabolism. Proteins particularly have this effect. A diet rich in proteins increases the total metabolism more than one containing less protein. In other words, more food is burned, and therefore more heat is produced in 24 hours due to the stimulating effect of the high protein diet than would be burned if the diet contained the same total number of calories but less protein. It is for this reason that persons trying to reduce are advised to eat diets containing a high proportion of protein, that is, so that their stored fat will burn up more rapidly. It is also the reason why summer diets should contain less meat than winter ones—so that less heat is produced in 24 hours.

Each of the three kinds of foods exerts a different degree of stimulation on the metabolic rate; therefore, the metabolism-stimulating effect of foods is known as the *specific dynamic action of foods.* Mixed diets stimulate the basal metabolic rate approximately 10 per cent, whereas proteins alone stimulate it 30 per cent, carbohydrates 6 per cent, and fats 4 per cent.

Adjusting to cold environmental temperatures increases metabolism because of additional muscular exercise performed, partly voluntary (moving arms, legs, etc.) and partly involuntary (shivering, muscle tension).

Relation of metabolic rates to weight control

Weight control is based on the simple fact that in every 24 hours period the body must burn up sufficient food to yield the number of calories required for the individual's total metabolic rate. Only in this way can sufficient energy be provided for maintaining life, for doing physical work, for digesting a mixed diet, and for adjusting to cool temperatures. The food burned obviously may come from either of two sources: either it can be eaten, or it can come from the body's stored foods. Reducing diets make use of both sources of supply. Only part of the food needed for the total metabolism is supplied by the daily diet, making it necessary for the rest to come from the body's stored food.

Foods are stored as glycogen, fats, and tissue proteins. And as you will recall, cells catabolize them preferentially in this same order: carbohydrates, fats, and proteins. With no food intake, almost all of the glycogen is estimated to be used up in a matter of one or two days. Then, with no more carbohydrate to act as a fat-sparer, fat is catabolized. How long it takes to deplete all of this reserve food depends, of course, upon how much adipose tissue the individual has when he starts his starvation diet. It takes perhaps about six weeks in an average sized individual. Finally, with no more fat available as a protein-sparer, tissue proteins are catabolized rapidly, and death soon ensues.[*]

Diets designed to increase body weight contain more calories than are required for the total metabolism of the individual and are, there-

---

[*]Guyton, Arthur: Textbook of medical physiology, ed. 2, Philadelphia, 1961, W. B. Saunders Co., p. 936.

fore, known as *high caloric diets*, whereas reducing diets are called *low caloric diets*. Moreover, many reducing diets are high protein, low fat diets. Do you think this is scientifically sound? Support your answer with facts given in this chapter. Patients having a high fever are given high caloric diets because their total metabolism is increased by the fever. In order to maintain their weight, they must, therefore, ingest more calories than usual.

HEAT REGULATION OF THE BODY

Warm-blooded animals, such as man, maintain a remarkably constant temperature despite variations in environmental temperatures. Normally, body temperature has a daily fluctuation of not more than 2° F., whereas in sickness the variation may reach several degrees. In order to maintain the even temperature characteristic of health, a nice balance must be maintained between the amount of heat produced in the body and that lost from the body.

Heat production

Heat is produced by one means—catabolism of foods. Because the muscles and glands (liver, especially) are the most active tissues, they carry on more catabolism and therefore produce more heat than any of the other tissues. The amount of heat produced depends mainly upon the amount of muscular work being done. Exercise and shivering, for example, increase heat production, whereas inactivity decreases the amount of heat generated.

Heat loss

Heat is lost from the body in several ways.

From the skin. Heat is lost from the skin by radiation, conduction, and evaporation of sweat; about 80 to 85 per cent of all heat lost from the body is lost from the skin.

Radiation. Radiation is the transfer of heat from the surface of one object to that of another without actual contact between the two. Heat radiates from the body surface to nearby objects that are cooler than the skin and radiates to the skin from those which are warmer than the skin. This is, of course, the principle of heating and cooling systems. From surfaces that have been heated to temperatures warmer than the skin, heat radiates to the skin, thereby warming it, whereas with cooled surfaces, heat radiates from the skin to them, thereby cooling the skin. The amount of heat lost by radiation from the skin is made to vary as needed by dilatation of surface blood vessels when more heat needs to be lost and by vasoconstriction when heat loss needs to be decreased. In cool environmental temperatures, radiation accounts for a greater percentage of heat loss from the skin than both conduction and evaporation combined. In hot environments, on the other hand, no heat is lost by radiation but instead may even be gained by radiation from warmer surfaces to the skin.

Conduction. Conduction means the transfer of heat to any substance actually in contact with the body, such as clothing or jewelry. This process accounts for a relatively small amount of heat loss compared to that due to radiation and evaporation.

Evaporation of water. Evaporation of water is a very important method by which heat is lost from the skin. At moderate temperatures it accounts for about half as much heat loss as does radiation, but at high environmental temperatures evaporation constitutes the only method by which heat can be lost from the skin. A humid atmosphere necessarily retards evaporation and therefore lessens the cooling effect derived from it—explanation of the fact that the same degree of temperature seems hotter in humid climates than in dry ones.

From the lungs (in the expired air). Heat is lost from the lungs by warming cold air inspired. The physical processes involved are conduction and evaporation.

From the digestive and urinary tracts (in feces and urine). Heat is lost from the digestive and urinary tracts by warming cold foods and liquids. The physical process involved is conduction.

Thermostatic control of heat produced and lost

The "physiological thermostat" or heat-regulating centers are located in the hypothalamus. Through their influence on various lower centers (vasomotor and muscular mainly), they regulate the amount of body heat produced and dissipated. The heat-regulating centers are controlled primarily by reflex mechanisms and secondarily by direct stimulation or inhibition by the temperature of the blood.

Reflex control

Afferent impulses from heat and cold receptors of the skin are transmitted to the heat-regulating centers. Stimulation of skin cold receptors, for example, leads to stimulation of neurons in the posterior hypothalamus (temperature-elevating centers). These centers send out efferent impulses which decrease the amount of heat loss from the body and increase the amount produced. For example, impulses for vasoconstriction of surface blood vessels lessen the amount of heat lost by radiation and conduction, and impulses for inhibition of the sweat glands prevent heat loss by evaporation. At the same time, the following impulses result in increased heat production; impulses to the arrector pili muscles of the hairs and to various skeletal muscles cause the hair to "stand on end" (gooseflesh) and shivering to occur. Stimulation of skin heat receptors leads to stimulation of neurons in the anterior hypothalamus (temperature-lowering center) and inhibition of the temperature-elevating center. As a result, reflex dilatation of surface blood vessels and increased sweat secretion occur.

Direct control

In addition to control of the heat-regulating centers, the *temperature of the blood* directly affects their activity. If blood temperature increases, as in muscular exercise, for example, the temperature-lowering center is stimulated, leading to vasodilatation and sweating. On the other hand, a drop in blood temperature acts as a stimulant for the temperature-elevating center. Surface vasoconstriction, inhibited sweat secretion, and increased muscle contraction result.

Correlations

When a fever or higher than normal temperature exists, it is thought to be due primarily to inability of the heat-loss mechanisms to keep pace with heat production. As a result body temperature rises.

The heat-regulating centers are present at birth but do not function well for a short time after birth; therefore, new babies need to be kept somewhat warmer than adults. If the baby is born prematurely, the heat-regulating centers do not function for a longer time, perhaps several weeks.

Outline summary

The digestive system

Functions and importance

1. Prepare food for absorption and metabolism
2. Absorption
3. Elimination of wastes
4. Vital importance

Organs of the digestive system

1. Main organs
   a. compose alimentary canal—mouth, pharynx, esophagus, stomach, and intestines
2. Accessory organs
   a. teeth, tongue, salivary glands, pancreas, liver, gallbladder, and appendix

Walls of organs

1. Coats composing walls
   a. mucous lining
   b. submucous coat of connective tissue—main blood vessels here
   c. muscular coat

459

d. fibroserous coat
2. Modifications of coats
    a. mucous lining
        1. rugae and microscopic gastric and hydrochloric acid glands in stomach
        2. circular folds, villi, intestinal glands, Peyer's patches, and solitary lymph nodes in small intestine
        3. solitary nodes and intestinal glands in large intestine
    b. muscle coat
        1. three layers (circular, longitudinal, oblique) in stomach instead of only two layers as in rest of tract
        2. three tapelike strips make up outer, longitudinal layer, and shirr large intestine into small sacs called haustra
    c. fibroserous coat
        1. peritoneum covers stomach and intestines
        2. greater omentum or lace apron—double fold of peritoneum, which hangs from lower edge of stomach like an apron over intestines; should not be confused with mesentery, also a double fold of peritoneum, but fan-shaped and attached at short side to posterior wall of abdominal cavity; small intestines anchored to posterior abdominal wall by means of mesentery

Mouth

Formed by cheeks, hard and soft palates, tongue, and muscles; hard palate—formed by two palatine bones and parts of two maxillary bones; soft palate — formed of muscle in shape of arch; forms partition between mouth and nasopharynx; fauces is archway or opening from mouth to oropharynx uvula is conical-shaped process suspended from midpoint of arch

Tongue

Many rough elevations on tongue's surface called papillae; contain taste buds; frenum —a fold of mucous membrane which helps anchor tongue to mouth floor

Salivary glands (three pairs)

1. Parotid—below and in front of ear; duct opens on inside of cheek, opposite upper, second molar tooth

2. Submaxillary—posterior part of mouth floor
3. Sublingual—anterior part of mouth floor

Teeth

1. Deciduous or baby teeth; 10 in each jaw or 20 in set
2. Permanent—16 per jaw or 32 per set
3. Structure of typical tooth (Fig. 228)

Pharynx

See pp. 348 and 349

Esophagus

1. Position and extent
    a. posterior to trachea and heart; pierces diaphragm
    b. extends from pharynx to stomach—distance of approximately 10 inches
2. Structure—collapsible, muscle tube

Stomach

1. Size, shape, and position
    a. size varies in different individuals; also according to whether distended or not
    b. shape—elongated pouch
    c. position—lies in epigastric and left hypochondriac portions of abdominal cavity
2. Divisions
    a. fundus—portion above esophageal opening
    b. body—central portion
    c. pylorus—constricted, lower portion
3. Curves
    a. lesser—upper, right border
    b. greater—lower, left border
4. Sphincter muscles
    a. cardiac—guarding opening of esophagus into stomach
    b. pyloric—guarding opening of pylorus into duodenum
5. Coats—see Table 44
6. Glands
    a. epithelial cells of gastric mucosa secrete mucus
    b. parietal cells secrete hydrochloric acid
    c. chief cells (zymogen cells) secrete enzymes of gastric juice
7. Functions
    a. serves as food reservoir
    b. secretes gastric juice
    c. contractions break food into small particles, mix them well with gastric juice, and move contents on into duodenum

d. secretes the antianemic intrinsic factor

e. carries on a limited amount of absorption—some water, alcohol, and certain other drugs

Small intestine

1. Size—approximately 1 inch in diameter, 20 feet in length
2. Divisions
   a. duodenum
   b. jejunum
   c. ileum
3. Functions
   a. completes digestion of foods
   b. absorbs end products of digestion
   c. secretes hormones which help control secretion of pancreatic juice, bile, and intestinal juice

Large intestine

1. Size—approximately 2½ inches in diameter, 5 or 6 feet in length
2. Divisions
   a. cecum
   b. colon
      1. ascending
      2. transverse
      3. descending
      4. sigmoid
   c. rectum
3. Functions
   a. absorption of water
   b. elimination of digestive wastes

Liver

1. Location and size—occupies most of right hypochondrium and part of epigastrium; is largest gland in body
2. Lobes—right lobe, subdivided into three smaller lobes (right lobe proper, caudate, and quadrate) and left lobe; lobes divided into lobules by blood vessels and fibrous partitions
3. Ducts—hepatic duct from liver; cystic duct from gallbladder; common bile duct formed by union of hepatic and cystic ducts and opens into duodenum at ampulla of Vater (duodenal papilla)
4. Functions
   a. secretes bile
   b. plays essential role in metabolism of carbohydrates, proteins, and fats, for example, carries on glycogenesis, glyco-

genolysis, glyconeogenesis, deamination, and ketogenesis; synthesizes various blood proteins

Gallbladder

1. Size, shape, and location—approximately size and shape of small pear; lies on undersurface of liver
2. Structure—sac of smooth muscle with mucous lining arranged in rugae
3. Functions
   a. concentrates and stores bile and ejects it into duodenum

Pancreas

1. Size, shape, and location—larger in men than in women but varies in different individuals; shaped something like a fish with head, body, and tail; lies in C-shaped curve of duodenum
2. Structure—similar to salivary glands; divided into lobes and lobules; pancreatic cells pour their secretion into duct which runs length of gland and empties into duodenum at ampulla of Vater; clusters of cells, not connected with any ducts, lie between pancreatic cells—called islets or islands of Langerhans—composed of alpha and beta type cells—latter thought to secrete insulin, former to secrete hyperglycemic factor (glucagon)
3. Functions
   a. secretes pancreatic juice
   b. beta cells of islands of Langerhans secrete insulin
   c. alpha cells of islands of Langerhans secrete glucagon

Vermiform appendix

1. Size, shape, and location—about size and shape of large angle worm; is blind-end tube off cecum
2. Structure—similar to rest of intestine

Digestion

Definition

All changes food undergoes in alimentary canal

Purpose

Conversion of foods into chemical and physical forms which can be absorbed and metabolized

Kinds

1. Mechanical—movements which change physical state of foods, propel them forward in alimentary tract, eliminate digestive wastes from tract, and facilitate absorption (see Table 47 for description of processes involved in mechanical digestion)
   a. mastication (chewing)
   b. swallowing (deglutition)
      1. movement of food through mouth into pharynx—a voluntary act
      2. movement of food through pharynx into esophagus—an involuntary or reflex act initiated by stimulation of mucosa of back of mouth, pharynx, or laryngeal region; paralysis of receptors here, for example, by Novocain, makes swallowing impossible
      3. movement of food through esophagus into stomach; accomplished by esophageal peristalsis—a reflex initiated by stimulation of esophageal mucosa
   c. peristalsis—wormlike movements that squeeze food downward in tract; emptying of stomach or opening of pyloric sphincter regulated by enterogastric reflex: fats and sugars in intestine stimulate mucosa to release enterogastrone into blood which, in turn, inhibits gastric peristalsis and slows stomach emptying; proteins and acid stimulate vagal nerve receptors in intestinal mucosa and thereby initiate this reflex
   d. churning
   e. mass peristalsis
   f. defecation—reflex initiated by stimulation of rectal mucosa
2. Chemical—series of hydrolytic processes dependent upon specific enzymes (see Table 48 for description of chemical changes)

Control of digestive gland secretion

Also see Table 49
1. Saliva—secretion is a reflex initiated by stimulation of taste buds, other receptors in mouth and esophagus, olfactory receptors, and visual receptors
2. Gastric secretion—controlled reflexly by same stimuli that initiate salivary secretion; also controlled chemically by hormone, gastrin, released by gastric mucosa in presence of certain substances, notably meat extractives; enterogastrone (hormone just mentioned as slowing stomach emptying) also has inhibitory effect on gastric secretion
3. Pancreatic secretion—controlled chemically by hormone secretin formed by intestinal mucosa when hydrocholoric acid enters duodenum
4. Bile
   a. secretion of—controlled chemically by same hormone (secretin) that regulates pancreatic secretin
   b. ejection of into duodenum—controlled chemically by hormone cholecystokinin formed by intestinal mucosa when fats present in duodenum
5. Intestinal juice—control still obscure, although believed to be both reflex and chemical

Absorption
Definition
Passage of substances through intestinal mucosa into blood or lymph

How accomplished
Probably mainly by active transport mechanisms

Metabolism
Meaning
In limited sense (more common use of word) means chemical changes in absorbed foods or utilization of foods by body cells; in more comprehensive sense means all changes which occur in foods after digestion and absorption, that is, circulation in blood and lymph, chemical changes, and elimination of wastes from chemical changes

Ways in which foods metabolized
1. Catabolism—breaks down food molecules to simpler compounds (carbon dioxide, water, and nitrogenous wastes), transferring some of their energy to phosphate compounds, notably, ATP, and releasing some of it as heat
2. Anabolism—building up food molecules into more complex compounds, notably, glycogen, enzymes and other cell proteins, hormones, etc.

Carbohydrate metabolism
1. Glycogenesis—conversion of glucose to glycogen for storage; occurs mainly in liver

cells; insulin necessary for normal rate of glycogenesis, presumably because necessary for active transport of glucose through cell membranes
2. Glycogenolysis—glycogen changed back to glucose; epinephrine and pancreatic glucagon stimulate rate of glycogenolysis
3. Gluconeogenesis—conversion, by a sequence of chemical reactions, of either proteins or fats into glucose; ACTH and glucocorticoids have stimulating effect on rate of gluconeogenesis; presumably ACTH and glucocorticoids accelerate mobilization of tissue proteins and fats, thereby furnishing liver cells with more of these substances to convert into glucose

Blood glucose homeostatic mechanisms
See Figs. 244, 245
1. Principles about normal carbohydrate metabolism
   a. principle of glycogenesis—glucose in excess of about 120 to 140 milligrams per 100 milliliters of blood brought to liver by portal veins and enters liver cells where it undergoes glycogenesis
   b. principle of the preferred energy fuel—cells catabolize first glucose, sparing fats and proteins; when their glucose supply becomes inadequate, they next catabolize fats, sparing proteins, and last they catabolize proteins
   c. principle of glucose storage as fat—when blood glucose is higher than normal and blood insulin content is adequate, excess glucose is converted to fat, mainly by liver cells, and stored as such in fat depots

Fat metabolism
1. Catabolism of fats
   a. hydrolysis of fats to fatty acids and glycerol, primarily in liver cells
   b. glycerol oxidized same as carbohydrates
   c. fatty acids converted to ketone bodies (ketogenesis); occurs mainly in liver; largest proportion of ketones enters blood from liver cells to be transported to tissues for oxidation to carbon dioxide and water via tricarboxylic acid cycle
2. Anabolism of fats—for tissue synthesis and for building various compounds; fats de-

posited in connective tissue converts it to adipose tissue
3. Fat mobilization—the release of fats from adipose tissue cells, followed by their catabolism; occurs when blood contains less glucose than normal or when it contains less insulin than normal; if excessive, leads to ketosis
4. Control of fat metabolism—by following major factors
   a. rate of glucose catabolism is one of main regulators of fat metabolism; in general, normal or high rates of glucose catabolism accompanied by low rates of fat mobilization and catabolism and high rates of fat deposition; converse also true
   b. Insulin helps control fat metabolism by its effects on glucose metabolism; in general, normal amounts of insulin and blood glucose tend to decrease fat mobilization and catabolism and to increase fat deposition; insulin deficiency increases fat mobilization and catabolism; converse also true
   c. Glucocorticoids help control fat metabolism. In general when blood glucose is lower than normal and in various stress situations, more glucocorticoids are secreted and accelerate fat mobilization and gluconeogenesis from them. And when blood glucose is higher than normal but the rate of glucose catabolism is low, glucocorticoids also increase fat mobilization, but it is followed by ketogenesis from them. When blood glucose is higher than normal, and providing its insulin content is adequate, glucocorticoids accelerate fat deposition

Protein metabolism
1. Anabolism of proteins—of primary importance, their catabolism, secondary; amino acids used to synthesize all kinds of tissue, for example, for growth and repair; also used to synthesize many other substances such as enzymes, hormones, and blood proteins
2. Catabolism of proteins
   a. deamination of amino acid molecule to form ammonia and a keto acid; mainly in liver cells

b. ammonia converted to urea (mainly in liver) and excreted via urine

c. keto acids may be converted to glucose in liver, or to fat, or oxidized via tricarboxylic acid cycle

3. Control of protein metabolism

a. STH and testosterone both have stimulating effect on protein synthesis or anabolism

b. glucocorticoids and ACTH have stimulating effect on protein mobilization and gluconeogenisis

c. thyroid hormone promotes protein anabolism when nutrition adequate and amount of hormone normal; therefore, adequate amounts necessary for normal growth

Metabolism of vitamins, mineral salts, and water

Vitamins essential for many physiological processes such as normal metabolism, growth, reproduction, resistance to infection, etc.; mineral salts essential for normal metabolism and for maintenance of favorable internal environment; water essential for all physiological reactions

Metabolic rates

1. Meaning—number of calories of heat produced in a given time

2. Ways of expressing—in calories or as "normal" or as a definite per cent above or below normal; for example, +10% or −10%

3. Basal metabolic rate—amount of heat produced in waking state when body is at complete rest, 12 to 18 hours after last meal, in a comfortably warm environment

4. Factors influencing basal metabolic rate

a. size—the greater the surface area, the higher the BMR (surface area computed from height and weight)

b. sex—approximately 5% higher in males

c. age—higher in youth than in age

d. abnormal functioning of certain endocrines, particularly thyroid

e. fever—each centigrade degree rise in temperature increases BMR approximately 13%

f. certain drugs, for example, dinitrophenol, increase BMR

g. other factors, for example, sleep (de-

creases BMR), pregnancy, and emotions (increase BMR)

5. How basal metabolic rate determined

a. direct calorimetry—too expensive and too time consuming for wide use

b. indirect calorimetry—measures amount of oxygen inspired in given time; 4.825 Calories of heat produced for each liter of oxygen consumed

6. Total metabolic rate—amount of heat produced by body in average 24 hours; equal to basal rate plus number of calories produced by muscular work, eating and digesting food, and adjusting to cool temperatures; expressed in calories per 24 hours

7. Relation of metabolic rates to weight control

a. reducing diets contain fewer calories than total metabolic requirement

b. fever diets and those designed to increase weight contain more calories than total metabolic requirement

Heat regulation of body
Heat production
By oxidation of foods in skeletal muscles and liver especially

Heat loss
1. From skin—by radiation, conduction, and evaporation of sweat

2. By warming cold inspired air

3. By warming cold foods and liquids

Thermostatic control of heat produced and lost by heat-regulating centers in hypothalamus
1. Reflex control initiated by cold or heat stimuli applied to skin: reflex responses to cold stimuli decrease heat loss and increase heat production—responses are surface vasoconstriction, inhibition of sweat secretion, and muscle contraction (shivering, etc.); reflex responses to heat stimuli are surface vasodilatation and stimulation of sweat secretion, promote heat loss

2. Temperature of blood affects heat-regulating centers; increased blood temperature causes centers to promote heat-losing mechanisms (vasodilatation and increased sweat); decreased blood temperature causes center

to stimulate heat-producing mechanisms (muscle contractions) and to inhibit heat loss by constricting surface blood vessels and inhibiting sweat secretion

Correlations

Review questions

The digestive system

1. Name and describe the coats that compose the walls of the esophagus, stomach, and intestines.
2. Differentiate between the peritoneum, the mesentery, and the omentum.
3. Explain what the tonsils and adenoids are and their locations.
4. Give the names and number of deciduous teeth; of permanent teeth.
5. Discuss the functions of gastric juice.
6. What juices digest proteins? Carbohydrates? Fats?
7. Differentiate between the end products of digestion and the end products of metabolism.
8. Contrast the function or purpose of digestion with the function or purpose of metabolism.
9. Compare anabolism and catabolism as to type chemical reactions involved and end products.
10. Compare digestion and anabolism as to type of chemical reactions.
11. Discuss the functions of the pancreas in digestion and metabolism.

12. Compare proteins, carbohydrates, and fats as to functions they serve in the body. Mention both similarities and differences.
13. Compare proteins, carbohydrates, and fats as to their metabolic wastes.
14. Differentiate between digestive and metabolic wastes.
15. Differentiate between basal and total metabolic rates.
16. Compare absorption of the three kinds of foods.

Situation: A patient has obstructive jaundice.

17. Which duct, or ducts, might be obstructed to produce the symptom jaundice? Explain.
18. Would this affect this patient's digestion, absorption, or metabolism? Explain.
19. Explain why vitamin K might be given to this patient.

Situation: A patient has advanced liver disease.

20. Discuss possible effects on digestion, absorption, or metabolism.
21. What other functions might be affected?

Situation: Mrs. A., who weighs 160 pounds, is 5 feet, 5 inches tall, and 50 years of age, has been given a reducing diet by her doctor. She complains to you that she "knows it won't work" because "it isn't what she eats that makes her fat." As proof, she says that both her husband and son "eat twice as much" as she and so does her younger sister.

22. How would you answer Mrs. A.?
23. Mrs. A. also tells you that she does not like so much meat and so many eggs and that she would rather do without some of these and have some pie or cake each day. How would you answer her?

The urinary system

The urinary system consists of those organs which produce urine and eliminate it from the body. They are two kidneys, two ureters, one bladder, and one urethra. The secretion of urine and its elimination from the body are vital functions since together they constitute one of the most important mechanisms for maintaining homeostasis. As one individual has phrased it, "The composition of the blood (and internal environment) is determined not by what the mouth ingests but by what the kidney keeps."*

Table 53 shows the substances excreted from the kidneys and other excretory organs.

KIDNEYS

Gross anatomy

Size, shape, and location

The kidneys resemble Lima beans in shape. An average-sized kidney measures approximately 4½ inches in length, from 2 to 3 inches in width, and 1 inch in thickness. Usually the left kidney is slightly larger than the right.

The kidneys lie behind the parietal peritoneum, against the posterior abdominal wall, at the level of the last thoracic and first three lumbar vertebrae (or just above the waistline). The liver pushes the right kidney down to a somewhat lower level than the left. A heavy cushion of fat normally keeps the kidneys up in position. Very thin individuals may suffer from ptosis (dropping) of one or both of these organs. Connective tissue (renal fasciae) anchors the kidneys to surrounding structures and helps to maintain their normal position.

External structure

The mesial surface of each kidney presents a concave notch called the *hilum*. Structures enter the kidneys through this notch just as

---

*From Smith, H. W.: Lectures on the kidney, Lawrence, Kansas, 1943, University of Kansas, p. 3.

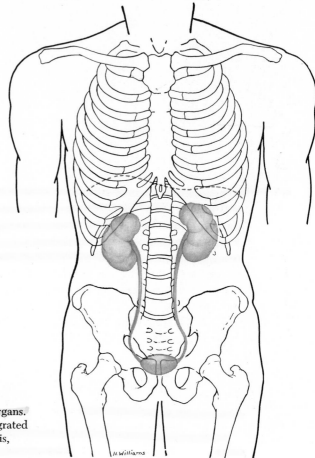

Fig. 255

Normal position of the urinary organs.
(From Francis and Farrell: Integrated
anatomy and physiology, St. Louis,
The C. V. Mosby Co.)

Table 53. Excretory organs of the body

Excretory organ	Substance excreted
Kidneys	Nitrogenous wastes (from protein catabolism) Toxins (from bacteria, for example) Water (from ingestion and from catabolism) Mineral salts
Skin (sweat glands)	Water Mineral salts Small amounts of nitrogenous wastes
Lungs	Carbon dioxide (from catabolism) Water
Intestine	Wastes from digestion (cellulose, connective tissue, etc.) Some metabolic wastes (bile pigments, for example; also salts of calcium and other heavy metals)

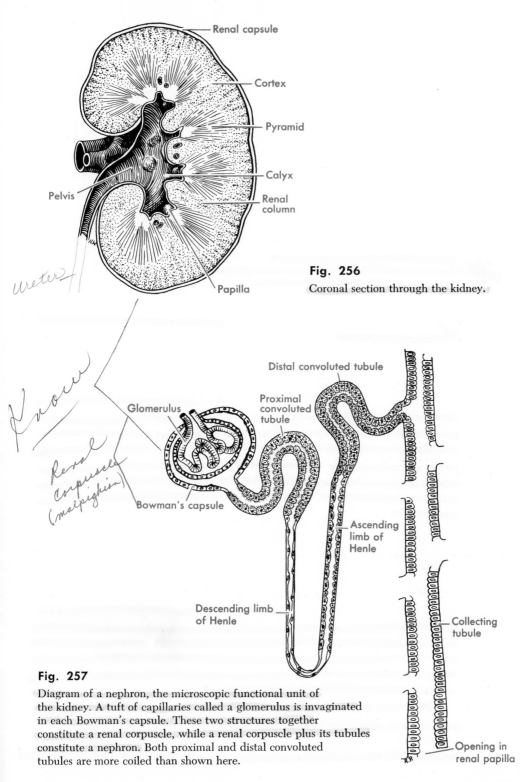

Renal capsule

Cortex

Pyramid

Calyx

Pelvis

Renal column

Ureter

Papilla

Fig. 256

Coronal section through the kidney.

Know

Renal corpuscle (malpighian)

Glomerulus

Distal convoluted tubule

Proximal convoluted tubule

Bowman's capsule

Ascending limb of Henle

Descending limb of Henle

Collecting tubule

Fig. 257

Diagram of a nephron, the microscopic functional unit of the kidney. A tuft of capillaries called a glomerulus is invaginated in each Bowman's capsule. These two structures together constitute a renal corpuscle, while a renal corpuscle plus its tubules constitute a nephron. Both proximal and distal convoluted tubules are more coiled than shown here.

Opening in renal papilla

469

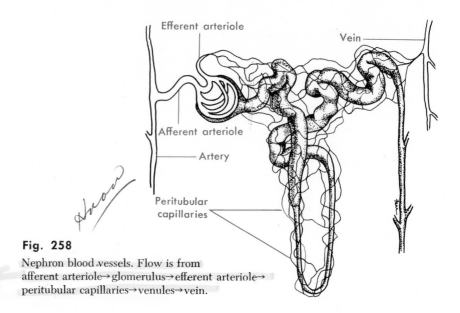

Fig. 258

Nephron blood vessels. Flow is from
afferent arteriole→glomerulus→efferent arteriole→
peritubular capillaries→venules→vein.

they enter the lung through its hilum. A tough white fibrous capsule
encases each kidney.

Internal structure

When a coronal section is made through the kidney, two kinds of
substances are seen composing its interior: an outer layer, the *cortex,*
and an inner portion, the *medulla.* The latter is divided into a dozen
or more triangular wedges, the *renal pyramids.* The bases of the
pyramids face the cortex, and their apices or *renal papillae* face the
center of the kidney. The pyramids have a striated appearance as
contrasted with the smooth texture of the cortical substance. The
cortex extends inward between each two pyramids, forming the *renal
columns.*

Microscopic anatomy

Microscopic examination reveals the kidney to be composed of pe-
culiarly shaped structures resembling tiny funnels with proportionately long convoluted stems. The upper portions of these anatomical
funnels are called *Bowman's capsules.* They consist of two layers of
flat epithelial cells with a space between the layers. Each capsule has
invaginated in it a cluster of capillaries designated as a *glomerulus.* A
Bowman's capsule and its partially incased glomerulus is named a
renal corpuscle (or *malpighian* corpuscle).

Blood flows into each glomerulus by way of an afferent arteriole
and out of it by way of an efferent arteriole—an unique arrangement.
Blood usually flows out of capillaries into what kind of vessels? Extending from each Bowman's capsule is a renal tubule. It consists of

several structurally different sections (Fig. 257). The first is known as the *proximal convoluted tubule:* proximal because it is the segment nearest the tubule's origin from the Bowman's capsule and convoluted because it pursues a tortuous rather than a straight course. The proximal tubule becomes the *descending limb* of the *loop of Henle* which becomes the *ascending limb,* which becomes the *distal convoluted tubule* which terminates in a straight or *collecting tubule.* Collecting tubules join larger tubules, and all the larger collecting tubules of one renal pyramid converge to form one tube which opens at a renal papilla into one of the small calyces. Bowman's capsules and both convoluted tubules lie in the cortex of the kidney, whereas the loops of Henle and collecting tubules lie in its medulla.

A glomerulus, Bowman's capsule, and its tubule—proximal, convoluted, loop of Henle, and distal convoluted portions—together constitute a *nephron,* the structural and functional unit of the kidney. *Gray's anatomy* says that there are about a million and a quarter nephrons in each kidney.

One of the ways in which the several parts of the nephron differ structurally is in the types of epithelial cells composing them (Fig. 257). And, as you might guess, they also differ functionally. But each part contributes a vital step in the process of urine formation.

Physiology

The function of the kidneys is to secrete urine, a life-preserving function because homeostasis depends upon it. Kidney failure, not relieved, means death because it means homeostasis failure. Consider, for instance, just a few of the blood constituents that cannot be held to their normal concentration ranges if the kidneys fail—all of the following plus many more: glucose, sodium, potassium, chloride, and nitrogenous wastes from protein metabolism.

In addition to excreting urine, the kidneys are now known to influence blood pressure, but exactly how they do this is still a matter of conflicting theories (p. 479).

How the kidneys secrete urine

Three processes are involved in the production of urine: filtration, reabsorption, and secretion.

Role of filtration in urine formation. Filtration, the first step in the formation of urine, takes place from the blood in the glomeruli out into the Bowman's capsules. Water and solutes filter out of the glomeruli even faster than out of ordinary capillaries. At least two structural features make renal corpuscles especially effective filtration membranes. For one thing, glomeruli have many more pores than other capillaries. And the fact that the efferent arteriole is smaller in diameter than the afferent arteriole makes for a higher resistance to blood flow out of glomeruli than out of other capillaries and, therefore, for a higher blood pressure (hydrostatic pressure, that is,) in glomeruli than in ordinary capillaries. Glomerular hydrostatic pressure, for instance, averages about 70 mm. Hg, whereas capillary hydrostatic pressure averages only about 30 mm. Hg.

Fluid moves out of the glomeruli into the Bowman's capsules for the same reason that it moves out of other capillaries into interstitial fluid or moves from any area to another—because a pressure gradient exists between the two areas. Normally, glomerular hydrostatic pressure, blood colloidal osmotic pressure, and capsular hydrostatic pressure together determine the pressure gradient (commonly spoken of as the *effective filtration pressure* or EFP) between glomeruli and capsules. And of these three pressures, glomerular hydrostatic pressure is the main driving force, the main determinant of the effective filtration pressure. It tends to move fluid out of the glomeruli. In contrast, the *capsular* hydrostatic pressure and the blood colloidal osmotic pressure both exert force in the opposite direction. (If you do not recall why osmotic pressure is a "water-pulling" rather than a "water-pushing" force, reread p. 39.) Suppose that there is a glomerular hydrostatic pressure of 70 mm. Hg and that it is opposed by a capsular hydrostatic pressure of 20 and a blood colloidal osmotic pressure of 30. There would then be a net or effective filtration pressure of 20 mm. Hg (70 − 20 − 30). In other words, there would be a pressure gradient of 20 mm. Hg, causing fluid to filter out of the glomeruli into the capsules.

Another factor, *capsular* colloidal osmotic pressure, operates when disease has increased glomerular permeability enough to allow blood protein molecules to diffuse* out of the blood into the capsular filtrate. Under these circumstances the capsular filtrate exerts an osmotic pressure in opposition to blood osmotic pressure. Capsular osmotic pressure tends to draw water out of the blood and so constitutes another force to be added to glomerular hydrostatic pressure in determining the

---

*Experiments have shown that the normal glomerular membrane is impermeable to molecules having a molecular weight of about 70,000 or more. Blood proteins have the following approximate molecular weights: Albumins, 70,000; globulins, over 165,000; fibrinogen, about 340,000, according to Kleiner, I. S., and Orten, J. M.: Human biochemistry, ed. 5, St. Louis, 1958, The C. V. Mosby Co.

effective filtration pressure. By using the following formula, you will be able to see how changes in the various pressures cause changes in the glomerular filtration rate.

$$
\begin{pmatrix} \text{Effective} \\ \text{filtration} \\ \text{pressure} \end{pmatrix} = \begin{pmatrix} \text{Glomerular} \\ \text{hydrostatic} \\ \text{pressure} \end{pmatrix} + \begin{pmatrix} \text{Capsular} \\ \text{osmotic} \\ \text{pressure} \end{pmatrix} - \begin{pmatrix} \text{Glomerular} \\ \text{osmotic} \\ \text{pressure} \end{pmatrix} + \begin{pmatrix} \text{Capsular} \\ \text{hydrostatic} \\ \text{pressure} \end{pmatrix}
$$

Glomerular hydrostatic pressure may decrease sharply under stress conditions such as following severe hemorrhage. Table 55 gives pressures which might exist under these circumstances. Using these figures, what do you compute the effective glomerular filtration pressure to be? Do you think it is true, after doing this computation, that glomerular filtration ceases entirely when glomerular hydrostatic pressure falls below a certain critical level?

Table 54. Normal glomerulocapsular pressures

	Hydrostatic pressure	Colloidal osmotic pressure
Glomerular blood	70 mm. Hg	30 mm. Hg
Capsular filtrate	20 mm. Hg	——

Table 55. Abnormal glomerulocapsular pressures

	Hydrostatic pressure	Colloidal osmotic pressure
Glomerular blood	44 mm. Hg	28 mm. Hg
Capsular filtrate	20 mm. Hg	4 mm. Hg

Kidney disease sometimes leads to a loss of blood proteins in the urine. How do you think this might change the glomerular and capsular pressures and glomerular filtration rate?

Glomerular hydrostatic pressure is regulated by mechanisms that change the size of the afferent and efferent arterioles and is also influenced by changes in systemic blood pressure and in blood protein concentration. For example, sympathetic impulses cause constriction of both afferent and efferent arterioles. But with intense sympathetic stimulation, the afferent arteriole becomes much more constricted than the efferent. Consequently glomerular hydrostatic pressure falls. Sometimes under severe stress conditions, it drops to a level too low to maintain filtration, and the kidneys "shut down" completely. In more technical language, renal suppression occurs. Glomerular hydrostatic pressure and filtration are directly related to systemic blood pressure. By

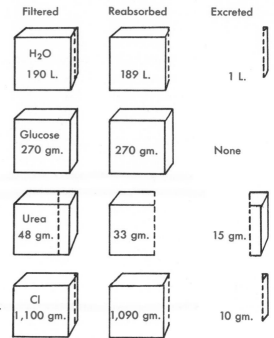

Filtered	Reabsorbed	Excreted
H₂O 190 L.	189 L.	1 L.
Glucose 270 gm.	270 gm.	None
Urea 48 gm.	33 gm.	15 gm.
Cl 1,100 gm.	1,090 gm.	10 gm.

Fig. 259

Left column shows amount of various substances filtered out of glomeruli into Bowman's capsules in twenty-four hours. Middle column shows amount reabsorbed back into blood—an index of tubular work. Right column shows amounts finally excreted in urine.

this we mean that an increase in blood pressure tends to produce an increase in glomerular pressure and in the filtration rate. The converse is also true.

Glomerular filtration is inversely related to blood colloidal osmotic pressure. Usually, for example, a decrease in blood osmotic pressure causes an increase in glomerular filtration. Normally the glomerular filtration rate averages about 125 milliliters per minute in men and somewhat less in women. The filtrate entering the proximal tubule has nearly the same composition as blood plasma except that it contains virtually no proteins when glomerular permeability is normal.

Role of tubule reabsorption in urine formation (Fig. 259). The second step in urine formation is reabsorption of substances needed by the body, that is, of most (usually from 97 to 99%) of the water and part of the solutes from the glomerular filtrate back into the blood. Reabsorption is the function of the cells composing the walls of the convoluted tubules and the loop of Henle. In the execution of this function these cells display astonishing powers of selection and discrimination; for example, they absorb most efficiently the substances that the body needs most vitally, such as Na^+, Cl^-, HCO_3^-, H_2O, and glucose.

Reabsorption is not merely a physical matter of diffusion and osmosis but consists also of somewhat obscure active transport mechanisms that require energy release by the cells, probably from a phosphate compound such as ATP (adenosine triphosphate). Because reabsorption is achieved partly by active transport mechanisms, it is one of the first powers diminished in kidney disease. Practical use is made of this fact in tests which measure the concentration of urine at different times of the day and thereby evaluate the active transport powers of the tubules.

Let us consider first the mechanism for reabsorption of solutes. Active transport mechanisms, whose precise nature is still unknown, absorb glucose, amino acids, and other nutrient substances and at least some electrolytes (salts). Proximal tubule cells transport glucose and other nutrients. So these vitally important materials, after filtering out of the glomeruli, return to the blood from the first part of the renal tubule. The transport mechanisms function so effectively that normally no glucose at all is lost in the urine. If, however, blood glucose exceeds a certain threshold amount (often around 150 milligrams per 100 milliliters of blood), the glucose transport mechanism cannot reabsorb all of it, and the excess remains in the urine. In other words, this mechanism has a maximum capacity for moving glucose molecules back into the blood. Occasionally this capacity is greatly reduced, in which case glucose appears in the urine (glycosuria or glucosuria), even though the blood sugar may be normal; this condition is known as renal diabetes or renal glycosuria.

Electrolytes are reabsorbed partly by active transport mechanisms and partly by diffusion. Sodium ions, for example, are known to be actively transported from all parts of the tubule. And this has important effects on the reabsorption of certain other ions and on water reabsorption. Sodium ions are positive ions. Therefore, when they are transported out of the tubules into the peritubular blood, the latter momentarily becomes electropositive to the tubular filtrate. This attracts negative ions (notably chloride) and causes an equal number of them to diffuse out of the tubule. Sodium transport out of the tubule also produces a momentary disequilibrium between the tubular filtrate and peritubular blood osmotic pressures. Because of the addition of extra sodium particles to the peritubular blood, the osmotic pressure of the peritubular blood increases above the level of the filtrate osmotic pressure.

Water, obeying the law of osmosis, follows rapidly along to re-establish osmotic equilibrium between the filtrate and blood. In short, the active transport of sodium out of the tubule is the main factor causing osmosis of water out of it. And, therefore, the water reabsorbed from the proximal tubule by this mechanism has been described as "obligatory water reabsorption"— obligatory because demanded by the law of osmosis. The volume of water reabsorbed from more distal parts of the tubule, on the other hand, being more variable than the volume of proximal reabsorption, is called "facultative water reabsorption."

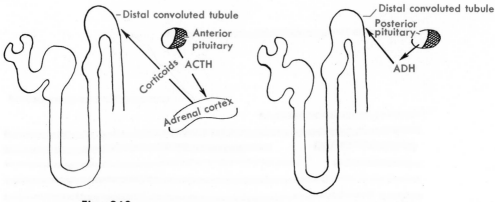

Fig. 260

ADH and corticoid control of distal renal tubule reabsorption.
ADH causes increased water reabsorption by distal
tubules and, it is now thought, by collecting tubules. Corticoids
increase sodium reabsorption and, therefore, water reabsorption.

How much water finally moves back into the blood depends upon the presence of a hormone released by the neurohypophysis (posterior pituitary gland). Its name, antidiuretic hormone (ADH), is appropriate because it works against diuresis (urine excretion in excess of the usual amount). In other words, ADH acts to decrease the amount of urine produced. The dynamics of the ADH mechanism are extremely complex,* but the results are clear—increased amounts of water are reabsorbed from the distal tubules (and from the collecting tubules too, it is now thought), and urine volume decreases while its concentration increases. It tends to become hypertonic to blood under the ADH influence. How important the ADH-tubule mechanism is can be appreciated from the fact that water balance depends upon it and cannot be maintained if it fails (discussed in Chapter XV).

Presumably other ions besides sodium are also actively transported by renal tubule cells, for example, potassium ions (probably by the proximal tubules).

Certain adrenal cortex hormones, classified as mineralocorticoids (M-C's), regulate the reabsorption of electrolytes, of ions, that is. Of the natural mineralocorticoids aldosterone is the most potent. It greatly increases reabsorption of sodium and thereby of chloride and water because active transport of sodium out of the tubule causes diffusion of chloride and osmosis of water out of it, as just noted.

---

*For a discussion of the ADH mechanism of facultative water reabsorption see Bard, P.: Medical physiology, ed. 11, St. Louis, 1961, The C. V. Mosby Co., pp. 351-356; Best, Charles H., and Taylor, M B.: The physiological basis of medical practice, ed. 7, Baltimore, 1961, Williams & Wilkins Co., pp. 546-552.

Role of secretion in urine formation. In addition to reabsorption, tubule cells can also secrete. Secretion means active transport from blood to tubule filtrate. Reabsorption, in contrast, means active transport from filtrate to blood—the opposite direction from secretion. For example, distal tubule cells actively transport hydrogen and ammonium ions out of the blood into the urine. In other words, they secrete these substances. And this is a matter of great physiological impor-

Table 56. Reabsorption and secretion mechanisms (for moving substances out of and into renal tubules)

Substance	Moved out of	By mechanism of	Into
Electrolytes, e.g.: Sodium ions	Blood in glomeruli Filtrate in tubules (all parts)	*Filtration* *Active transport*	Bowman's capsules Blood in peritubular capillaries
Potassium ions	Blood in glomeruli Filtrate in proximal tubules Blood in peritubular capillaries	*Filtration* *Active transport* (reabsorption) *Active transport* (secretion)	Bowman's capsules Blood in peritubular capillaries Filtrate in tubules
Chloride ions	Blood in glomeruli Filtrate in tubules	*Filtration* *Diffusion* (secondary to Na⁺-transport)	Bowman's capsules Blood in peritubular capillaries
Nutrients, e.g.: Glucose	Blood in glomeruli Filtrate in proximal tubules	*Filtration* *Active transport*	Bowman's capsules Blood in peritubular capillaries
Wastes, e.g.: Urea (most abundant solute in urine)	Blood in glomeruli Filtrate in tubules	*Filtration* *Diffusion*	Bowman's capsules Blood in peritubular capillaries
Water	Blood in glomeruli Filtrate in proximal tubules Filtrate in distal and collecting tubules	*Filtration* *Osmosis* (obligatory water reabsorption) *Osmosis* (facultative water reabsorption)	Bowman's capsules Blood in peritubular capillaries Blood in peritubular capillaries
Hydrogen ions and *ammo- nium* ions	Blood in peritubular capillaries	*Active transport* (secretion)	Filtrate in distal tubules

Table 57. Functions of different parts of nephron in urine formation

Part of nephron	Function	Substance moved
Glomerulus	Filtration	Water All solutes except colloids such as blood proteins
Proximal tubule and loop of Henle	Reabsorption by active transport	Na$^+$, K$^+$ and probably some other ions; nutrients—glucose and amino acids
	Reabsorption by diffusion (secondary to active transport)	Cl$^-$ and probably some other ions
	Obligatory water reabsorption by osmosis	Water
Distal tubule	Reabsorption by active transport	Na$^+$, K$^+$, probably some other ions
	Facultative water reabsorption by osmosis (ADH-controlled)	Water
	Secretion by active transport	H$^+$, NH$_3^+$, and some drugs
Collecting tubule	Facultative water reabsorption by osmosis	Water

tance. The maintenance of acid-base balance depends upon it (discussed in Chapter XVI). Tubule cells also secrete penicillin and para-aminohippuric acid (PAH), two clinically important substances. For example, by administering a known amount of PAH and then measuring the amount excreted in the urine, tubular secretion can be evaluated. If the tubules are impaired, they, of course, cannot move as much PAH out of the blood, and less appears in the urine within a given time.

In Table 56 is summarized the reabsorption and secretion mechanisms. In Table 57 and Fig. 261 are summarized the functions of the different parts of the nephron in forming urine.

Mechanisms that control volume of urine secreted

The amount of urine secreted is regulated primarily by the factors cited which change the amount of water reabsorption by the distal tubule cells (p. 476). It is thought that only under pathological conditions does the rate of glomerular filtration change enough to alter the volume of urine produced.

The total volume of extracellular fluid is known to influence the volume of urine secreted, although the mechanism by which it accomplishes this is still unproved. At any rate, when ECF volume increases, increased urinary output soon follows. Conversely, when ECF volume decreases, decreased urinary output follows. Evidence that the first of these principles operates is the common experience of increased output following rapid ingestion of a large amount of fluid. Evidence of the second principle is the oliguria or even anuria in dehydrated patients.

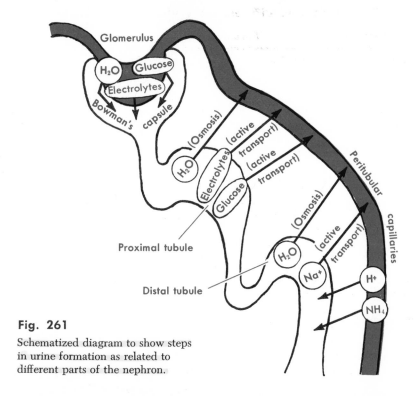

Fig. 261

Schematized diagram to show steps
in urine formation as related to
different parts of the nephron.

Another factor which helps regulate the amount of urine secreted
is the total amount of solutes excreted through the kidneys. The more
solutes to be excreted, the greater the volume of urine. In diabetes,
for example, more solids are excreted than normally due to the excess glucose which "spills over" into the urine, and therefore the volume of urine secreted daily is greater than in the normal individual.

Influence of kidneys on blood pressure

Clinical observation and animal experiments have established the
fact that destruction of a large proportion of total kidney tissue usually
results in the development of hypertension. This happens frequently,
for example, in patients who have severe renal arteriosclerosis or glo-
merulonephritis. Many experiments have been performed and various
theories devised to explain the mechanism responsible for "renal hypertension." Ischemic kidneys are known to produce a proteolytic enzyme, *renin,* which hydrolyzes one of the blood proteins (a globulin)
to produce *angiotonin* (hypertensin) which causes arteriolar constriction and a temporary rise in blood pressure. It is also known that
the kidneys execute a blood pressure-reducing function, but the way
in which they do this is not known. Some investigators think the kidneys probably secrete a hormonal substance that acts in some way
to reduce blood pressure, as well as secreting renin which has the
opposite effect.

479

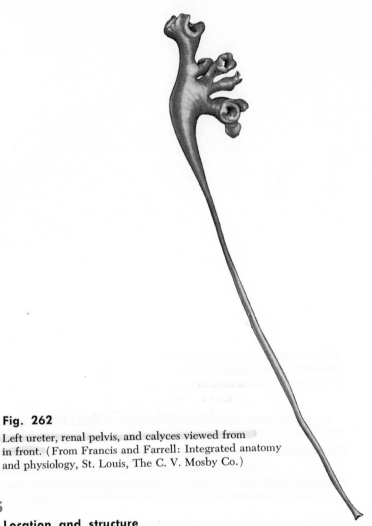

Fig. 262

Left ureter, renal pelvis, and calyces viewed from
in front. (From Francis and Farrell: Integrated anatomy
and physiology, St. Louis, The C. V. Mosby Co.)

URETERS

Location and structure

The two ureters are tubes from 10 to 12 inches long and are one
fifth of an inch in diameter. They lie behind the parietal peritoneum
and extend from the kidneys to the posterior surface of the bladder.
As the upper end of each ureter enters the kidney, it enlarges into a
funnel-shaped basin named the *renal pelvis*. The pelvis expands into
several branches called *calyces*. Each calyx contains a renal papilla. As
urine is secreted, it drops out of the collecting tubules, whose openings
are in the papillae, into the calyces, thence into the pelvis, and down
the ureters into the bladder.

The walls of the ureters are composed of three coats: a lining coat
of mucous membrane, a middle coat of two layers of smooth muscle,
and an outer fibrous coat.

Where the ureters empty into the bladder there is a fold of mucus
membrane which serves as a valve preventing the backflow of urine
into the ureter when the bladder contracts.

Function

The ureters, together with their expanded upper portions, the pelves and calyces, collect the urine as it forms and drain it into the bladder. Peristaltic waves (about one to five per minute) force the urine down the ureters and into the bladder.

Correlations

Stones known as *renal calculi* sometimes develop within the kidney. Urine may wash them into the ureter where they cause extreme pain if they are large enough to distend its walls.

BLADDER

Structure

The bladder is a collapsible bag located directly behind the symphysis pubis. It lies below the parietal peritoneum which covers only its superior surface. Three layers of smooth muscle (known collectively as the detrusor muscle) fashion its walls, while mucous membrane, arranged in rugae, forms its lining. Because of the rugae and the elasticity of its walls, the bladder is capable of considerable distention, although its capacity varies greatly with individuals. There are three openings in the floor of the bladder—two from the ureters and one into the urethra. The ureter openings lie at the posterior corners of the triangular-shaped floor (the trigone) and the urethral opening at the anterior and lower corner.

Functions

The bladder performs two functions:
1. It serves as a reservoir for urine before it leaves the body.
2. Aided by the urethra, it expels urine from the body. Distention of the bladder with urine stimulates stretch receptors in the bladder wall. This initiates reflex contraction of the bladder wall but simultaneous relaxation of the internal sphincter, followed rapidly by relaxation of the external sphincter and emptying of the bladder. Parasympathetic fibers transmit the impulses that cause contractions of the bladder and relaxation of the internal sphincter. Voluntary contraction of the external sphincter, however, to prevent or terminate micturition is learned. Voluntary control of micturition is possible only if the nerves supplying the bladder and urethra, the projection tracts of the cord and brain, and the motor area of the cerebrum are all intact. Injury to any of these parts of the nervous system, by a cerebral hemorrhage or cord injury, for example, results in involuntary emptying of the bladder at intervals. Involuntary micturition is called *incontinence*.

481

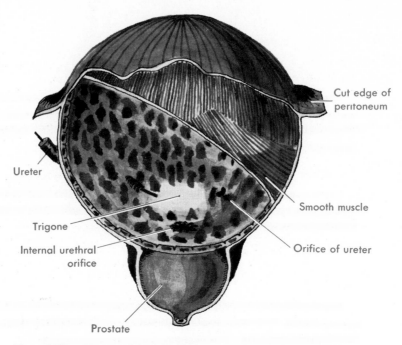

Fig. 263
Bladder. Part of wall cut away to show muscle coat and interior.

In the average bladder, 250 milliliters of urine will cause a moderately distended sensation and therefore the desire to void.

Occasionally an individual is unable to void even though the bladder contains an excessive amount of urine. This condition is known as *retention;* it often follows pelvic operations and childbirth. Catheterization (introduction of rubber tube through urethra into bladder to remove urine) is used to relieve the discomfort accompanying retention. A more serious complication, which is also characterized by the inability to void, is called *suppression.* In this condition the patient cannot void because the kidneys are not secreting any urine, and therefore the bladder is empty. Catheterization, of course, gives no relief for this condition.

URETHRA

Structure and location

The urethra is a small tube leading from the floor of the bladder to the exterior. In the female it lies directly behind the symphysis pubis and anterior to the vagina. It extends up, in, and back for a distance of about 1 to 1½ inches. The male urethra follows a tortuous course for a distance of approximately 8 inches. Immediately below the bladder, it passes through the center of the prostate gland, then between two sheets of white fibrous tissue connecting the pubic bones,

Table 58.   Physical characteristics of normal urine

Amount (24 hours)	Three pints (1500 ml.) but varies greatly according to fluid intake, amount of perspiration, and several other factors
Clearness	Transparent or clear; upon standing, becomes cloudy
Color	Amber or straw-colored; varies according to amount voided—the less voided, the darker the color, usually; diet also may change color; for example, reddish color from beets
Odor	"Characteristic"; upon standing, develops ammonia odor due to formation of ammonium carbonate
Specific gravity	1.015 to 1.020; highest in morning specimen
Reaction	Acid but may become alkaline if diet is largely vegetables; high protein diet increases acidity; stale urine has alkaline reaction due to decomposition of urea forming ammonium carbonate; normal range for urine pH 4.8-7.5; average about 6; rarely becomes more acid than 4.5 or more alkaline than 8

and then through the penis, the external male reproductive organ. These three parts of the urethra are known, respectively, as the prostatic portion, the membranous portion, and the cavernous portion.

The opening of the urethra to the exterior is named the *urinary meatus.*

Mucous membrane lines the urethra as well as the rest of the urinary tract.

Functions

As the terminal portion of the urinary tract, the urethra serves as the passageway for eliminating urine from the body. In addition, the male urethra is the terminal portion of the reproductive tract and serves as the passageway for eliminating the reproductive fluid (semen) from the body. The female urethra serves only the urinary tract.

URINE

Physical characteristics

In Table 58 are listed the physical characteristics of normal urine.

Chemical composition

Urine is approximately 95% water, in which are dissolved several kinds of substances, the most important of which are listed as follows:
1. *nitrogenous wastes* from protein metabolism—such as urea (most abundant solute in urine), uric acid, ammonia and creatinine.
2. *electrolytes*—mainly the following ions: sodium, potassium, ammonium, chloride, bicarbonate, phosphate, and sulfate; amounts and kinds of minerals vary with diet and other factors.

3. *toxins*—during disease, bacterial poisons leave the body in the urine—an important reason for "forcing fluids" on patients suffering with infectious diseases, so as to dilute the toxins which might damage the kidney cells if they were eliminated in a concentrated form.
4. *pigments.*
5. *hormones.*
6. various *abnormal constituents* sometimes found in urine—such as glucose, albumin, blood, casts, calculi, etc.

DEFINITIONS

1. *glycosuria,* or *glucosuria*—sugar (glucose) in the urine.
2. *hematuria*—blood in the urine.
3. *pyuria*—pus in the urine.
4. *casts*—substances, such as mucus, which harden and form molds inside the uriniferous tubules and then are washed out into the urine; microscopic in size.
5. *dysuria*—painful urination.
6. *polyuria*—unusually large amounts of urine.
7. *oliguria*—scanty urine.
8. *anuria*—absence of urine.

Outline summary

The urinary system

Kidneys

Gross anatomy

1. Size, shape, and location—4½ by 2 to 3 by 1 inch; shaped like Lima beans; lie against posterior abdominal wall, behind peritoneum, at level of last thoracic and first three lumbar vertebrae; right kidney slightly lower than left
2. External structure—hilum, concave notch on mesial surface; enveloping capsule of white fibrous tissue
3. Internal structure—outer layer called cortex; inner portion called medulla; renal pyramids are triangular wedges of medullary substance, apices of which are called papillae; renal columns are inward extensions of cortex between pyramids

Microscopic anatomy

Cluster of capillaries invaginated in Bowman's capsule called *glomerulus;* Bowman's capsule together with glomerulus constitute renal (malpighian) corpuscle; physiological unit of kidney called nephron—consists of renal corpuscle, convoluted tubules, loop of Henle, and straight tubule

Physiology

1. Function—secrete urine, by which various toxins and metabolic wastes are excreted and composition and volume of blood regulated; influence blood pressure
2. How urine secreted (see Table 56 and Fig. 261)

a. filtration of substances from blood in glomeruli into Bowman's capsules
b. reabsorption of most of water and part of solutes from tubular urine back into blood
c. secretion of certain substances by tubule cells

3. Mechanisms that control volume of urine formed are factors which change
a. amount of water reabsorbed by tubule cells—most important determinant of amount of urine formed; posterior pituitary ADH stimulates distal tubule water reabsorption; corticoids increase sodium reabsorption and therefore also increase water absorption
b. rate of filtration from glomeruli—normally quite constant at about 125 ml. per minute; varies directly with changes in glomerular blood pressure, that is, increased glomerular blood pressure tends to increase urine formation and vice versa but glomerular blood pressure normally quite constant; decreased blood colloidal osmotic pressure (an abnormal condition) tends to increase urine formation and vice versa
c. total extracellular fluid volume; urine output increases following increase in total ECF and decreases following decrease in ECF
d. amount of solutes excreted in urine; urine output increases when solutes increase

Ureters
Location and structure
Lie retroperitoneally; extend from kidneys to posterior part of bladder flood; ureter expands as it enters kidney, becoming renal pelvis which is subdivided into calyces, each of which contains renal papilla; walls of smooth muscle with mucous lining and fibrous outer coat

Functions
Collect urine and drain it into bladder

Bladder
Structure and location
Collapsible bag of smooth muscle lined with mucosa; lies behind symphysis pubis, below parietal peritoneum; three openings—one into urethra and two into ureters

Functions
1. Reservoir for urine
2. Expels urine from body by way of urethra, called micturition, urination, or voiding; retention is inability to expel urine from bladder and suppression is failure of kidneys to secrete urine

Urethra
Structure and location
Musculomembranous tube lined with mucosa; lies behind symphysis, in front of vagina in female; extends through prostate gland, fibrous sheet, and penis in male; opening to exterior called urinary meatus

Functions
1. Female—passageway for expulsion of urine from body
2. Male—passageway for expulsion of urine and of reproductive fluid (semen)

Urine
Physical characteristics
See Table 58

Chemical composition
Consists of approximately 95% water in which are dissolved
1. Wastes from protein metabolism (urea, uric acid, creatinine, etc.)
2. Mineral salts (sodium chloride main one but various others according to diet)
3. Toxins—from bacteria, for example
4. Pigments
5. Sex hormones
6. Abnormal constituents—for example, glucose in diabetes and numerous others such as albumin, blood, casts, and calculi

Definitions
1. Glycosuria—sugar in urine
2. Hematuria—blood in urine
3. Pyuria—pus in urine
4. Casts—microscopic bits of substances which harden and form molds inside tubules
5. Dysuria—painful urination
6. Polyuria—excessive amounts of urine
7. Oliguria—scanty urine
8. Anuria—absence of urine

Review questions

The urinary system

1. What four organs are excretory organs? Which of these eliminate wastes of protein metabolism? Of digestion? Of carbohydrate and fat metabolism?
2. Name, locate, and give main function of each organ of the urinary system.
3. Distinguish between secretion, excretion, and elimination.
4. How far and in which direction must a catheter be inserted to reach the bladder in the female? In the male?
5. Describe the microscopic structure of the kidney.
6. Describe the mechanism of urine formation, relating each step to part of the nephron which performs it.

Situation: An artificial kidney consists of a long cellophane or plastic tube coiled around a large fluid-containing drum. Crystalloids diffuse freely through the tube, but colloids and blood cells cannot pass through it. Blood from a patient is made to flow through the tube. The tube is submerged in the drum fluid. Consult the column below for characteristic quantities of blood and dialyzing fluid constituents.

	Blood plasma (in coiled tube) mEq./L.	Dialyzing fluid (around coiled tube) mEq./L.
Na	142	126
K	5	5
Ca	5	0
Mg	3	0
Cl	103	110
HCO_3	27	25
HPO_4	2	0
SO_4	1	0
	mg./100 ml.	mg./100 ml.
Glucose	100	1750
Urea	26	0
Uric acid	4	0
Creatinine	1	0

7. What body structures do you think the cellophane tube substitutes for?
8. Which, if any, of the above substances diffuse out of the blood into the dialyzing fluid? Give your reasons.
9. Which, if any, of the above substances diffuse into the blood from the dialyzing fluid? Give your reasons.
10. Which, if any, of the above substances do not pass through the cellophane membrane in either direction? Give your reasons.
11. What reasons can you see for having the dialyzing fluid contain the concentration of each substance given above? What does it accomplish?

Situation: Results of a blood urea clearance test indicate that the glomerular filtration rate of a patient who has had a severe hemorrhage is less than 50% of normal.

12. Explain the mechanism responsible for the drop in the glomerular filtration rate.
13. Do you consider this a homeostatic mechanism? Does it serve a useful purpose? If so, what purpose?
14. What is the normal glomerular filtration rate?
15. What would you expect to be true of the volume of urine this patient would excrete—normal, polyuria, oliguria?
16. Define the following terms briefly:

Bowman's capsule	polyuria
calculi	ptosis
calyces	pyelitis
casts	renal capsule
cystitis	renal cortex
dysuria	renal hilum
glomerulus	renal medulla
glycosuria	renal papilla
hematuria	renal pelvis
incontinence	renal pyramids
nephritis	retention
oliguria	suppression

Reproduction of the
human being

Chapter XIII

The reproductive system

Meaning and function

Male reproductive organs
Testis
Excretory ducts of testes
Male accessory reproductive
   glands
Supporting structures of male
   reproductive system
Composition and course of
   seminal fluid

Female reproductive system
Names of organs
Uterus
Uterine tubes
Ovaries
Vagina
Vulva
Perineum
Breasts
Recurring female sexual cycles
Control of female sexual cycles
Function served by female
   sexual cycles
Menarche and menopause

Embryology
Meaning and scope
Value of knowledge of
   embryology
Steps in development of a new
   individual

MEANING AND FUNCTION

The reproductive system consists of those organs whose function is to produce a new individual, that is, to accomplish reproduction and to produce certain hormones. Different forms of life reproduce in different ways, but all living organisms, no matter how simple or how complex, are able to perform this miracle.

Reproduction of cells, of course, must occur in order that reproduction of a multicellular organism may occur. But before pursuing this idea any further, we shall describe the various reproductive organs.

MALE REPRODUCTIVE ORGANS

Glands, ducts, and supporting structures compose the male reproductive system. Glands are the testes, seminal vesicles, prostate, and bulbourethral glands. Epididymis, seminal ducts, and urethra are the names of the ducts. Supporting structures are the scrotum, penis, and spermatic cords.

Testes

Structure and location

The testes are small ovoid glands which lie in a pouchlike, skin-covered structure called the *scrotum*. A white fibrous capsule encases each testis and sends partitions through its interior, dividing it into lobules. Each lobule contains a tiny, coiled *seminiferous tubule* (Fig. 269) and numerous interstitial cells (of Leydig). The seminiferous tubules come together to form a plexus from which a few ducts emerge and enter the head of the epididymis.

Functions

The testes perform two primary functions:

1. Seminiferous tubules produce the male *gametes* or reproductive cells which are called *spermatozoa* or simply sperm. *Spermatogenesis*, then, is one of the testes' functions.

489

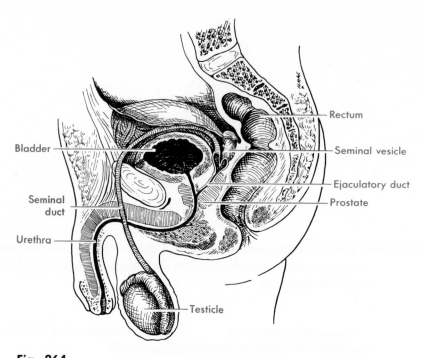

Fig. 264

Sagittal section through the male pelvis. The seminal
duct, encased in the spermatic cord, enters the pelvic cavity from the
scrotum by way of the inguinal canal.

2. Interstitial cells of the testes secrete the hormone testosterone
(androgen or masculinizing hormone) directly into the blood for circulation to structures which it influences. It serves the following general functions:

(a) Testosterone promotes "maleness," the development and maintenance of male secondary sex characteristics.

(b) Testosterone promotes development and maintenance of male
accessory organs such as the prostate, seminal vesicles, etc.

(c) Testosterone promotes development of adult male sexual
behavior.

(d) Testosterone promotes protein synthesis; classed as an anabolic
hormone.

(e) Testosterone inhibits secretion of the gonadotrophic hormone
ICSH (interstitial cell-stimulating hormone; LH or luteinizing
hormone in the female) by the adenohypophysis.

An interesting relationship exists between the adenohypophysis and
the testes and their hormones. It is a kind of seesaw relationship, or in
newer and more scientific terminology, it is a feedback relationship.
The adenohypophysis secrets ICSH. ICSH stimulates the testes (their
interstitial cells). The testes then secrete more testosterone. Testosterone feeds back to inhibit the adenohypophysis. The adenohypophy-

sis then secretes less ICSH. Diagrammed, this relationship is as follows:

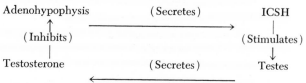

Removal of the testes (orchiectomy, castration) results in both sterility and various changes in the secondary sex characteristics. Why?

Structure of spermatozoa

Fig. 265, A, shows the characteristic parts of a spermatozoon: head, middle piece, and elongated, lashlike tail.

Excretory ducts of the testes
Epididymis
Structure and location

Each epididymis consists of a single tightly coiled tube enclosed in a fibrous casing. The tube has a very small diameter (just barely macroscopic) but measures approximately 20 feet in length. It lies along the top and side of the testis.

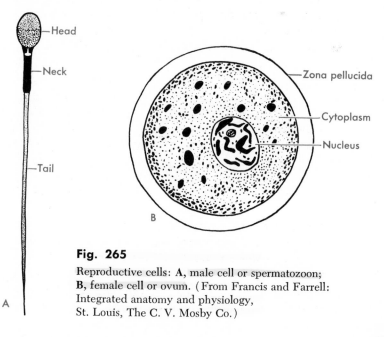

Fig. 265

Reproductive cells: **A**, male cell or spermatozoon; **B**, female cell or ovum. (From Francis and Farrell: Integrated anatomy and physiology, St. Louis, The C. V. Mosby Co.)

Functions

1. It serves as one of the ducts through which sperm pass in their journey from the testis to the exterior.

2. It stores a small quantity of sperm prior to ejaculation. During their stay in the epididymis, sperm become capable of motility, a characteristic necessary to their fertility.

3. It secretes part of the semen.

Seminal duct (vas deferens, ductus deferens)
Structure and location

The seminal duct, like the epididymis, is a tube, in fact, it is an extension of the epididymis. It passes through the inguinal canal where it is enclosed in a fibrous cylinder, the spermatic cord, into the abdominal cavity. Here it extends over the top and down the posterior surface of the bladder where it joins the duct from the seminal vesicle to form the ejaculatory duct (Figs. 266 and 267).

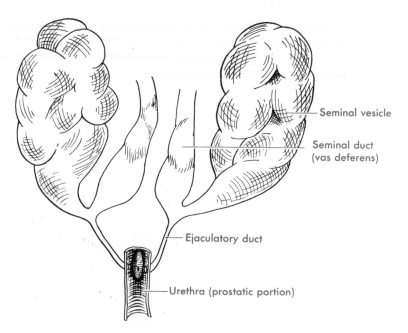

Seminal vesicle

Seminal duct (vas deferens)

Ejaculatory duct

Urethra (prostatic portion)

Fig. 266

Diagram showing formation of the ejaculatory ducts by the union of the seminal duct with the seminal vesicle duct. The ejaculatory ducts join the prostatic portion of the urethra.

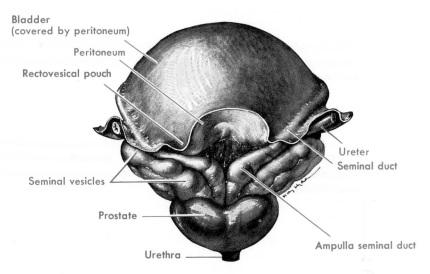

Bladder
(covered by peritoneum)

Peritoneum

Rectovesical pouch

Ureter
Seminal duct

Seminal vesicles

Prostate

Ampulla seminal duct

Urethra

Fig. 267

Bladder and male pelvic reproductive organs viewed from behind.
(From Callander: Surgical anatomy, Philadelphia, W. B. Saunders Co.)

Function

The seminal duct serves as one of the excretory ducts for the testis, connecting the epididymis with the ejaculatory duct.

Correlation

Severing of the seminal ducts, usually through incision in the groin, renders the patient sterile for the obvious reason that sperm can no longer pass all the way through the epididymis to reach the exterior.

Ejaculatory duct

The two ejaculatory ducts are short tubes which pass through the prostate gland to terminate in the urethra. They are formed by the union of the seminal ducts with the ducts from the seminal vesicles.

Urethra

See pp. 482 to 483 for a discussion of the urethra.

Male accessory reproductive glands
Seminal vesicles
Structure and location

The seminal vesicles are convoluted pouches which lie along the lower part of the posterior surface of the bladder, directly in front of the rectum.

493

Function

They secrete the viscous liquid portion of the semen. It contains nutrients that support sperm metabolism. The seminal vesicles, it is now known, do not store sperm.

Prostate gland
Structure and location

This compound tubuloalveolar gland, which lies just below the bladder, is doughnut-shaped. The fact that the urethra passes through the small hole in the center of the prostate is a matter of considerable clinical significance. Many older men suffer from enlargement of this gland. As it enlarges, it squeezes the urethra, frequently closing it so completely that urination becomes impossible and retention results. Surgical removal of the gland (prostatectomy) is resorted to as a cure for this condition when other less radical methods of treatment fail.

Function

The prostate adds a thin alkaline secretion to the seminal fluid. This helps protect the sperm from acid present in the male urethra and female vagina and thereby increases sperm motility. (Acid depresses or, if strong enough, kills sperm. Sperm motility is greatest in neutral or slightly alkaline media.)

Bulbourethral glands
Structure and location

The two bulbourethral or Cowper's glands resemble peas in both size and shape. These compound tubuloalveolar glands lie below the prostate glands. A duct approximately 1 inch long connects them with the membranous portion of the urethra.

Function

Like the prostate, these glands secrete an alkaline fluid important for counteracting the acid present in the male urethra and female vagina.

Supporting structures of the male reproductive system
Supporting structures located externally
Scrotum

The scrotum is a skin-covered pouch suspended from the perineal region. It is more deeply pigmented than the rest of the skin and contains a few coarse hairs. Internally it is divided into two sacs by a septum, each sac containing a testis, epididymis, and lower part of the spermatic cord.

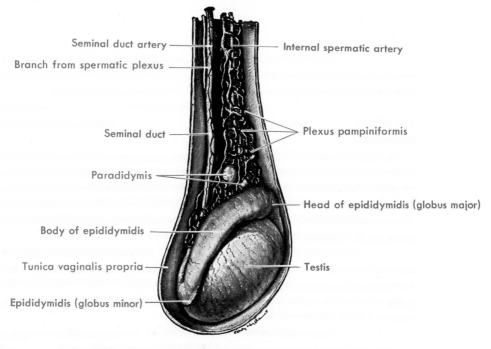

Seminal duct artery —
Branch from spermatic plexus —

— Internal spermatic artery

Seminal duct —

— Plexus pampiniformis

Paradidymis —

— Head of epididymidis (globus major)

Body of epididymidis —

Tunica vaginalis propria —

— Testis

Epididymidis (globus minor) —

Fig. 268

Lateral view of the right spermatic cord and testis. (From Callander: Surgical anatomy, Philadelphia, W. B. Saunders Co.)

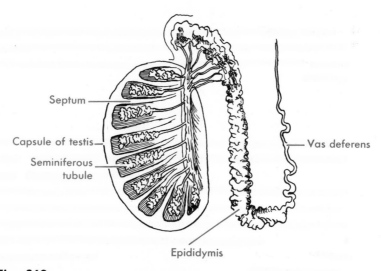

Septum —

Capsule of testis —
Seminiferous tubule —

— Vas deferens

Epididymis

Fig. 269

Diagram of testis to show seminiferous tubules and formation of the epididymis.

Penis

Structure. Three cylindrical masses of erectile or cavernous tissue, enclosed in separate fibrous coverings and held together by a covering of skin, compose the penis. The two larger and uppermost of these cylinders are named the *corpora cavernosa penis*, whereas the smaller, lower one, which contains the urethra, is called the *corpus cavernosum urethrae.*

Erectile tissue which composes these structures resembles a rubber sponge in structure, consisting, as it does, of many irregular cavernous spaces, the venous sinuses. Under the influence of the sexual emotion, the arteries and arterioles of the penis dilate, flooding and distending the cavernous spaces with blood and thereby causing the organ to become enlarged, rigid, and erect.

At the distal end of the penis there is a slightly bulging structure, the *glans penis*, over which the skin is folded doubly to form a more or less loose-fitting, retractable casing known as the *prepuce* or foreskin. If the foreskin fits too tightly about the glans, a circumcision is usually performed to prevent irritation.

Functions. The penis fulfills two functions: it contains the urethra, the terminal duct for both urinary and reproductive tracts, and is the copulatory organ by means of which spermatazoa are introduced into the female vagina. The scrotum and penis together constitute the *external genitals* of the male.

Supporting structure located internally

The *spermatic cords* are cylindrical casings of white fibrous tissue located in the inguinal canals between the scrotum and the abdominal cavity. They enclose the seminal ducts, blood vessels, lymphatics, and nerves.

Composition and course of seminal fluid

The seminal fluid consists of secretions from the epididymides, seminal vesicles, prostate, and bulbourethral glands. Each drop of fluid is said to contain as many as 300 million sperm, formed in the seminiferous tubules in the testes. In traversing the distance from their place of origin to the exterior, the sperm must pass from the testis through the epididymis, seminal duct, ejaculatory duct, and urethra. Note that the male gametes originate in an organ located outside the body (that is, not within a body cavity), travel inside, and finally are expelled outside. Early in fetal life the testes are located in the abdominal cavity but normally descend through the spermatic cord into the scrotum some time before birth. Occasionally a baby is born with undescended testes, a condition readily observed by palpation of the scrotum. Because the higher temperature inside the abdominal cavity makes sperm infertile, measures are taken to bring the testes down into the scrotum in order to prevent sterility.

Ejaculation of the seminal fluid occurs at irregular intervals due to arousal of the sexual emotion.

Male fertility

Male fertility relates to many factors—for example, to the size, shape, and number of sperm ejaculated. Fertile sperm have a uniform size and shape. They are highly motile. Although only one sperm fertilizes an ovum, millions of sperm seem to be necessary for fertilization to occur. When the sperm count falls below about 60 million per milliliter of semen, sterility usually results.

One hypothesis suggested to explain this puzzling fact is this: semen that contains an adequate number of sperm also contains enough hyaluronidase to liquefy the intercellular cement between the cells that encase each ovum. Without this, a single sperm cannot penetrate the layers of cells (corona radiata) around the ovum and hence cannot fertilize it.

FEMALE REPRODUCTIVE SYSTEM

Names of organs

The following organs compose the female reproductive system:
1. *primary sex organs*—the two ovaries (female gonads).
2. *secondary sex organs*—two uterine tubes (fallopian tubes or oviducts), one uterus, one vagina, one vulva (pudendum or external genitals), and two breasts or mammary glands.

Uterus

Structure

Size, shape, and divisions

The uterus is pear-shaped in its virgin state and measures approximately three inches in length, two inches in width at its widest part, and one inch in thickness. It is composed of two parts: an upper portion, the *body*, and a lower, narrow section, the *cervix*. The body rounds into a bulging prominence above the level at which the uterine tubes enter; this bulging upper surface is called the *fundus*.

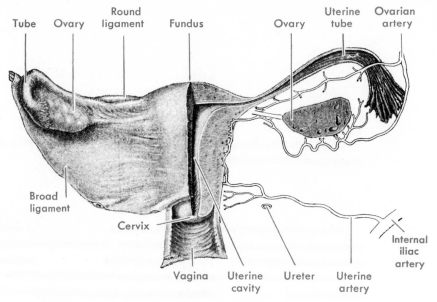

Tube   Ovary   Round   Fundus   Ovary   Uterine   Ovarian
                 ligament   tube   artery

Broad
ligament

Cervix

Internal
iliac
artery

Vagina   Uterine   Ureter   Uterine
          cavity   artery

Fig. 270

Female reproductive organs. The left half shows the tube and ovary in their natural relationship; the right half is a diagrammatic section. (From Pitzman: Fundamentals of human anatomy, St. Louis, The C. V. Mosby Co.)

Wall

Three coats compose the walls of the uterus.

1. A lining of mucous membrane called *endometrium*. Three layers of tissues compose the endometrium: a compact surface layer of columnar epithelium, a spongy middle layer of loose connective tissue, and a basal layer of dense connective tissue that attaches the endometrium to the underlying myometrium. During menstruation and following delivery of a baby, the compact and spongy layers slough off.

2. A thick, middle coat (the *myometrium*) consists of three layers of smooth muscle fibers which extend in all directions, longitudinally, transversely, obliquely, and give the uterus great strength. The myometrium is thickest in the fundus and thinnest in the cervix—a good example of the principle of structural adaptation to function. In order to expel a fetus, that is, move it down and out of the uterus, the fundus must contract more forcibly than the lower part of the uterine wall and the cervix must be stretched or dilated.

3. An external coat of serous membrane, the parietal peritoneum—this coat is incomplete as it covers none of the cervix and only part of the body (all except the lower one-fourth of its anterior surface). The fact that the entire uterus is not covered with peritoneum has clinical value because it makes it possible to perform operations on this organ without the risk of infection which attends cutting into the peritoneum.

Cavities

The cavities of the uterus are small due to the thickness of its walls. The body cavity is flat and triangular; its apex is directed downward and constitutes the *internal os* which opens into the *cervical canal.* The cervical canal is constricted on its lower end also, forming the *external os,* which opens into the vagina. The uterine tubes open into the body cavity at its upper, outer angles.

Blood supply

The uterus receives a generous supply of blood from uterine arteries, branches of the internal iliac arteries.

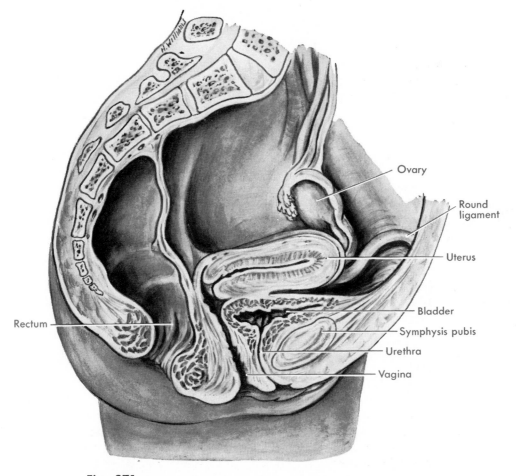

Fig. 271
Sagittal section of the female pelvis.

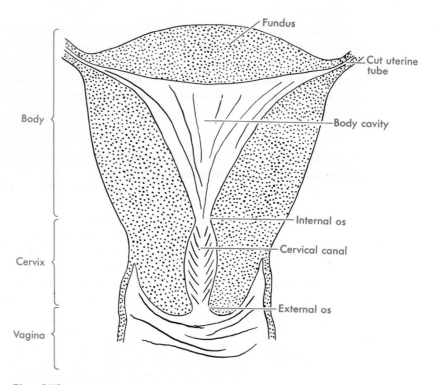

Fig. 272

Diagram of a frontal section view of the uterus showing the divisions.

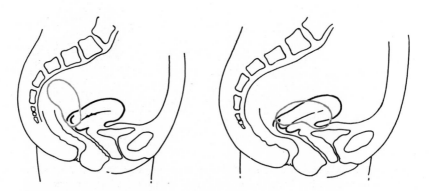

Fig. 273

Normal and abnormal positions of the uterus. Dotted lines show the abnormal positions: **A,** retroflexion; **B,** anteflexion.

Location

The uterus is located in the pelvic cavity between the bladder and rectum.

Position

1. *Normally* the uterus is flexed between the body and cervix, with the body lying over the superior surface of the bladder, pointing forward and slightly upward. The cervix points downward and backward from the point of flexion, joining the vagina at approximately a right angle. Several ligaments hold the uterus in place but allow its body considerable movement, a characteristic which often leads to malpositions of the organ.

2. The uterus may lie in any one of several *abnormal positions;* a common one is retroversion or backward tilting of the entire organ.

3. *Eight ligaments* (three pairs, two single ones) anchor the uterus in the pelvic cavity. Six of these so-called ligaments are actually extensions of the parietal peritoneum in different directions. The other two are fibromuscular cords. The names and brief descriptions of these are as follows:

    1. *two broad ligaments*—double folds of parietal peritoneum which form a kind of partition across the pelvic cavity; the uterus is suspended between these two folds.

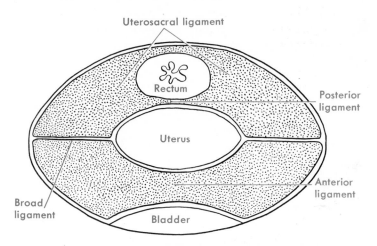

Fig. 274

Scheme to show the relative positions of the six uterine ligaments formed by folds of the peritoneum: the two broad ligaments, double folds of peritoneum extending from the uterus to the side walls of the pelvic cavity; the two uterosacral ligaments, foldlike extensions of peritoneum from the uterus to the sacrum; the posterior ligament, a fold of peritoneum between the uterus and rectum; and the anterior ligament, a fold of peritoneum between the uterus and bladder.

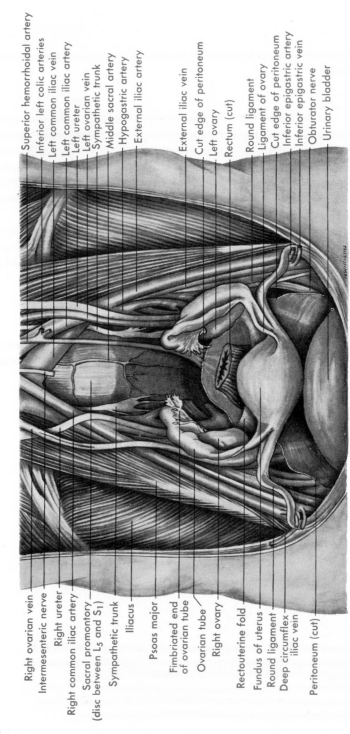

Right ovarian vein
Intermesenteric nerve
Right ureter
Right common iliac artery
Sacral promontory
(disc between L$_5$ and S$_1$)
Sympathetic trunk
Iliacus
Psoas major
Fimbriated end
of ovarian tube
Ovarian tube
Right ovary
Rectouterine fold
Fundus of uterus
Round ligament
Deep circumflex
iliac vein
Peritoneum (cut)

Superior hemorrhoidal artery
Inferior left colic arteries
Left common iliac vein
Left common iliac artery
Left ureter
Left ovarian vein
Sympathetic trunk
Middle sacral artery
Hypogastric artery
External iliac artery
External iliac vein
Cut edge of peritoneum
Left ovary
Rectum (cut)
Round ligament
Ligament of ovary
Cut edge of peritoneum
Inferior epigastric artery
Inferior epigastric vein
Obturator nerve
Urinary bladder

Fig. 275

Female pelvis viewed from in front and above. (From Francis and Farrell:
Integrated anatomy and physiology, St. Louis, The C. V. Mosby Co.)

2. *two uterosacral ligaments*—foldlike extensions of the peritoneum from the posterior surface of the uterus to the sacrum, one on each side of the rectum.
3. *one posterior ligament*—a fold of peritoneum extending from the posterior surface of the uterus to the rectum; this ligament forms a deep pouch known as the *cul-de-sac of Douglas* (or rectouterine pouch) between the uterus and rectum. Since this is the lowest point in the pelvic cavity, pus collects here in pelvic inflammations. To secure drainage, an incision may be made at the top of the posterior wall of the vagina (posterior colpotomy).
4. *one anterior ligament*—the fold of peritoneum formed by the extension of the peritoneum on the anterior surface of the uterus to the posterior surface of the bladder; this fold also forms a cul-de-sac but one which is less deep than the posterior pouch.
5. *two round ligaments*—fibromuscular cords extending from the upper, outer angles of the uterus through the inguinal canals and disappearing in the labia majora.

Functions

The uterus or womb accomplishes three highly important, though nonvital, functions.

1. *Menstruation* is a sloughing away of the compact and spongy layers of the endometrium, attended by bleeding from the torn vessels.

2. *Pregnancy.* The embryo implants itself in the endometrium and there lives as a parasite throughout the fetal period.

3. *Labor* consists of powerful, rhythmic contractions of the muscular uterine wall which result in expulsion of the fetus or birth.

Uterine tubes (fallopian tubes, oviducts)

Location

The uterine tubes are attached to the uterus at its upper outer angles. They lie between the folds of the broad ligaments and extend upward and outward toward the sides of the pelvis and then curve downward and backward.

Structure

The same three coats (mucous, smooth muscle, serous) of the uterus compose the tubes. The mucosa of the tubes, however, is ciliated. At the distal end, each tube expands into a funnel-like portion called the *infundibulum*. The open outer margin of the infundibulum resembles a fringe in its irregular outline; the fringelike projections are known as *fimbriae*. Here the mucous lining of the tubes is directly continuous

503

with the peritoneum—a fact of great clinical significance because the tubal mucosa is continuous with that of the uterus and vagina, and, therefore, often becomes infected by gonococci or other organisms introduced into the vagina. And inflammation of the tubes (salpingitis) may readily spread to become inflammation of the peritoneum (peritonitis), a serious condition. In the male there is no such direct route by which microorganisms can reach the peritoneum from the exterior.

Each tube is approximately 4 inches long.

Function

The tubes serve as ducts for the female gametes (ova) even though they are not actually connected to the ovaries, the organs which produce the ova. Fertilization, the union of a spermatazoon with an ovum, normally occurs in the tubes.

Ovaries (female gonads)

Location and size

These glands, which resemble large almonds in size and shape, are located one on either side of the uterus, below and behind the uterine tubes. Each ovary lies between the folds of the broad ligament and is attached to its posterior surface by the mesovarian ligament. The ovarian ligament anchors it to the uterus. The distal portion of the tube curves about the ovary in such a way that the fimbriae cup over the ovary but do not actually attach to it. Here, then, is a gland whose duct is detached from it, a fact which makes possible pregnancy in the pelvic cavity instead of in the uterus as is normal.

Microscopic structure

The surface of the ovary consists of a single layer of germinal epithelial cells, whereas its interior is made up of connective tissue in which are embedded thousands of microscopic structures known as *graafian follicles*. After puberty the follicles are present in varying stages of development (Fig. 276). The primordial follicles consist of an *ovum* encased in a nest of epithelial cells. Before puberty, all the follicles are in this stage. Development of the follicles after puberty is discussed on p. 510.

Functions

The ovary develops and matures the ova and discharges them into the pelvic cavity (ovulation). It also secretes the female hormones—estrogens and progesterone. More details about their secretion and their functions appear on pp. 510 to 517.

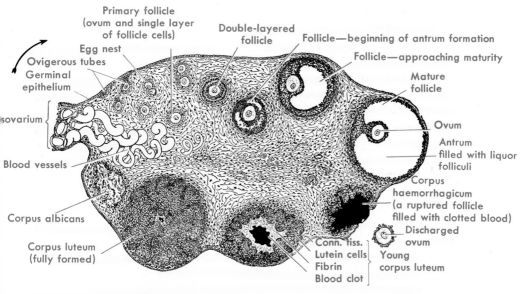

Fig. 276

Diagram of a mammalian ovary showing the life cycle of an ovarian follicle and egg. The successive stages are arranged clockwise starting with the arrow. (From Patten: Embryology of the pig, New York, The Blakiston Co.)

Fig. 277

Uterine tube and ovary with mature graafian follicle. (From Arey: Developmental anatomy, Philadelphia, W. B. Saunders Co.)

Vagina

Location

The vagina is situated between the rectum which lies posterior, and the urethra and bladder which lie anterior to it; it extends upward and backward from its external orifice.

Structure

The vagina is a collapsible tube, capable of great distention, is composed mainly of smooth muscle, and is lined with mucous membrane arranged in rugae. Its anterior wall, which measures from 2½ to 3 inches in length, is about 1 inch shorter than the posterior wall because the cervix protrudes into the uppermost portion of the anterior wall. A fold of mucous membrane, the *hymen*, forms a border around the external opening of the vagina, partially closing the orifice, in the virginal state. Occasionally, this structure completely covers the vaginal outlet, a condition referred to as *imperforate hymen*. Perforation has to be done before the menstrual flow can escape.

Functions

The vagina constitutes an essential part of the reproductive tract because of the following:

1. It is the organ which receives the seminal fluid from the male.
2. It serves as the lower part of the birth canal.
3. It acts as the excretory duct for uterine secretions and the menstrual flow.

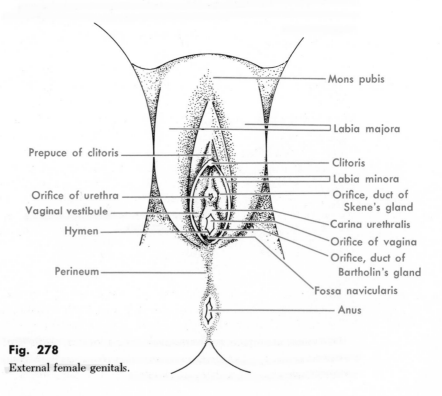

Fig. 278

External female genitals.

Vulva

Fig. 278 shows the structures which together constitute the female external genitals (reproductive organs) or vulva. They are as follows.

1. *mons veneris* or mons pubis—a skin-covered pad of fat over the symphysis pubis; coarse hairs appear on this structure at puberty and persist throughout life.
2. *labia majora* or large lips—covered with pigmented skin and hair on the outer surface and smooth and free from hair on the inner surface; composed mainly of fat and numerous glands.
3. *labia minora* or "small lips"—located within the labia majora, covered with modified skin; these two lips come together anteriorly in the midline; the area between the labia minora is the *vestibule*.
4. *clitoris*—a small organ composed of erectile tissue, located just behind the junction of the labia minora and homologous to the corpora cavernosa and glans of the penis; the *prepuce* or foreskin covers the clitoris, as it does the glans penis in the male.
5. *urinary meatus*—the small opening of the urethra, situated between the clitoris and vaginal orifice.
6. *vaginal orifice*—an opening, which, in the virginal state, is usually only slightly larger than the urinary meatus because of the constricting border formed by the hymen. In the marital state the vaginal orifice is noticeably larger than the meatus. It is located posterior to the meatus.
7. *Bartholin's glands* or the *greater vestibular glands*—two bean-shaped glands, one on either side of the vaginal orifice; each gland opens by means of a single, long duct into the space between the hymen and the labium minus; are of clinical importance because they are frequently infected (bartholinitis or Bartholin's abscess), particularly by the gonococcus; are homologous to the bulbourethral glands in the male; secrete a lubricating fluid. Opening into the vestibule near the urinary meatus by way of two small ducts is a group of tiny mucous glands, the *lesser vestibular* or *Skene's glands*. These have clinical interest because gonococci which lodge there are difficult to eradicate.

Perineum

The perineum is the skin-covered muscular region between the vaginal orifice and the anus. This area has great clinical importance because of the danger of its being torn during childbirth. If the tear is deep, it may extend all the way through the perineum and even through the anal sphincter, resulting in involuntary seepage from the rectum until the laceration is repaired. To avoid this possibility, an incision known as an *episiotomy* is usually made in the perineum, particularly at the birth of a first baby.

Breasts

Location and size

The breasts lie over the pectoral muscles and are attached to them by a layer of connective tissue (fascia). Estrogens and progesterone, two ovarian hormones, control their development during puberty. Estrogens stimulate growth of the ducts of the mammary glands, whereas progesterone stimulates development of the alveoli, the actual secreting cells. Breast size is determined more by the amount of fat around the glandular tissue than by the amount of glandular tissue itself. Hence, the size of the breast does not relate to its functional ability.

Structure

Each breast consists of several lobes separated by septa of connective tissue. Each lobe consists of several lobules, which, in turn, are composed of connective tissue in which are embedded the secreting cells (alveoli) of the gland, arranged in grapelike clusters around

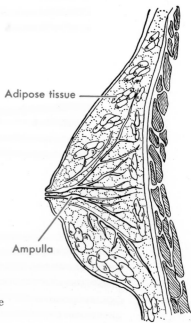

Adipose tissue

Ampulla

Fig. 279

Structure of the breast. Note the position of the breast superficial to the pectoralis major muscle.

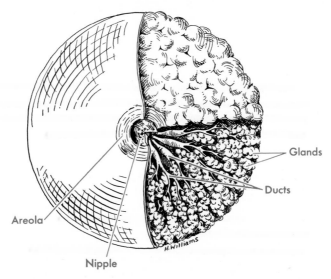

Fig. 280

Anterior view of breast. The skin has been removed in the upper right
quadrant to show the deposits of adipose tissue. In the lower right
quadrant the adipose tissue has been removed to show the mammary glands.

minute ducts. The ducts from the various lobules unite, forming a
single excretory duct for each lobe, or between fifteen and twenty in
each breast. These main ducts converge toward the nipple, like the
spokes of a wheel. They enlarge slightly before reaching the nipple
into ampullae or small "reservoirs" (Fig. 279). Each of these main
ducts terminates in a tiny opening on the surface of the nipple. Adipose tissue is deposited around the surface of the gland, just under the
skin, and between the lobes (Fig. 280). The nipples are bordered by a
circular pigmented area, the *areola*. It contains numerous sebacous
glands which appear as small nodules under the skin. The areola and
nipple change color from delicate pink to brown early in pregnancy,
a fact of value in diagnosing a first pregnancy. The color decreases
after lactation has ceased but never entirely returns to the virginal hue.

Function

The function of the mammary glands is lactation, that is, the secretion of milk for the nourishment of newborn infants.

Mechanism controlling lactation

Very briefly, lactation is controlled as follows:

1. Estrogens and progesterone make the breasts structurally ready
for secretion.

2. The baby's suckling movements initiate reflex secretion of prolactin (lactogenic hormone or luteotrophin) by the adenohypophysis.

3. Prolactin stimulates alveoli of the mammary glands to secrete
milk.

509

Milk secretion starts about the third or fourth day after delivery of a baby, supplanting a thin, yellowish secretion called *colostrum*. With repeated stimulation by the suckling infant, the milk usually continues to form for six to nine months or even longer.

Recurring female sexual cycles

Many changes recur periodically in the female during the years between the onset of the menses (menarche) and their cessation (menopause or climacteric). Most obvious, of course, is menstruation—the outward sign of changes in the endometrium. Most women also note periodic changes in the breasts. But these are only two of many behind-the-scenes changes that occur over and over again at fairly uniform intervals during the thirty some years of female reproductive maturity. Rhythmical changes also take place in the ovaries, the myometrium, the vagina, hormone secretion, body temperature, and even in mood or "emotional tone." We shall investigate some of the details known or postulated about changes in the ovaries, endometrium, myometrium, and hormones and the relations between these changes.

Ovarian cycles

Once each month, on about the first day of menstruation, several primordial graafian follicles and their enclosed ova begin to grow and develop. The follicular cells proliferate and start to secrete estrogens, one kind of female hormone, in increasing amounts for about two weeks. Usually only one follicle matures and migrates to the surface of the ovary (Fig. 277). The surface of the follicle degenerates, causing expulsion of the mature ovum into the pelvic cavity (ovulation). When does ovulation occur? This is a question of great practical importance and one that has been given many answers. Present-day physiologists most frequently answer that ovulation usually occurs fourteen days before the next menstrual period begins. But, they quickly add, there are exceptions to this general rule. Ovulation may even take place nineteen or more days before the onset of the next menses. (A few women experience pain within a few hours after ovulation. This is referred to as *mittelschmerz*—German for middle pain. It has been ascribed to irritation of the peritoneum by hemorrhage from the ruptured follicle.)

Shortly before ovulation the ovum undergoes a special type of mitosis (called miosis) in which its number of chromosomes is reduced by half. Immediately after ovulation, cells of the ruptured follicle enlarge and, due to the appearance of lipoid substances in them, become transformed into a golden-colored body, the *corpus luteum*. The corpus luteum grows for seven or eight days. During this time it secretes the hormones progesterone and estrogens in increasing amounts. Then, provided that fertilization of the ovum did not occur, the size of the corpus luteum and the amount of its secretions gradually diminish. By the twenty-sixth or twenty-seventh day following onset of the menses, progesterone secretion has ceased entirely and estrogen production has reached a minimum. About two days later another menses starts presumably because of the low blood levels of estrogens and progesterones.

Endometrial cycle or menstrual cycle

During menstruation, necrotic bits of the compact and spongy layers of the endometrium slough off, leaving denuded bleeding areas. Following menstruation, the cells of these layers proliferate, causing the endometrium to reach a thickness of 2 or 3 millimeters by the time of ovulation. During this period, endometrial glands and arterioles have lengthened and become more coiled—two factors that also contribute to the thickening of the endometrium. After ovulation the endometrium grows still thicker (reaching a maximum of about 4 to 6 millimeters), but most of this increase is believed due to swelling produced by fluid retention rather than to further proliferation of endometrial cells. The increasingly tortuous endometrial glands start to secrete during the time between ovulation and the next menses. Then, the day before menstruation starts again, the tightly coiled arterioles constrict, producing endometrial ischemia. This leads to necrosis, sloughing, and, once again, menstrual bleeding.

The menstrual cycle is customarily divided into phases, named for major events occurring in them. Their names and the approximate times they take place are as follows:

1. *menses* or menstrual period—cycle days 1 to 5; some individual variation.

2. *preovulatory phase*—days between the end of the menses and ovulation; usually cycle days 6 to 13, but may be considerably longer. Also called estrogenic or follicular phase because of high blood estrogen content due to secretion by the developing follicle. Proliferative phase is still another name for this phase because proliferation of endometrial cells occurs at this time.

3. *ovulation*—day on which mature follicle ruptures, expelling its ovum into pelvic cavity (between the folds of the broad ligaments). Occurs frequently on cycle day 15 in a 28-day cycle but differs according to the length of the preovulatory phase. For example, in a 32-day cycle, the preovulatory phase would

511

probably last until cycle day 18, and ovulation would then occur on cycle day 19 instead of 15.

4. *premenstrual phase*—days between ovulation and onset of menses. Also called luteal phase because corpus luteum secretes during this time, and progesterone phase because this hormone is secreted only during this phase. Length of this premenstrual phase is pretty constant, lasting usually 14 days, that is, cycle days 15 to 28. Differences in length of total menstrual cycle, therefore, exist mainly because of differences in duration of the preovulatory rather than of the premenstrual phase.

Myometrial cycle

The myometrium contracts mildly but with increasing frequency during the two weeks preceding ovulation. Contractions decrease or disappear between ovulation and the next menses, thereby lessening the probability of expulsion of an implanted ovum.

Gonadotrophic cycles

The adenohypophysis (anterior pituitary gland) secretes three hormones which influence female reproductive organs and their functions. They are the follicle-stimulating hormone (FSH), the luteinizing hormone (LH), and luteotrophic hormone (LTH, prolactin, or lactogenic hormone). Collectively FSH, LH, and LTH are called gonadotrophins. The amount of each gonadotrophin secreted varies with a rhythmical regularity that can be related, as we shall see, to the rhythmical ovarian and uterine changes just described.

Control of female sexual cycles

Physiologists agree that hormones play the major role in producing the cyclic changes characteristic in the female during the years of reproductive maturity. Much, however, remains unknown or controversial about the specific actions of the hormones involved. By correlating the changing concentrations of the three pituitary gonadotrophins with the monthly ovarian and uterine changes, investigators have arrived at a working hypothesis about the main features of the control mechanisms.

A brief description follows of the mechanisms which produce cyclical changes in the ovaries, uterus, and in the amounts of gonadotrophins secreted.

Cyclical changes in the ovaries result from cyclical changes in the amounts of gonadotrophins secreted by the adenohypophysis. An increasing blood FSH concentration has two effects: it stimulates one or

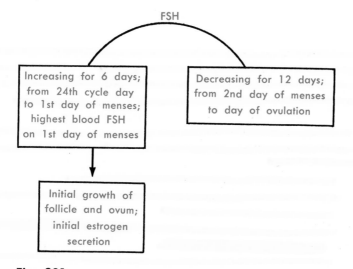

Fig. 281

Ovarian changes produced by FSH. Cycle days shown in
the diagram are approximate.

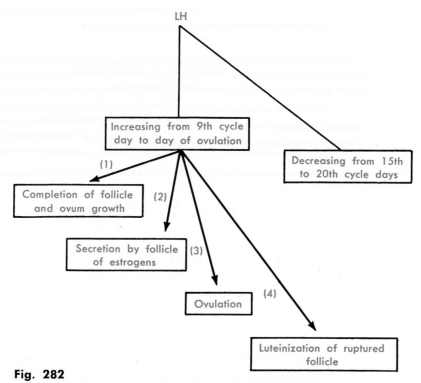

Fig. 282

Ovarian changes produced by LH. Because LH causes ovulation
and luteinization, it is known as both the ovulating and the
luteinizing hormone. Cycle days stated in diagram are approximate.

513

more primitive graafian follicles and ova to start growing, and it stimulates the follicles to start secreting estrogens. Blood FSH concentration increases during the premenstrual phase, from about the twenty-fourth day of the menstrual cycle until menstruation starts (Fig. 281 shows ovarian change produced by FSH).

Several days before ovulation, the adenohypophysis starts to release increasing amounts of LH into the blood. LH brings about four ovarian changes:

1. Completion of growth of the follicle and ovum.
2. Increasing secretion of estrogens by the follicle during preovulatory phase in menstrual cycle.
3. Rupturing of the mature follicle with expulsion of its ripe ovum (process known as *ovulation*).
4. Formation of a golden body, the corpus luteum, in the ruptured follicle (process called *luteinization*). The name luteinizing hormone refers, obviously, to the fourth of the foregoing LH functions. And because of the third function LH is also called "the ovulating hormone." Blood LH concentration increases from about the ninth cycle day until ovulation (Fig. 282 shows ovarian changes produced by LH).

LTH secretion by the adenohypophysis starts to increase about two days before ovulation. The increase in blood LTH concentration stimulates the corpus luteum to secrete progesterone and estrogens (Fig. 283). If pregnancy does not occur, the corpus luteum reaches its maximum development in about 8 days and then starts to regress. Gradually, fibrous tissue (corpus albicans) replaces it. On or about cycle day 25 the corpus luteum stops secreting both progesterone and estrogens. Their blood concentrations drop precipitously. Without their

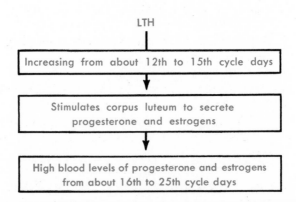

Fig. 283

Ovarian changes produced by LTH.

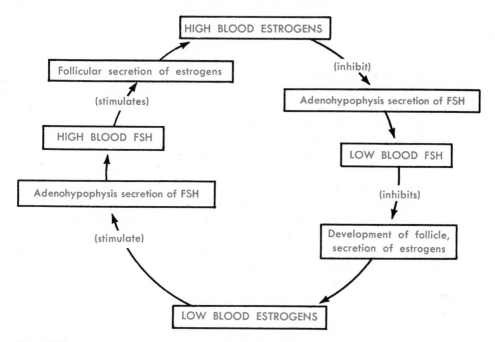

Fig. 284

Feedback mechanism for controlling secretion of FSH and estrogens.
High blood level of FSH stimulates estrogen secretion, whereas
resulting high estrogen level inhibits FSH secretion. How does
this compare with ICSH-testosterone feedback mechanism? (See
p. 491 if you want to check your answer.)

stimulation, the endometrium degenerates rapidly and starts to bleed.
Menstruation, in other words, occurs, and another menstrual cycle has
begun.

Cyclical changes in the uterus are brought about by changing blood
concentrations of estrogens and progesterone. As blood estrogens increase during the preovulatory phase of the menstrual cycle, they produce the following main changes in the uterus:

1. Proliferation of endometrial cells, producing a thickening of the
   endometrium.
2. Growth of endometrial glands.
3. Increase in the water content of the endometrium.
4. Increased myometrial contractions.

Increasing blood progesterone concentration during the premenstrual
phase of the menstrual cycle produces the following main changes
in the uterus:

1. Secretion by endometrial glands.
2. Slight enlargement and tight coiling of the spiral arteries of the
   uterus.
3. Increase in the water content of the endometrium.
4. Decreased myometrial contractions.

515

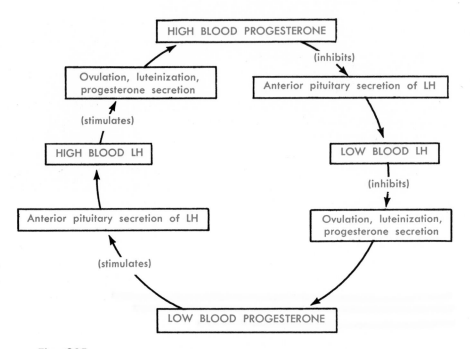

Fig. 285

Feedback mechanism for controlling LH and progesterone secretion. Note inverse relationship between blood concentration of progesterone and rate of LH secretion but direct relationship between blood concentration of LH and rate of progesterone secretion.

Cyclical changes in the amounts of gonadotrophins secreted by the adenohypophysis result from changes in the blood levels of estrogens and progesterone. For example, high blood estrogens inhibit FSH secretion, and low blood estrogens stimulate FSH secretion. High blood levels of progesterone, on the other hand, are thought to inhibit LH secretion. In recent years this information has been applied as a birth control method. Commercial preparations containing progesterone and estrogens are given daily for a number of days to produce a high concentration of both hormones in the blood. This in turn inhibits pituitary secretion of FSH and LH, and because of their deficiency in the blood, a follicle and its ovum are not stimulated to mature that month. With no mature ovum to be expelled, ovulation does not occur, and therefore pregnancy cannot occur. The next menses, however, does take place—because the progesterone and estrogen dosage is stopped in time to allow their blood levels to decrease as they normally do near the end of the cycle to bring on menstruation.

Function served by female sexual cycles

The major function seems to be to prepare the endometrium each month for a pregnancy. If it does not occur, the thick vascular lining, no longer needed, is shed.

If fertilization of the ovum (pregnancy) occurs, the menstrual cycle is modified as follows:

1. The corpus luteum does not disappear but persists and continues to secrete progesterone and estrogens for six months or more of pregnancy. If it is removed by any means during the early months of pregnancy, spontaneous abortion results.

2. The fertilized ovum, which immediately starts developing into an embryo, travels down the tube and implants itself in the endometrium, so carefully prepared for this event.

Menarche and menopause

The menstrual flow first occurs (menarche) at puberty, at about the age of 13 years, although there is wide individual variation according to race, nutrition, health, heredity, etc. Normally it recurs about every twenty-eight days for some thirty odd years, except during pregnancy, and then ceases (menopause or climacteric) at the age of 45 years or thereabout.

EMBRYOLOGY
Meaning and scope

Embryology is the science of the development of the individual before birth. It is a story of miracles, describing the means by which a new human life is started and the steps by which a single microscopic cell is transformed into a complex human being. In a work of this kind, it seems feasible to include only a few of the main points in the de-

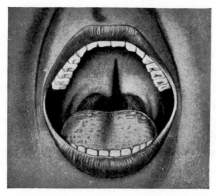

Fig. 286

Cleft palate, the result of an embryological malformation. (From Campbell: A textbook of surgical anatomy, Philadelphia, W. B. Saunders Co.)

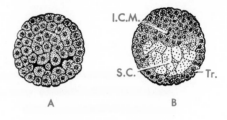

Fig. 287

Stages in the development of the human embryo. **A,** the hypothetical morula, a solid, spherical mass of cells; **B,** the blastocyst, a hollow ball of cells with an inner cell mass; **I.C.M.,** inner cell mass: **S.C.,** blastocyst cavity; **Tr.,** trophoblast. (From Arey: Developmental anatomy, Philadelphia, W. B. Saunders Co.)

velopment of the new individual since the facts amassed by the science of embryology are so many and so intricate that volumes have been written about them.

Value of knowledge of embryology

The main value to the medical profession of knowing the steps by which a new individual is evolved lies in their explanation of various congenital deformities. For example, one of the most common malformations is harelip, a condition which results from imperfect fusion of the frontal and maxillary processes during embryonic development.

Steps in the development of a new individual
Preliminary processes

Production of a new human being starts with the union of a spermotozoon and an ovum to form a single cell. Several preliminary steps, however, are necessary before such a union can take place.

Maturation of the sex cells (miosis*). Reduction in number of chromosomes to one-half original number. Only when maturation has occurred are the ovum and spermatozoon mature and ready to unite with each other. The necessity for chromosome reduction as a preliminary to union of the sex cells is explained by the fact that the cells of each species of living organisms contain a specific number of chromosomes. Human cells, for example, contain 46 chromosomes. If the male and female cells united without first halving their respective chromosomes, the resulting cell would contain twice as many chromosomes as is specific for human beings. Mature ova and sperm, therefore, contain only 23 chromosomes or one-half as many as other human cells. Of these, one is the sex chromosome and may be either one of two types, known as X or Y. All ova contain an X chromosome. Sperm, on the other hand, have either an X or a Y chromosome. As far as is known at the present time, a female child results from the union of an X chromosome-bearing sperm with an ovum and a male child from the union of a Y chromosome-bearing sperm with an ovum.

---

*For a discussion of miosis consult a textbook of histology or of biology.

Ovulation and insemination. The second preliminary step necessary for conception of a new individual consists in bringing the sperm and ovum into proximity with each other so that the union of the two can take place. Two processes are involved in the accomplishment of this step.

1. Ovulation or expulsion of the mature ovum from the graafian follicle into the pelvic cavity, from which it enters one of the uterine tubes.

2. Insemination or expulsion of the seminal fluid from the male urethra into the female vagina. Several million sperm enter the female reproductive tract with each ejaculation of semen. By lashing movements of their flagella-like tails, assisted somewhat by muscular contractions of surrounding structures, the sperm make their way into the external os of the cervix, through the cervical canal and uterine cavity, and into the tubes.

Developmental processes

Fertilization or union of a male and a female gamete to produce a one-celled individual called a zygote. The sperm "swim" up the tube toward the ovum. Although numerous sperm surround the ovum, only one is permitted to penetrate it. As soon as the head and middle piece of one spermatozoon enter the ovum (the tailpiece dropping off), the remaining sperm are repulsed and cannot enter. The sperm head then forms itself into a nucleus which approaches and eventually fuses with the nucleus of the ovum, producing, at that moment, a new single-celled individual or *zygote*. One-half of the 46 chromosomes in the zygote nucleus came from the sperm and one-half from the ovum. Since chromosomes are composed of *genes* or inheritance determinants, the new being inherits one-half of its characteristics from its father and one-half from its mother.

Normally fertilization occurs in the uterine tube. Occasionally, however, it takes place in the pelvic cavity, as evidenced by pregnancies which start to develop in the pelvic cavity instead of in the uterus.

Inasmuch as the ovum lives only a short time (probably less than forty-eight hours) after leaving the graafian follicle, fertilization can occur only around the time of ovulation (p. 511). Sperm also have short-lived fertility, probably only about 24 hours after entering the female tract.

Cleavage or segmentation. Cleavage consists of repeated mitotic divisions, first of the zygote to form two cells, then of those two cells to form four cells, and so on, resulting, in about three days' time, in the formation of a solid, spherical mass of cells known as a *morula.* About this time the embryo reaches the uterus, where it starts to implant itself in the endometrium. Occasionally, implantation occurs in the tube or pelvic cavity instead of in the uterus; the condition is known as an *ectopic pregnancy*.

As the cells of the morula continue to divide, a hollow ball of cells or *blastocyst*, consisting of an outer layer of cells and an inner cell mass, is formed. Implantation in the uterine lining is now complete. About ten days have elapsed since fertilization. The cells which compose the outer wall of the blastocyst are known as trophoblasts; they eventually become part of the placenta, the structure which anchors the fetus to the uterus.

Differentiation. As the cells composing the inner mass of the blastocyst continue to divide, they arrange themselves into a structure shaped like a figure eight, containing two cavities separated by a double-layered plate of cells known as the *embryonic disc.* The youngest human embryos examined have been at this stage or about two weeks old dated from the time of fertilization. The cells which form the cavity above the embryonic disc eventually become a fluid-filled, shock-absorbing sac (the amnion) in which the fetus floats. The cells of the lower cavity form the yolk sac, a small vesicle attached to the belly of the embryo until about the middle of the second month, when it breaks away. Only the double layer of cells which compose the embryonic disc is destined to form the new individual. The upper layer of cells is called the *ectodermal layer* and the lower layer the *entoderm*. A third layer of cells, known as the *mesoderm*, develops between the ectoderm and entoderm. Up to this time all the cells have appeared alike, but now they are differentiated into three distinct types, ectodermal, mesodermal, and entodermal, known as the *primary germ layers*, each of which will give rise to definite structures. For example, the ectoderm cells will form the skin and its appendages and the nervous system; the mesoderm, the muscles, bones, and various other connective tissues; the entoderm, the epithelium of the digestive and respiratory tracts, etc.

Histogenesis and organogenesis. The story of how the primary germ layers develop into many different kinds of tissues (histogenesis) and how those tissues arrange themselves into organs (organogenesis) is long and complicated. Its telling belongs to the science of embryology. Enough for the beginning student of anatomy to appreciate that life begins when two sex cells unite to form a single cell, that the new human body evolves by a series of processes consisting of cell multiplication, cell growth, cell differentiation, and cell rearrangements, all of which take place in definite, orderly sequence. By the end of the second month, a recognizable human form has been attained. At the end of another month the sex is clearly distinguishable, and from then until birth, development is mainly a matter of growth.

Outline summary

The reproductive system

Meaning and function

Consists of organs which together produce new individual

Male reproductive organs

1. Gonads, testes (paired)
2. Series of ducts
   a. epididymis (paired)
   b. seminal ducts, vas deferens, or ductus deferens (paired)
   c. ejaculatory ducts (paired)
   d. urethra
3. Accessory glands
   a. seminal vesicles (paired)
   b. prostate gland
   c. bulbourethral (Cowper's) glands paired
4. Supporting structures
   a. external—scrotum and penis
   b. internal—spermatic cords (paired)

Testis

1. Structure and location—several lobules composed of seminiferous tubules and interstitial cells (of Leydig), separated by septa, encased in fibrous capsule; few ducts emerge from top of organ and enter head of epididymis; located in scrotum, one testis in each of two scrotal compartments
2. Functions
   a. spermatogenesis—formation of mature male gametes (spermatozoa) by seminiferous tubules
   b. secretion of hormone (testosterone) by interstitial cells
3. Structure of spermatozoon—consists of head, middle piece, and whiplike tail

Excretory ducts of testis

1. Epididymis
   a. structure and location—single, tightly coiled tube enclosed in fibrous casing; lies along top and side of testis
   b. function—duct for seminal fluid; also secretes part of seminal fluid; sperm become capable of motility while they are stored in epididymis
2. Seminal duct (vas deferens)
   a. structure and location—tube, extension of epididymis; extends through inguinal canal, into abdominal cavity, over top and down posterior surface of bladder to join duct from seminal vesicle
   b. function—one of excretory ducts for seminal fluid; connects epididymis with ejaculatory duct
3. Ejaculatory duct—formed by union of seminal duct with duct from seminal vesicle; passes through prostate gland, terminating in urethra
4. Urethra—see p. 482

Male accessory reproductive glands

1. Seminal vesicles
   a. structure and location—convoluted pouches on posterior surface of bladder
   b. function—secrete nutrient-rich part of seminal fluid
2. Prostate gland
   a. structure and location—doughnut-shaped; encircles urethra just below bladder
   b. function—adds alkaline secretion to seminal fluid
3. Bulbourethral glands
   a. structure and location—small, pea-shaped structures with 1-inch long ducts leading into urethra; lie below prostate gland
   b. function—secrete alkaline fluid which is part of semen

Supporting structures of male reproductive system

1. External
   a. scrotum—skin-covered pouch suspended from perineal region; divided into two compartments; contains testis, epididymis, and first part of seminal duct
   b. penis—composed of three cylindrical masses of erectile tissue, one of which contains urethra
2. Internal — spermatic cords, fibrous cylinders located in inguinal canals, enclose seminal ducts, blood vessels, lymphatics, and nerves

521

Composition and course of seminal fluid

Consists of secretions from testes, epididymides, seminal vesicles, prostate, and bulbourethral glands; each drop contains millions of sperm; passes from testes through epididymis, seminal duct, ejaculatory duct, and urethra

Female reproductive system

Names of organs

Two ovaries, two uterine tubes, one uterus, one vagina, one set of external genitals (vulva), two breasts

Uterus

1. Structure
   a. size, shape, and divisions—pear-shaped; 3 by 2 by 1 inch in virginal state; consists of body and cervix; fundus is bulging upper surface of body
   b. walls—lining of mucosa called endometrium; thick, middle coat of muscle (myometrium), partial external coat of peritoneum
   c. cavities—body cavity small and triangular in shape with three openings; two from tubes and one, the internal os, into cervical canal; external os is opening of cervical canal into vagina
   d. blood supply—generous, from uterine arteries
2. Location—in pelvic cavity between bladder and rectum
3. Position—flexed between body and cervix, with body lying over bladder pointing forward and slightly upward; cervix joins vagina at right angles; capable of considerable mobility, therefore, often in abnormal positions, such as retroverted; eight ligaments anchor it—two broad, two uterosacral, one posterior, one anterior, and two round
4. Functions
   a. menstruation
   b. pregnancy
   c. labor and expulsion of fetus

Uterine tubes

1. Location—attached to uterus at upper, outer angles
2. Structure—same three coats as uterus; distal ends open with fimbriated margins; mucosa and peritoneum in direct contact here
3. Function—duct for female gametes; fertilization occurs here normally

Ovaries (female gonads)

1. Location and size—size and shape of large almonds; lie behind and below uterine tubes; anchored to uterus and broad ligament
2. Microscopic structure—consists of several thousand graafian follicles embedded in connective tissue base; follicles in all stages of development; usually each month one matures, ruptures surface of ovary, and expels its ovum into abdominal cavity
3. Functions
   a. oogenesis—formation of mature female gametes (ova)
   b. secretion of hormones, estrogens and progesterone

Vagina

1. Location—between rectum and urethra
2. Structure—collapsible, musculomembranous tube, capable of great distention; external outlet protected by fold of mucous membrane, hymen
3. Functions
   a. receive seminal fluid
   b. is lower part of birth canal
   c. is excretory duct for uterine secretions and menstrual flow

Vulva

Consists of numerous structures which together constitute external genitals; main ones are
1. Mons veneris—skin-covered pad of fat over symphysis pubis
2. Labia majora—hairy, skin-covered lips
3. Labia minora—small lips covered with modified skin
4. Clitoris—small mound of erectile tissue just below junction of two labia minora
5. Urinary meatus—just below clitoris; opens into urethra
6. Vaginal orifice—below urethra
7. Bartholin's glands—comparable to bulbourethral glands of male; open by means of

long duct in space between hymen and labia minora; ducts from lesser vestibular or Skene's glands open near urinary meatus

Perineum

Region between vaginal orifice and anus; frequently torn at childbirth

Breasts

1. Location and size—just under skin, over pectoral muscles; size depends on deposits of adipose tissue
2. Structure—divided into lobes and lobules; latter composed of racemose glands; single excretory duct per lobe opens in nipple; circular, pigmented area called areola borders nipple
3. Function—secrete milk for infant

Recurring female sexual cycles—Figs. 281 to 285

1. Ovarian cycles—each month, follicle and ovum develop; follicle secretes estrogens; ovum matures and follicle ruptures (ovulation); corpus luteum forms and secretes progesterone and estrogens; if no pregnancy, corpus luteum gradually degenerates and is replaced by fibrous tissue; remains if there is pregnancy
2. Endometrial cycle (menstrual cycle)—surface of endometrium sloughs off during menses, with bleeding from denuded area; regeneration and proliferation of lining occurs; endometrial glands and arterioles become longer and more tortuous; glands secrete viscous mucus and cycle repeats
3. Myometrial cycle—contractility increases before ovulation and subsides following
4. Gonadotrophic cycles—FSH starts to increase few days before menses, reaches maximum by onset of menses, and decreases to minimum by ovulation; LH secretion increases few days before ovulation and reaches maximum by ovulation and minimum few days later; LTH secretion begins day or so before ovulation, reaches maximum within day or so after ovulation, remains high for several days, and decreases to minimum 2 or 3 days before menstruation

Control of female sexual cycles

By feed back relationship between adenohypophysis and ovarian hormones (Fig. 283)

Function served by female sexual cycles

Preparation of endometrium for pregnancy during preovulatory and premenstrual periods; shedding of progestational endometrium if no pregnancy occurs

Menarche and menopause

Menarche—onset of menses; about 13 years of age

Menopause (climateric)—cessation of menses; about 45 years of age

Embryology

Meaning and scope

Science of development of individual before birth; long and complex study

Value of knowledge of embryology

Interprets many abnormal formations

Steps in development of new individual

1. Preliminary processes
   a. maturation of ovum and sperm or reduction of their chromosomes to one-half original number; that is, one-half of 46
   b. ovulation and insemination—ovulation once every 28 days, usually about 14 days before beginning of next menstrual period; insemination, indefinite occurrence; sperm introduced into vagina, swim up to meet ovum in tube
2. Developmental processes
   a. fertilization or union of ovum and sperm; normally occurs in tube; only one sperm penetrates ovum; one-celled new individual called zygote formed by union
   b. cleavage or segmentation — multiplication of cells from zygote by repeated mitosis; morula or solid ball of cells formed; becomes hollow with a cluster of cells attached at one point on inner surface of sphere; called blastocyst at this stage; now implanted in endometrium
   c. differentiation of cells into three primary

germe layers—ectoderm, mesoderm, and entoderm

d. histogenesis or formation of various tissues from primary germ layers; organogenesis or formation of various organs by rearrangements of tissues, such as fusions, shiftings, foldings, etc.

Review questions

The reproductive system

1. Name the male sex glands. Where are they located?
2. Of what is the seminal fluid composed? Trace its course from its formation in the gonads to the exterior.
3. What and where is the prostate gland?
4. What and where are Cowper's glands?
5. What is the spermatic cord? From what to what does it extend, and what does it contain?
6. Name the female sex glands. Name all the internal female reproductive organs.
7. What name is given to the external female genitals?
8. What is the perineum? Of what clinical importance is it in the female?
9. Name the three openings to the exterior from the female pelvis. How many are there in the male?
10. What is a graafian follicle? What does it contain?
11. How many ova mature in a month, usually?
12. When, in the menstrual cycle, is ovulation thought to occur?
13. Discuss the mechanism thought to control menstruation.
14. Name the periods in the menstrual cycle with the approximate length of days in each and the main events.
15. What two organs are necessary for menstruation to occur?
16. What structures hold the uterus in place? Name them.
17. Name the divisions of the uterus.

18. What and where are the fallopian tubes? Approximately how long are they? With what are they lined? Their lining is continuous on their distal ends with what? On their proximal ends? Why is an infection of the lower part of the female reproductive tract likely to develop into a very serious condition?
19. What is the cul-de-sac of Douglas?
20. Approximately how long is the posterior wall of the vagina? The anterior wall? In what direction does it extend from the outside?
21. Where does fertilization take place?
22. Which of the following patients will no longer menstruate? Why? (1) One who has had a bilateral salpingectomy (removal of the tubes)? (2) A panhysterectomy (removal of the entire uterus)? (3) A bilateral oophorectomy (removal of both ovaries)? (4) A cervical hysterectomy (body and fundus removed)? (5) A unilateral oophorectomy?
23. Which of the patients described in Question 22 could no longer become pregnant? Explain.
24. After the menopause, would you expect blood to have a high concentration of any of the following hormones? FSH, LH, LTH, estrogens, progesterone. Explain your reasoning.
25. Define or make an identifying statement about each of the following:

adolescence	maturation
climacteric	miosis
colostrum	menarche
corpus luteum	menstruation
ectopic pregnancy	mitosis
embryology	morula
endometrium	oophorectomy
episiotomy	ovum
estrogens	ovulation
fertilization	progesterone
fimbriae	puberty
gamete	salpingitis
genes	semen
gonad	spermatozoon
hysterectomy	zygote

Integration and control of body functions by hormones

The endocrine system

MEANING OF THE ENDOCRINE SYSTEM

The endocrine system consists of those glands which pour their secretions directly into the blood instead of into ducts. In other words, the endocrines are the *ductless* glands or glands of *internal secretion*. Like the duct glands, the ductless glands extract substances from the blood and synthesize them into new, more complex compounds.

NAMES OF ORGANS

Six structures are definitely known to be endocrine glands: the pituitary, thyroid, parathyroid, and adrenal glands, the gonads (testes or ovaries), and the islands of Langerhans in the pancreas. Several other structures, however, also manufacture hormones, for example, the gastric and duodenal mucosa and perhaps the liver and the pineal and thymus glands.

GENERAL FUNCTIONS AND IMPORTANCE

The general function of the endocrine glands is to secrete substances called *hormones*. Since hormones enter the blood rather than ducts, they circulate all over the body and theoretically can act upon any or all tissues. Thyroid hormone, for example, affects virtually every cell in the body. But, at the other extreme, some hormones, such as FSH described in Chapter 13, noticeably affect only one organ. In any case, the structures acted upon by a given hormone are referred to as its *target organs*. The ovary is the target organ for FSH.

Hormones, then, constitute a kind of messenger service by which one part of the body can communicate directions to another part and by which the body's multiple and diverse activities can be controlled and integrated. As you of course know, the nervous system performs these same functions of communication, control, and integration. So, too, do various other chemicals besides hormones—carbon dioxide, to cite just one example, helps control the activity of the respiratory center cells. Interestingly enough, the two kinds of control mechanisms, nervous and chemical, do not exert exactly the same kind of control.

527

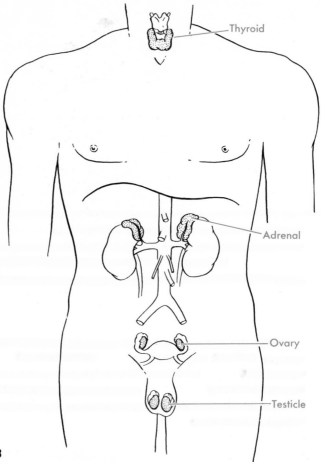

Fig. 288

Location of some of the endocrine
glands. The pituitary, parathyroids, and
islands of Langerhans are not shown.

And this is fortunate. It makes for better timing and more precision of
control. The reason it does is that nervous and chemical mechanisms
differ as to their speed, duration, and locale of action. In general,
nerve impulses produce their effects more rapidly, but they last a
shorter time, and involve a smaller area than effects produced by
chemicals. For example, vasoconstriction may result from either nerve
impulses or chemicals acting on blood vessel walls. If nerve impulses
bring about the constriction, it occurs almost instantaneously in a
limited area and remains only as long as the impulses continue. In
contrast, if a hormone such as epinephrine causes the constriction, it
occurs only after enough time has elapsed for the chemical to circulate
through the body, is widespread, and persists for considerable time.
Another illustration—bone growth regulation by hormones—is a widespread effect that takes place over a period of several years.

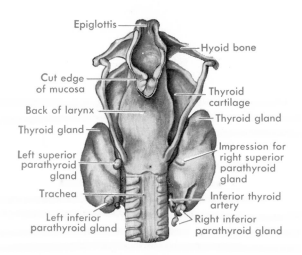

Fig. 289

Thyroid and parathyroid glands viewed from behind. The right inferior parathyroid gland is double in this specimen. (From Francis and Farrell: Integrated anatomy and physiology, St. Louis, The C. V. Mosby Co.)

Exaggerating the importance of endocrine glands is almost impossible. Hormones play a major role in metabolism and are therefore crucial for normal physical and mental development, for reproduction, and for the maintenance of homeostasis. In fact, if you were to try to find a bodily function completely unaffected by any hormone, you would fail. Thyroid hormone, as already mentioned, affects all of our billions of cells. Excesses or deficiencies of hormones make the difference between normalcy and all sorts of abnormalities such as idiocy, dwarfism, gigantism, and sterility and even the difference between life and death in some instances.

Research over a period of many years by many investigators has yielded our rather extensive present-day knowledge concerning endocrine physiology. Investigation has followed along two lines: experimentation on animals and observation and treatment of human beings. For example, in the early efforts to discover pancreatic functions, the pancreas was removed from dogs, and careful observations of all symptoms were recorded. Later, pancreatic islet hormone was administered to depancreatized dogs (made possible in 1922 by the work of Dr. F. G. Banting and his associates at the University of Toronto), and more observations were recorded. Similarly, in many instances, by studying the effects of a lack of a certain gland's secretions and then the changes resulting from a restoration of those secretions, a great deal of information has been amassed concerning endocrine functions. Also, by observing the symptoms of human beings suffering with glandular disease and their response to hormone administration, more knowledge has been compiled.

HYPOPHYSIS (PITUITARY GLAND)

Location and structure

The *hypophysis* lies in the small depression in the sphenoid bone known as the sella turcica. A stemlike portion attaches it to the undersurface of the cerebrum. Formerly its parts were classified according to their relative positions as the anterior, median, and posterior lobes. This classification is still used but is being replaced by a classification based on the embryological development of the parts and their functions. This newer classification divides the gland into two main parts: the *adenohypophysis* (main part of which is the anterior lobe) and the *neurohypophysis* (main part of which is the posterior lobe). The adenohypophysis arises from the ectoderm of the posterior nasopharynx, whereas the neurohypophysis develops as a downward projection from the brain from the diencephalon. As the prefix adeno suggests, this part of the pituitary is glandular in nature, both as to function and as to microscopic structure. The neurohypophysis, on the other hand, bears structural resemblances to nervous tissue, but it, too, functions as an endocrine gland.

Functions of the adenohypophysis

The paramount importance of this tiny gland, as far as normal life is concerned, can scarcely be overemphasized. Its secretions, in proper amounts, are essential for normal growth and metabolism. In addition, they control certain other ductless glands. In fact, so important is pituitary influence on other endocrines (Fig. 290) that it is known as the master gland of the endocrine system. Ham speaks of it as "the chairman of the endocrine society."[*] It does indeed conduct a great deal of endocrine business. And indirectly, through its control of other endocrines, it helps control many other structures as well.

The adenohypophysis secretes the following hormones: somatotrophin, thyrotrophin, adenocorticotrophin, and gonadotrophin. By means of the last three of these hormones, the adenohypophysis exerts its control over other endocrine glands, namely, the thyroid, adrenal cortex, and gonads (ovaries or testes).

Somatotrophin. The name of this hormone comes from two Greek words, *soma* which means body and *trophe* which means nourishment. It is an apt name because the outstanding physiological effect of somatotrophin is bodily growth, a phenomenon which certainly implies nourishment. In short, somatotrophin is an anabolic hormone. A popular shorter name for somatotrophin is growth hormone; a longer one

---

[*]From Ham, Arthur W., and Leeson, Thomas S.: Histology, ed. 4, Philadelphia, 1961, J. B. Lippincott Co.

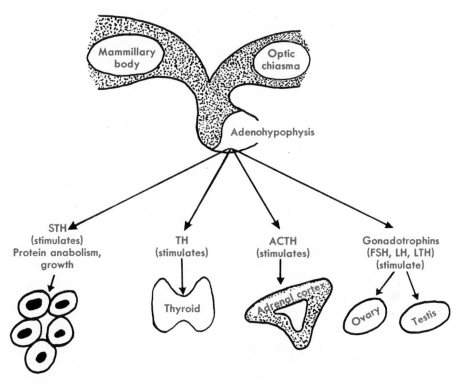

Fig. 290

Adenohypophyseal (anterior pituitary) hormones.

is somatotrophic hormone or abbreviated, STH. The mechanism by which STH accelerates growth is not completely established, but it apparently promotes amino acid transport into cells—evidence, blood amino acid content decreases within hours after administration of STH to a fasting animal. With the faster entrance of amino acid into cells, tissue protein synthesis and therefore cellular growth also accelerate. It stimulates both bone and soft tissue growth during the growth years, that is, before closure of the epiphyseal cartilages. So an excess of STH early in life while the skeleton is still growing produces *gigantism*.

If oversecretion occurs during adult life, the condition known as *acromegaly* develops. Characteristic of this disease are enlargement of the bones of the hands, feet, jaws, and cheeks and an increase, too, in their overlying soft tissues (Figs. 292 and 293). Undersecretion of the growth hormone produces *dwarfism* when it occurs during the years of skeletal growth and *pituitary cachexia* (Simmond's disease), a much rarer condition, when the deficiency develops during adult life. Premature aging with marked tissue atrophy characterizes this disease.

STH sometimes has a diabetogenic effect in addition to its growth-promoting effect. Prolonged high blood concentrations of STH are

531

Fig. 291

A pituitary giant and dwarf contrasted with normal-sized men. Excessive
secretion of the somatotrophic hormone by the adenohypophysis
during the early years of an individual's life produces giants of this
type, while deficient secretion of this substance produces
well-formed dwarfs. (Courtesy Dr. Edmund E. Beard.)

often followed by hyperglycemia (diabetes), thought to be brought
about in the following way. High blood STH accelerates liver gluconeogenesis which increases blood glucose which increases insulin
secretion. Eventually many of the overstimulated beta cells of
the islands of Langerhans degenerate, insulin secretion and therefore glucose transport decrease, and hyperglycemia or diabetes
results.

STH tends to decrease fat deposition. "It is well established that
the increase in tissue protein content which is produced by administration of growth hormone is accompanied by a loss of tissue fat."*

---

*From Bard, P.: Medical physiology, ed. 11, St. Louis, 1961, The C. V. Mosby
Co., p. 753.

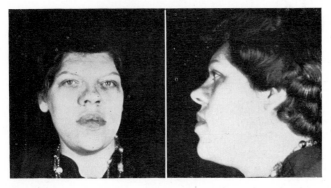

Fig. 292

Acromegaly, a condition in which the bones of the face, hands, and feet enlarge in adult life. Hypersecretion of the somatotrophic hormone by the adenohypophysis during adulthood produces this abnormality. (Courtesy Dr. Edmund E. Beard.)

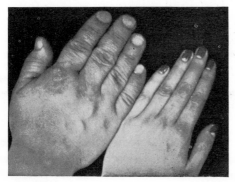

Fig. 293

Hand of an individual suffering from acromegaly contrasted with a normal hand. (Courtesy Dr. Edmund E. Beard.)

Presumably at least some of the mobilized fats are converted by liver cells to glucose (gluconeogenesis).

Thyrotrophin. The thyrotrophic hormone primarily stimulates the release of thyroid hormone. It constitutes the chief mechanism for controlling thyroid secretion. If the gland is unable to synthesize its hormone—as it is, for example, on iodine-deficient diets—thyrotrophin then causes hypertrophy of the thyroid rather than an increase in its secretion. Thyrotrophin and thyroid hormone reciprocally regulate each other's secretion by a feedback mechanism analogous to the one which controls ACTH and corticoid secretion (Fig. 294). High blood concentrations of thyrotrophin stimulate secretion of thyroid hormone, whereas the resulting high blood concentration of thyroid hormone inhibits secretion of thyrotrophin.

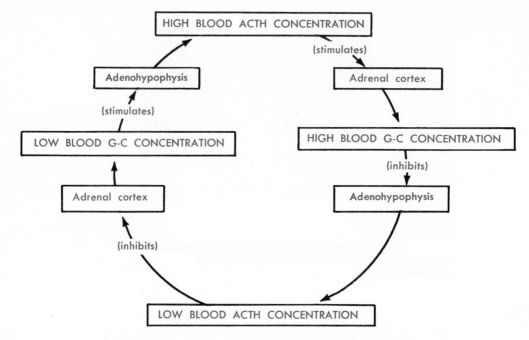

Fig. 294

Control of ACTH secretion by the adenohypophysis—a feedback
mechanism and also a homeostatic mechanism. High blood
concentration of ACTH (adrenocorticotrophic hormone) stimulates G-C
(glucocorticoids) secretion, whereas resulting high blood G-C concentration
inhibits ACTH secretion.

Adrenocorticotrophin (ACTH). The adrenocorticotrophic hormone
stimulates activity of the adrenal cortex—particularly to produce glucocorticoids, hormones which affect the metabolism of sugar and protein.
Glucocorticoids accelerate tissue protein mobilization and liver gluconeogenesis and so tend to increase blood glucose. Therefore, high
blood concentration of ACTH tends to produce hyperglycemia and
eventually possibly diabetes by this indirect route of accelerating gluconeogenesis. Therefore, ACTH, like STH, is classed as a hyperglycemic and diabetogenic hormone.

Gonadotrophins. Actions of the gonadotrophic hormones in the female during the years of reproductive maturity were discussed on
pp. 512 to 516 and in the male on p. 490. Gonadotrophins also help
regulate growth and development of reproductive organs earlier in life.

Until a few years before puberty, the adenohypophysis secretes
only very slight amounts of these hormones. Gradually this amount
increases. Then shortly before puberty, it takes a sudden spurt. The
greatly increased concentration of gonadotrophins in the blood produces the changes characteristic of the onset of puberty.

Deficient secretion of pituitary gonadotrophins causes the sexual infantilism characteristic of the disease known as *Fröhlich's syndrome.*

During pregnancy the placenta produces chorionic gonadotrophins, so-called because they are secreted by cells of the chorion, the outermost fetal membrane. In addition to gonadotrophins the placenta also produces estrogens and progesterone. Gonadotrophic substances are excreted in the urine during pregnancy. In fact, their presence in the latter forms the basis for the Aschheim-Zondek and Friedman tests for pregnancy.

Some evidence suggests that the adenohypophysis helps control the parathyroids, but existence of a parathyrotrophic hormone is still doubtful.

Control of hormone secretion by the adenohypophysis

Two kinds of mechanisms—chemical and neural—together control adenohypophysis secretion. The chemical mechanism operates on what is currently called the feedback principle. Very briefly this means that the hormone of one gland controls hormone secretion by another gland whose hormone then feeds back to control secretion of the first hormone.

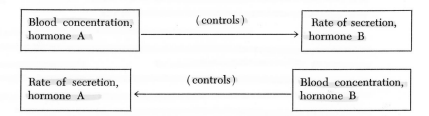

Fig. 294 shows in diagram form the application of the feedback principle to control of the pituitary.

Neural control of the adenohypophysis is achieved indirectly rather than directly by nerve impulses. Axons of neurons in the hypothalamus presumably liberate a substance into blood flowing through a plexus of capillaries and thence through hypophysial portal vessels which carry it to the adenohypophysis. That portal blood supply helps control anterior pituitary secretion is no longer doubted, but exactly how it mediates its control is not certain. At any rate the hypothalamo-hypophyseal portal system forms an important connecting link by which the nervous system can help control the endocrine system. It is one of the means of integrating the activities of these two great integrating systems. More specifically, it is the means by which autonomic centers in the hypothalamus can help control adenohypophyseal secretion and thereby help control secretion by the adrenal cortex, thyroid, and gonads—a fact that assumes crucial importance under stress conditions. Hypothalamic-adenohypophyseal control of ACTH secretion is one of the body's major defenses against trauma; it is one of its major stress responses.

Function of neurohypophysis (posterior pituitary gland)

The neurohypophysis secretes two hormones—oxytocin (Pitocin) and pitressin (ADH, the antidiuretic hormone). But strangely enough, posterior pituitary cells do not themselves make these hormones. Neurons in the hypothalamus (supraoptic and paraventricular nuclei) synthesize them. From their cell bodies the hormones pass down along axons into the neurohypophysis which later secretes them into the blood.

Oxytocin (from Greek words meaning *swift childbirth*) stimulates the smooth muscle of the pregnant uterus and therefore is generally said to be at least one of the factors initiating and maintaining labor. Commercial preparations of oxytocin are sometimes used to increase uterine contractions during labor and after delivery of the placenta to decrease hemorrhage. Oxytocin has a second action; it acts on the lactating breast to cause release of milk from glandular cells into ducts from which a baby can obtain it by suckling. Incidentally, suckling constitutes the stimulus for oxytocin secretion.

Pitressin (ADH) accelerates water reabsorption from renal tubules and also stimulates the smooth muscle of the blood vessels and intestines. Pitressin preparations are, therefore, used to treat diabetes insipidus and sometimes to relieve intestinal distension. But because they are not as effective in raising blood pressure as certain other drugs, they are not often given for their hypertensive effect.

Control of neurohypophyseal secretion

Unlike secretion by the adenohypophysis, secretion by the neurohypophysis is controlled only by nerve impulses. They reach the gland via fibers from the supraoptic and paraventricular nuclei of the hypothalamus. Impulses over these fibers regulate the rate of release of neurohypophyseal hormones.

THYROID GLAND

Location and structure

Two fairly large lateral lobes and a connecting portion, the isthmus, constitute the thyroid gland. It is located in the neck just below the larynx. The isthmus lies across the anterior surface of the upper part of the trachea. Thyroid tissue contains numerous small follicles. Colloid, composed largely of an iodine-containing protein known as thyroglobulin, fills these tiny sacs.

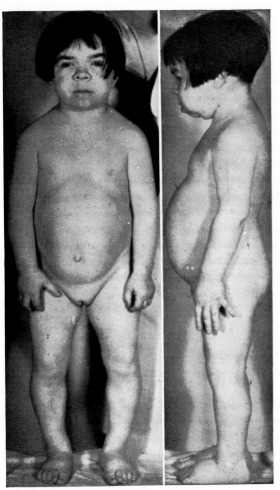

Fig. 295

Cretinism, a type of dwarfing produced by deficient secretion by the thyroid gland during the developmental years. The subject is 16 years of age. (Courtesy Dr. Edmund E. Beard.)

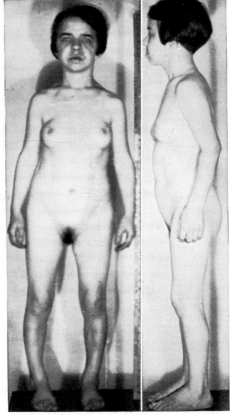

Fig. 296

Cretinism. The same individual shown in Fig. 295 after approximately two years of treatment with thyroid extract. (Courtesy Dr. Edmund E. Beard.)

Functions

The thyroid gland synthesizes thyroglobulin, stores large amounts of it (unlike the other endocrines), and secretes thyroid hormone, now known to consist mainly of thyroxin with small amounts of tri-iodo-thyronine. Thyroxin becomes bound to blood proteins and circulates in the blood in this form. How much hormone the thyroid gland releases depends upon the blood level of thyrotrophin (see p. 533).

Thyroid hormone's main physiological actions are to help regulate the metabolic rate and the processes of growth and tissue differentiation. It increases the metabolic rate, an effect evidenced by increased oxygen consumption following thyroid administration. Like pituitary somatotrophin, thyroid hormone stimulates growth, but unlike somatotrophin, it also influences tissue differentiation and development. For example, cretins (thyroid deficiency) are not only dwarfed, but they are also usually mentally retarded because the brain fails to develop normally. Their bones and many other tissues also show an abnormal pattern of development (Figs. 295 and 296).

Effects of hypersecretion and hyposecretion of thyroid hormone

Hypersecretion of thyroid hormone produces the disease *exophthalmic goiter* (Graves' disease, Basedow's disease, and several other names), characterized by increased metabolism (plus 30 or more), an accompanying increased appetite, loss of weight, increased nervous irritability, and exophthalmus. Marked edema of the fatty tissue behind the eye, attributed to the high blood titer of thyrotrophic hormone, produces the exophthalmus.

Hyposecretion during the formative years leads to malformed dwarfism or *cretinism*, a condition characterized by retarded mental, physical, and sexual development and lowered metabolic rate. Later in life deficient thyroid secretion produces the disease *myxedema*, characterized by decreased metabolic rate which, in turn, leads to lessened mental and physical vigor and a gain in weight, loss of hair, and a thickening of the skin due to an accumulation of fluid in the subcutaneous tissues. Because of a high mucoprotein content, this fluid is viscous; therefore, it gives a firmness to the skin, and the skin does not pit when pressed, as it does in other types of edema (Fig. 297).

PARATHYROIDS

Location and structure

The parathyroids are small round bodies attached to the posterior surfaces of the lateral thyroid lobes. Usually there are four, but sometimes there are fewer and sometimes more of these glands.

Fig. 297

Myxedema, a condition produced when the thyroid gland fails to secrete sufficiently during the adult years. (Courtesy Dr. Edmund E. Beard.)

Functions

Parathyroid hormone's primary action, it seems well established, is to increase the breakdown and resorption of bone. Through this action it tends secondarily to increase the blood calcium level. And reciprocally, the blood calcium level feeds back to control parathyroid secretion. Parathyroid hormone, therefore, seems to constitute an important controller of blood calcium homeostasis, a mineral important primarily because of its effect on neuromuscular irritability but also for blood clotting and for normal permeability of cell membranes. As the blood calcium content decreases below normal, neuromuscular irritability increases—that is, an inverse relation exists between the amount of blood calcium and neuromuscular irritability.

Deficiency of parathyroid hormone may produce tetany, a serious condition characterized by abnormally low blood calcium and various signs of increased neuromuscular irritability, such as muscle spasms. Parathyroid hormone excess, on the other hand, may produce a bone disease known as osteitis fibrosa generalisata. Bone mass decreases (as a result of increased bone destruction followed by fibrous tissue replacement), decalcification occurs, and cystlike cavities appear in the bone.

539

ADRENALS

Location and structure

The adrenal glands are located atop the kidneys, fitting like a cap over these organs. The outer portion of the gland is called the *cortex* and the inner substance the *medulla*. Both the adrenal cortex and adrenal medulla are endocrines.

Functions

The cortex secretes hormones designated as *corticoids.** Numerous steroids have been isolated from dead cortical tissue. Although the exact compounds secreted by the cortex still are not known, it now

---

*Steroid compounds have the following nucleus:

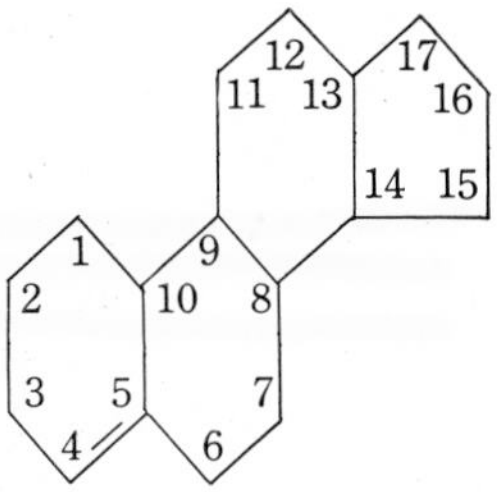

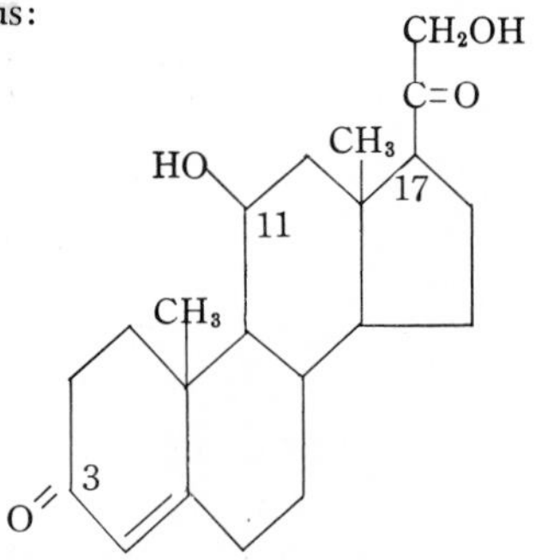

Corticosterone (compound B)

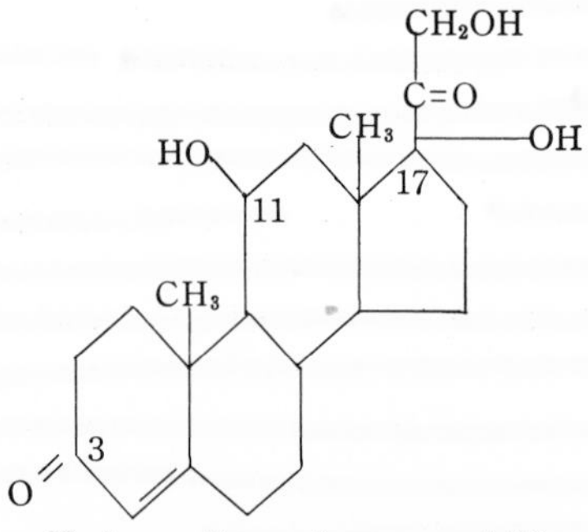

Hydrocortisone (compound F)

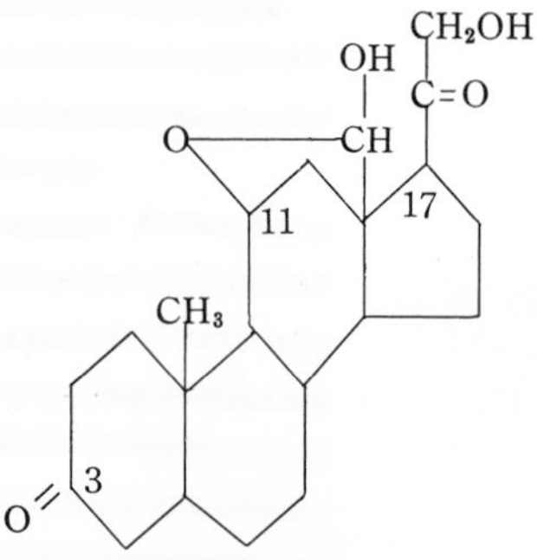

Aldosterone

Corticosterone (compound B) may be parent substance of other corticoids.

Compound E or cortisone (chemical name, 17-hydroxy-11-dehydrocorticoster-one, signifying that the molecule is the same as corticosterone with −OH instead of −H on C-17, and minus H on C-11).

DOC (11-desoxycorticosterone—corticosterone molecules without any oxygen on C-11).

In addition to the corticoids, various other biologically important compounds are steroids—cholesterol, bile acids, and sex hormones, for example.

seems probable that hydrocortisone and aldosterone are the predominant hormones produced. In addition, the adrenal cortex secretes a small amount of sex hormones or their precursors. Most of these are androgens (masculinizing). But there are some female hormones (estrogens and progesterone) too. Corticoids help control the activities of probably all body cells. Especially important, it seems, is their influence on muscle, fat, liver, and renal tubule cells. Thereby, they exert a major control over the metabolism of all three kinds of foods—proteins, carbohydrates, and fats—and of electrolytes and fluids as well. They also play a part in the body's defense against stress. They sometimes influence sexual characteristics.

Glucocorticoids

Hydrocortisone and cortisone are classified functionally as glucocorticoids. As described on p. 449, they promote tissue protein mobilization and liver gluconeogenesis. For example, in Cushing's disease the rate of tissue protein mobilization exceeds that of tissue protein synthesis—a fact that accounts for the diminished muscular mass so characteristic of this disease. It also explains the description of glucocorticoids as protein catabolic hormones. But glucocorticoids not only accelerate tissue protein catabolism, they also are essential for normal protein deposition or synthesis. Addison's disease (corticoid deficiency) attests to this fact. Less than normal amounts of proteins are deposited in tissues, a fact which may partially explain the marked weakness characteristic of this condition. One theory interprets the action of glucocorticoids on protein metabolism as facilitating the movement of amino acids through cell membranes in either direction, that is, into or out of the cell (Fig. 300). If this is true, then amino acid movement out of cells seems to be stimulated by excess glucocorticoids, as in Cushing's disease, whereas their movement into cells is apparently depressed by deficient glucocorticoids such as exists in Addison's disease.

Glucocorticoids
↑
(stimulate)
↓
Protein mobilization from tissues
into blood
↓
Increased amounts of amino acids
transported to liver
↓
Increased rate of gluconeogenesis
from amino acids
↓
Increased blood sugar

Fig. 298

Scheme showing postulated mechanism by which corticoid control of carbohydrate metabolism may stem from corticoid control of protein metabolism.

541

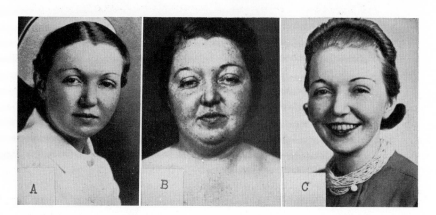

Fig. 299

Cushing's syndrome; adrenal cortical tumor in a patient 25 years of age:
A, before illness; **B,** at height of illness; **C,** one year after removal of the
tumor. (Overdosage of sustained therapy with cortisone, hydrocortisone,
or ACTH may produce symptoms very similar to the naturally occurring
Cushing's syndrome.) (From Kepler, E. J., Sprague, R. G., Mason,
H. L., and Power, M. H.: The pathologic physiology of adrenal
cortical tumors and Cushing's syndrome, Recent Progr.
Hormone Research **2:** 345, 1948, Academic Press, Inc.)

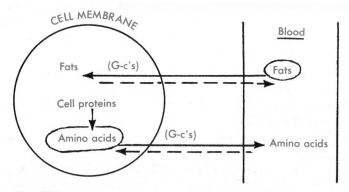

Fig. 300

Diagram illustrates the following two principles: (1) glucocorticoids
promote fat deposition but are also essential for fat mobilization, and
(2) glucocorticoids promote amino acid mobilization but are also essential
for normal amino acid deposition and protein synthesis.

Effects on carbohydrate metabolism. Glucocorticoids influence carbohydrate metabolism indirectly through their stimulating effects on protein and fat mobilization and on liver gluconeogenesis. Glucocorticoids, therefore, tend to increase blood glucose. That is, they have a hyperglycemic effect. Since this is the opposite effect of insulin, it is also spoken of as the antiinsulin action of glucocorticoids. It is, of course, important clinically. For example, if a diabetic person receives corticoid therapy, his diabetic condition probably becomes aggravated, and his insulin dosage probably has to be increased.

Effects on fat metabolism. Glucocorticoids sometimes promote fat deposition and sometimes fat mobilization (p. 446). Cushing's disease illustrates both glucocorticoid fat-depositing and protein-mobilizing actions. Addison's disease illustrates glucocorticoid fat mobilization.

Effects on the body's reactions to stress. Dr. Hans Selye of the University of Montreal and a host of other investigators in recent years have contributed greatly to our knowledge of the body's responses to stress conditions. One of the first responses seems to be an increase in ACTH secretion and therefore in glucocorticoid secretion. What initiates this response is still unknown. But in some way the hypothalamus is thought to be informed of the stress condition present in the body. It then stimulates the adenohypophysis, presumably, as you will recall, by means of a chemical released into the hypophyseal portal system and transported from the hypothalamus to the adenohypophysis. Next, the adenohypophysis responds by greatly increasing its output of ACTH. ACTH circulates to the adrenal cortex and stimulates it to hypertrophy and to secrete more glucocorticoids. Their blood concentration increases and brings about various other stress responses. Notable among them are the following:

1. Atrophy of lymphatic tissue, particularly the thymus gland and lymph nodes.
2. Eosinopenia and lymphocytopenia (decreased number of eosinophils and lymphocytes).
3. Decreased antibody formation, therefore less immunity and allergy.
4. Slower connective tissue proliferation, therefore less inflammation but greater tendency for an infection to spread and also slower wound healing.
5. Increased mobilization (catabolism) of tissue proteins and fats.
6. Increased liver gluconeogenesis.

Dr. Selye apparently considers the inhibiting of inflammation the main function of glucocorticoids since he speaks of them as "A-C's," meaning anti-inflammatory corticoids.

Corticoids are known to be essential for resistance to stress of every

543

type. Without adequate amounts of these hormones, homeostasis cannot be maintained. Consider just one example. A patient with Addison's disease (corticoid deficiency), if given a water load, will develop water intoxication. He excretes the extra water much more slowly than a normal individual. Tubular reabsorption does not decrease sufficiently to offset the added intake. On the other hand, such a patient becomes dehydrated more rapidly than a normal person when deprived of water. Tubule reabsorption in this instance does not increase sufficiently to offset the decreased intake.

Mineralocorticoids

Aldosterone and desoxycorticosterone are classified functionally as mineralocorticoids because their main action concerns mineral salt (electrolyte) metabolism. Aldosterone exerts much more potent effects

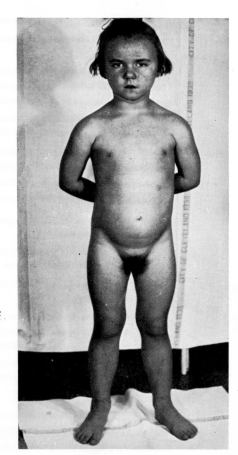

Fig. 301

A virilizing tumor of the adrenal cortex produced the precocious development of this 3-year-old-girl. Note the masculine muscular development of the body. Excessive secretion by the adrenal cortex is responsible also for bearded women. (Courtesy Dr. Edmund E. Beard.)

than desoxycorticosterone and is believed to be the main mineralo-corticoid secreted by the adrenal cortex. An important principle about the effects of aldosterone is that it tends to increase electrolyte and therefore fluid movement through cell membranes. Most important, presumably, is this action on renal tubule cells. Specifically, aldo-sterone causes sodium to move more rapidly out of the tubule urine into and through the tubule cells on into the blood. This tends to increase blood and interstitial fluid sodium concentration. In exchange for sodium, potassium moves more rapidly in the opposite direction, that is, out of the blood into the tubule urine. And this, in turn, tends to decrease extracellular potassium concentration. Thus aldosterone accelerates both renal tubule reabsorption of sodium and excretion of potassium. In other words, aldosterone promotes sodium retention and potassium loss. As a result, it tends to increase extracellular so-dium and to decrease extracellular potassium. Aldosterone also tends to produce similar changes in intracellular electrolyte con-centration, namely, increased intracellular sodium and decreased potassium.

By stimulating tubule reabsorption of sodium ions, aldosterone in-directly accelerates chloride ions and water reabsorption. Briefly, then, in summary aldosterone tends to produce the following effects: faster tubular reabsorption of sodium and excretion of potassium, increased extracellular sodium and chloride, increased extracellular volume, de-creased extracellular potassium, increased intracellular sodium, and decreased intracellular potassium. As a result of these aldosterone actions, fluid and electrolytes soon deviate from normal when the blood concentration of mineralocorticoids deviates from nor-mal.

Sex corticoids

Because normally the cortex secretes such small amounts of male and female hormones, the sex corticoids are thought to be insignificant physiologically (Fig. 301).

Control of adrenal cortex secretion

The adenohypophyseal hormone, ACTH, as previously noted, con-trols the amount of glucocorticoids secreted but may be assisted in this function by other factors too. Selye, for example, suggests that chemicals released by injured tissues may stimulate the production of corticoids either indirectly by influencing the amount of ACTH se-creted or perhaps directly by their effect on adrenal cortical cells. Epinephrine is known to stimulate cortical secretion, presumably by increasing ACTH production.

So far as is known, **ACTH** does not control mineralocorticoid secretion. Instead, extracellular volume, sodium concentration, and potassium concentration act in some way to regulate aldosterone secretion. The exact mechanism, however, is obscure. At any rate, low extracellular volume or sodium concentration and high extracellular potassium concentration all have an accelerating effect on aldosterone secretion. And of these, low sodium concentration seems to have the most potent influence; it leads to the greatest increase in aldosterone output.

Adrenal medulla

The adrenal medulla secretes epinephrine (adrenalin) and norepinephrine. Like the adrenal corticoids, the adrenal medulla hormones help the body meet stressful situations, but, unlike them, they are not essential for the maintenance of life. Epinephrine affects smooth and cardiac muscle and glands similarly to sympathetic stimulation of these structures. It serves to increase and prolong sympathetic effects. Norepinephrine produces more widespread vasoconstriction than epinephrine; therefore, when administered as a drug, it usually brings about a greater rise in blood pressure than epinephrine. The cooperative functioning of the sympathetic system and adrenal medulla serve as a very fast acting defense reaction against stress stimuli of various kinds. Severe or prolonged stress stimuli, according to Selye, activate the anterior pituitary-adrenal cortex mechanism as a further protective device.

OVARIES

The ovaries produce two hormones: estrogens and progesterone.

Estrogens

The estrogens consist chiefly of estradiol and two other sterols, estrone (estrin or theelin) and estriol. They are secreted by the graafian follicles and during pregnancy by the placenta. They carry on the following functions:

1. Estrogens promote growth and development of the secondary sex organs (breasts, vagina, and myometrium) and maintain them in the adult state. They promote development and maintenance of other secondary sex characteristics such as pubertal and axillary hair, distribution of body fat, etc.

2. Estrogens promote repair of the endometrium following the menses.

3. Estrogens stimulate endometrial cell proliferation and therefore

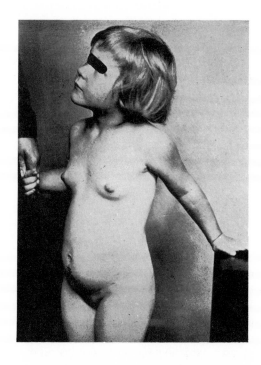

Fig. 302

Premature sexual development in a 3-year-old girl caused by a granulosa cell tumor of the ovary. (Courtesy Dr. Edmund E. Beard.)

cause the endometrium to repair itself following the menses and to thicken during the preovulatory phase.

4. Estrogens promote water retention by the endometrium.

5. Estrogens promote myometrial contractions.

6. Estrogens help control development and functioning of breasts. During adolescence and pregnancy they especially promote development of ducts in the mammary glands. They inhibit LTH (prolactin) formation by the pituitary gland and thereby inhibit lactation. Shedding of the placenta following delivery cuts off a major source of estrogens. Blood estrogen content drops rapidly and markedly. This decrease in blood estrogen concentration stimulates prolactin secretion which, in turn, stimulates lactation.

7. Estrogens have an inhibiting effect on the production of FSH and LTH by the anterior lobe of the pituitary gland.

8. Estrogens may contribute to normal sexual desire.

Hyposecretion of estrogens tends to produce disturbances of the menstrual cycle and either underdevelopment or atrophy of the uterus and breasts.

Progesterone (progestin or lutin)

Progesterone, secreted by the corpus luteum and by the placenta, has the following effects.

1. Increases secretion by endometrial glands.

2. Causes spiral arteries of the uterus to enlarge slightly and coil tightly.
3. Increases the endometrium's water content.
4. Decreases myometrial contractions.
5. Promotes development of the secreting cells of the breasts to the stage where they can secrete milk when stimulated by prolactin following delivery.

Hyposecretion of progesterone leads to abortion in the pregnant woman and to menstrual disorders in the nonpregnant woman.

TESTES

The interstitial cells of the testes secrete testosterone, a steroid hormone classed as an androgen, that is, a substance that promotes "maleness." It promotes development of the secondary sex organs and characteristics, maintains them in the adult state, and contributes to normal sexual behavior. Urine of both men and women contains androsterone and possibly other androgens of the class of compounds known as 17-ketosteroids. Part of the urinary 17-ketosteroids derive from adrenal cortex secretions and part from testosterone.

Hyposecretion may cause the male characteristics to fail to develop. Castration after puberty leads to a decrease in size of the external genitals and the prostate.

ISLANDS OF LANGERHANS

The beta cells of the islands of Langerhans secrete insulin which is necessary for normal carbohydrate metabolism and therefore for normal fat metabolism (pp. 445 to 446). *Hypersecretion* causes ravenous hunger and insulin shock due to lowered blood sugar. *Hyposecretion* produces diabetes mellitus.

Alpha cells of the pancreas secrete glucagon. Glucagon stimulates glycogenolysis and thereby tends to increase blood sugar.

THYMUS GLAND AND PINEAL GLAND

Although some evidence seems to indicate that these structures are endocrines, neither gland has been proved to secrete any hormones of physiological significance. The thymus atrophies following puberty. The pineal gland (also called epiphysis cerebri) degenerates at about 7 years of age and is composed of fibrous tissue in the adult.

PLACENTA

The placenta functions as a temporary endocrine gland. It secretes large amounts of estrogens and progesterone and a chorionic hormone which resembles the gonadotrophic hormone of the adenohypophysis in that it postpones menstruation, maintaining the endometrium in the premenstrual or progestational state.

Outline summary
The endocrine system

Meaning
Composed of glands which pour secretions into blood instead of into ducts

Names of organs
Pituitary, thyroid, parathyroids, adrenals, gonads, and islands of Langerhans in pancreas; possibly pineal body and thymus also

General functions and importance
Secretions of these glands, called hormones, comprise one of integrating mechanisms of body, comparable to nervous system function; of great importance since are essential for normal growth, reproduction, and metabolism

Adenohypophysis (pituitary gland)
Location and structure

Located in sella turcica of sphenoid bone, attached to undersurface of cerebrum; parts formerly classified as anterior, median, and posterior lobes; newer classification divides gland into adenohypophysis (anterior lobe) and neurohypophysis (posterior lobe)

Functions of adenohypophysis

1. Somatotrophin (STH) promotes growth, protein deposition, and fat mobilization and tends to increase blood sugar
2. Thyrotrophin (TH) stimulates thyroid
3. Adrenocorticotrophin (ACTH) stimulates adrenal cortex
4. Gonadotrophins FSH (follicle-stimulating hormone), LH (luteinizing hormone, ovulating hormone), and LTH (luteotrophin, prolactin) stimulate gonads; LTH stimulates secretion of milk by mammary glands
5. Effects of hypersecretion and hyposecretion
   a. hypersecretion may result in giantism, acromegaly, sexual prematurity, hyperactivity of thyroid or adrenal cortex, or pituitary diabetes
   b. hyposecretion may result in dwarfism, pituitary cachexia, sexual infantilism, Fröhlich's syndrome, or thyroid or adrenal cortex atrophy

Control of hormone secretion by adenohypophysis

1. Feedback control by blood concentration of corticoids, thyroid hormone, and gonadotrophins
2. Neural control via hyopthalamus and hypophyseal portal vessels

Functions of posterior pituitary gland (neurohypophysis)

1. Secretes hormones synthesized by neurons in hypothalamus, namely, contains oxytocin and pitressin (ADH)
2. Oxytocin stimulates contractions of pregnant uterus and release of milk by lactating breast
3. Pitressin stimulates water reabsorption by distal and collecting tubules and stimulates smooth muscle of blood vessels and intestine

549

Control of neurohypophyseal secretion of ADH

By impulses from hypothalamus

Thyroid gland
Location and structure

Located in neck just below larynx; two lateral lobes connected by isthmus

Functions

1. Stores iodine-containing protein, thyroglobulin
2. Secretes thyroid hormone which stimulates rate of oxygen consumption (metabolic rate) of all cells and thereby helps regulate physical and mental development, development of sexual maturity, and numerous other processes
3. Hypersecretion produces exophthalmic goiter
4. Hyposecretion in early life produces malformed dwarfism or cretinism; in later life, myxedema

Parathyroids
Location and structure

Attached to posterior surfaces of thyroid; small round bodies, usually four in number

Functions

1. Stimulates bone resorption, thereby regulating blood calcium and neuromuscular irritability
2. Hypersecretion causes decrease in bone mass with replacement by fibrous tissue
3. Hyposecretion produces hypocalcemia and tetany and death in few hours

Adrenals
Location and structure

Located atop kidneys; outer portion of gland called cortex and inner portion called medulla

Functions

1. Glucocorticoids (mainly hydrocortisone secreted; cortisone also glucocorticoid)
   a. promotes mobilization of proteins from cells; also necessary for deposit of proteins in cells
   b. effect is to increase liver gluconeogenesis from proteins, thereby increasing blood sugar
   c. promote deposition of fat in tissues; necessary for fat mobilization
   d. necessary for resistance to stress
2. Mineralocorticoids (mainly aldosterone secreted) important regulators of fluid and electrolyte balance; increase electrolyte and therefore water movement through cell membranes, notably, increase renal tubule reabsorption of sodium, chloride, and water, and increase tubule excretion of potassium
3. Cortical sex hormones—normally insignificant because of small amounts secreted; both androgens and female hormones secreted by adrenal cortex of both sexes, hence description of adrenal cortex as "bisexual accessory gland"
4. Control of adrenal cortex secretion
   a. glucocorticoids — by adenohypophyseal hormone, ACTH; epinephrine also stimulates cortical secretion, presumably via ACTH; Selye suggests that injured tissues may release chemicals that stimulate production of corticoids directly or indirectly by stimulating ACTH production
   b. mineralocorticoids—by sodium and potassium concentrations and volume of extracellular fluid; low sodium, high potassium, low volume increase aldosterone secretion
5. Functions of adrenal medulla
   a. secrete epinephrine and norepinephrine; epinephrine produces effects similar to sympathetic stimulation—increases and prolongs sympathetic effects; norepinephrine causes more widespread vasoconstriction and greater rise in blood pressure than epinephrine

Ovaries
Estrogens

1. Promote growth and development of secondary sex organs and maintain them in adult state
2. Promote repair of endometrium following menses
3. Stimulate endometrial cell proliferation
4. Promote water retention by endometrium

5. Promote myometrial contractions
6. Promote development of mammary glands during adolescence and pregnancy; inhibit LTH production by anterior pituitary gland, thereby inhibiting lactation
7. Inhibit production of FSH and LTH by anterior pituitary gland
8. May contribute to normal sexual desire

Progesterone

1. Increases secretion by endometrial glands
2. Causes spiral arteries of the uterus to enlarge slightly and coil tightly
3. Increases endometrium's water content
4. Decreases myometrial motility
5. Promotes development of secreting cells of breasts to stage at which they can secrete milk when stimulated by prolactin

Testes

Secrete testosterone which
1. Promotes development of secondary sex organs and characteristics and maintains them in adult condition
2. Contributes to normal sexual behavior

Islands of Langerhans

Beta cells secrete insulin which is essential for normal carbohydrate metabolism; hypersecretion causes "insulin shock"; hyposecretion causes diabetes mellitus; alpha cells of islets secrete glucagon which promotes glycogenolysis

Thymus gland and pineal gland

Probably not endocrine glands

Placenta

A temporary endocrine; secretes estrogens, progesterone, and chorionic gonadotrophin; helps maintain progestational state of endometrium

Review questions

The endocrine system

1. Name the endocrine glands and locate each one.
2. Name the hormone or hormones which help control each of the following: (a) blood sugar level, (b) blood calcium level, (c) blood sodium level, and (d) blood potassium level. Explain mechanisms involved.
3. Name the hormone or hormones which help control each of the following: (a) growth, (b) development of secondary male characteristics and female characteristics, (c) fluid and electrolyte balance, (d) resistance to stress, (e) functions of adrenal cortex, thyroid, and ovaries, and (f) secretion of ACTH, TH, and FSH.
4. What hormone enhances and prolongs sympathetic effects?
5. What hormones help control protein metabolism? Explain.
6. What hormones help control fat metabolism? Explain.
7. What hormones help control carbohydrate metabolism? Explain.
8. What condition results from a deficiency of thyroid extract early in life? Later in life?
9. What disease results from too much thyroid secretion? From too much pituitary somatotrophic hormone early in life? Too much later in life? Too little early in life?
10. Giantism results from an oversupply of which endocrine secretion? Cretinism from a deficiency of which one? Acromegaly from an oversupply of which one? Myxedema from a deficiency of which one?
11. Which gland is called the "master gland"? Why?

Situation: A patient goes to his doctor because he feels "so terribly weak and tired all the time and has lost so much weight." After hospital admission and various tests, the doctor tells him he has "something wrong with his adrenal glands." Blood chemistry tests reveal low blood concentrations of sodium and chloride and high potassium.

12. Do you think this patient had a disease of the adrenal medulla or adrenal cortex? State reasons.
13. Was the condition hyperfunctioning or hypofunctioning of the gland? State reasons.
14. How would you explain the patient's chief complaints?

551

15. Might this patient have any type of water imbalance? If so, what and why? Explain mechanisms involved.

16. Eosinophil counts were done on this patient following injections of epinephrine. Do you think the counts would be normal or not? Explain why. Significance?

17. Blood sugar was measured after a 24-hour fast. Would it be higher or lower than it would be in a normal individual under the same conditions? Why?

Situation: A patient who has a severe form of Cushing's disease is given insulin each day.

18. Should the nurse watch this patient for signs of hypoglycemia or hyperglycemia? Explain.

19. Would this patient be likely to be "insulin sensitive" or "insulin resistant"? Explain.

20. Explain the meaning of the statement "hormone functions are interrelated." Give examples to support or refute this statement.

Fluid, electrolyte, and acid-base balance

Fluid and electrolyte balance

INTRODUCTION

The term fluid balance means several things. It, of course, means the same thing as homeostasis of fluids. To say that the body is in a state of fluid balance is to say that the total amount of water in the body is normal and that it remains relatively constant. But fluid balance also means something more. It also means relative constancy of the distribution of water in the body's three fluid compartments. The volume of water inside the cells, in the interstitial spaces, and in the blood vessels all remain relatively constant when a condition of fluid balance exists. Fluid imbalance, then, means that both the total volume of water in the body and the amount in one or more of its fluid compartments have increased or decreased beyond normal limits.

Fluid balance and electrolyte balance are interdependent. If one deviates from normal, so does the other (Fig. 303). A discussion of one, therefore, necessitates a discussion of the other.

Modern medicine attaches great importance to fluid and electrolyte balance. Today, a large proportion of hospital patients receive some kind of fluid and electrolyte therapy. To help you understand the rationale underlying such treatment, this chapter is included. We shall consider successively some general principles about fluid balance, the portals by which water enters and leaves the body, the mechanisms that control the total volume of body water, and the mechanisms that regulate the distribution of water in the three fluid compartments.

SOME GENERAL PRINCIPLES ABOUT FLUID BALANCE

1. The cardinal principle about fluid balance is that intake must equal output. Obviously, if more water or less leaves the body than enters it, fluid balance cannot exist.

2. Devices for varying output so that it equals intake constitute the major mechanism for maintaining fluid balance, but mechanisms for adjusting intake to output also operate.

3. Mechanisms for controlling water movement between the fluid compartments also play a major role in the maintenance of fluid and electrolyte balance.

555

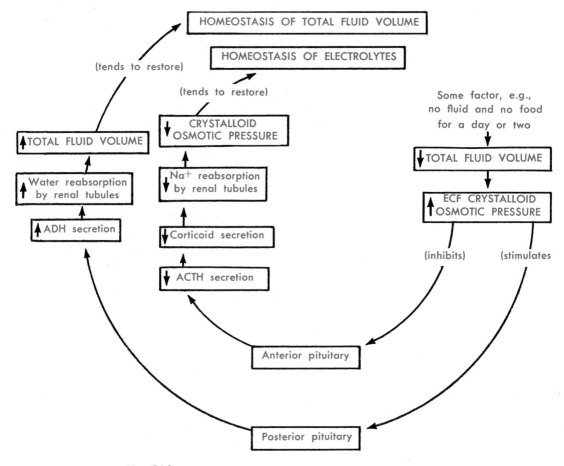

Fig. 303

A homeostatic mechanism for restoring fluid and electrolyte balance. Note interdependence of fluid and electrolyte balances. Descending arrows (↓), decreased; ascending arrows (↑), increased.

AVENUES BY WHICH WATER ENTERS AND LEAVES BODY

Water normally enters the body from three sources: from liquids the individual drinks, from water in the foods he eats, and from water formed when the food he eats is metabolized. Water normally leaves the body by four exits: kidneys, lungs, skin, and feces (Fig. 304). In accord with the cardinal principle of fluid balance, the total volume of water entering the body normally equals the total volume leaving, or, briefly, intake normally equals output. Table 59 gives normal volumes for each portal of water entry and exit, though, of course, these could vary considerably and still be considered normal.

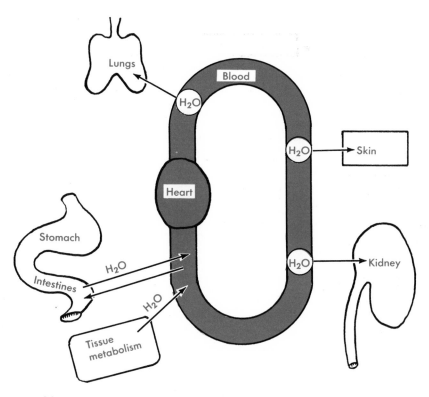

Fig. 304

Normal portals of water entry and exit from blood.

Table 59. Typical normal values for each portal of water entry and exit

Intake		Output	
Ingested liquids	1500 ml.	Kidneys (urine)	1400 ml.
Water in foods	700 ml.	Lungs (water in expired air)	350 ml.
Water formed in metabolism	200 ml.	Skin	
		(By diffusion)	350 ml.
		(By sweat)	100 ml.
		Intestine (in feces)	200 ml.
Totals	2400 ml.		2400 ml.

MECHANISMS THAT MAINTAIN
HOMEOSTASIS OF TOTAL FLUID VOLUME
Control of urine volume

Homeostasis of the total volume of water in the body is maintained or restored primarily by devices that adjust output to intake. Most important of these are the mechanisms which control the volume of urine excreted.

Two factors together determine urine volume: the glomerular filtration rate and the renal tubule water reabsorption rate. The glomerular filtration rate, except under abnormal conditions, remains fairly constant, hence does not normally cause urine volume to fluctuate. The rate of tubular reabsorption of water, on the other hand, fluctuates considerably (pp. 475 and 476 and Fig. 303). The rate of tubular reabsorption, therefore, rather than the glomerular filtration rate, normally adjusts urine volume to fluid intake.

Although changes in the volume of fluid loss via the skin, lungs, and intestines also affect the fluid intake-output ratio, these volumes are not automatically adjusted to intake volume, as is the volume of urine.

Factors that alter fluid loss under abnormal conditions

Both the rate of respiration and the volume of sweat secreted may greatly alter fluid output under certain abnormal conditions. For example, a patient who hyperventilates for an extended time loses an excessive amount of water via the expired air. If, as frequently happens, he also takes in less water by mouth than normal, his fluid output then exceeds his intake and dehydration (that is, a decrease in total body water) develops. Other abnormal conditions characterized by greater output than intake are vomiting, diarrhea, intestinal drainage, etc.

Control of fluid intake

Physiologists disagree about the details of the mechanism for controlling intake so that it increases when output increases and decreases

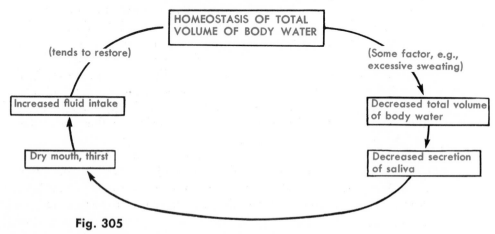

Fig. 305

Diagram illustrates the basic principle of a
postulated homeostatic mechanism for adjusting intake to output.

when output decreases. In general, it operates in this way: when dehydration starts to develop, salivary secretion decreases, producing a "dry mouth" feeling and the sensation of thirst. The individual then drinks water, thereby increasing his fluid intake to offset his increased output, and this tends to restore fluid balance (Fig. 305). If, however, an individual takes nothing by mouth for several days, fluid balance cannot be maintained despite every effort of homeostatic mechanisms to compensate for the zero intake. Obviously under this condition the only way balance could be maintained would be for fluid output to also decrease to zero. This is not possible. Some output is obligatory. For example, as long as respirations continue, some water leaves the body by way of the expired air; as long as life continues, an irreducible minimum of water diffuses through the skin.

MECHANISMS THAT MAINTAIN
HOMEOSTASIS OF FLUID DISTRIBUTION
Comparison of plasma, interstitial fluid, and intracellular fluid

Structurally speaking, body fluids occupy three fluid compartments: blood vessels, tissue spaces, and cells. Thus, we speak of the plasma, interstitial fluid, and intracellular fluid. Functionally, however, these three fluids may be considered as only two fluids: that which lies outside the cells and that which lies within them. Functionally, then, we speak of the extracellular fluid (ECF), meaning both the plasma and interstitial fluid, and the intracellular fluid (ICF), meaning the water inside all the cells. Extracellular fluid constitutes the internal environment of the body. It, therefore, serves the dual functions of providing the relatively constant environment vital to cells and of transporting substances to and from them. Intracellular fluid, on the other hand, because it is a solvent, functions to facilitate intracellular chemical reactions that maintain life. Compared as to volume, intracellular fluid is the largest, plasma the smallest, and interstitial fluid in between. The volumes, of course, vary according to size and age. In a normal adult, according to an eminent authority,* intracellular fluid constitutes roughly 50% of body weight, interstitial fluid about 15%, and plasma about 5% (Fig. 306).

Compared chemically, plasma and interstitial fluid (the two extracellular fluids) are almost identical. Intracellular fluid, on the other hand, shows striking differences from either of the two extracellular fluids. Let us examine first the chemical structure of plasma and in-

---

*Gamble, James L.: Chemical anatomy, physiology, and pathology of extracellular fluid, ed. 6, Cambridge, Mass., 1958, Harvard University Press, pp. 2-4.

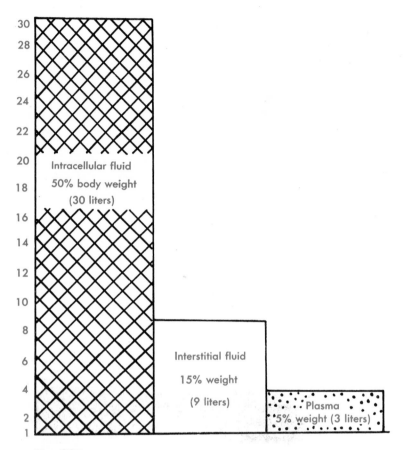

Fig. 306

Relative volumes of three body fluids.
(Modified from Gamble.)

terstitial fluid as shown in Fig. 307. Perhaps the first difference to
catch your eye is that blood contains a slightly larger total of electrolytes (ions) than does interstitial fluid. If you compare the two fluids,
ion for ion, you will discover the most important difference between
blood plasma and interstitial fluid. Look at the anions (negative
ions) in these two extracellular fluids. Note that blood contains an
appreciable amount of protein anions. Interstitial fluid, in contrast,
contains hardly any protein anions. This is the only functionally important difference between blood and interstitial fluid. It exists because the normal capillary membrane is practically impermeable to
proteins. Hence, almost all of them remain behind in the blood instead
of filtering out into the interstitial fluid. And because proteins remain

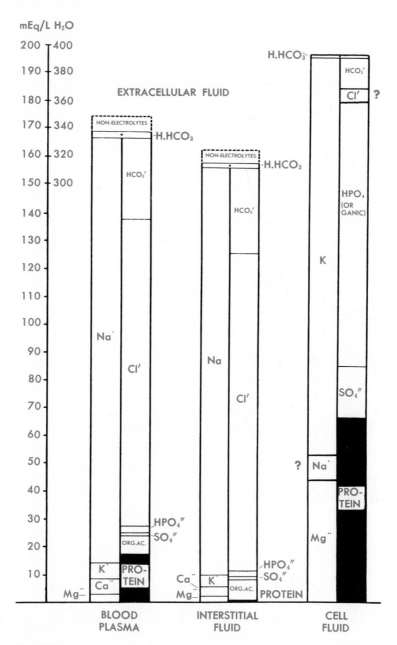

Fig. 307

Diagram showing chief chemical constituents of three fluid compartments.
Height of left half of each column indicates total concentration of cations;
that of right half, concentrations of anions. Both are expressed in
milliequivalents per liter (mEq./L.) of water. Note that chloride and
sodium values in cell fluid are questioned. It is probable that at least
muscle intracellular fluid contains some sodium but no chloride. (From
Bard: Medical physiology, ed. 11, St. Louis, 1961, The C. V. Mosby Co.;
modified from Gamble: Harvey Lect. **42:**247, 1950.)

in the blood, certain other differences also exist between blood and interstitial fluid: notably, blood contains more sodium ions and fewer chloride ions than does interstitial fluid.*

Table 60. Electrolyte composition of blood plasma*

Cations		Anions	
142 mEq. Na⁺		103 mEq. Cl⁻	
5 mEq. K⁺		27 HCO3⁻	
5 mEq. Ca⁺⁺		16 protein⁻	
3 mEq. Mg⁺⁺		6 org. ac.⁻	
		2 HPO4⁼	
		1 SO4⁼	
Totals	155 mEq./L. plasma	155 mEq./L. plasma	

*From Gamble, James L.: Chemical anatomy, physiology, and pathology of extracellular fluid, ed. 6, Cambridge, Mass., 1958, Harvard University Press.

Extracellular fluids and intracellular fluid are more unlike than like chemically. Chemical difference predominates between the extracellular and intracellular fluids. Chemical similarity predominates between the two extracellular fluids. Study Fig. 307 and make some generalizations about the main chemical differences between the extracellular and intracellular fluids. For example: What is the most abundant cation in the extracellular fluids? In the intracellular fluid? What is the most abundant anion in the extracellular fluids? In the intracellular fluid? What about the relative concentrations of protein anions in extracellular fluid and intracellular fluid?

The only reason we have called attention to the chemical structure of the three body fluids is that here, as elsewhere, structure determines function. In this instance the chemical structure of the three fluids helps control water and electrolyte movement between them. Or phrased differently, the chemical structure of body fluids, if normal, helps maintain homeostasis of fluid distribution, and, if abnormal, results in fluid imbalance. Hypervolemia (excess blood volume) is a case in point. Edema, too, frequently stems from changes in the chemical structure of body fluids (Fig. 308).

---

*According to the Donnan equilibrium principle, when nondiffusible anions (negative ions) are present on one side of a membrane, there are on that side of the membrane fewer diffusible anions and more diffusible cations (positive ions) than on the other side. Applying this principle to the blood and interstitial fluid: because blood contains nondiffusible protein anions, it contains fewer chloride ions (diffusible anions) and more sodium ions (diffusible cations) than does interstitial fluid.

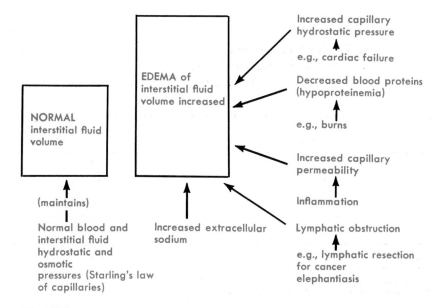

Fig. 308

Diagram to illustrate principle that any one or more of several factors
may produce interstitial fluid edema.

We are ready now to try to answer the following question: How does
the chemical structure of body fluids control water movement between
them, and thereby control fluid distribution in the body?

Control of water movement between plasma and interstitial fluid

Over sixty years ago Starling advanced an hypothesis about the
nature of the mechanism that controls water movement between
plasma and interstitial fluid, that is, across the capillary membrane.
This hypothesis has since become one of the major premises of physiology and is often spoken of as Starling's "law of the capillaries." According to this law, the control mechanism for water exchange between
plasma and interstitial fluid consists of four pressures: blood hydrostatic and colloid osmotic pressures* on one side of the capillary membrane and interstitial fluid hydrostatic and colloid† osmotic pressures
on the other side.

---

*Osmotic pressure due to concentrations of protein in blood and interstitial
fluid. Since the capillary membrane is permeable to other plasma solutes, they
quickly diffuse through the membrane so cause no osmotic pressure to develop
against it. Only the proteins, to which the capillary membrane is practically impermeable, cause an actual osmotic pressure against the capillary membrane (explained on p. 38).

†A small amount of blood proteins passes through the capillary membrane
and tends to concentrate around the venous end of capillaries, hence this pressure.

Table 61. Pressures at arterial end of tissue capillaries

Arterial end of capillary	Hydrostatic pressure	Colloid osmotic pressure
Blood	35 mm. Hg	25 mm. Hg
Interstitial fluid	2 mm. Hg	0 mm. Hg

According to the physical laws governing filtration and osmosis (p. 40), blood hydrostatic pressure (HP) tends to force fluid out of capillaries into interstitial fluid (IF), but blood colloid osmotic pressure (OP) tends to draw it back into them. Interstitial fluid, hydrostatic pressure, in contrast, tends to force fluid out of the interstitial fluid into the capillaries, and interstitial fluid colloid osmotic pressure tends to draw it back out of capillaries. In short, two of these pressures constitute vectors in one direction and two in the opposite direction. Does this remind you of another mechanism studied earlier? (To check your answer, see p. 473.)

The difference between the two sets of opposing forces obviously represents the net or effective force (pressure gradient) tending to produce the net fluid movement between blood and interstitial fluid. In general terms, Starling's law of the capillaries might be stated, therefore, in this way: The rate and direction of fluid exchange between capillaries and interstitial fluid is determined by the hydrostatic and colloid osmotic pressures of the two fluids. Or, written as a formula:

$$(\text{Blood HP} + \text{IFOP}) - (\text{IFHP} + \text{Blood OP}) = \text{EFP*}$$

Note that the factors enclosed in the first set of brackets tend to move fluid out of capillaries, those in the second set tend to move fluid into them.

To illustrate operation of Starling's law, let us consider how it controls water exchange at the arterial end of tissue capillaries. Table 61 gives hypothetical normal pressures although these vary somewhat.

Applying Starling's law of the capillaries:

(35 + 0) − (25 + 2) = 8 mm. Hg net or effective pressure, causing water to move out of the blood at arterial ends of capillaries into interstitial fluid

The same law operates at the venous end of capillaries (Table 62). Again apply Starling's law of the capillaries. What is the net effec-

---

*Effective filtration pressure between capillary blood and interstitial fluid.

Table 62. Pressures at venous end of tissue capillaries

Venous end of capillary	Hydrostatic pressure	Colloid osmotic pressure
Blood	15 mm. Hg	25 mm. Hg
Interstitial fluid	1 mm. Hg	3 mm. Hg*

*A small amount of blood proteins passes through the capillary membrane and tends to concentrate around the venous end of capillaries, hence this pressure.

tive pressure at the venous ends of capillaries? In which direction does it cause water to move? Assuming that the figures given in Table 62 are normal, do you agree that "about the same amount of water returns to the blood at the venous ends of capillaries as left it at the arterial ends"?

On the basis of our discussion thus far, we can formulate a principle about the conditions which must exist in order for blood and interstitial fluids to remain in balance with the same amount of water moving out of the blood into the interstitial fluid as moves back into the blood: No net transfer of water occurs between blood and interstitial fluid when the effective filtration pressure (EFP) equals zero. And a corollary necessarily follows: A net shift of water does occur between blood and interstitial fluid whenever the effective filtration pressure does not equal zero.

Starling's law of the capillaries may be used to explain several types of fluid imbalance seen clinically. Edema, for example, frequently develops in patients who have cardiac decompensation. Because of impaired venous return, capillary hydrostatic pressure may increase above normal in this condition. Suppose that it rises to 40 mm. Hg (average for entire capillary) and that when it first increases blood osmotic pressure and interstitial fluid hydrostatic and osmotic pressures are normal, as shown in Fig. 309. According to Starling's law, the two forces that tend to move water out of the blood total 41 mm. Hg and are opposed by two forces that total only 27 mm. Hg. A net loss of water from the blood to the interstitial fluid, therefore, neccessarily occurs. Interstitial volume increases accordingly until the inward moving forces again equal the outward moving forces and a new balance in water exchange between the two fluids is established. In this case, when the edema becomes sufficiently marked to produce an interstitial fluid hydrostatic pressure of 16 mm. Hg, the amount of water leaving the blood for the interstitial fluid and the amount entering it from the interstitial fluid again become equal. Thus the increased interstitial fluid volume, that is, the edema, becomes stabilized.

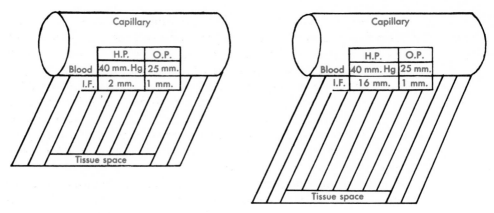

Fig. 309

A mechanism of cardiac edema formation; application of Starling's
law of the capillaries. Left, Initial rise in capillary
hydrostatic pressure establishes effective filtration pressure which
causes net fluid shift out of blood into interstitial fluid.
Right, Edema (increased interstitial fluid volume) develops as a
result of this shift and increases the interstitial fluid hydrostatic
pressure enough to cancel the effective filtration pressure and
re-establish the equilibrium of fluid exchange across the capillary membrane.

Control of water movement between interstitial fluid and intracellular fluids

The chemical structure of interstitial fluid and intracellular fluid
normally controls the exchange of water between them (across the
cell membrane), just as the chemical structure of blood and interstitial
fluid helps control the exchange of water between these two fluids.
The control of water movement between interstitial and intracellular
fluids differs, however, from the control of water movement between
blood and interstitial fluid in that the former depends primarily upon
the relative crystalloid osmotic pressures of the two fluids rather than
upon their relative colloid osmotic and hydrostatic pressures.

Practically speaking, this means that the sodium concentration of
interstitial fluid and the potassium concentration of intracellular fluid
exert the dominant control over water movement between interstitial
and intracellular fluids. This is true for two reasons: They are the
most abundant solutes of these fluids and the normal cell membrane
acts as if it were almost impermeable to them. Hence, these crystalloids are mainly responsible for the osmotic pressure against both
sides of the cell membrane. As a consequence, normal interstitial and
intracellular volumes are maintained only when interstitial sodium
and intracellular potassium concentrations remain normal.

Extracellular fluid sodium (Na⁺) ion concentration is many times greater than that of the intracellular fluid. And the intracellular fluid potassium (K⁺) ion concentration is much higher than that of the extracellular fluid. So the question arises as to why diffusion does not equilibrate these ionic concentrations. What force operates against diffusion to maintain such an ionic imbalance? Today's explanation postulates a "sodium pump" mechanism, that is, active transport of sodium ions out of cells. A negatively charged carrier substance is postulated which transports sodium ions outward and exchanges them for potassium ions which it carries into the cell.

Normal sodium concentration in the interstitial fluid and potassium concentration in the intracellular fluid depend upon many factors. Reabsorption of these ions by renal tubules and active transport of them across the cell membrane (controlled, as we have noted, by aldosterone) are two of the most important ones. Homeostasis of interstitial and intracellular fluid volumes depends upon these pump mechanisms. For example, if the active transport mechanism which reabsorbs sodium into blood from renal tubules accelerates, extracellular fluid sodium concentration may increase above normal (sodium retention), and extracellular fluid crystalloid osmotic pressure temporarily increases—to a level higher than that of the intracellular fluid. The law of osmosis operates, and a shift of water from cells to interstitial fluid takes place until a new equilibrium is established between extracellular fluid and intracellular fluid osmotic pressures.

Outline summary
Fluid and electrolyte balance
Introduction
1. Meaning of fluid balance
   a. same as homeostasis of fluids, that is, total volume of water in body is normal and remains relatively constant
   b. volume of blood plasma, of interstitial fluid, and of intracellular fluid all remain relatively constant, that is, homeostasis of distribution of water as well as of total volume
2. Fluid balance and electrolyte balance interdependent—See Fig. 303

Some general principles about fluid balance
1. Cardinal principle—intake must equal output
2. Fluid and electrolyte balance maintained primarily by mechanisms that adjust output to intake; secondarily by mechanisms that adjust intake to output
3. Fluid balance also maintained by mechanisms that control movement of water between fluid compartments

Avenues by which water normally enters and leaves body

1. Water enters body through digestive tract in
   a. liquids
   b. foods
2. Water formed in body by metabolism of foods
3. Water leaves body via kidneys, lungs, skin, and intestine

Mechanisms that adjust fluid output to fluid intake

Control of urine volume

1. Factors that control reabsorption of water by distal and collecting tubules: ECF electrolyte concentration (crystalloid osmotic pressure) controls ADH secretion which controls tubule H_2O reabsorption; ECF volume controls aldosterone secretion which controls tubule Na^+ reabsorption and therefore water reabsorption
2. Factors that control reabsorption of water by distal and collecting tubules (mainly crystalloid osmotic pressure of ECF which indirectly controls corticoid and ADH secretion which regulate sodium, potassium, and water reabsorption

Factors that alter fluid loss under abnormal conditions

Hyperventilation, hypoventilation, vomiting, diarrhea, etc.

Control of fluid intake

See Fig. 305
Mechanism by which intake adjusted to output not completely known; one controlling factor seems to be degree of moistness of mucosa of mouth—if output exceeds intake, mouth feels dry, sensation of thirst occurs, and individual ingests liquids

Mechanisms that maintain homeostasis of fluid distribution

Comparison of plasma, interstitial fluid, and intracellular fluid

1. Plasma and interstitial fluid constitute extracellular fluid (ECF) the internal environment of body or, in other words, environment of cells
2. Intracellular fluid (ICF) volume is largest, plasma volume smallest; ICF about 50% of body weight, IF about 15%, and plasma about 5% or ICF volume about 10 times that of plasma and IF volume about 3 times plasma volume
3. Chemically plasma and IF almost identical except that plasma contains slightly more electrolytes and considerably more proteins than IF; also blood contains somewhat more sodium and fewer chloride ions
4. Chemically, ECF and ICF strikingly different; sodium main cation of ECF, potassium main cation of ICF; chloride main anion of ECF; phosphate main anion of ICF; protein concentration much higher in ICF than in IF

Control of water movement between plasma and interstitial fluid

By four pressures—blood hydrostatic and colloid osmotic pressures and interstitial fluid hydrostatic and colloid osmotic pressures; effect of these pressures on water movement between plasma and interstitial fluid expressed in Starling's "law of the capillaries"; when (blood hydrostatic pressure + IF colloid osmotic pressure) − (blood colloid osmotic pressure + IF hydrostatic pressure) = 0, equal amounts of water leave blood for IF and return to it from IF, or, in other words, water balance exists between these two fluids under these conditions

Control of water movement between interstitial fluid and intracellular fluid

Primarily by relative crystalloid osmotic pressures of ECF and ICF, which depend mainly upon sodium concentration of ECF and potassium concentration of ICF which, in turn, depend upon cellular and renal sodium transport mechanisms

Review questions

Fluid and electrolyte balance

1. Explain in your own words the meaning of the term fluid balance.
2. How is total volume of body fluids kept relatively constant—that is, what other factors must be controlled in order to keep the total volume of water in the body relatively constant?
3. What, if any, are functionally important differences between the chemical composition of plasma and interstitial fluid?
4. What, if any, are functionally important differences between the chemical composition of extracellular and intracellular fluids?
5. Are plasma and interstitial fluid more accurately described as "similar" or "different" as to chemical composition? Volume?
6. Support your answer to question 5 with some specific facts.
7. Are interstitial fluid and intracellular fluid more accurately described as "similar" or "different" as to chemical composition? Volume?
8. Explain Starling's law of the capillaries in your own words. Be as brief and clear as you can. This law describes the mechanism for controlling what?

Situation: Edema characterizes a certain stage of starvation.

9. Explain why edema develops, applying Starling's law of the capillaries to this situation.

Situation: A patient has had marked diarrhea for several days.

10. Explain the homeostatic mechanisms that would tend to compensate for this excessive fluid loss.
11. Do you think they could succeed in maintaining fluid balance or would fluid therapy probably be necessary?
12. What, if any, abnormality of fluid distribution do you think would occur in this patient without fluid therapy? Explain your reasoning.
13. Why does dehydration necessarily develop if an individual takes nothing by mouth for several days and receives no fluid therapy? Why cannot homeostatic mechanisms prevent this?

Acid-base balance

Acid-base balance is vitally important. Acid-base balance means maintenance of homeostasis of the hydrogen ion concentration of body fluids. Even a slight deviation from normal causes pronounced changes in the rate of cellular chemical reactions. This, in turn, threatens survival.

MECHANISMS THAT CONTROL pH OF BODY FLUIDS

Meaning of term pH

The term pH is a symbol used to mean the hydrogen ion concentration of a solution. Actually, pH stands for the negative logarithm of the hydrogen ion concentration.* pH indicates the degree of acidity and alkalinity of a solution—the latter because as hydrogen ion concentration increases, OH ion concentration (alkalinity) necessarily decreases. A pH of 7 indicates neutrality (equal amounts of H+ and OH−), a pH of less than 7 indicates acidity (more H+ than OH−), and one greater than 7 indicates alkalinity (more OH− than H+).

Types of pH control mechanisms

Since various acids and bases continually enter the blood from absorbed foods and from metabolism of food, some kind of mechanism for neutralizing or eliminating these substances is necessary if blood pH is to remain constant. Actually three different devices operate together to maintain constancy of pH. Collectively these devices—buffers, respirations, and kidney excretion of acids and bases—might be said to constitute the pH homeostatic mechanism.

---

*A pH of 7, for example, means that a solution contains 10^{-7} grams hydrogen ions per liter. Or, translating this logarithm into a number, a pH of 7 means that a solution contains 0.0000001 (that is, 1/10,000,000) gram hydrogen ions per liter. A solution of pH 6 contains 0.000001 (1/1,000,000) gram hydrogen ions per liter and one of pH 8 contains 0.00000001 (1/100,000,000) gram hydrogen ions per liter. Note that a solution with pH 7 contains 10 times as many hydrogen ions as a solution with pH 8 and that pH decreases as hydrogen ion concentration increases.

Effectiveness of pH control mechanisms; range of pH

The most eloquent evidence of the effectiveness of the pH control mechanism is the extremely narrow range of pH, normally 7.35 to 7.45. In terms of hydrogen ion concentration, this means that normally there is a little more than 1/100,000,000 of a gram of hydrogen ions (pH 8) in a liter of blood but a little less than 1/10,000,000 of a gram (pH 7). Also, the greatest normal amount of hydrogen ions is only about 1/100,000,000 of a gram more than the smallest normal amount. What incredible constancy! Acids continually stream into capillary blood from cell metabolism and yet a liter of venous blood (pH 7.35) contains only about 1/100,000,000 of a gram more hydrogen ions than does a liter of arterial blood (pH 7.45)! The pH homeostatic mechanism does indeed control effectively—astonishingly so.

BUFFER MECHANISM FOR CONTROLLING pH OF BODY FLUIDS

Buffers defined

In terms of action, a buffer is a substance that prevents marked changes in the pH of a solution when an acid or a base is added to it. Let us suppose that a small amount of the strong acid HCl is added to a solution that contains a buffer (to blood, for example), and that its pH decreases from 7.41 to 7.27. But if the same amount of HCl were added to pure water containing no buffers, its pH would decrease much more markedly, from 7 to perhaps 3.4. In both instances pH decreased upon addition of the acid, but much less so with buffers present than without them.

In terms of chemical composition, buffers consist of two kinds of substances and are, therefore, often referred to as "buffer pairs." Most of the body fluid buffer pairs consist of a weak acid and a salt of that acid, as shown in the next paragraph.

Buffer pairs present in body fluids

The main buffer pairs present in body fluids are as follows:

Bicarbonate pairs $\dfrac{NaHCO_3}{H_2CO_3}, \dfrac{KHCO_3}{H_2CO_3},$ etc.

Plasma protein pair $\dfrac{Na \cdot proteinate}{Proteins \ (weak \ acids)}$

Hemoglobin pairs $\dfrac{K \cdot Hb}{Hb}, \dfrac{K \cdot HbO_2}{HbO_2}$ (Hb and HbO_2 are weak acids)

Phosphate buffer pair $\dfrac{Na_2HPO_4}{NaH_2PO_4} \ \dfrac{(basic \ phosphate)}{(acid \ phosphate)}$

Action of buffers to prevent marked changes in pH of body fluids

Buffers react with a relatively strong acid (or base) to replace it by a relatively weak acid (or base). That is to say, an acid which highly dissociates to yield many H ions is replaced by one which dissociates less highly to yield fewer H ions. Thus, by the buffer reaction, instead of the strong acid remaining in the solution and contributing many H ions to drastically lower the pH of the solution, a weaker acid takes its place, contributes fewer additional H ions to the solution, and thereby lowers its pH only slightly. Therefore, because blood contains buffer pairs, its pH fluctuates much less widely than it would without them. In other words, blood buffers constitute one of the devices for preventing marked changes in blood pH. Let us consider some specific examples of buffer action. More carbonic acid is formed in the body than any other acid. It continuously enters tissue capillaries where it is buffered primarily by the potassium salt of hemoglobin inside the red blood cells as shown in Fig. 310.

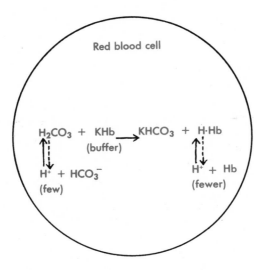

Fig. 310

Buffering of carbonic acid inside red blood cell by potassium salt of hemoglobin. Note that each molecule of carbonic acid is replaced by a molecule of the acid, hemoglobin. Since hemoglobin is a weaker acid than carbonic acid, fewer of these hemoglobin molecules dissociate to form hydrogen ions. Hence, fewer hydrogen ions are present in red blood cell intracellular fluid than would have been present without the buffering of carbonic acid by the potassium salt of hemoglobin. Also, since the carbonic acid in the red blood cells has come from plasma, fewer hydrogen ions remain in blood than would if there were no buffering of carbonic acid.

$$\text{Lactic acid} + \text{NaHCO}_3 \longrightarrow \text{Na·lactate} + \text{H}_2\text{CO}_3$$
$$\updownarrow$$
$$\text{H}^+ + \text{lactate}^- \qquad\qquad\qquad\qquad \text{H}^+ + \text{HCO}_3^-$$
(few) (fewer)

Fig. 311

Buffering of lactic acid (a fixed or nonvolatile acid) by basic
carbonate salt which also buffers other nonvolatile acids.
Carbonic acid (a weaker acid than lactic acid) replaces lactic acid
Result: fewer hydrogen ions are added to blood than would be if
lactic acid were not buffered.

$$\text{NaOH} + \text{H}_2\text{CO}_3 \longrightarrow \text{NaHCO}_3 + \text{HOH}$$
$$\updownarrow$$
$$\text{Na}^+ + \text{OH}^- \qquad\qquad\qquad\qquad \text{H}^+ + \text{OH}^-$$
(many) (very few)

Fig. 312

Buffering of base NaOH by carbonic acid.

Note how this reaction applies the principle of buffering. As a result
of the buffering action of KHb, the weaker acid, H·Hb, replaces the
stronger acid, H_2CO_3, and, therefore, the hydrogen ion concentration
of blood increases much less than it would if carbonic acid were not
buffered.

The potassium salt of oxyhemoglobin, sodium proteinate (sodium
salts of blood proteins), and basic sodium phosphate also buffer carbonic acid.

Nonvolatile, or fixed acids, such as lactic acid and ketone bodies, are
buffered mainly by the basic member of the bicarbonate buffer pair
as shown in the equation given in Fig. 311.

Buffering of bases by carbonic acid is illustrated by the equation
given in Fig. 312.

When blood pH is normal and a state of acid-base balance exists,
components of the bicarbonate buffer pair are present in the extracellular fluid in a ratio of 20 parts of base bicarbonate (primarily
$NaHCO_3$) to 1 part of carbonic acid. Actually, a liter of plasma normally contains about 27 milliequivalents of base bicarbonate and 1.3
milliequivalents of carbonic acid:

$$\frac{27 \text{ mEq.} \bullet \text{B} \bullet \text{HCO}_3}{1.3 \text{ mEq.} \bullet \text{ H}_2\text{CO}_3} = \frac{20}{1} = \text{pH 7.4}$$

An increase in this ratio causes pH to increase (uncompensated alkalosis), and a decrease in it causes pH to decrease (uncompensated acidosis).

Buffering of nonvolatile acids (for example, lactic and acetoacetic acid, one of the ketone bodies from fat catabolism) adds some carbonic acid and removes some base bicarbonate from blood (see Fig. 311). This decreases the base bicarbonate-carbonic acid ratio, which in turn decreases venous blood pH below arterial blood pH.

Evaluation of role of buffers in pH control

Buffering alone cannot maintain homeostasis of pH. As we have seen, extra hydrogen ions continually enter capillary blood despite buffering. If even a few more hydrogen ions were added to blood every time it circulated and no way were provided for eliminating them, blood hydrogen ion concentration would gradually but continually increase and pH continually decrease. The additional respiratory and urinary devices must, therefore, function concurrently with the buffers in order to maintain constancy of pH.

RESPIRATORY MECHANISM OF pH CONTROL

Explanation of mechanism

Respirations play a vital part in controlling pH. With every expiration carbon dioxide leaves the body in the expired air. This necessarily reduces the amount of carbonic acid in the extracellular fluids. Why? Because less carbon dioxide remains in the extracellular fluids to combine with water to form carbonic acid. And, since some of the carbonic acid molecules dissociate to yield hydrogen ions, if the amount of carbonic acid in blood decreases, the concentration of hydrogen ions also decreases and the pH increases. In short, expiration eliminates from the blood and from the body some of the carbon dioxide that enters blood in the tissue capillaries and that combines with water to form carbonic acid which, despite buffering, still adds hydrogen ions, sufficient in amount, in fact, to decrease blood pH from about 7.41, a characteristic average for arterial blood, to about 7.36, a characteristic average for venous blood. As carbon dioxide leaves the blood from the pulmonary capillaries, blood hydrogen ion concentration again decreases and blood pH increases from the venous to arterial level.

Adjustment of respirations to pH of arterial blood

Obviously in order for respirations to serve as a mechanism of pH control, there must be some arrangement so respirations can vary as needed to maintain or restore normal pH. Suppose that blood pH has

575

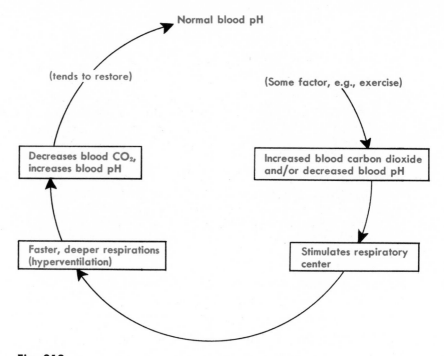

Normal blood pH

(tends to restore)

(Some factor, e.g., exercise)

Decreases blood CO₂, increases blood pH

Increased blood carbon dioxide and/or decreased blood pH

Faster, deeper respirations (hyperventilation)

Stimulates respiratory center

Fig. 313

Respiratory mechanism of pH control. A rise in arterial blood
CO_2 content or a drop in its pH (below about 7.38) stimulates
respiratory center neurons. Hyperventilation results. Less
CO_2 and therefore less carbonic acid and less hydrogen ions
remain in blood so that its pH increases back up toward normal.

decreased (that is, hydrogen ion concentration has increased). Respirations then need to increase in order to eliminate some of the carbon dioxide from the blood. Less carbon dioxide in the blood means
fewer hydrogen ions in blood formed from the following reaction:

$$CO_2 + H_2O \xrightarrow{\text{(carbonic anhydrase)}} H_2CO_3 \longrightarrow H^+ + HCO_3^-$$

The mechanism for adjusting respirations to arterial blood carbon
dioxide content or pH operates in this way. Neurons of the respiratory
center are sensitive to changes in arterial blood carbon dioxide content and to changes in its pH. If the amount of carbon dioxide in
arterial blood increases beyond a certain level, or if arterial blood pH
decreases below about 7.38, the respiratory center is stimulated and
respirations accordingly increase in rate and depth. This, in turn,
eliminates more carbon dioxide, reduces carbonic acid and hydrogen
ions, and increases pH back toward the normal level (Fig. 313). The
carotid chemoreflex (p. 343) is another device by which respirations
adjust to blood pH and, in turn, adjust pH.

Some principles relating respirations and pH of body fluids

1. A decrease in blood pH below normal (that is, acidosis) tends to cause increased respirations (hyperventilation) which tends to increase pH back toward normal. In other words, acidosis causes hyperventilation which acts as a compensating mechanism for the acidosis.

2. Prolonged hyperventilation may increase blood pH enough to produce alkalosis.

3. An increase in blood pH above normal (or alkalosis) causes hypoventilation which serves as a compensating mechanism for the alkalosis by decreasing blood pH back toward normal.

4. Prolonged hypoventilation may decrease blood pH enough to produce acidosis.

URINARY MECHANISM OF pH CONTROL

General principles about the mechanism

Because the kidneys can excrete varying amounts of acid and base, they, like the lungs, play a vital role in pH control. Kidney tubules, by excreting many or few hydrogen ions, in exchange for reabsorbing many or few sodium ions, control urine pH and thereby help control blood pH. If, for example, blood pH decreases below normal, kidney tubules remove more hydrogen ions from the blood to the urine and reabsorb more sodium ions from the urine back into the blood, thereby decreasing urine pH but increasing blood pH back toward normal. In brief, the urinary mechanism of pH control, like the respiratory mechanism, is a device for actually eliminating more or fewer hydrogen ions from the body at a rate matching the number entering the blood. The buffering mechanism, in contrast, merely reduces the amount of hydrogen ions or OH ions coming into the blood at one time. Inadequate or excessive respirations or urinary excretion, therefore, throw the body into an acid-base disturbance despite adequate buffering action. Only when all three parts of the pH control mechanism—buffering, respirations, and urine secretion—function adequately can acid-base balance be maintained.

Let us turn our attention now to the mechanisms that adjust urine pH to counteract changes in blood pH.

Mechanisms that control urine pH

When the pH of body fluids decreases, urine pH also decreases due to certain activities of the distal tubule cells which acidify urine. The following paragraphs describe these mechanisms.

1. Distal tubules secrete hydrogen ions into the urine in exchange for basic ions which they reabsorb. Fig. 314 illustrates the mechanism

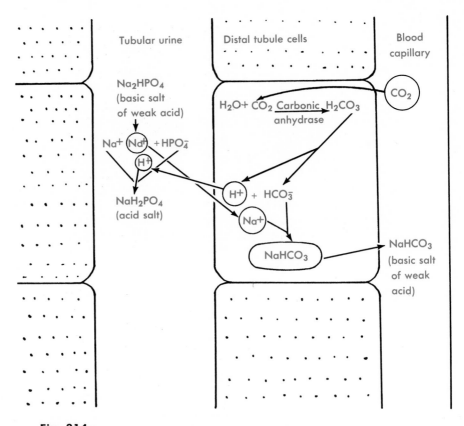

Fig. 314

Acidification of urine and conservation of base by distal
renal tubule secretion of H ions (discussed below).

by which they do this. Carbon dioxide diffuses from tubule capillaries
into distal tubule cells where the enzyme carbonic anhydrase accelerates the combining of carbon dioxide with water to form carbonic
acid. The latter dissociates into hydrogen ions and bicarbonate ions.
The hydrogen ions then diffuse into the tubular urine, where they displace basic ions (most often sodium) from a basic salt of a weak acid
and thereby change the basic salt to an acid salt or to a weak acid
which is eliminated in the urine. While this is happening, the displaced
sodium or other basic ion diffuses into a tubule cell. Here it combines
with the bicarbonate ion left over from the carbonic acid dissociation
to form sodium bicarbonate. The sodium bicarbonate then diffuses,
is reabsorbed, that is, into the blood. Note the various results of this
mechanism. Sodium bicarbonate (or other base bicarbonate) is con-
served for the body. Instead of all the basic salts that filter out of
glomerular blood being eliminated in the urine, considerable amounts
are recovered into peritubular capillary blood. In addition, extra hydrogen ions are added to the urine and thereby eliminated from the

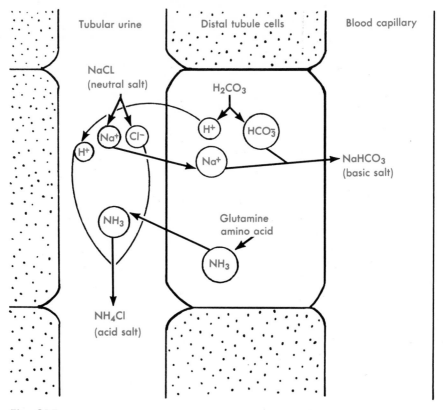

Fig. 315

Acidification of urine by NH₃ synthesis and
conservation of base (discussed below).

body. And, finally, this increases blood pH back upward toward normal and decreases urine pH. In short, distal tubule secretion of hydrogen ions in exchange for sodium ions makes blood more alkaline by
making urine more acid.

2. Distal tubule cells synthesize ammonia which diffuses into the
tubular urine, there to combine with hydrogen to form an ammonium
ion (Fig. 315). The ammonium ion displaces sodium or some other
basic ion from a salt of a strong acid to form an ammonium salt. The
basic ion then diffuses back into a tubule cell and combines with bicarbonate ion to form a basic salt which, in turn, diffuses into tubular
blood. The effects of distal tubule ammonium secretion on pH control
are thus the same as the effects of distal tubule hydrogen secretion.
Distal tubules secrete more hydrogen and ammonium ions or, in other
words, make the urine more acid when the pH of body fluid decreases
below its normal mean. Fig. 316 indicates how this homeostatic mechanism may be set in operation and its effects. Quantitatively, ammonium
ion excretion is more important than hydrogen ion excretion.

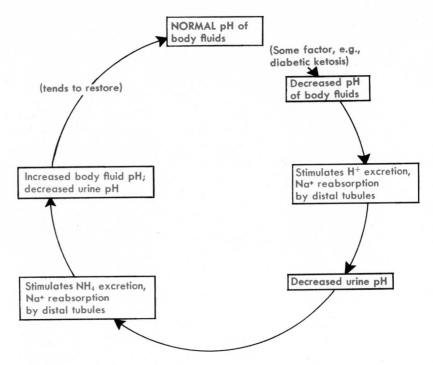

Fig. 316

Urinary mechanism for maintaining homeostasis of pH.

CLINICAL DISTURBANCES IN ACID-BASE BALANCE
Acidosis

During the course of certain diseases, such as diabetic ketosis or starvation, for instance, abnormally large amounts of nonvolatile acids enter the blood. All three types of pH control mechanisms—buffers, respiratory and urinary—are enlisted in the effort to compensate for the excess acid and to maintain acid-base balance. Basic bicarbonate buffers immediately react with the acids (Fig. 311). This decreases the ratio of base bicarbonate-carbonic acid of blood, which decreases blood pH. Respirations become faster and deeper (hyperventilation), removing more carbon dioxide and thereby decreasing the carbonic acid and hydrogen ion content of blood toward normal. The kidneys increase their excretion of H^+ and NH_4^+ in exchange for reabsorbed Na^+ (Figs. 314 and 315). This removes some of the added acid ions and lessens the decrease in blood base carbonate. If hyperventilation and urine acidification together succeed in preventing a decrease in the base bicarbonate-carbonic acid ratio, blood pH remains normal and a state of *compensated acidosis* exists. But if, despite these homeostatic devices, the ratio and pH decrease, *uncompensated acidosis* develops.

Increased blood hydrogen ion concentration, as we have noted, stimulates the respiratory center. For this reason hyperventilation is an outstanding clinical sign of acidosis. Increases in hydrogen ion concentration above a certain level depress the central nervous system and, therefore, produce such symptoms as disorientation and coma.

A matter of clinical importance about tubule excretion of hydrogen ions is its relationship to tubule excretion of potassium ions. Renal tubules can excrete either hydrogen or potassium in exchange for the sodium they reabsorb. Therefore, in general, the more hydrogen they excrete, the less potassium is excreted. In acidosis, therefore, in which tubule excretion of hydrogen increases, potassium excretion decreases. This may lead to hyperkalemia (increased blood potassium), a dangerous condition because it can cause heart block.

Alkalosis

Alkalosis develops less often than acidosis. Some circumstances, however, such as ingestion of an excessive amount of an alkaline drug, hyperventilation, or excessive vomiting can produce alkalosis. Base bicarbonate increases above normal in alkalosis. In compensated alkalosis, carbonic acid also increases but the base bicarbonate-carbonic acid ratio and pH remain normal. In uncompensated alkalosis, the ratio and pH increase.

Outline summary
Acid-base balance
Mechanisms that control pH of body fluids
Meaning of term pH
Negative logarithm of H ion concentration of solution

Types of pH control mechanisms
1. Buffers
2. Respirations
3. Secretion of urine of varying pH

Effectiveness of pH control mechanisms; range of pH
Extremely effective, normally maintain pH within very narrow range of 7.35 to 7.45

Buffer mechanism for controlling pH of body fluids
Buffers defined
Substances that prevent marked change in pH of solution when acid or base added to it; consist of weak acid (or its acid salt) and basic salt of that acid

Buffer pairs present in body fluids
Mainly carbonic acid, proteins, hemoglobin, acid phosphate, and sodium and potassium salts of these weak acids.

Action of buffers to prevent marked changes in pH of body fluids
1. Carbonic acid, a volatile acid, buffered mainly by potassium salt of hemoglobin and oxyhemoglobin
2. Nonvolatile acids, such as lactic acid, buffered mainly by sodium bicarbonate
3. Bases buffered mainly by carbonic acid

(Ratio $\dfrac{B \cdot HCO_3}{H_2CO_3} = \dfrac{20}{1}$ when homeostasis of pH at 7.4 exists)

Evaluation of role of buffers in pH control

Cannot maintain normal pH without adequate functioning of respiratory and urinary pH control mechanisms

Respiratory mechanism of pH control

Explanation of mechanism

Amount of blood carbon dioxide directly related to amount of carbonic acid and, therefore, to concentration of H ions; with increased respirations, less carbon dioxide remains in blood, hence less carbonic acid and fewer H ions; with decreased respirations, more carbon dioxide remains in blood, hence more carbonic acid and more H ions

Adjustment of respirations to pH of arterial blood

See Fig. 313, p. 576

Some principles relating respirations and pH of body fluids

1. Acidosis $\longrightarrow$ Hyperventilation
  $\downarrow$
  increases elimination of CO_2
  $\downarrow$
  decreases blood CO_2
  $\downarrow$
  decreases blood H_2CO_3
  $\downarrow$
  decreases blood H ions, that is, increases blood pH
  $\downarrow$
  tends to correct acidosis, that is, to restore normal pH
2. Prolonged hyperventilation, by decreasing blood H ions excessively, may produce alkalosis
3. Alkalosis causes hypoventilation which tends to correct alkalosis by increasing blood CO_2 and, therefore, blood H_2CO_3 and H ions
4. Prolonged hypoventilation by eliminating too little CO_2, causes increase in blood H_2CO_3 and, consequently, in blood H ions, thereby may produce acidosis

Urinary mechanism of pH control

General principles about the mechanism

Plays vital role in acid-base balance because kidneys can eliminate more H ions from body while reabsorbing more base when pH tends toward acid side and eliminate fewer H ions while reabsorbing less base when pH tends toward alkaline side

Mechanisms that control urine pH

1. Secretion of H ions into urine—as blood CO_2, H_2CO_3, and H ions increase above normal, distal tubules secrete more H ions into urine to displace basic ion (mainly sodium) from a urine salt and then reabsorb sodium into blood in exchange for the H ions excreted
2. Synthesis of NH_3—as blood H ion concentration increases, distal tubules synthesize more NH_3 which combines with H ion of urine to form NH_4 ion which displaces basic ion from a salt; basic ion then is reabsorbed back into blood in exchange for ammonium ion excreted

Clinical disturbances in acid-base balance

Acidosis

1. Compensated metabolic acidosis—decreased alkaline reserve (base bicarbonate, mainly $NaHCO_3$), but ratio $\dfrac{NaHCO_3}{H_2CO_3}$ maintained at normal $\dfrac{20}{1}$ by proportionately decreasing blood carbonic acid by hyperventilation
2. Uncompensated acidosis—alkaline reserve, $\dfrac{NaHCO_3}{H_2CO_3}$ ratio, and blood pH all decrease below normal

Alkalosis

1. Compensated alkalosis—opposite to compensated acidosis
2. Uncompensated alkalosis—opposite to uncompensated acidosis

Review questions

Acid-base balance

1. Explain, in your own words, what the term pH means.
2. What is the normal range for pH of body fluids?
3. Explain what a buffer is in terms of its chemical composition and in terms of its function. Cite specific equations to illustrate your explanation.
4. What is the numerical value of the ratio of $B \cdot HCO_3/H_2CO_3$ when blood pH is 7.4 and the body is in a state of acid-base balance?
5. Is the ratio $B \cdot HCO_3/H_2CO_3$ necessarily abnormal when an acid-base disturbance is present? Give reasons to support your answer.
6. Is blood pH always abnormal when an acid-base disturbance is present? Give reasons for your answer.
7. Explain how the "respiratory mechanism of pH control" operates.
8. Why is hyperventilation a characteristic clinical sign in acidosis?

Situation: A patient has suffered a severe head injury. Respirations are markedly depressed.

9. Which, if either, do you think is a potential danger—acidosis or alkalosis? State your reasons.
10. Describe the homeostatic mechanisms that would operate to try to maintain acid-base balance in this patient.

Situation: A mother brings her baby to the hospital and reports that he has seemed very sick for the past 24 hours and that he has not eaten during that time and has passed no urine.

11. Do you think acidosis or alkalosis may be present in this baby?
12. Why?

Suggested supplementary readings

Chapter II

Allfrey, V. G., and Mirsky, A. E.: How cells make molecules, Scient. Am. **205**:74, 1961.

Bearn, A. G., and German, J. L., III: Chromosomes and disease, Scient. Am. **205**:66, 1961.

Benzer, S.: The fine structure of the gene, Scient. Am. **206**:70, 1962.

Brachet, J.: The living cell, Scient. Am. **205**:50, 1961.

Ham, Arthur W., and Leeson, Thomas S.: Histology, ed. 4, Philadelphia, 1961, J. B. Lippincott Co.

Harary, J.: Heart cells in vitro, Scient. Am. **206**:141, 1962.

Hayashi, T.: How cells move, Scient. Am. **205**:184, 1961.

Holter, H.: How things get into cells, Scient. Am. **205**:167, 1961.

Hurwitz, J., and Furth, J. J.: Messenger RNA, Scient. Am. **206**:41, 1962.

Hyden, H.: Satellite cells in the nervous system, Scient. Am. **205**:62, 1961.

In the beginning—DNA, Science Newsletter, **82**:262, 1962.

Katz, B.: How cells communicate, Scient. Am. **205**:209, 1961.

Lehninger, A. L.: How cells transform energy, Scient. Am. **205**:62, 1961.

McElroy, W. D.: Cellular physiology and biochemistry, Englewood Cliffs, N. J., 1960, Prentice-Hall, Inc.

Miller, W. H.: How cells receive stimuli, Scient. Am. **205**:222, 1961.

Swanson, Carl P.: The cell, Englewood Cliffs, N. J., 1960, Prentice-Hall, Inc.

Chapter III

Ham, Arthur W., and Leeson, Thomas S.: Histology, ed. 4, Philadelphia, 1961, J. B. Lippincott Co.

Chapter IV

Calin, M. M.: The skin from infancy to old age, Am. J. Nursing **60**:993, 1960.

Chapter V

Lonergan, R. C.: Osteoporosis of the spine, Am. J. Nursing **61**:79, 1961.

Chapter VI

Morehouse, L. E., and Miller, Augustus T., Jr.: Physiology of exercise, ed. 3, St. Louis, 1959, The C. V. Mosby Co.

Wells, K. S.: Kinesiology, ed. 3, St. Louis, 1960, The C. V. Mosby Co.

Chapter VII

Dasser and O'Connor: Continuous epidural block for obstetric anesthesia, Am. J. Nursing **60**:1296, 1960.

O'Brien, R.: We're learning more about the brain, Today's Health **60**:32, 1962.

Peele, T. L.: The neuroanatomic basis for clinical neurology, ed. 2, New York, 1961, McGraw Hill Book Co., Inc.

Penfield, W., and Rasmussen, T.: The cerebral

cortex of man, New York, 1957, The Macmillan Co.

Chapter VIII

Ariagno, R. P.: Ultrasonic surgery for Meniére's disease, Am. J. Nursing 60:1778, 1960.

Peele, T. L.: The neuroanatomic basis for clinical neurology, ed. 2, New York, 1961, McGraw Hill Book Co., Inc.

Rosenzweig, M. R.: Auditory localization, Scient. Am. 205:132, 1961.

Chapter IX

Harary, I.: Heart cells in vitro, Scient. Am. 206:141, 1962.

Chapter X

Knowles, J. H.: Respiratory physiology and its clinical applications, Cambridge, Mass., Harvard University Press.

Chapter XI

Mayer, J.: Obesity, causes and treatment, Am. J. Nursing 59:1732, 1959.

Nugent, G. R.: Prolonged hypothermia, Am. J. Nursing 60:967, 1960.

Symposium on obesity, New York Academy of Medicine, June, 1960.

Chapter XIII

Tyler, E. T.: Oral contraceptives, Am. J. Nursing 61:51, 1961.

Chapter XIV

Greenblatt, R. B., and Metts, J. C., Jr.: Addison's disease, Am. J. Nursing 60:1249, 1960.

Lanes, P.: Primary aldosteronism, Am. J. Nursing 61:46, 1961.

Reich, B. H., and Ault, L. P.: Nursing care of the patient with Addison's disease, Am. J. Nursing 60:1249, 1960.

Chapter XV

Bard, P.: Medical physiology, ed. 11, St. Louis, 1961, The C. V. Mosby Co., pp. 301-359.

Best, Charles H., and Taylor, M. B.: The physiological basis of medical practice, ed. 7, Baltimore, 1961, Williams & Wilkins Co., pp. 17-32.

Gamble, J. L.: Chemical anatomy, physiology, and pathology of extracellular fluid, ed. 6, Cambridge, Mass., 1958, Harvard University Press.

Chapter XVI

Bard, P.: Medical physiology, ed. 11, St. Louis, 1961, The C. V. Mosby Co., pp. 359-361.

Best, Charles H., and Taylor, M. B.: The physiological basis of medical practice, ed. 7, Baltimore, 1961, Williams & Wilkins Co., pp. 556-563.

Additional references

Biochemistry

Kleiner, and Orten, J. M.: Biochemistry, ed. 6, St. Louis, 1962, The C. V. Mosby Co.

Gross anatomy, atlases

Sobotta-Uhlenhuth, E.: Atlas of human anatomy, 3 vols., ed. 7, New York, 1957, Hafner Publishing Co.

Spalteholz, Werner: Atlas of human anatomy, 2 vols., ed. 15, New York, 1954, Little, Brown & Co.

Gross anatomy, textbooks

Brash, James Couper, editor: Cunningham's textbook of anatomy, ed 9, New York, 1951, Oxford University Press.

Edwards, Linden F.: Concise anatomy, ed. 2, New York, 1956, McGraw-Hill Book Co., Inc.

Gray, Henry: Anatomy of the human body, ed. 26, edited by Charles Mayo Goss, Philadelphia, 1954, Lea & Febiger.

Hamilton, W. J., editor: Textbook of human anatomy, New York, 1957, The Macmillan Co.

Microscopic anatomy

Ham, Arthur W., and Leeson, Thomas S.: Histology, ed. 4, Philadelphia, 1961, J. B. Lippincott Co.

Jordan, Harvey Ernest: A textbook of histology, ed. 9, New York, 1952, Appleton-Century-Crofts, Inc.

Maximow, Alexander A., and Bloom, William: A Textbook of histology, ed. 7, Philadelphia, 1957, W. B. Saunders Co.

Developmental anatomy

Arey, Leslie Brainerd: Developmental anatomy—a textbook and laboratory manual of embryology, ed. 6, Philadelphia, 1954, W. B. Saunders Co.

Physiology

Best, Charles Herbert, and Taylor, Norman Burke: The physiological basis of medical practice, ed. 7, Baltimore, 1961, Williams & Wilkins Co.

Cannon, W. B.: The wisdom of the body, rev. ed., New York, 1939, W. W. Norton & Co.

Elkinton, J. Russell, and Danowski, T. S.: The body fluids: basic physiology and practical therapeutics, Baltimore, 1955, Williams and Wilkins Co.

Fulton, John F.: Howell's textbook of physiology, ed. 17, Philadelphia, 1955, W. B. Saunders Co.

Goldschmidt, R. B.: Theoretical genetics, Berkeley, 1955, University of California Press.

Guyton, Arthur C.: Textbook of medical physiology, Philadelphia, 1956, W. B. Saunders Co.

Montagu, A.: Human heredity, New York, 1959, New American Library.

Steen, E. B.: Medical abbreviations, Philadelphia, 1960, F. A. Davis Co.

Steen, E. B., and Montagu, A.: Anatomy and physiology (college outline series), vols. 1 and 2, New York, 1959, Barnes & Noble, Inc.

Zoethout, William D., and Tuttle, W. W.: Textbook of physiology, ed. 13, St. Louis, 1958, The C. V. Mosby Co.

Periodicals

American Journal of Medical Sciences
American Journal of Physiology
Annual Review of Physiology
Harvey Lectures
Journal of Anatomy
Journal of Neurophysiology
Journal of the American Medical Association

Glossary

abdomen body area between the diaphragm and pelvis.

abduct to move away from the midline; opposite of adduct.

absorption passage of a substance through a membrane (for example, skin or mucosa) into blood.

acapnia marked decrease in blood carbon dioxide content.

acetabulum socket in the hip bone (os coxae or innominate bone) into which the head of the femur fits.

acetone bodies ketone bodies, acids formed during the first part of fat catabolism; namely—acetoacetic acid, beta-hydroxybutyric acid, and acetone.

Achilles tendon tendon inserted on calcaneus; so-called because of the Greek myth that Achilles' mother held him by the heels when she dipped him in the river Styx, thereby making him invulnerable except in this area.

acidosis condition in which there is an excessive proportion of acid in the blood.

acromion bony projection of the scapula; forms point of the shoulder.

adduct to move toward the midline; opposite of abduct.

adenoids glandlike; adenoids or pharyngeal tonsils are paired lymphoid structures in the nasopharynx.

adolescence period between puberty and adulthood.

adventitia, externa outer coat of a tube-shaped structure such as blood vessels.

aerobic requiring free oxygen; opposite of anaerobic.

afferent neuron transmitting impulses to the central nervous system.

albuminuria albumin in the urine.

alkaline reserve bicarbonate salts present in body fluids; mainly sodium bicarbonate.

alkalosis condition in which there is an excessive proportion of alkali in the blood; opposite of acidosis.

alveolus literally a small cavity; alveoli of lungs are microscopic saclike dilatations of terminal bronchioles.

ameboid movement movement characteristic of amebae; that is, by projections of protoplasm (pseudopodia) toward which the rest of the cell's protoplasm flows.

amenorrhea absence of the menses.

amino acid organic compound having an NH_3 and a COOH group in its molecule; has both acid and basic properties; amino acids are the structural units from which proteins are built.

amphiarthrosis slightly movable joint.

ampulla saclike dilatation of a tube or duct.

anabolism synthesis by cells of complex compounds (for example, protoplasm, hormones) from simpler compounds (amino acids, simple sugars, fats, minerals); opposite of catabolism, the other phase of metabolism.

anaerobic not requiring free oxygen; opposite of aerobic.

anastomosis connection between vessels; the

587

circle of Willis, for example, is an anastomosis of certain cerebral arteries.

anemia deficient number of red blood cells or deficient hemoglobin.

anesthesia loss of sensation.

aneurysm blood-filled saclike dilatation of the wall of an artery.

angina any disease characterized by spasmodic suffocative attacks; for example, angina pectoris, paroxysmal thoracic pain with feeling of suffocation.

anisocytosis irregularity in size of red blood cells.

ankylosis abnormal immobility of a joint.

anorexia loss of appetite.

anoxemia deficient blood oxygen content.

anoxia deficient oxygen supply to tissues.

antagonistic muscles those having opposing actions; for example, muscles that flex the upper arm are antagonistic to muscles that extend it.

anterior front or ventral; opposite of posterior or dorsal.

antibody, immune body substance produced by the body that destroys or inactivates a specific substance (antigen) that has entered the body; for example, diphtheria antitoxin is the antibody against diphtheria toxin.

antigen substance which, when introduced into the body, causes formation of antibodies against it.

antiketogenic inhibiting ketone formation.

antiseptic preventing bacterial growth and multiplication.

antrum cavity; for example, the antrum of Highmore, the space in each maxillary bone, or the maxillary sinus.

anus distal end or outlet of the rectum.

apex pointed end of a conical structure.

aphasia loss of a language faculty such as the ability to use words or to understand them.

apnea temporary cessation of breathing.

aponeurosis flat sheet of white fibrous tissue that serves as a muscle attachment.

aqueduct tube for conduction of liquid; for example, the cerebral aqueduct conducts cerebrospinal fluid from the third to the fourth ventricle.

arachnoid delicate, weblike middle membrane of the meninges.

areola small space; the pigmented ring around the nipple.

arteriole small branch of an artery.

artery vessel carrying blood away from the heart.

arthrosis joint or articulation.

articular of a joint.

articulation joint.

arytenoid ladle-shaped; two small cartilages of the larynx.

ascites accumulation of serous fluid in the abdominal cavity.

asphyxia loss of consciousness due to deficient oxygen supply.

aspirate to remove by suction.

asthenia bodily weakness.

ataxia loss of power of muscle coordination.

atrium chamber or cavity; for example, atrium of each side of the heart.

atrophy wasting away of tissue; decrease in size of a part.

auricle part of the ear attached to the side of the head; earlike appendage of each atrium.

autonomic self-governing, independent.

axilla armpit.

axon nerve cell process that transmits impulses away from the cell body.

Bartholin seventeenth century Danish anatomist.

basophil white blood cell that stains readily, with basic dyes.

biceps two headed.

bilirubin red pigment in the bile.

biliverdin green pigment in the bile.

B. N. A. (Basle Nomina Anatomica) anatomic terminology accepted at Basle by the Anatomical Society in 1895.

Bowman nineteenth century English physician.

brachial pertaining to the arm.

bronchiectasis dilatation of the bronchi.

bronchiole small branch of a bronchus.

bronchus one of the two branches of the trachea.

buccal pertaining to the cheek.

buffer compound which combines with an acid or with a base to form a weaker acid or base, thereby lessening the change in hydrogen ion concentration that would occur without the buffer.

bulimia voracious appetite.

bursa fluid-containing sac or pouch lined with synovial membrane.

buttock prominence over the gluteal muscles.

calculus stone formed in various parts of the body; may consist of different substances.

calorie heat unit; a large calorie is the amount of heat needed to raise the temperature of 1 kilogram of water 1 degree centigrade.

calyx cup-shaped division of the renal pelvis.

canaliculus little canal.

capillary microscopic blood vessel; capillaries connect arterioles with venules; also, microscopic lymphatic vessels.

carbhemoglobin, carbaminohemoglobin compound formed by union of carbon dioxide with hemoglobin.

carbohydrate organic compounds containing carbon, hydrogen, and oxygen in certain specific proportions; for example, sugars, starches, cellulose.

carcinoma cancer, a malignant tumor.

caries decay of teeth or of bone.

carotid from Greek word meaning to plunge into deep sleep; carotid arteries of the neck so called because pressure on them may produce unconsciousness.

carpal pertaining to the wrist.

casein protein in milk.

cast mold; for example, formed in renal tubules.

castration removal of testes or ovaries.

catabolism breakdown of food compounds or of protoplasm into simpler compounds; opposite of anabolism, the other phase of metabolism.

catalyst substance which alters the speed of a chemical reaction.

cataract opacity of the lens of the eye.

caudal pertaining to the tail of an animal; opposite of cephalic.

cecum blind pouch; the pouch at the proximal end of the large intestine.

celiac pertaining to the abdomen.

cellulose polysaccharide, the main plant carbohydrate.

centimeter 1/100 of a meter, about ⅖ of an inch.

cephalic pertaining to the head; opposite of caudal.

cerumen earwax.

cervix neck; any necklike structure.

chemoreceptor distal end of sensory dendrites especially adapted for chemical stimulation.

chiasm crossing; specifically, a crossing of the optic nerves.

cholecystectomy removal of the gallbladder.

cholesterol organic alcohol present in bile, blood, and various tissues.

choroid, chorioid skinlike.

chromatin deep-staining substance in the nucleus of cells; divides into chromosomes during mitosis.

chromosome one of the segments into which chromatin divides during mitosis; involved in transmitting hereditary characteristics.

chyle milky fluid; the fat-containing lymph in the lymphatics of the intestine.

chyme partially digested food mixture leaving the stomach.

cilia hairlike projections of protoplasm.

cochlea snail shell or structure of similar shape.

coenzyme nonprotein substance which activates an enzyme.

collagen principal organic constituent of connective tissue.

colloid solute particles with diameters of 1 to 100 millimicrons.

colostrum first milk secreted after childbirth.

commissure bundle of nerve fibers passing from one side to the other of the brain or cord.

concha shell-shaped structure; for example, bony projections into the nasal cavity.

condyle rounded projection at the end of a bone.

congenital present at birth.

contralateral on the opposite side.

coracoid like a raven's beak in form.

corium true skin or derma.

coronal of or like a crown.

coronary encircling; in the form of a crown.

corpus body.

corpuscles very small body or particle.

cortex outer part of an internal organ; for example, of the cerebrum and of the kidneys.

costal pertaining to the ribs.

crenation, plasmolysis shriveling of a cell due to water withdrawal.

cretinism dwarfism due to hypofunction of the thyroid gland.

cribriform sievelike.

cricoid ring-shaped; a cartilage of this shape in the larynx.

cruciate cross shaped.

crystalloid solute particle less than 1 millimicron in diameter.

cubital pertaining to the forearm.

cutaneous pertaining to the skin.

cyanosis bluish appearance of the skin due to deficient oxygenation of blood.

cytoplasm the protoplasm of a cell exclusive of the nucleus.

deamination chemical reaction by which the amino group NH_3 is split from an amino acid.

deciduous temporary; shedding at a certain stage of growth; for example, deciduous teeth.

decussation crossing over like an X.

defecation elimination of waste matter from the intestines.

deferens carrying away.

deglutition swallowing.

deltoid triangular; for example, deltoid muscle.

dendrite, dendron branching or treelike; a nerve cell process that transmits impulses toward the cell body.

dens tooth.

dentate having toothlike projections.

dentine main part of a tooth, under the enamel.

dentition teething; also, number, shape, and arrangement of the teeth.

dermis, corium true skin.

dextrose glucose, a monosaccharide, the principal blood sugar.

dialysis separation; the separation of crystalloids from colloids by the faster diffusion of the former through a membrane.

diapedesis passage of blood cells through intact blood vessel walls.

diaphragm membrane or partition that separates one thing from another; the muscular partition between the thorax and abdomen; the midriff.

diarthrosis freely movable joint.

diastole relaxation of the heart interposed between its contractions; opposite of systole.

diencephalon "tween" brain; parts of the brain between the cerebral hemispheres and the mesencephalon or midbrain.

diffusion spreading; for example, scattering of solute particles.

digestion conversion of food into assimilable compounds.

diplopia double vision; seeing one object as two.

disaccharide sugar formed by the union of two monosaccharides; contains twelve carbon atoms.

distal toward the end of a structure; opposite of proximal.

diverticulum outpocketing from a tubular organ such as the intestine.

dorsal, posterior pertaining to the back; opposite of ventral.

Douglas Scottish anatomist of the late seventeenth and early eighteenth centuries.

dropsy accumulation of serous fluid in a body cavity, in tissues; edema.

duct canal or passage.

dura mater literally strong or hard mother; outermost layer of the meninges.

dyspnea difficult or labored breathing.

dystrophy faulty nutrition.

ectopic displaced; not in the normal place; for example, extrauterine pregnancy.

edema excessive fluid in tissues; dropsy.

effector responding organ; for example, voluntary and involuntary muscle, the heart, and glands.

efferent carrying from, as neurons which transmit impulses from the central nervous system to the periphery; opposite of afferent.

electrolyte substance that ionizes in solution, rendering the solution capable of conducting an electric current.

electron minute, negatively charged particle.

elimination expulsion of wastes from the body.

embolism obstruction of a blood vessel by foreign matter carried in the blood stream.

embryo animal in early stages of intrauterine development; the human fetus the first three months after conception.

emesis vomiting.

emphysema dilatation of pulmonary alveoli. *CAVITY*

empyema pus in a cavity; for example, in the chest cavity.

encephalon brain.

endocrine secreting into the blood or tissue fluid rather than into a duct; opposite of exocrine.

energy capacity for doing work.

enzyme catalytic agent formed in living cells.

eosinophil, acidophil white blood cell readily stained by eosin.

epidermis "false" skin; outermost layer of the skin.

epinephrine adrenaline; secretion of the adrenal medulla.

erythrocyte red blood cell.

ethmoid sievelike.

eupnea normal respiration.

Eustachio Italian anatomist of the sixteenth century.

exocrine secreting into a duct; opposite of endocrine.

exophthalmos abnormal protrusion of the eyes.

extrinsic coming from the outside; opposite of intrinsic.

Fallopius sixteenth century Italian anatomist.

fascia sheet of connective tissue.

fasciculus little bundle.

fetus unborn young, especially in the later stages; in human beings, from third month of intrauterine period until birth.

fiber threadlike structure.

fibrin insoluble protein in clotted blood.

fibrinogen soluble blood protein which is converted to insoluble fibrin during clotting.

fimbria fringe.

fissure groove.

flaccid soft, limp.

follicle small sac or gland.

fontanelle "soft spots" of the infant's head; unossified areas in the infant skull.

foramen small opening.

fossa cavity or hollow.

fovea small pit or depression.

fundus base of a hollow organ; for example, the part farthest from its outlet.

ganglion cluster of nerve cell bodies outside the central nervous system.

gasserian named for Gasser, a sixteenth century Austrian surgeon.

gastric pertaining to the stomach.

gene part of the chromosome that transmits a given hereditary trait.

genitalia reproductive organs.

gestation pregnancy.

gland secreting structure.

glomerulus compact cluster; for example, of capillaries in the kidneys.

glossal of the tongue.

glucose monosaccharide or simple sugar; the principal blood sugar.

gluteal of or near the buttocks.

glycerin, glycerol product of fat digestion.

glycogen polysaccharide; animal starch.

gonad sex gland in which reproductive cells are formed.

graafian named for Graaf, a seventeenth century Dutch anatomist.

gustatory pertaining to taste.

gyrus convoluted ridge.

haversian named for Havers, English anatomist of the late seventeenth century.

hemiplegia paralysis of one side of the body.

hemoglobin iron-containing protein in red blood cells.

hemopoiesis blood cell formation.

hemorrhage bleeding.

hepar liver.

heparin substance obtained from the liver which inhibits blood clotting.

heredity transmission of characteristics from a parent to a child.

hernia, "rupture" protrusion of a loop of an organ through an abnormal opening.

hilus, hilum depression where vessels enter an organ.

His German anatomist of the late nineteenth century.

histology science of minute structure of tissues.

homeostasis relative uniformity of the normal body's internal environment.

hormone substance secreted by an endocrine gland.

hyaline glasslike.

hydrolysis literally "split by water"; chemical

591

reaction in which a compound reacts with water.

hymen Greek for skin; mucous membrane that may partially or entirely occlude the vaginal outlet.

hyoid shaped like the letter U; bone of this shape at the base of the tongue.

hyperemia increased blood in a part.

hyperopia farsightedness.

hyperplasia increase in the size of a part due to an increase in the number of its cells.

hyperpnea abnormally rapid breathing, panting.

hypertension abnormally high blood pressure.

hypertrophy increased size of a part due to an increase in the size of its cells.

hypophysis Greek for undergrowth; hence the pituitary gland which grows out from the undersurface of brain.

incus anvil; the middle ear bone which is shaped like an anvil.

inferior lower; opposite of superior.

inguinal of the groin.

inhalation inspiration or breathing in; opposite of exhalation or expiration.

inhibition checking or restraining of action.

innominate not named, anonymous; for example, ossa coxae (hip bones) formerly known as innominate bones.

insulin hormone secreted by islands of Langerhans in the pancreas.

intercellular between cells; interstitial.

internuncial like a messenger between two parties; hence, an internuncial neuron is one which conducts impulses from one neuron to another.

interstitial of or forming small spaces between things; intercellular.

intima innermost.

intrinsic not dependent upon externals; located within something; opposite of extrinsic.

involuntary not willed; opposite of voluntary.

involution return of an organ to its normal size after enlargement; also retrograde or degenerative change.

ion electrically charged atom or group of atoms.

ipsilateral on the same side; opposite of contralateral.

irritability excitability; ability to react to a stimulus.

ischemia local anemia; temporary lack of blood supply to an area.

isotonic of the same tension or pressure.

ketones acids (acetoacetic, beta-hydroxybutyric, and acetone) produced during fat catabolism.

kilogram 1000 grams; approximately 2.2 pounds.

kinesthesia "muscle sense"; that is, sense of position and movement of body parts.

labia lips.

lacrimal pertaining to tears.

lactation secretion of milk.

lactose milk sugar, a disaccharide.

lacuna space or cavity; for example, lacunae in bone contain bone cells.

lamella thin layer, as of bone.

lateral of or toward the side; opposite of medial.

leukocyte white blood cell.

ligament bond or band connecting two objects; in anatomy a band of white fibrous tissue connecting bones.

lipid fats and fatlike compounds.

loin part of the back between the ribs and hip bones.

lumbar of or near the loins.

lumen passageway or space within a tubular structure.

luteum golden yellow.

lymph watery fluid in the lymphatic vessels.

lymphocyte one type of white blood cells.

malleolus small hammer; projections at the distal ends of the tibia and fibula.

malleus hammer; the tiny middle ear bone which is shaped like a hammer.

Malpighii seventeenth century Italian anatomist.

maltose disaccharide or "double" sugar.

mammary pertaining to the breast.

mammillary like a nipple.

manometer instrument used for measuring the pressure of fluids.

manubrium handle; upper part of the sternum.

mastication chewing.

matrix ground substance in which cells are embedded.

meatus passageway.

medial of or toward the middle; opposite of lateral.

mediastinum middle section of the thorax; that is, between the two lungs.

medulla Latin for marrow; hence the inner portion of an organ in contrast to the outer portion or cortex.

Meibom seventeenth century German anatomist.

membrane thin layer or sheet.

menstruation monthly discharge of blood from the uterus.

mesencephalon midbrain.

mesentery fold of peritoneum which attaches the intestine to the posterior abdominal wall.

mesial situated in the middle; median.

metabolism complex process by which food is utilized by a living organism.

metacarpus "after" the wrist; hence the part of the hand between the wrist and fingers.

metatarsus "after" the instep; hence the part of the foot between the tarsal bones and toes.

micturition urination, voiding.

mitochondria threadlike structures.

mitosis indirect cell division involving complex changes in the nucleus.

mitral shaped like a miter.

monosaccharide simple sugar.

Monro eighteenth century English surgeon.

myelin lipoid substance found in the myelin sheath around some nerve fibers.

myocardium muscle of the heart.

myopia nearsightedness.

nares nostrils.

neurilemma nerve sheath.

neuron nerve cell, including its processes.

neutrophil white blood cell that stains readily with neutral dyes.

nuchal pertaining to the nape of the neck.

nucleus spherical structure within a cell; a group of neuron cell bodies in the brain or cord.

occiput back of the head.

olecranon elbow.

olfactory pertaining to the sense of smell.

ophthalmic pertaining to the eyes.

os Latin for mouth and for bone.

osmosis movement of a fluid through a semipermeable membrane.

ossicle little bone.

palate roof of the mouth.

palpebrae eyelids.

papilla small nipple-shaped elevation.

paralysis loss of the power of motion or sensation, especially voluntary motion.

parenchyma essential or functional tissue of an organ.

parietal of the walls of an organ or cavity.

parotid located near the ear.

parturition act of giving birth to an infant.

patella small, shallow pan; the kneecap.

Pavlov Russian physiologist of the late nineteenth and early twentieth centuries.

pectineal pertaining to the pubic bone.

pectoral pertaining to the chest or breast.

pelvis basin or funnel-shaped structure.

Peyer Swiss anatomist of the late seventeenth and early eighteenth centuries.

peripheral pertaining to an outside surface.

peroneus, peroneal of or near the fibula.

petrous rocklike.

pH hydrogen ion concentration; the negative logarithm of hydrogen ion concentration.

phagocytosis ingestion and digestion of particles by a cell.

phalanges finger or toe bones.

phrenic pertaining to the diaphragm.

pia mater gentle mother; the vascular innermost covering (meninges) of the brain and cord.

pilomotor mover of a hair.

pineal shaped like a pine cone.

piriformis pear shaped.

pisiform pea shaped.

plantar pertaining to the sole of the foot.

plasma liquid part of the blood.

plasmolysis shrinking of a cell due to water loss by osmosis.

plexus network.

plica fold.

polymorphonuclear having many-shaped nuclei.

polysaccharide complex sugar.

pons bridge.

593

popliteal behind the knee.

posterior following after; hence located behind; opposite of anterior.

Poupart seventeenth century French anatomist.

presbyopia "oldsightedness"; farsightedness of old age.

pronate to turn palm downward.

protoplasm living substance.

proximal next or nearest; located nearest the center of the body or the point of attachment of a structure.

psoas pertaining to the loin, the part of the back between the ribs and hip bones.

pterygoid wing shaped.

puberty age at which the reproductive organs become functional.

racemose like a cluster of grapes.

ramus branch.

Ranvier French pathologist of the late nineteenth and early twenties centuries.

receptor peripheral ending of a sensory neuron.

reflex involuntary action.

refraction bending of a ray of light as it passes from a medium of one density to one of a different density.

refractory resisting stimulation.

renal pertaining to the kidney.

rugae wrinkles or folds.

reticular netlike.

sagittal like an arrow; longitudinal.

salpinx tube; oviduct.

sartorius tailor; hence the thigh muscle used to sit cross-legged like a tailor.

sciatic pertaining to the ischium.

sclera from Greek for hard.

scrotum bag.

sebum Latin for tallow; secretion of sebaceous glands.

sella turcica Turkish saddle; saddle-shaped depression in the sphenoid bone.

semen Latin for seed; male reproductive fluid.

semilunar half-moon shaped.

senescence old age.

serratus saw toothed.

serum any watery animal fluid; clear, yellowish liquid that separates from a clot of blood.

sesamoid shaped like a sesame seed.

sigmoid S shaped.

sinus cavity.

soleus pertaining to a sole; a muscle in the leg shaped like the sole of a shoe.

somatic of the body framework or walls, as distinguished from the viscera or internal organs.

sphenoid wedge shaped.

sphincter ring-shaped muscle.

splanchnic visceral.

squamous scalelike.

stapes stirrup; tiny stirrup-shaped bone in the middle ear.

Starling English physiologist of the late nineteenth and early twentieth centuries.

stimulus agent that causes a change in the activity of a structure.

stratum layer.

striated marked with parallel lines.

stroma Greek for mattress or bed; hence the framework or matrix of a structure.

sudoriferous secreting sweat.

sulcus furrow or groove.

superior higher; opposite of inferior.

supinate to turn the palm of the hand upward; opposite of pronate.

Sylvius seventeenth century anatomist.

symphysis Greek for a growing together.

synapse joining; point of contact between adjacent neurons.

synovia literally "with egg"; secretion of the synovial membrane resembles egg white.

synthesis putting together of parts to form a more complex whole.

systole contraction of the heart muscle.

talus ankle; one of the bones of the ankle.

tarsus instep.

Tawara Japanese physiologist (1873-   ).

tendon band or cord of fibrous connective tissue which attaches a muscle to a bone or other structure.

thrombosis formation of a clot in a blood vessel.

tibia Latin for shin bone.

tonus continued, partial contraction of muscle.

trochlear pertaining to a pulley.

trophic having to do with nutrition.

tropic having to do with a turning or a change.

tunica covering.
turbinate shaped like a cone or like a scroll or spiral.
tympanum drum.

umbilicus navel.
utricle little sac.
uvula Latin for a little grape; a projection hanging from the soft palate.

vagina sheath.
vagus Latin for wandering.
valve structure which permits flow of a fluid in one direction only.
vas vessel or duct.
vastus wide, of great size.

Vater German anatomist of the late seventeenth and early eighteenth centuries.
vein vessel carrying blood to the heart.
ventral of or near the belly; in man, front or anterior; opposite of dorsal or posterior.
ventricle small cavity.
vermiform worm shaped.
villus hairlike projection.
viscera internal organs.
vomer ploughshare.

Willis seventeenth century English anatomist.

xiphoid sword shaped.

zygoma yoke.

Index

Ceruminous glands, 74, 279
Cervical canal, 499
  curve, 98
  glands, 360
  lymph nodes, 360
  plexus, 235
  spinal nerves, 235
  vertebrae, 97, 107
Cervix of uterus, 497
Chemical changes in digestion, 426-430
  in metabolism, 434-457
  composition of blood, 298, 559-562
Chemoreceptors, 337, 396, 397, 399
Chemoreflex, 342, 396-399
Chest cavity, changes in size of, 381-382
Chewing muscles, 163
Cheyne-Stokes respirations, 388, 401
Chiasm or chiasma, optic, 222, 278
Chief cells, 413
Chloride shift, 476
Chlorolabe, 277
Choanae, 373
Choking reflex, 399
Cholecystectomy, 420
Cholecystitis, 420
Cholecystokinin, 431
Cholesterol, 540
Cholinergic fibers, 253
Cholinesterase, 195
Chondrocytes, 81
Chordae tendineae, 307
Chorioid coat of eye, 267, 268, 270
Choroid plexus, 199
Chromaphil substance, 191
Chromatid, 50
Chromatin, 33, 51
Chromatolysis, 191
Chromidial, 191
Chromosomes, 33, 51, 518
Churning, 424
Chyle, 358
Chylomicrons, 434
Ciliary body of eye, 268
  ganglion, 223, 248
  muscle of eye, 268, 272
Circle of Willis, 317
Circular folds, 408
Circulation, changes after birth, 329-330
  collateral, 310

Circulation—cont'd
  control, 332-347
  fetal, 328-330
  how to trace, 331
  in veins, 347
  kinds of, 330
  meaning, 330
  of lymph, 355-359
  physiology of, 330-350
  portal, 327, 330
  pulmonary, 330
  relation to repirations, 347, 397
  scheme of, 332
  systemic, 330
  through heart, 330
Circulatory system, functions of, 289, 332
Circumcision, 496
Circumduction, 126
Cisterna chyli, 358
Citrate, 303
Citric acid cycle, 43-48
Clasmatocytes, 63
Claustrum, 204
Clavicle, 83, 109
Clay-colored stool, 420
Cleavage of ovum, 519
Cleft palate, 371, 517
Climacteric, 510, 517
Clitoris, 507
Clotting, hastening of, 303-304
  mechanism of, 299-302
  prevention of, 302, 303
CMO, 334, 335
Coagulation, 299-304
Cobalt, 292
Coccygeus muscle, 161
Coccyx, 107
Cochlea, 281
Cochlear duct, 281
Coenzyme, 426, 442, 443
Cold receptors, 267
Collagenous fibers, 60
Collar bone, 83, 109
Collateral ganglion, 248
Collecting tubules, 471
Colliculi, 201, 217
Colloid, 28, 298
  osmotic pressure, 563-565
Colon, 415
  divisions of, 416
  mechanical digestion in, 424, 425
Color perception, 277

Colostrum, 510
Colpotomy, posterior, 503
Columns of spinal cord, 218
Common bile duct, 418
  carotid artery, 316, 354
  iliac artery, 317
  vein, 322
Compensatory mechanisms (see Homeostatic mechanisms)
Complemental air, 386
Compound B, 540
Compound E, 540
Compound F, 540
Conchae, nasal, 82, 106, 373
Condensation, 443
Conduction, heat loss by, 458
  over reflex arc, 196
Conductivity, 34
  of nervous tissue, 195
Condyle(s), 88
  occipital, 94
  of femur, 101, 115
  of mandible, 95
  of tibia, 101
Condyloid joint, 123
Cones, visual, 270, 277
Conjunctiva, 273
Conjunctivitis, 273
Connective tissue, 60-63, 543
Constriction of blood vessels, 342, 343
Contraceptive pills, 516
Contractility, 34, 135, 492
Contraction of muscle, 137-139, 237
  isometric, 137
  isotonic, 137
  strength of, 145
Contracture, 137
Contralateral reflex arc, 196
Convergence, 241, 276, 277
Convoluted tubules, 471, 474-478
Convolutions of cerebrum, 202
Convulsion, 138
Copper, 292
Coracobrachialis, 152
Coracoid process, 98
Cornea, 268, 274
Corona radiata, 497
Coronal, 19
  suture, 92, 95
Coronary arteries, 309, 310, 316
Coronoid fossa, 99, 111

Meatus—cont'd
  internal auditory, 93
  urinary, 483, 507
Medial, 19
Medial lemniscus, 240
Mediastinum, 381, 386
Medulla oblongata, 201, 215-217
  of adrenal glands, 546
  of kidney, 470
Medullary cavity of bone, 86, 127, 128
  sheath, 192
Medullated nerve fibers (see Myelinated fibers)
Megakaryocytes, 297
Meiosis (see Miosis)
Meissner's corpuscles, 266, 267
Melanin, 72
Melanoblasts, 72
Membrane(s), alveolar-capillary, 392, 394
  arachnoid, 198
  basilar, 281, 284
  cell, 31-40
  cutaneous, 70-71
  mucous, 69
  of brain (see Meninges)
  of spinal cord (see Meninges)
  Reissner's, 281, 284
  serous, 69
  synovial, 69
  tympanic, 279, 283
  types of, 69
  vestibular, 281
Membrani tympani (see Tympanic membrane)
Membranous labyrinth, 280
Memory, 210
Menarche, 510, 517
Meninges, 197, 217
Meningitis, 197
Menopause, 510, 517
Menstrual cycle, 511-512
Menstruation, 503, 511, 515
Mental foramen, 95
  processes, 210
Merkel's disks, 267
Mesencephalon (see Midbrain)
Mesenteric arteries, 317
  veins, 327
Mesentery, 406
Mesial, 19

Mesoderm, 520
Mesothelium, 51
Mesovarian ligament, 504
Metabolic rate, 451-457, 538
  basal, 451
    effect of age on, 452, 455
    effect of drugs on, 453
    effect of exercise on, 455
    factors determining, 452-453
  how measured, 452-454
  meaning of, 451
  relation to weight control, 456
  total, 455
  ways of expressing, 451
Metabolism, 434-457
  meaning of, 22, 43, 435
  of carbohydrates, 418, 436, 437
  of fats, 400, 435, 442-446
  of mineral salts, 450
  of proteins, 435, 446-450, 531, 534, 541
  of vitamins, 450
  of water, 450-451
  summary of, 449
Metacarpal bones, 84, 111
Metamyelocyte, 295
Metaphase, 51
Metatarsal arch, 116, 118, 119
  bones, 84, 111, 116
Methacoline, 257
Microglia, 63, 188
Microscope, electron, 29
Micturition, 481
Midbrain, 201, 216-217
Milk, secretion of, 509-510
  sugar, 428
Millimeter, 28
Millimicron, 28
"Milk leg," 315
Mineral salts (see Electrolytes)
Mineralocorticoids, 476, 544-545
Minimal air, 386
Miosis, 510, 518
Mitochondria, 29, 30, 32, 44, 48
Mitosis, 49-51, 510
Mitral stenosis, 309
  valve, 307
Mittelschmerz, 510
Mixed nerves, 236
Modiolus, 281
Molar teeth, 410
Monocytes, 294

Monosaccharides, 428
Mons pubis, 507
  veneris, 507
Morula, 519
Motility (see Contractility)
Motor areas of brain, 209
  end plate, 143
  pathways, 206, 219, 241-245
  neuron, 189, 245
  tracts, 206, 219, 241-245
  unit, 143
Mouth, anatomy of, 409
  digestion in, 428
Mucosa or mucous membrane, 69
  modifications of, in alimentary tract, 408
Multiple sclerosis, 145
Mumps, 410
Murmurs, heart, 313
Muscle(s), action or actions, 144-147
  adductor group, 148, 155
  antagonist, 145
  arrector pili, 73
  attachment of, 142, 147
  biceps brachii, 153
    femoris, 156
  brachialis, 153
  brachioradialis, 153
  buccinator, 163
  cardiac, 57
  cells (see Muscle tissue)
  chewing, 163
  ciliary, 268, 272
  coccygeus, 161
  coracobrachialis, 152
  corrugator supercilli, 163
  deltoid, 152
  detrusor, 481
  diaphragm, 160, 384
  epicranius, 163
  erector spinae (see Sacrospinalis)
  extensors carpi radialis and ulnaris, 154
  external oblique of abdomen, 159
  fascia, 142
  fatigue of, 137
  fibers, 57, 139
  flexor carpi radialis, 154
    ulnaris, 154
  functions, 133
  gastrocnemius, 157
  geniohyoid, 107

611

617

619

621